Y0-AQW-897

McGraw Hill Education create™

Course Complex Variables

Course Number **MAT 342**

Stony Brook University

Mathematics

McGraw Hill Education create™

http://create.mheducation.com

ISBN-10: 1308020783 ISBN-13: 9781308020785

Contents

Credits

PREFACE

This book is a thorough revision of its earlier eighth edition, which was published in 2009. That edition has served, just as the earlier ones did, as a textbook for a one-term introductory course in the theory and application of functions of a complex variable. This new edition preserves the basic content and style of the earlier ones, the first two of which were written by the late Ruel V. Churchill alone.

The book has always had two main objectives.

(*a*) The first is to develop those parts of the theory that are prominent in applications of the subject.

(*b*) The second objective is to furnish an introduction to applications of residues and conformal mapping. The applications of residues include their use in evaluating real improper integrals, finding inverse Laplace transforms, and locating zeros of functions. Considerable attention is paid to the use of conformal mapping in solving boundary value problems that arise in studies of heat conduction and fluid flow. Hence the book may be considered as a companion volume to the authors' text *Fourier Series and Boundary Value Problems,* where another classical method for solving boundary value problems in partial differential equations is developed.

The first nine chapters of this book have for many years formed the basis of a three-hour course given each term at The University of Michigan. The final three chapters have fewer changes and are mostly intended for self-study and reference. The classes using the book have consisted mainly of seniors concentrating in mathematics, engineering, or one of the physical sciences. Before taking the course, the students have completed at least a three-term calculus sequence and a first course in ordinary differential equations. If mapping by elementary functions is desired earlier in the course, one can skip to Chap. 8 immediately after Chap. 3 on elementary functions and then return to Chap. 4 on integrals.

We mention here a sample of the changes in this edition, some of which were suggested by students and people teaching from the book. A number of topics have been moved from where they were. For example, although harmonic functions are still introduced in Chap. 2, harmonic conjugates have been moved to Chap. 9, where they are actually needed. Another example is the moving of the derivation of an important inequality needed in proving the fundamental theorem of algebra (Chap. 4) to Chap. 1, where related inequalities are introduced. This has the advantage of enabling the reader to concentrate on such inequalities when they are grouped together and also of making the proof of the fundamental theorem of algebra reasonably brief and efficient without taking the reader on a distracting side-trip. The introduction to the concept of mapping in Chap. 2 is shortened somewhat in this edition, and only the mapping $w = z^2$ is emphasized in that chapter. This was suggested by some users of the last edition, who felt that a detailed consideration of $w = z^2$ is sufficient in Chap. 2 in order to illustrate concepts needed there. Finally, since most of the series, both Taylor and Laurent, that are found and discussed in Chap. 5 rely on the reader's familiarity with just six Maclaurin series, those series are now grouped together so that the reader is not forced to hunt around for them whenever they are needed in finding other series expansions. Also, Chap. 5 now contains a separate section, following Taylor's theorem, devoted entirely to series representations involving negative powers of $z - z_0$. Experience has shown that this is especially valuable in making the transformation from Taylor to Laurent series a natural one.

This edition contains many new examples, sometimes taken from the exercises in the last edition. Quite often the examples follow in a separate section immediately following a section that develops the theory to be illustrated.

The clarity of the presentation has been enhanced in other ways. Boldface letters have been used to make definitions more easily identified. The book has fifteen new figures, as well as a number of existing ones that have been improved. Finally, when the proofs of theorems are unusually long, those proofs are clearly divided into parts. This happens, for instance, in the proof (Sec. 49) of the three-part theorem regarding the existence and use of antiderivatives. The same is true of the proof (Sec. 51) of the Cauchy-Goursat theorem. Finally, there is a Student's Solutions Manual (ISBN: 978-0-07-352899-1; MHID: 0-07-352899-4) that is available. It contains solutions of selected exercises in Chapters 1 through 7, covering the material through residues.

In order to accommodate as wide a range of readers as possible, there are footnotes referring to other texts that give proofs and discussions of the more delicate results from calculus and advanced calculus that are occasionally needed. A bibliography of other books on complex variables, many of which are more advanced, is provided in Appendix 1. A table of conformal transformations that are useful in applications appears in Appendix 2.

As already indicated, some of the changes in this edition have been suggested by users of the earlier edition. Moreover, in the preparation of this new edition, continual interest and support has been provided by a variety of other people, especially the staff at McGraw-Hill and my wife Jacqueline Read Brown.

James Ward Brown

CHAPTER

1

COMPLEX NUMBERS

In this chapter, we survey the algebraic and geometric structure of the complex number system. We assume various corresponding properties of real numbers to be known.

1. SUMS AND PRODUCTS

Complex numbers can be defined as ordered pairs (x, y) of real numbers that are to be interpreted as points in the ***complex plane***, with rectangular coordinates x and y, just as real numbers x are thought of as points on the real line. When real numbers x are displayed as points $(x, 0)$ on the ***real axis***, we write $x = (x, 0)$; and it is clear that the set of complex numbers includes the real numbers as a subset. Complex numbers of the form $(0, y)$ correspond to points on the y axis and are called ***pure imaginary numbers*** when $y \neq 0$. The y axis is then referred to as the ***imaginary axis***.

It is customary to denote a complex number (x, y) by z, so that (see Fig. 1)

$$z = (x, y). \tag{1}$$

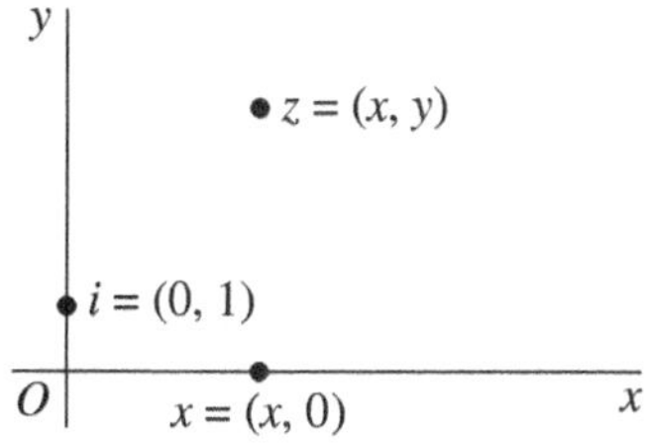

FIGURE 1

The real numbers x and y are, moreover, known as the ***real and imaginary parts*** of z, respectively, and we write

$$x = \operatorname{Re} z, \qquad y = \operatorname{Im} z. \tag{2}$$

Two complex numbers z_1 and z_2 are ***equal*** whenever they have the same real parts and the same imaginary parts. Thus the statement $z_1 = z_2$ means that z_1 and z_2 correspond to the same point in the complex, or z, plane.

The ***sum*** $z_1 + z_2$ and ***product*** $z_1 z_2$ of two complex numbers

$$z_1 = (x_1, y_1) \quad \text{and} \quad z_2 = (x_1, y_1)$$

are defined as follows:

$$(x_1, y_1) + (x_2, y_2) = (x_1 + x_2, y_1 + y_2), \tag{3}$$

$$(x_1, y_1)(x_2, y_2) = (x_1x_2 - y_1y_2, y_1x_2 + x_1y_2). \tag{4}$$

Note that the operations defined by means of equations (3) and (4) become the usual operations of addition and multiplication when restricted to the real numbers:

$$(x_1, 0) + (x_2, 0) = (x_1 + x_2, 0),$$
$$(x_1, 0)(x_2, 0) = (x_1x_2, 0).$$

The complex number system is, therefore, a natural extension of the real number system.

Any complex number $z = (x, y)$ can be written $z = (x, 0) + (0, y)$, and it is easy to see that $(0, 1)(y, 0) = (0, y)$. Hence

$$z = (x, 0) + (0, 1)(y, 0);$$

and if we think of a real number as either x or $(x, 0)$ and let i denote the pure imaginary number (0,1), as shown in Fig. 1, it is clear that*

$$z = x + iy. \tag{5}$$

Also, with the convention that $z^2 = zz$, $z^3 = z^2z$, etc., we have

$$i^2 = (0, 1)(0, 1) = (-1, 0),$$

or

$$i^2 = -1. \tag{6}$$

Because $(x, y) = x + iy$, definitions (3) and (4) become

$$(x_1 + iy_1) + (x_2 + iy_2) = (x_1 + x_2) + i(y_1 + y_2), \tag{7}$$

$$(x_1 + iy_1)(x_2 + iy_2) = (x_1x_2 - y_1y_2) + i(y_1x_2 + x_1y_2). \tag{8}$$

*In electrical engineering, the letter j is used instead of i.

Observe that the right-hand sides of these equations can be obtained by formally manipulating the terms on the left as if they involved only real numbers and by replacing i^2 by -1 when it occurs. Also, observe how equation (8) tells us that *any complex number times zero is zero*. More precisely,

$$z \cdot 0 = (x + iy)(0 + i0) = 0 + i0 = 0$$

for any $z = x + iy$.

2. BASIC ALGEBRAIC PROPERTIES

Various properties of addition and multiplication of complex numbers are the same as for real numbers. We list here the more basic of these algebraic properties and verify some of them. Most of the others are verified in the exercises.

The commutative laws

$$z_1 + z_2 = z_2 + z_1, \quad z_1 z_2 = z_2 z_1 \tag{1}$$

and the associative laws

$$(z_1 + z_2) + z_3 = z_1 + (z_2 + z_3), \quad (z_1 z_2) z_3 = z_1 (z_2 z_3) \tag{2}$$

follow easily from the definitions in Sec. 1 of addition and multiplication of complex numbers and the fact that real numbers have corresponding properties. The same is true of the distributive law

$$z(z_1 + z_2) = z z_1 + z z_2. \tag{3}$$

EXAMPLE. If

$$z_1 = (x_1, y_1) \quad \text{and} \quad z_2 = (x_2, y_2),$$

then

$$z_1 + z_2 = (x_1 + x_2, y_1 + y_2) = (x_2 + x_1, y_2 + y_1) = z_2 + z_1.$$

According to the commutative law for multiplication, $iy = yi$. Hence one can write $z = x + yi$ instead of $z = x + iy$. Also, because of the associative laws, a sum $z_1 + z_2 + z_3$ or a product $z_1 z_2 z_3$ is well defined without parentheses, as is the case with real numbers.

The additive identity $0 = (0, 0)$ and the multiplicative identity $1 = (1, 0)$ for real numbers carry over to the entire complex number system. That is,

$$z + 0 = z \quad \text{and} \quad z \cdot 1 = z \tag{4}$$

for every complex number z. Furthermore, 0 and 1 are the only complex numbers with such properties (see Exercise 8).

There is associated with each complex number $z = (x, y)$ an additive inverse

$$-z = (-x, -y), \tag{5}$$

satisfying the equation $z + (-z) = 0$. Moreover, there is only one additive inverse for any given z, since the equation

$$(x, y) + (u, v) = (0, 0)$$

implies that

$$u = -x \quad \text{and} \quad v = -y.$$

For any *nonzero* complex number $z = (x, y)$, there is a number z^{-1} such that $zz^{-1} = 1$. This multiplicative inverse is less obvious than the additive one. To find it, we seek real numbers u and v, expressed in terms of x and y, such that

$$(x, y)(u, v) = (1, 0).$$

According to equation (4), Sec. 1, which defines the product of two complex numbers, u and v must satisfy the pair

$$xu - yv = 1, \quad yu + xv = 0$$

of linear simultaneous equations; and simple computation yields the unique solution

$$u = \frac{x}{x^2 + y^2}, \quad v = \frac{-y}{x^2 + y^2}.$$

So *the* multiplicative inverse of $z = (x, y)$ is

$$z^{-1} = \left(\frac{x}{x^2 + y^2}, \frac{-y}{x^2 + y^2}\right) \qquad (z \neq 0). \tag{6}$$

The inverse z^{-1} is not defined when $z = 0$. In fact, $z = 0$ means that $x^2 + y^2 = 0$; and this is not permitted in expression (6).

EXERCISES

1. Verify that

(*a*) $(\sqrt{2} - i) - i(1 - \sqrt{2}i) = -2i$;

(*b*) $(2, -3)(-2, 1) = (-1, 8)$;

(*c*) $(3, 1)(3, -1)\left(\frac{1}{5}, \frac{1}{10}\right) = (2, 1)$.

2. Show that

(*a*) $\text{Re}(iz) = -\text{Im}\, z$;

(*b*) $\text{Im}(iz) = \text{Re}\, z$.

3. Show that $(1+z)^2 = 1 + 2z + z^2$.

4. Verify that each of the two numbers $z = 1 \pm i$ satisfies the equation $z^2 - 2z + 2 = 0$.

5. Prove that multiplication of complex numbers is commutative, as stated at the beginning of Sec. 2.

6. Verify

(*a*) the associative law for addition of complex numbers, stated at the beginning of Sec. 2;

(*b*) the distributive law (3), Sec. 2.

7. Use the associative law for addition and the distributive law to show that

$$z(z_1 + z_2 + z_3) = zz_1 + zz_2 + zz_3.$$

8. (*a*) Write $(x, y) + (u, v) = (x, y)$ and point out how it follows that the complex number $0 = (0, 0)$ is unique as an additive identity.

(*b*) Likewise, write $(x, y)(u, v) = (x, y)$ and show that the number $1 = (1, 0)$ is a unique multiplicative identity.

9. Use $-1 = (-1, 0)$ and $z = (x, y)$ to show that $(-1)z = -z$.

10. Use $i = (0, 1)$ and $y = (y, 0)$ to verify that $-(iy) = (-i)y$. Thus show that the additive inverse of a complex number $z = x + iy$ can be written $-z = -x - iy$ without ambiguity.

11. Solve the equation $z^2 + z + 1 = 0$ for $z = (x, y)$ by writing

$$(x, y)(x, y) + (x, y) + (1, 0) = (0, 0)$$

and then solving a pair of simultaneous equations in x and y.

Suggestion: Use the fact that no real number x satisfies the given equation to show that $y \neq 0$.

Ans. $z = \left(-\frac{1}{2}, \pm\frac{\sqrt{3}}{2}\right)$.

3. FURTHER ALGEBRAIC PROPERTIES

In this section, we mention a number of other algebraic properties of addition and multiplication of complex numbers that follow from the ones already described in Sec. 2. Inasmuch as such properties continue to be anticipated because they also apply to real numbers, the reader can easily pass to Sec. 4 without serious disruption.

We begin with the observation that the existence of multiplicative inverses enables us to show that *if a product* $z_1 z_2$ *is zero, then so is at least one of the factors* z_1 *and* z_2. For suppose that $z_1 z_2 = 0$ and $z_1 \neq 0$. The inverse z_1^{-1} exists; and any complex number times zero is zero (Sec. 1). Hence

$$z_2 = z_2 \cdot 1 = z_2\left(z_1 z_1^{-1}\right) = \left(z_1^{-1} z_1\right) z_2 = z_1^{-1}(z_1 z_2) = z_1^{-1} \cdot 0 = 0.$$

That is, if $z_1 z_2 = 0$, either $z_1 = 0$ or $z_2 = 0$; or possibly both of the numbers z_1 and z_2 are zero. Another way to state this result is that *if two complex numbers z_1 and z_2 are nonzero, then so is their product $z_1 z_2$.*

Subtraction and division are defined in terms of additive and multiplicative inverses:

(1) $$z_1 - z_2 = z_1 + (-z_2),$$

(2) $$\frac{z_1}{z_2} = z_1 z_2^{-1} \qquad (z_2 \neq 0).$$

Thus, in view of expressions (5) and (6) in Sec. 2,

(3) $$z_1 - z_2 = (x_1, y_1) + (-x_2, -y_2) = (x_1 - x_2, y_1 - y_2)$$

and

(4) $$\frac{z_1}{z_2} = (x_1, y_1)\left(\frac{x_2}{x_2^2 + y_2^2}, \frac{-y_2}{x_2^2 + y_2^2}\right) = \left(\frac{x_1x_2 + y_1y_2}{x_2^2 + y_2^2}, \frac{y_1x_2 - x_1y_2}{x_2^2 + y_2^2}\right) \qquad (z_2 \neq 0)$$

when $z_1 = (x_1, y_1)$ and $z_2 = (x_2, y_2)$.

Using $z_1 = x_1 + iy_1$ and $z_2 = x_2 + iy_2$, one can write expressions (3) and (4) here as

(5) $$z_1 - z_2 = (x_1 - x_2) + i(y_1 - y_2)$$

and

(6) $$\frac{z_1}{z_2} = \frac{x_1x_2 + y_1y_2}{x_2^2 + y_2^2} + i\frac{y_1x_2 - x_1y_2}{x_2^2 + y_2^2} \qquad (z_2 \neq 0).$$

Although expression (6) is not easy to remember, it can be obtained by writing (see Exercise 7)

(7) $$\frac{z_1}{z_2} = \frac{(x_1 + iy_1)(x_2 - iy_2)}{(x_2 + iy_2)(x_2 - iy_2)},$$

multiplying out the products in the numerator and denominator on the right, and then using the property

(8) $$\frac{z_1 + z_2}{z_3} = (z_1 + z_2)z_3^{-1} = z_1 z_3^{-1} + z_2 z_3^{-1} = \frac{z_1}{z_3} + \frac{z_2}{z_3} \qquad (z_3 \neq 0).$$

The motivation for starting with equation (7) appears in Sec. 5.

EXAMPLE. The method is illustrated below:

$$\frac{4 + i}{2 - 3i} = \frac{(4 + i)(2 + 3i)}{(2 - 3i)(2 + 3i)} = \frac{5 + 14i}{13} = \frac{5}{13} + \frac{14}{13}i.$$

There are some expected properties involving quotients that follow from the relation

$$\frac{1}{z_2} = z_2^{-1} \qquad (z_2 \neq 0), \tag{9}$$

which is equation (2) when $z_1 = 1$. Relation (9) enables us, for instance, to write equation (2) in the form

$$\frac{z_1}{z_2} = z_1\left(\frac{1}{z_2}\right) \qquad (z_2 \neq 0). \tag{10}$$

Also, by observing that (see Exercise 3)

$$(z_1z_2)(z_1^{-1}z_2^{-1}) = (z_1z_1^{-1})(z_2z_2^{-1}) = 1 \qquad (z_1 \neq 0,\ z_2 \neq 0),$$

and hence that $z_1^{-1}z_2^{-1} = (z_1z_2)^{-1}$, one can use relation (9) to show that

$$\left(\frac{1}{z_1}\right)\left(\frac{1}{z_2}\right) = z_1^{-1}z_2^{-1} = (z_1z_2)^{-1} = \frac{1}{z_1z_2} \qquad (z_1 \neq 0,\ z_2 \neq 0). \tag{11}$$

Another useful property, to be derived in the exercises, is

$$\left(\frac{z_1}{z_3}\right)\left(\frac{z_2}{z_4}\right) = \frac{z_1z_2}{z_3z_4} \qquad (z_3 \neq 0,\ z_4 \neq 0). \tag{12}$$

Finally, we note that the ***binomial formula*** involving real numbers remains valid with complex numbers. That is, if z_1 and z_2 are any two nonzero complex numbers, then

$$(z_1 + z_2)^n = \sum_{k=0}^{n} \binom{n}{k} z_1^k z_2^{n-k} \qquad (n = 1, 2, \ldots) \tag{13}$$

where

$$\binom{n}{k} = \frac{n!}{k!(n-k)!} \qquad (k = 0, 1, 2, \ldots, n)$$

and where it is agreed that $0! = 1$. The proof is left as an exercise. Because addition of complex numbers is commutative, the binomial formula can, of course, be written

$$(z_1 + z_2)^n = \sum_{k=0}^{n} \binom{n}{k} z_1^{n-k} z_2^k \qquad (n = 1, 2, \ldots). \tag{14}$$

EXERCISES

1. Reduce each of these quantities to a real number:

(*a*) $\dfrac{1+2i}{3-4i} + \dfrac{2-i}{5i}$; (*b*) $\dfrac{5i}{(1-i)(2-i)(3-i)}$; (*c*) $(1-i)^4$.

Ans. (*a*) $-\dfrac{2}{5}$; (*b*) $-\dfrac{1}{2}$; (*c*) -4.

2. Show that

$$\frac{1}{1/z} = z \qquad (z \neq 0).$$

3. Use the associative and commutative laws for multiplication to show that

$$(z_1 z_2)(z_3 z_4) = (z_1 z_3)(z_2 z_4).$$

4. Prove that if $z_1 z_2 z_3 = 0$, then at least one of the three factors is zero.

Suggestion: Write $(z_1 z_2) z_3 = 0$ and use a similar result (Sec. 3) involving two factors.

5. Derive expression (6), Sec. 3, for the quotient z_1/z_2 by the method described just after it.

6. With the aid of relations (10) and (11) in Sec. 3, derive the identity

$$\left(\frac{z_1}{z_3}\right)\left(\frac{z_2}{z_4}\right) = \frac{z_1 z_2}{z_3 z_4} \qquad (z_3 \neq 0,\, z_4 \neq 0).$$

7. Use the identity obtained in Exercise 6 to derive the cancellation law

$$\frac{z_1 z}{z_2 z} = \frac{z_1}{z_2} \qquad (z_2 \neq 0,\, z \neq 0).$$

8. Use mathematical induction to verify the binomial formula (13) in Sec. 3. More precisely, note that the formula is true when $n = 1$. Then, assuming that it is valid when $n = m$ where m denotes any positive integer, show that it must hold when $n = m + 1$.

Suggestion: When $n = m + 1$, write

$$\begin{aligned}(z_1 + z_2)^{m+1} &= (z_1 + z_2)(z_1 + z_2)^m = (z_2 + z_1)\sum_{k=0}^{m}\binom{m}{k} z_1^k z_2^{m-k} \\ &= \sum_{k=0}^{m}\binom{m}{k} z_1^k z_2^{m+1-k} + \sum_{k=0}^{m}\binom{m}{k} z_1^{k+1} z_2^{m-k}\end{aligned}$$

and replace k by $k - 1$ in the last sum here to obtain

$$(z_1 + z_2)^{m+1} = z_2^{m+1} + \sum_{k=1}^{m}\left[\binom{m}{k} + \binom{m}{k-1}\right] z_1^k z_2^{m+1-k} + z_1^{m+1}.$$

Finally, show how the right-hand side here becomes

$$z_2^{m+1} + \sum_{k=1}^{m}\binom{m+1}{k} z_1^k z_2^{m+1-k} + z_1^{m+1} = \sum_{k=0}^{m+1}\binom{m+1}{k} z_1^k z_2^{m+1-k}.$$

4. VECTORS AND MODULI

It is natural to associate any nonzero complex number $z = x + iy$ with the directed line segment, or vector, from the origin to the point (x, y) that represents z in the complex plane. In fact, we often refer to z as the point z or the vector z. In Fig. 2 the numbers $z = x + iy$ and $-2 + i$ are displayed graphically as both points and radius vectors.

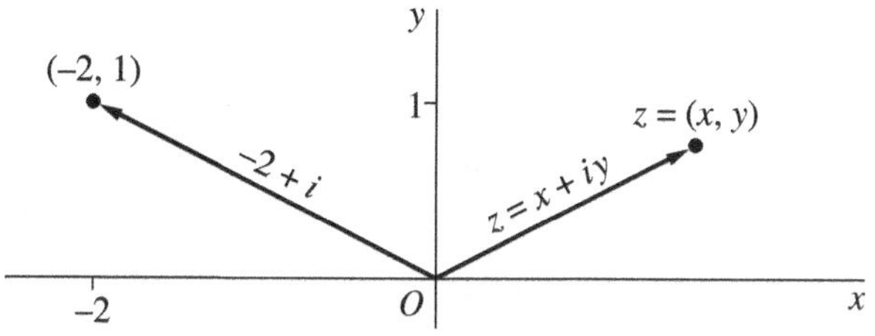

FIGURE 2

When $z_1 = x_1 + iy_1$ and $z_2 = x_2 + iy_2$, the sum

$$z_1 + z_2 = (x_1 + x_2) + i(y_1 + y_2)$$

corresponds to the point $(x_1 + x_2, y_1 + y_2)$. It also corresponds to a vector with those coordinates as its components. Hence $z_1 + z_2$ may be obtained vectorially as shown in Fig. 3.

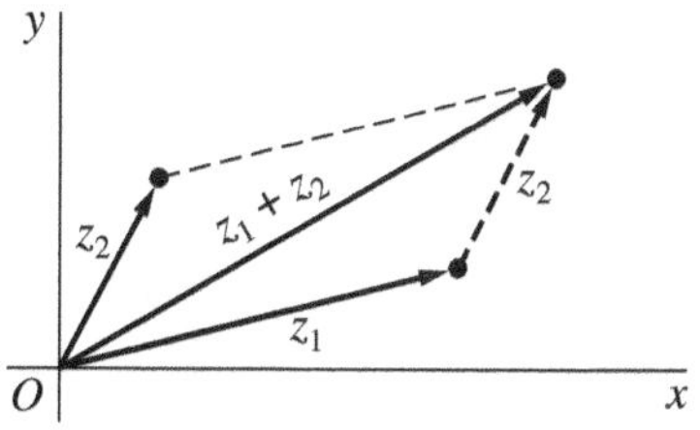

FIGURE 3

Although the product of two complex numbers z_1 and z_2 is itself a complex number represented by a vector, that vector lies in the same plane as the vectors for z_1 and z_2. Evidently, then, this product is neither the scalar nor the vector product used in ordinary vector analysis.

The vector interpretation of complex numbers is especially helpful in extending the concept of absolute values of real numbers to the complex plane. The ***modulus***, or absolute value, of a complex number $z = x + iy$ is defined as the nonnegative real number $\sqrt{x^2 + y^2}$ and is denoted by $|z|$; that is,

$$|z| = \sqrt{x^2 + y^2}. \tag{1}$$

It follows immediately from definition (1) that the real numbers $|z|$, $x = \operatorname{Re} z$, and $y = \operatorname{Im} z$ are related by the equation

$$|z|^2 = (\operatorname{Re} z)^2 + (\operatorname{Im} z)^2. \tag{2}$$

Thus

$$\operatorname{Re} z \le |\operatorname{Re} z| \le |z| \quad \text{and} \quad \operatorname{Im} z \le |\operatorname{Im} z| \le |z|. \tag{3}$$

Geometrically, the number $|z|$ is the distance between the point (x, y) and the origin, or the length of the radius vector representing z. It reduces to the usual absolute value in the real number system when $y = 0$. Note that while *the inequality $z_1 < z_2$ is meaningless unless both z_1 and z_2 are real,* the statement $|z_1| < |z_2|$ means that the point z_1 is closer to the origin than the point z_2 is.

EXAMPLE 1. Since $|-3+2i| = \sqrt{13}$ and $|1+4i| = \sqrt{17}$, we know that the point $-3+2i$ is closer to the origin than $1+4i$ is.

The distance between two points (x_1, y_1) and (x_2, y_2) is $|z_1 - z_2|$. This is clear from Fig. 4, since $|z_1 - z_2|$ is the length of the vector representing the number

$$z_1 - z_2 = z_1 + (-z_2);$$

and, by translating the radius vector $z_1 - z_2$, one can interpret $z_1 - z_2$ as the directed line segment from the point (x_2, y_2) to the point (x_1, y_1). Alternatively, it follows from the expression

$$z_1 - z_2 = (x_1 - x_2) + i(y_1 - y_2)$$

and definition (1) that

$$|z_1 - z_2| = \sqrt{(x_1 - x_2)^2 + (y_1 - y_2)^2}.$$

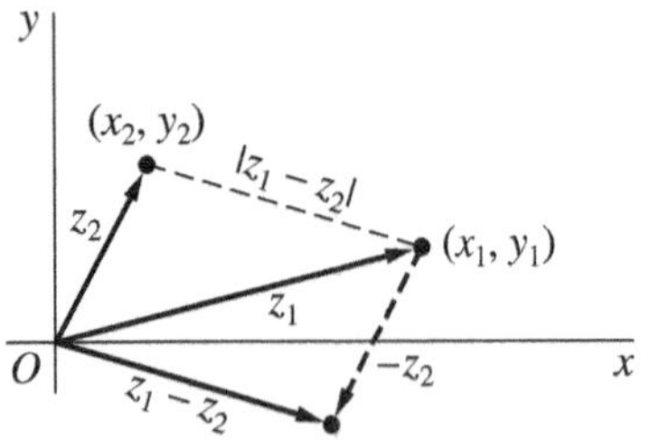

FIGURE 4

The complex numbers z corresponding to the points lying on the circle with center z_0 and radius R thus satisfy the equation $|z - z_0| = R$, and conversely. We refer to this set of points simply as the circle $|z - z_0| = R$.

EXAMPLE 2. The equation $|z - 1 + 3i| = 2$ represents the circle whose center is $z_0 = (1, -3)$ and whose radius is $R = 2$.

Our final example here illustrates the power of geometric reasoning in complex analysis when straightforward computation can be somewhat tedious.

EXAMPLE 3. Consider the set of all points $z = (x, y)$ satisfying the equation

$$|z - 4i| + |z + 4i| = 10.$$

Upon writing this as

$$|z - 4i| + |z - (-4i)| = 10,$$

one can see that it represents the set of all points $P(x, y)$ in the $z = (x, y)$ plane the sum of whose distances from two fixed points $F(0, 4)$ and $F'(0, -4)$ is the constant 10. This is, of course, an ellipse with foci $F(0, 4)$ and $F'(0, -4)$.

5. TRIANGLE INEQUALITY

We turn now to the ***triangle inequality***, which provides an upper bound for the modulus of the sum of two complex numbers z_1 and z_2:

$$|z_1 + z_2| \leq |z_1| + |z_2|. \tag{1}$$

This important inequality is geometrically evident in Fig. 3 of Sec. 4 since it is merely a statement that the length of one side of a triangle is less than or equal to the sum of the lengths of the other two sides. We can also see from Fig. 3 that inequality (1) is actually an equality when 0, z_1, and z_2 are collinear. Another, strictly algebraic, derivation is given in Exercise 15, Sec. 6.

An immediate consequence of the triangle inequality is the fact that

$$|z_1 + z_2| \geq ||z_1| - |z_2||. \tag{2}$$

To derive inequality (2), we write

$$|z_1| = |(z_1 + z_2) + (-z_2)| \leq |z_1 + z_2| + |-z_2|,$$

which means that

$$|z_1 + z_2| \geq |z_1| - |z_2|. \tag{3}$$

This is inequality (2) when $|z_1| \geq |z_2|$. If $|z_1| < |z_2|$, we need only interchange z_1 and z_2 in inequality (3) to arrive at

$$|z_1 + z_2| \geq -(|z_1| - |z_2|),$$

which is the desired result. Inequality (2) tells us, of course, that the length of one side of a triangle is greater than or equal to the difference of the lengths of the other two sides.

Because $|-z_2| = |z_2|$, one can replace z_2 by $-z_2$ in inequalities (1) and (2) to write

$$|z_1 - z_2| \leq |z_1| + |z_2| \quad \text{and} \quad |z_1 - z_2| \geq ||z_1| - |z_2||.$$

In actual practice, however, one need use only inequalities (1) and (2). This is illustrated in the following example.

EXAMPLE 1. If a point z lies on the unit circle $|z| = 1$, inequalities (1) and (2) tell us that

$$|z - 2| = |z + (-2)| \leq |z| + |-2| = 1 + 2 = 3$$

and

$$|z - 2| = |z + (-2)| \geq ||z| - |-2|| = |1 - 2| = 1.$$

The triangle inequality (1) can be generalized by means of mathematical induction to sums involving any finite number of terms:

$$|z_1 + z_2 + \cdots + z_n| \le |z_1| + |z_2| + \cdots + |z_n| \qquad (n = 2, 3, \ldots). \tag{4}$$

To give details of the induction proof here, we note that when $n = 2$, inequality (4) is just inequality (1). Furthermore, if inequality (4) is valid when $n = m$, it must also hold when $n = m + 1$ since by inequality (1),

$$\begin{aligned}|(z_1 + z_2 + \cdots + z_m) + z_{m+1}| &\le |z_1 + z_2 + \cdots + z_m| + |z_{m+1}| \\ &\le (|z_1| + |z_2| + \cdots + |z_m|) + |z_{m+1}|.\end{aligned}$$

EXAMPLE 2. Let z denote any complex number lying on the circle $|z| = 2$. Inequality (4) tells us that

$$\left|3 + z + z^2\right| \le 3 + |z| + \left|z^2\right|.$$

Since $|z^2| = |z|^2$, according to Exercise (8),

$$|3 + z + z^2| \le 9.$$

EXAMPLE 3. If n is a positive integer and if $a_0, a_1, a_2, \ldots, a_n$ are complex constants, where $a_n \ne 0$, the quantity

$$P(z) = a_0 + a_1 z + a_2 z^2 + \cdots + a_n z^n \tag{5}$$

is a ***polynomial*** of degree n. We shall show here that for some positive number R, the reciprocal $1/P(z)$ satisfies the inequality

$$\left|\frac{1}{P(z)}\right| < \frac{2}{|a_n|R^n} \quad \text{whenever} \quad |z| > R. \tag{6}$$

Geometrically, this tells us that the modulus of the reciprocal $1/P(z)$ is bounded from above when z is exterior to the circle $|z| = R$. This important property of polynomials will be used later on in Sec. 58 of Chap. 4, and we verify it here since it illustrates the use of inequalities presented in this section, as well as the identities

$$|z_1 z_2| = |z_1||z_2| \quad \text{and} \quad |z^n| = |z|^n \quad (n = 1, 2, \ldots)$$

to be obtained in Exercises 8 and 9.

We first write

$$w = \frac{a_0}{z^n} + \frac{a_1}{z^{n-1}} + \frac{a_2}{z^{n-2}} + \cdots + \frac{a_{n-1}}{z} \qquad (z \ne 0), \tag{7}$$

so that

$$P(z) = (a_n + w)z^n \tag{8}$$

when $z \neq 0$. Next, we multiply through equation (7) by z^n:

$$wz^n = a_0 + a_1 z + a_2 z^2 + \cdots + a_{n-1} z^{n-1}.$$

This tells us that

$$|w||z|^n \leq |a_0| + |a_1||z| + |a_2||z|^2 + \cdots + |a_{n-1}||z|^{n-1},$$

or

$$(9) \qquad |w| \leq \frac{|a_0|}{|z|^n} + \frac{|a_1|}{|z|^{n-1}} + \frac{|a_2|}{|z|^{n-2}} + \cdots + \frac{|a_{n-1}|}{|z|}.$$

Now that a sufficiently large positive number R can be found such that each of the quotients on the right in inequality (9) is less than the number $|a_n|/(2n)$ when $|z| > R$, and so

$$|w| < n\frac{|a_n|}{2n} = \frac{|a_n|}{2} \quad \text{whenever} \quad |z|>R.$$

Consequently,

$$|a_n + w| \geq ||a_n| - |w|| > \frac{|a_n|}{2} \quad \text{whenever} \quad |z| > R;$$

and, in view of equation (8),

$$(10) \qquad |P_n(z)| = |a_n + w||z|^n > \frac{|a_n|}{2}|z|^n > \frac{|a_n|}{2}R^n \quad \text{whenever} \quad |z| > R.$$

Statement (6) follows immediately from this.

EXERCISES

1. Locate the numbers $z_1 + z_2$ and $z_1 - z_2$ vectorially when

(*a*) $z_1 = 2i, \quad z_2 = \frac{2}{3} - i$;

(*b*) $z_1 = (-\sqrt{3}, 1), \quad z_2 = (\sqrt{3}, 0)$;

(*c*) $z_1 = (-3, 1), \quad z_2 = (1, 4)$;

(*d*) $z_1 = x_1 + iy_1, \quad z_2 = x_1 - iy_1$.

2. Verify inequalities (3), Sec. 4, involving $\text{Re}\, z$, $\text{Im}\, z$, and $|z|$.

3. Use established properties of moduli to show that when $|z_3| \neq |z_4|$,

$$\frac{\text{Re}(z_1 + z_2)}{|z_3 + z_4|} \leq \frac{|z_1| + |z_2|}{||z_3| - |z_4||}.$$

4. Verify that $\sqrt{2}\,|z| \geq |\text{Re}\, z| + |\text{Im}\, z|$.

Suggestion: Reduce this inequality to $(|x| - |y|)^2 \geq 0$.

5. In each case, sketch the set of points determined by the given condition:

(*a*) $|z - 1 + i| = 1$; (*b*) $|z + i| \leq 3$; (*c*) $|z - 4i| \geq 4$.

6. Using the fact that $|z_1 - z_2|$ is the distance between two points z_1 and z_2, give a geometric argument that $|z - 1| = |z + i|$ represents the line through the origin whose slope is -1.

7. Show that for R sufficiently large, the polynomial $P(z)$ in Example 3, Sec. 5, satisfies the inequality

$$|P(z)| < 2|a_n||z|^n \quad \text{whenever} \quad |z| > R.$$

Suggestion: Observe that there is a positive number R such that the modulus of each quotient in inequality (9), Sec. 5, is less than $|a_n|/n$ when $|z| > R$.

8. Let z_1 and z_2 denote any complex numbers

$$z_1 = x_1 + iy_1 \quad \text{and} \quad z_2 = x_2 + iy_2.$$

Use simple algebra to show that

$$|(x_1 + iy_1)(x_2 + iy_2)| \quad \text{and} \quad \sqrt{(x_1^2 + y_1^2)(x_2^2 + y_2^2)}$$

are the same and then point out how the identity

$$|z_1 z_2| = |z_1||z_2|$$

follows.

9. Use the final result in Exercise 8 and mathematical induction to show that

$$|z^n| = |z|^n \qquad (n = 1, 2, \ldots),$$

where z is any complex number. That is, after noting that this identity is obviously true when $n = 1$, assume that it is true when $n = m$ where m is any positive integer and then show that it must be true when $n = m + 1$.

6. COMPLEX CONJUGATES

The ***complex conjugate***, or simply the conjugate, of a complex number $z = x + iy$ is defined as the complex number $x - iy$ and is denoted by $\bar{z}$; that is,

$$\bar{z} = x - iy. \tag{1}$$

The number $\bar{z}$ is represented by the point $(x, -y)$, which is the reflection in the real axis of the point (x, y) representing z (Fig. 5). Note that

$$\bar{\bar{z}} = z \quad \text{and} \quad |\bar{z}| = |z|$$

for all z.

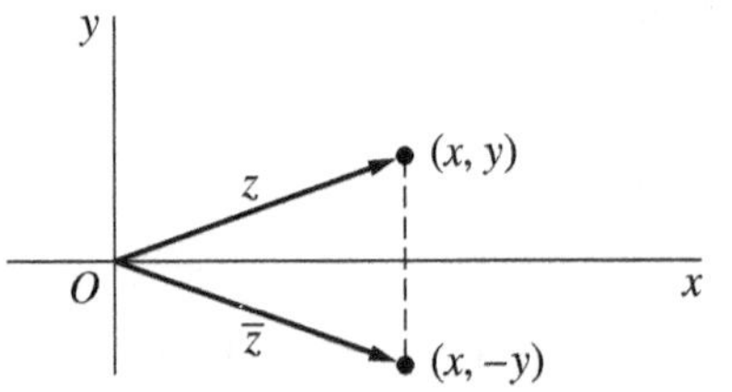

FIGURE 5

If $z_1 = x_1 + iy_1$ and $z_2 = x_2 + iy_2$, then

$$\overline{z_1 + z_2} = (x_1 + x_2) - i(y_1 + y_2) = (x_1 - iy_1) + (x_2 - iy_2).$$

So the conjugate of the sum is the sum of the conjugates:

$$\overline{z_1 + z_2} = \overline{z_1} + \overline{z_2}. \tag{2}$$

In like manner, it is easy to show that

$$\overline{z_1 - z_2} = \overline{z_1} - \overline{z_2}, \tag{3}$$

$$\overline{z_1 z_2} = \overline{z_1}\,\overline{z_2}, \tag{4}$$

and

$$\overline{\left(\frac{z_1}{z_2}\right)} = \frac{\overline{z_1}}{\overline{z_2}} \qquad (z_2 \neq 0). \tag{5}$$

The sum $z + \overline{z}$ of a complex number $z = x + iy$ and its conjugate $\overline{z} = x - iy$ is the real number $2x$, and the difference $z - \overline{z}$ is $2iy$. Hence

$$\operatorname{Re} z = \frac{z + \overline{z}}{2} \quad \text{and} \quad \operatorname{Im} z = \frac{z - \overline{z}}{2i}. \tag{6}$$

An important identity relating the conjugate of a complex number $z = x + iy$ to its modulus is

$$z\overline{z} = |z|^2, \tag{7}$$

where each side is equal to $x^2 + y^2$. It suggests the method for determining a quotient z_1/z_2 that begins with expression (7), Sec. 3. That method is, of course, based on multiplying both the numerator and the denominator of z_1/z_2 by $\overline{z_2}$, so that the denominator becomes the real number $|z_2|^2$.

EXAMPLE 1. As an illustration,

$$\frac{-1 + 3i}{2 - i} = \frac{(-1 + 3i)(2 + i)}{(2 - i)(2 + i)} = \frac{-5 + 5i}{|2 - i|^2} = \frac{-5 + 5i}{5} = -1 + i.$$

See also the example in Sec. 3.

Identity (7) is especially useful in obtaining properties of moduli from properties of conjugates noted above. We mention that (compare with Exercise 8, Sec. 5)

$$|z_1 z_2| = |z_1||z_2|. \tag{8}$$

Also,

$$\left|\frac{z_1}{z_2}\right| = \frac{|z_1|}{|z_2|} \qquad (z_2 \neq 0). \tag{9}$$

Property (8) can be established by writing

$$|z_1 z_2|^2 = (z_1 z_2)(\overline{z_1 z_2}) = (z_1 z_2)(\overline{z_1}\,\overline{z_2}) = (z_1\overline{z_1})(z_2\overline{z_2}) = |z_1|^2|z_2|^2 = (|z_1||z_2|)^2$$

and recalling that a modulus is never negative. Property (9) can be verified in a similar way.

EXAMPLE 2. Property (8) tells us that $|z^2| = |z|^2$ and $|z^3| = |z|^3$. Hence if z is a point inside the circle centered at the origin with radius 2, so that $|z| < 2$, it follows from the generalized triangle inequality (4) in Sec. 5 that

$$|z^3 + 3z^2 - 2z + 1| \le |z|^3 + 3|z|^2 + 2|z| + 1 < 25.$$

EXERCISES

1. Use properties of conjugates and moduli established in Sec. 6 to show that

(*a*) $\overline{\bar{z} + 3i} = z - 3i$; (*b*) $\overline{iz} = -i\bar{z}$;

(*c*) $\overline{(2+i)^2} = 3 - 4i$; (*d*) $|(2\bar{z}+5)(\sqrt{2}-i)| = \sqrt{3}\,|2z+5|$.

2. Sketch the set of points determined by the condition

(*a*) $\text{Re}(\bar{z} - i) = 2$; (*b*) $|2\bar{z} + i| = 4$.

3. Verify properties (3) and (4) of conjugates in Sec. 6.

4. Use property (4) of conjugates in Sec. 6 to show that

(*a*) $\overline{z_1 z_2 z_3} = \bar{z}_1\,\bar{z}_2\,\bar{z}_3$; (*b*) $\overline{z^4} = \bar{z}^4$.

5. Verify property (9) of moduli in Sec. 6.

6. Use results in Sec. 6 to show that when z_2 and z_3 are nonzero,

(*a*) $\overline{\left(\dfrac{z_1}{z_2 z_3}\right)} = \dfrac{\bar{z}_1}{\bar{z}_2\,\bar{z}_3}$; (*b*) $\left|\dfrac{z_1}{z_2 z_3}\right| = \dfrac{|z_1|}{|z_2||z_3|}$.

7. Show that

$$|\text{Re}(2 + \bar{z} + z^3)| \le 4 \qquad \text{when } |z| \le 1.$$

8. It is shown in Sec. 3 that if $z_1 z_2 = 0$, then at least one of the numbers z_1 and z_2 must be zero. Give an alternative proof based on the corresponding result for real numbers and using identity (8), Sec. 6.

9. By factoring $z^4 - 4z^2 + 3$ into two quadratic factors and using inequality (2), Sec. 5, show that if z lies on the circle $|z| = 2$, then

$$\left|\frac{1}{z^4 - 4z^2 + 3}\right| \le \frac{1}{3}.$$

10. Prove that

(*a*) z is real if and only if $\bar{z} = z$;

(*b*) z is either real or pure imaginary if and only if $\bar{z}^2 = z^2$.

11. Use mathematical induction to show that when $n = 2, 3, \ldots,$

(*a*) $\overline{z_1 + z_2 + \cdots + z_n} = \bar{z}_1 + \bar{z}_2 + \cdots + \bar{z}_n$;

(*b*) $\overline{z_1 z_2 \cdots z_n} = \bar{z}_1\,\bar{z}_2 \cdots \bar{z}_n$.

12. Let $a_0, a_1, a_2, \ldots, a_n$ $(n \geq 1)$ denote *real* numbers, and let z be any complex number. With the aid of the results in Exercise 11, show that

$$\overline{a_0 + a_1 z + a_2 z^2 + \cdots + a_n z^n} = a_0 + a_1 \bar{z} + a_2 \bar{z}^2 + \cdots + a_n \bar{z}^n.$$

13. Show that the equation $|z - z_0| = R$ of a circle, centered at z_0 with radius R, can be written

$$|z|^2 - 2\,\mathrm{Re}(z\bar{z}_0) + |z_0|^2 = R^2.$$

14. Using expressions (6), Sec. 6, for $\mathrm{Re}\, z$ and $\mathrm{Im}\, z$, show that the hyperbola $x^2 - y^2 = 1$ can be written

$$z^2 + \bar{z}^2 = 2.$$

15. Follow the steps below to give an algebraic derivation of the triangle inequality (Sec. 5)

$$|z_1 + z_2| \leq |z_1| + |z_2|.$$

(*a*) Show that

$$|z_1 + z_2|^2 = (z_1 + z_2)(\bar{z}_1 + \bar{z}_2) = z_1\bar{z}_1 + (z_1\bar{z}_2 + \overline{z_1\bar{z}_2}) + z_2\bar{z}_2.$$

(*b*) Point out why

$$z_1\bar{z}_2 + \overline{z_1\bar{z}_2} = 2\,\mathrm{Re}(z_1\bar{z}_2) \leq 2|z_1||z_2|.$$

(*c*) Use the results in parts (*a*) and (*b*) to obtain the inequality

$$|z_1 + z_2|^2 \leq (|z_1| + |z_2|)^2,$$

and note how the triangle inequality follows.

7. EXPONENTIAL FORM

Let r and θ be polar coordinates of the point (x, y) that corresponds to a *nonzero* complex number $z = x + iy$. Since $x = r\cos\theta$ and $y = r\sin\theta$, the number z can be written in ***polar form*** as

$$z = r(\cos\theta + i\sin\theta). \tag{1}$$

If $z = 0$, the coordinate θ is undefined; and so it is understood that $z \neq 0$ whenever polar coordinates are used.

In complex analysis, the real number r is not allowed to be negative and is the length of the radius vector for z; that is, $r = |z|$. The real number θ represents the angle, measured in radians, that z makes with the positive real axis when z is interpreted as a radius vector (Fig. 6). As in calculus, θ has an infinite number of possible values, including negative ones, that differ by integral multiples of 2π. Those values can be determined from the equation $\tan\theta = y/x$, where the quadrant containing the point corresponding to z must be specified. Each value of θ is called an ***argument*** of z, and the set of all such values is denoted by $\arg z$. The ***principal value*** of $\arg z$, denoted by

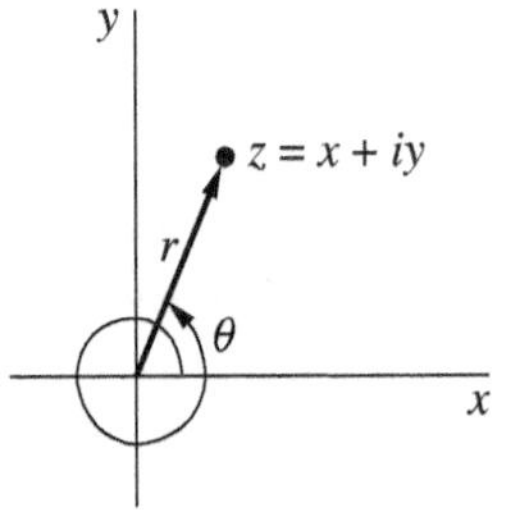

FIGURE 6

Arg z, is the unique value Θ such that $-\pi < \Theta \le \pi$. Evidently, then,

$$\arg z = \text{Arg}\, z + 2n\pi \qquad (n = 0, \pm 1, \pm 2, \ldots). \tag{2}$$

Also, when z is a negative real number, Arg z has the value π, not $-\pi$.

EXAMPLE 1. The complex number $-1 - i$, which lies in the third quadrant, has principal argument $-3\pi/4$. That is,

$$\text{Arg}(-1 - i) = -\frac{3\pi}{4}.$$

It must be emphasized that because of the restriction $-\pi < \Theta \le \pi$ of the principal argument Θ, it is *not* true that $\text{Arg}(-1 - i) = 5\pi/4$.

According to equation (2),

$$\arg(-1 - i) = -\frac{3\pi}{4} + 2n\pi \qquad (n = 0, \pm 1, \pm 2, \ldots).$$

Note that the term Arg z on the right-hand side of equation (2) can be replaced by any particular value of arg z and that one can write, for instance,

$$\arg(-1 - i) = \frac{5\pi}{4} + 2n\pi \qquad (n = 0, \pm 1, \pm 2, \ldots).$$

The symbol $e^{i\theta}$, or $\exp(i\theta)$, is defined by means of ***Euler's formula*** as

$$e^{i\theta} = \cos\theta + i\sin\theta, \tag{3}$$

where θ is to be measured in radians. It enables us to write the polar form (1) more compactly in ***exponential form*** as

$$z = re^{i\theta}. \tag{4}$$

The choice of the symbol $e^{i\theta}$ will be fully motivated later on in Sec. 30. Its use in Sec. 8 will, however, suggest that it is a natural choice.

EXAMPLE 2. The number $-1 - i$ in Example 1 has exponential form

$$-1 - i = \sqrt{2}\exp\left[i\left(-\frac{3\pi}{4}\right)\right]. \tag{5}$$

With the agreement that $e^{-i\theta} = e^{i(-\theta)}$, this can also be written $-1 - i = \sqrt{2}\, e^{-i3\pi/4}$. Expression (5) is, of course, only one of an infinite number of possibilities for the exponential form of $-1 - i$:

$$(6) \qquad -1 - i = \sqrt{2}\exp\left[i\left(-\frac{3\pi}{4} + 2n\pi\right)\right] \qquad (n = 0, \pm 1, \pm 2, \ldots).$$

Note how expression (4) with $r = 1$ tells us that the numbers $e^{i\theta}$ lie on the circle centered at the origin with radius unity, as shown in Fig. 7. Values of $e^{i\theta}$ are, then, immediate from that figure, without reference to Euler's formula. It is, for instance, geometrically obvious that

$$e^{i\pi} = -1, \quad e^{-i\pi/2} = -i, \quad \text{and} \quad e^{-i4\pi} = 1.$$

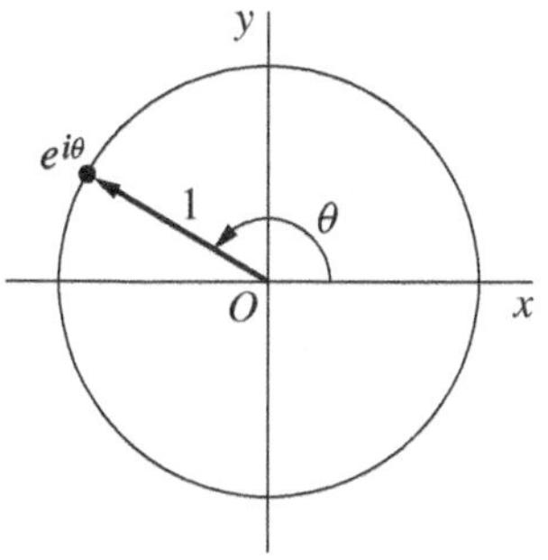

FIGURE 7

Note, too, that the equation

$$(7) \qquad z = Re^{i\theta} \qquad (0 \le \theta \le 2\pi)$$

is a parametric representation of the circle $|z| = R$, centered at the origin with radius R. As the parameter θ increases from $\theta = 0$ to $\theta = 2\pi$, the point z starts from the positive real axis and traverses the circle once in the counterclockwise direction. More generally, the circle $|z - z_0| = R$, whose center is z_0 and whose radius is R, has the parametric representation

$$(8) \qquad z = z_0 + Re^{i\theta} \qquad (0 \le \theta \le 2\pi).$$

This can be seen vectorially (Fig. 8) by noting that a point z traversing the circle $|z - z_0| = R$ once in the counterclockwise direction corresponds to the sum of the fixed vector z_0 and a vector of length R whose angle of inclination θ varies from $\theta = 0$ to $\theta = 2\pi$.

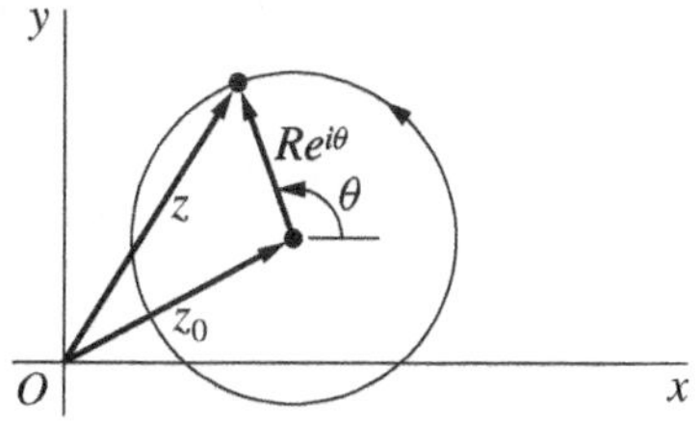

FIGURE 8

8. PRODUCTS AND POWERS IN EXPONENTIAL FORM

Simple trigonometry tells us that $e^{i\theta}$ has the familiar additive property of the exponential function in calculus:

$$\begin{aligned} e^{i\theta_1}e^{i\theta_2} &= (\cos\theta_1 + i\sin\theta_1)(\cos\theta_2 + i\sin\theta_2) \\ &= (\cos\theta_1\cos\theta_2 - \sin\theta_1\sin\theta_2) + i(\sin\theta_1\cos\theta_2 + \cos\theta_1\sin\theta_2) \\ &= \cos(\theta_1+\theta_2) + i\sin(\theta_1+\theta_2) = e^{i(\theta_1+\theta_2)}. \end{aligned}$$

Thus, if $z_1 = r_1e^{i\theta_1}$ and $z_2 = r_2e^{i\theta_2}$, the product z_1z_2 has the exponential form

$$z_1z_2 = r_1e^{i\theta_1}r_2e^{i\theta_2} = r_1r_2e^{i\theta_1}e^{i\theta_2} = (r_1r_2)e^{i(\theta_1+\theta_2)}. \tag{1}$$

Furthermore,

$$\frac{z_1}{z_2} = \frac{r_1e^{i\theta_1}}{r_2e^{i\theta_2}} = \frac{r_1}{r_2}\cdot\frac{e^{i\theta_1}e^{-i\theta_2}}{e^{i\theta_2}e^{-i\theta_2}} = \frac{r_1}{r_2}\cdot\frac{e^{i(\theta_1-\theta_2)}}{e^{i0}} = \frac{r_1}{r_2}e^{i(\theta_1-\theta_2)}. \tag{2}$$

Note how it follows from expression (2) that the inverse of any nonzero complex number $z = re^{i\theta}$ is

$$z^{-1} = \frac{1}{z} = \frac{1e^{i0}}{re^{i\theta}} = \frac{1}{r}e^{i(0-\theta)} = \frac{1}{r}e^{-i\theta}. \tag{3}$$

Expressions (1), (2), and (3) are, of course, easily remembered by applying the usual algebraic rules for real numbers and e^x.

Another important result that can be obtained formally by applying rules for real numbers to $z = re^{i\theta}$ is

$$z^n = r^ne^{in\theta} \qquad (n = 0, \pm1, \pm2, \ldots). \tag{4}$$

It is easily verified for positive values of n by mathematical induction. To be specific, we first note that it becomes $z = re^{i\theta}$ when $n = 1$. Next, we assume that it is valid when $n = m$, where m is any positive integer. In view of expression (1) for the product of two nonzero complex numbers in exponential form, it is then valid for $n = m + 1$:

$$z^{m+1} = z^mz = r^me^{im\theta}re^{i\theta} = (r^mr)e^{i(m\theta+\theta)} = r^{m+1}e^{i(m+1)\theta}.$$

Expression (4) is thus verified when n is a positive integer. It also holds when $n = 0$, with the convention that $z^0 = 1$. If $n = -1, -2, \ldots,$ on the other hand, we define z^n in terms of the multiplicative inverse of z by writing

$$z^n = (z^{-1})^m \quad \text{where} \quad m = -n = 1, 2, \ldots.$$

Then, since equation (4) is valid for positive integers, it follows from the exponential form (3) of z^{-1} that

$$z^n = \left[\frac{1}{r}e^{i(-\theta)}\right]^m = \left(\frac{1}{r}\right)^m e^{im(-\theta)} = \left(\frac{1}{r}\right)^{-n} e^{i(-n)(-\theta)} = r^ne^{in\theta}$$
$$(n = -1, -2, \ldots).$$

Expression (4) is now established for all integral powers.

Expression (4) can be useful in finding powers of complex numbers even when they are given in rectangular form and the result is desired in that form.

EXAMPLE 1. In order to put $(-1+i)^7$ in rectangular form, write

$$(-1+i)^7 = (\sqrt{2}\, e^{i3\pi/4})^7 = 2^{7/2} e^{i\,21\pi/4} = (2^3 e^{i5\pi})(2^{1/2} e^{i\,\pi/4}).$$

Because

$$2^3 e^{i5\pi} = (8)(-1) = -8$$

and

$$2^{1/2} e^{i\,\pi/4} = \sqrt{2}\left(\cos\frac{\pi}{4} + i\sin\frac{\pi}{4}\right) = \sqrt{2}\left(\frac{1}{\sqrt{2}} + \frac{i}{\sqrt{2}}\right) = 1+i,$$

we arrive at the desired result: $(-1+i)^7 = -8\,(1+i)$.

Finally, we observe that if $r = 1$, equation (4) becomes

$$(5) \qquad (e^{i\theta})^n = e^{in\theta} \quad (n = 0, \pm 1, \pm 2, \ldots).$$

When written in the form

$$(6) \qquad (\cos\theta + i\sin\theta)^n = \cos n\theta + i\sin n\theta \quad (n = 0, \pm 1, \pm 2, \ldots),$$

this is known as ***de Moivre's formula***. The following example uses a special case of it.

EXAMPLE 2. Formula (6) with $n = 2$ tells us that

$$(\cos\theta + i\sin\theta)^2 = \cos 2\theta + i\sin 2\theta,$$

or

$$\cos^2\theta - \sin^2\theta + i2\sin\theta\cos\theta = \cos 2\theta + i\sin 2\theta.$$

By equating real parts and then imaginary parts here, we have the familiar trigonometric identities

$$\cos 2\theta = \cos^2\theta - \sin^2\theta, \quad \sin 2\theta = 2\sin\theta\cos\theta.$$

(See also Exercises 10 and 11, Sec. 9.)

9. ARGUMENTS OF PRODUCTS AND QUOTIENTS

If $z_1 = r_1 e^{i\theta_1}$ and $z_2 = r_2 e^{i\theta_2}$, the expression

$$(1) \qquad z_1 z_2 = (r_1 r_2) e^{i(\theta_1 + \theta_2)}$$

in Sec. 8 can be used to obtain an important identity involving arguments:

$$(2) \qquad \arg(z_1 z_2) = \arg z_1 + \arg z_2.$$

Equation (2) is to be interpreted as saying that if values of two of the three (multiple-valued) arguments are specified, then there is a value of the third such that the equation holds.

We start the verification of statement (2) by letting θ_1 and θ_2 denote any values of $\arg z_1$ and $\arg z_2$, respectively. Expression (1) then tells us that $\theta_1 + \theta_2$ is a value of $\arg(z_1 z_2)$. (See Fig. 9.) If, on the other hand, values of $\arg(z_1 z_2)$ and $\arg z_1$ are specified, those values correspond to particular choices of n and n_1 in the expressions

$$\arg(z_1 z_2) = (\theta_1 + \theta_2) + 2n\pi \qquad (n = 0, \pm 1, \pm 2, \ldots)$$

and

$$\arg z_1 = \theta_1 + 2n_1\pi \qquad (n_1 = 0, \pm 1, \pm 2, \ldots).$$

Since

$$(\theta_1 + \theta_2) + 2n\pi = (\theta_1 + 2n_1\pi) + [\theta_2 + 2(n - n_1)\pi],$$

equation (2) is evidently satisfied when the value

$$\arg z_2 = \theta_2 + 2(n - n_1)\pi$$

is chosen. Verification when values of $\arg(z_1 z_2)$ and $\arg z_2$ are specified follows from the fact that statement (2) can also be written

$$\arg(z_2 z_1) = \arg z_2 + \arg z_1.$$

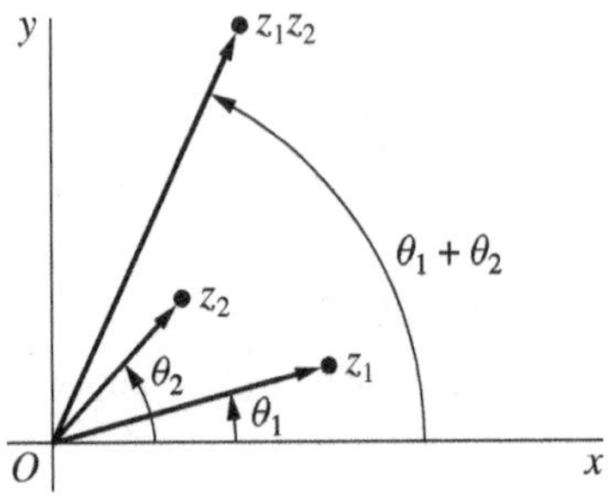

FIGURE 9

Statement (2) is sometimes valid when *arg* is replaced everywhere by *Arg* (see Exercise 6). But, as the following example illustrates, that is *not always* the case.

EXAMPLE 1. When $z_1 = -1$ and $z_2 = i$,

$$\text{Arg}(z_1 z_2) = \text{Arg}(-i) = -\frac{\pi}{2} \quad \text{but} \quad \text{Arg } z_1 + \text{Arg } z_2 = \pi + \frac{\pi}{2} = \frac{3\pi}{2}.$$

If, however, we take the values of $\arg z_1$ and $\arg z_2$ just used and select the value

$$\text{Arg}(z_1 z_2) + 2\pi = -\frac{\pi}{2} + 2\pi = \frac{3\pi}{2}$$

of $\arg(z_1 z_2)$, we find that equation (2) *is* satisfied.

Statement (2) tells us that

$$\arg\left(\frac{z_1}{z_2}\right) = \arg\left(z_1 z_2^{-1}\right) = \arg z_1 + \arg\left(z_2^{-1}\right);$$

and, since (Sec. 8)

$$z_2^{-1} = \frac{1}{r_2} e^{-i\theta_2},$$

one can see that

$$\arg\left(z_2^{-1}\right) = -\arg z_2. \tag{3}$$

Hence

$$\arg\left(\frac{z_1}{z_2}\right) = \arg z_1 - \arg z_2. \tag{4}$$

Statement (3) is, of course, to be interpreted as saying that the set of all values on the left-hand side is the same as the set of all values on the right-hand side. Statement (4) is, then, to be interpreted in the same way that statement (2) is.

EXAMPLE 2. In order to illustrate statement (4), let us use it to find the principal value of $\text{Arg}\, z$ when

$$z = \frac{i}{-1-i}.$$

We start by writing

$$\arg z = \arg i - \arg(-1-i).$$

Since

$$\text{Arg}\, i = \frac{\pi}{2} \quad \text{and} \quad \text{Arg}(-1-i) = -\frac{3\pi}{4},$$

one value of $\arg z$ is $5\pi/4$. But this is not a *principal* value Θ, which must lie in the interval $-\pi < \Theta \le \pi$. We can, however, obtain that value by adding some integral multiple, possibly negative, of 2π:

$$\text{Arg}\left(\frac{i}{-1-i}\right) = \frac{5\pi}{4} - 2\pi = -\frac{3\pi}{4}.$$

EXERCISES

1. Find the principal argument $\text{Arg}\, z$ when

(a) $z = \dfrac{-2}{1+\sqrt{3}i}$; (b) $z = \left(\sqrt{3}-i\right)^6$.

Ans. (a) $2\pi/3$; (b) π.

2. Show that (a) $|e^{i\theta}| = 1$; (b) $\overline{e^{i\theta}} = e^{-i\theta}$.

3. Use mathematical induction to show that

$$e^{i\theta_1}e^{i\theta_2}\cdots e^{i\theta_n} = e^{i(\theta_1+\theta_2+\cdots+\theta_n)} \qquad (n = 2, 3, \ldots).$$

4. Using the fact that the modulus $|e^{i\theta} - 1|$ is the distance between the points $e^{i\theta}$ and 1 (see Sec. 4), give a geometric argument to find a value of θ in the interval $0 \le \theta < 2\pi$ that satisfies the equation $|e^{i\theta} - 1| = 2$.

Ans. π.

5. By writing the individual factors on the left in exponential form, performing the needed operations, and finally changing back to rectangular coordinates, show that

(*a*) $i(1 - \sqrt{3}i)(\sqrt{3} + i) = 2(1 + \sqrt{3}i)$; (*b*) $5i/(2 + i) = 1 + 2i$;

(*c*) $(\sqrt{3} + i)^6 = -64$; (*d*) $(1 + \sqrt{3}\,i)^{-10} = 2^{-11}(-1 + \sqrt{3}\,i)$.

6. Show that if $\operatorname{Re} z_1 > 0$ and $\operatorname{Re} z_2 > 0$, then

$$\operatorname{Arg}(z_1 z_2) = \operatorname{Arg} z_1 + \operatorname{Arg} z_2,$$

where principal arguments are used.

7. Let z be a nonzero complex number and n a negative integer $(n = -1, -2, \ldots)$. Also, write $z = re^{i\theta}$ and $m = -n = 1, 2, \ldots$. Using the expressions

$$z^m = r^m e^{im\theta} \quad \text{and} \quad z^{-1} = \left(\frac{1}{r}\right) e^{i(-\theta)},$$

verify that $(z^m)^{-1} = (z^{-1})^m$ and hence that the definition $z^n = (z^{-1})^m$ in Sec. 7 could have been written alternatively as $z^n = (z^m)^{-1}$.

8. Prove that two nonzero complex numbers z_1 and z_2 have the same moduli if and only if there are complex numbers c_1 and c_2 such that $z_1 = c_1 c_2$ and $z_2 = c_1\overline{c_2}$.

Suggestion: Note that

$$\exp\left(i\frac{\theta_1 + \theta_2}{2}\right)\exp\left(i\frac{\theta_1 - \theta_2}{2}\right) = \exp(i\theta_1)$$

and [see Exercise 2(*b*)]

$$\exp\left(i\frac{\theta_1 + \theta_2}{2}\right)\overline{\exp\left(i\frac{\theta_1 - \theta_2}{2}\right)} = \exp(i\theta_2).$$

9. Establish the identity

$$1 + z + z^2 + \cdots + z^n = \frac{1 - z^{n+1}}{1 - z} \qquad (z \ne 1)$$

and then use it to derive ***Lagrange's trigonometric identity:***

$$1 + \cos\theta + \cos 2\theta + \cdots + \cos n\theta = \frac{1}{2} + \frac{\sin[(2n+1)\theta/2]}{2\sin(\theta/2)} \qquad (0 < \theta < 2\pi).$$

Suggestion: As for the first identity, write $S = 1 + z + z^2 + \cdots + z^n$ and consider the difference $S - zS$. To derive the second identity, write $z = e^{i\theta}$ in the first one.

10. Use de Moivre's formula (Sec. 8) to derive the following trigonometric identities:

(*a*) $\cos 3\theta = \cos^3\theta - 3\cos\theta\sin^2\theta$;

(*b*) $\sin 3\theta = 3\cos^2\theta\sin\theta - \sin^3\theta$.

11. (*a*) Use the binomial formula (14), Sec. 3, and de Moivre's formula (Sec. 8) to write

$$\cos n\theta + i\sin n\theta = \sum_{k=0}^{n}\binom{n}{k}\cos^{n-k}\theta\,(i\sin\theta)^k \qquad (n = 0, 1, 2, \ldots).$$

Then define the integer m by means of the equations

$$m = \begin{cases} n/2 & \text{if } n \text{ is even,} \\ (n-1)/2 & \text{if } n \text{ is odd} \end{cases}$$

and use the above summation to show that [compare with Exercise 10(*a*)]

$$\cos n\theta = \sum_{k=0}^{m}\binom{n}{2k}(-1)^k\cos^{n-2k}\theta\sin^{2k}\theta \qquad (n = 0, 1, 2, \ldots).$$

(*b*) Write $x = \cos\theta$ in the final summation in part (*a*) to show that it becomes a polynomial*

$$T_n(x) = \sum_{k=0}^{m}\binom{n}{2k}(-1)^k x^{n-2k}(1-x^2)^k$$

of degree n $(n = 0, 1, 2, \ldots)$ in the variable x.

10. ROOTS OF COMPLEX NUMBERS

Consider now a point $z = re^{i\theta}$, lying on a circle centered at the origin with radius r (Fig. 10). As θ is increased, z moves around the circle in the counterclockwise direction. In particular, when θ is increased by 2π, we arrive at the original point; and the same is true when θ is decreased by 2π. It is, therefore, evident from Fig. 10 that *two nonzero complex numbers*

$$z_1 = r_1e^{i\theta_1} \quad \textit{and} \quad z_2 = r_2e^{i\theta_2}$$

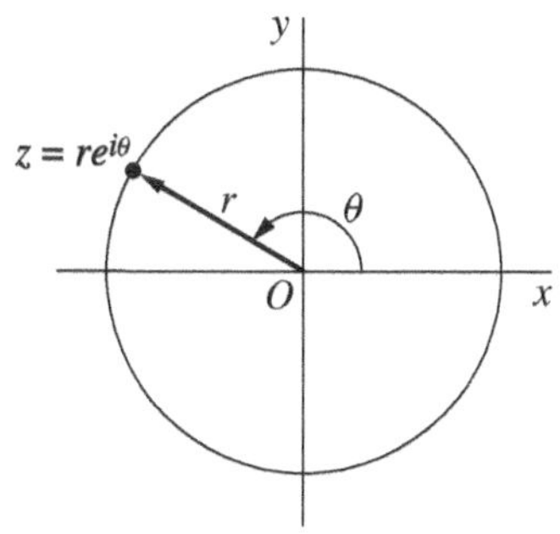

FIGURE 10

*These are called ***Chebyshev polynomials*** and are prominent in approximation theory.

are equal if and only if

$$r_1 = r_2 \quad and \quad \theta_1 = \theta_2 + 2k\pi,$$

where k is any integer $(k = 0, \pm 1, \pm 2, \ldots)$.

This observation, together with the expression $z^n = r^n e^{in\theta}$ in Sec. 8 for integral powers of complex numbers $z = re^{i\theta}$, is useful in finding the nth roots of any nonzero complex number $z_0 = r_0 e^{i\theta_0}$, where n has one of the values $n = 2, 3, \ldots$. The method starts with the fact that an nth root of z_0 is a nonzero number $z = re^{i\theta}$ such that $z^n = z_0$, or

$$r^n e^{in\theta} = r_0 e^{i\theta_0}.$$

According to the statement in italics just above, then,

$$r^n = r_0 \quad \text{and} \quad n\theta = \theta_0 + 2k\pi,$$

where k is any integer $(k = 0, \pm 1, \pm 2, \ldots)$. So $r = \sqrt[n]{r_0}$, where this radical denotes the unique *positive* nth root of the positive real number r_0, and

$$\theta = \frac{\theta_0 + 2k\pi}{n} = \frac{\theta_0}{n} + \frac{2k\pi}{n} \qquad (k = 0, \pm 1, \pm 2, \ldots).$$

Consequently, the complex numbers

$$z = \sqrt[n]{r_0} \exp\left[i\left(\frac{\theta_0}{n} + \frac{2k\pi}{n}\right)\right] \qquad (k = 0, \pm 1, \pm 2, \ldots)$$

are nth roots of z_0. We are able to see immediately from this exponential form of the roots that they all lie on the circle $|z| = \sqrt[n]{r_0}$ about the origin and are equally spaced every $2\pi/n$ radians, starting with argument θ_0/n. Evidently, then, all of the *distinct* roots are obtained when $k = 0, 1, 2, \ldots, n-1$, and no further roots arise with other values of k. We let c_k $(k = 0, 1, 2, \ldots, n-1)$ denote these distinct roots and write

$$(1) \qquad c_k = \sqrt[n]{r_0} \exp\left[i\left(\frac{\theta_0}{n} + \frac{2k\pi}{n}\right)\right] \qquad (k = 0, 1, 2, \ldots, n-1).$$

(See Fig. 11.)

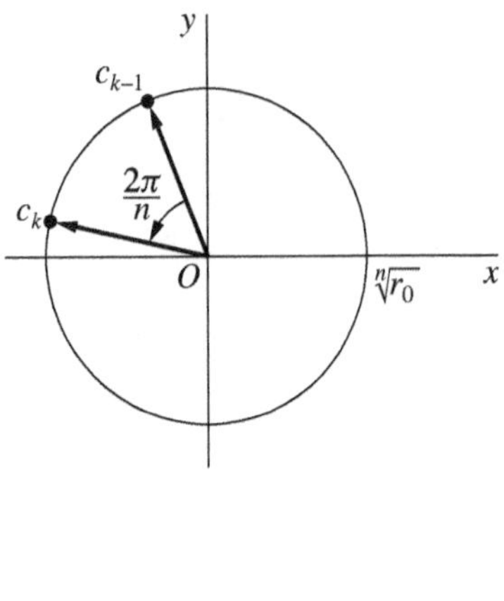

FIGURE 11

The number $\sqrt[n]{r_0}$ is the length of each of the radius vectors representing the n roots. The first root c_0 has argument θ_0/n; and the two roots when $n = 2$ lie at the opposite ends of a diameter of the circle $|z| = \sqrt[n]{r_0}$, the second root being $-c_0$. When $n \geq 3$, the roots lie at the vertices of a regular polygon of n sides inscribed in that circle.

We shall let $z_0^{1/n}$ denote the *set* of nth roots of z_0. If, in particular, z_0 is a positive real number r_0, the symbol $r_0^{1/n}$ denotes the entire set of roots; and the symbol $\sqrt[n]{r_0}$ in expression (1) is reserved for the one positive root. When the value of θ_0 that is used in expression (1) is the principal value of $\arg z_0$ $(-\pi < \theta_0 \leq \pi)$, the number c_0 is referred to as the ***principal root.*** Thus when z_0 is a positive real number r_0, its principal root is $\sqrt[n]{r_0}$.

Observe that if we write expression (1) for the roots of z_0 as

$$c_k = \sqrt[n]{r_0} \exp\left(i\frac{\theta_0}{n}\right) \exp\left(i\frac{2k\pi}{n}\right) \quad (k = 0, 1, 2, \ldots, n-1),$$

and also write

$$\omega_n = \exp\left(i\frac{2\pi}{n}\right), \tag{2}$$

it follows from property (5), Sec. 8, of $e^{i\theta}$ that

$$\omega_n^k = \exp\left(i\frac{2k\pi}{n}\right) \quad (k = 0, 1, 2, \ldots, n-1) \tag{3}$$

and hence that

$$c_k = c_0\omega_n^k \quad (k = 0, 1, 2, \ldots, n-1). \tag{4}$$

The number c_0 here can, of course, be replaced by any particular nth root of z_0, since ω_n represents a counterclockwise rotation through $2\pi/n$ radians.

Finally, a convenient way to remember expression (1) is to write z_0 in its most general exponential form (compare with Example 2 in Sec. 7)

$$z_0 = r_0\, e^{i(\theta_0 + 2k\pi)} \qquad (k = 0, \pm 1, \pm 2, \ldots) \tag{5}$$

and to *formally* apply laws of fractional exponents involving real numbers, keeping in mind that there are precisely n roots:

$$c_k = \left[r_0\, e^{i(\theta_0+2k\pi)}\right]^{1/n} = \sqrt[n]{r_0} \exp\left[\frac{i(\theta_0 + 2k\pi)}{n}\right] = \sqrt[n]{r_0} \exp\left[i\left(\frac{\theta_0}{n} + \frac{2k\pi}{n}\right)\right]$$
$$(k = 0, 1, 2, \ldots, n-1).$$

The examples in the next section serve to illustrate this method for finding roots of complex numbers.

11. EXAMPLES

In each of the examples here, we start with expression (5), Sec. 10, and proceed in the manner described just after it.

EXAMPLE 1. Let us find all four values of $(-16)^{1/4}$, or all of the fourth roots of the number -16. One need only write

$$-16 = 16\exp[i(\pi + 2k\pi)] \qquad (k = 0, \pm 1, \pm 2, \ldots)$$

to see that the desired roots are

$$(1) \qquad c_k = 2\exp\left[i\left(\frac{\pi}{4} + \frac{k\pi}{2}\right)\right] \qquad (k = 0, 1, 2, 3).$$

They lie at the vertices of a square, inscribed in the circle $|z| = 2$, and are equally spaced around that circle, starting with the principal root (Fig. 12)

$$c_0 = 2\exp\left[i\left(\frac{\pi}{4}\right)\right] = 2\left(\cos\frac{\pi}{4} + i\sin\frac{\pi}{4}\right) = 2\left(\frac{1}{\sqrt{2}} + i\frac{1}{\sqrt{2}}\right) = \sqrt{2}(1+i).$$

Without any further calculations, it is then evident that

$$c_1 = \sqrt{2}(-1+i), \quad c_2 = \sqrt{2}(-1-i), \quad \text{and} \quad c_3 = \sqrt{2}(1-i).$$

Note how it follows from expressions (2) and (4) in Sec. 10 that these roots can be written

$$c_0, \; c_0\omega_4, \; c_0\omega_4^2, \; c_0\omega_4^3 \qquad \text{where} \qquad \omega_4 = \exp\left(i\frac{\pi}{2}\right).$$

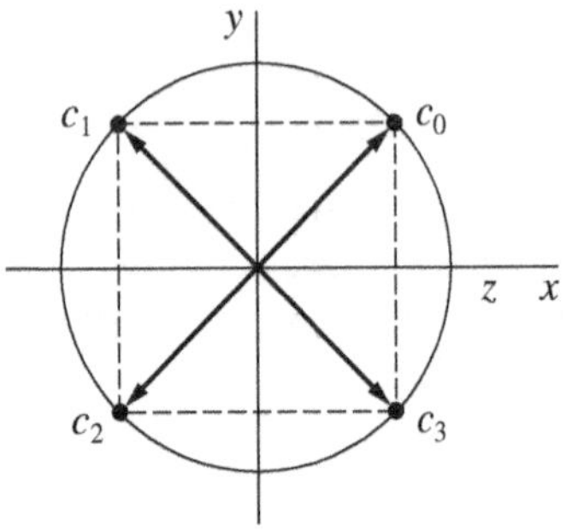

FIGURE 12

EXAMPLE 2. In order to determine the nth roots of unity, we start with

$$1 = 1\exp[i(0 + 2k\pi)] \qquad (k = 0, \pm 1, \pm 2 \ldots)$$

and find that

$$(2) \quad c_k = \sqrt[n]{1}\exp\left[i\left(\frac{0}{n} + \frac{2k\pi}{n}\right)\right] = \exp\left(i\frac{2k\pi}{n}\right) \qquad (k = 0, 1, 2, \ldots, n-1).$$

When $n = 2$, these roots are, of course, ± 1. When $n \geq 3$, the regular polygon at whose vertices the roots lie is inscribed in the unit circle $|z| = 1$, with one vertex corresponding to the principal root $z = 1$ ($k = 0$). In view of expression (3), Sec. 10, these roots are simply

$$1, \omega_n, \omega_n^2, \ldots, \omega_n^{n-1} \quad \text{where} \quad \omega_n = \exp\left(i\frac{2\pi}{n}\right).$$

See Fig. 13, where the cases $n = 3, 4,$ and 6 are illustrated. Note that $\omega_n^n = 1$.

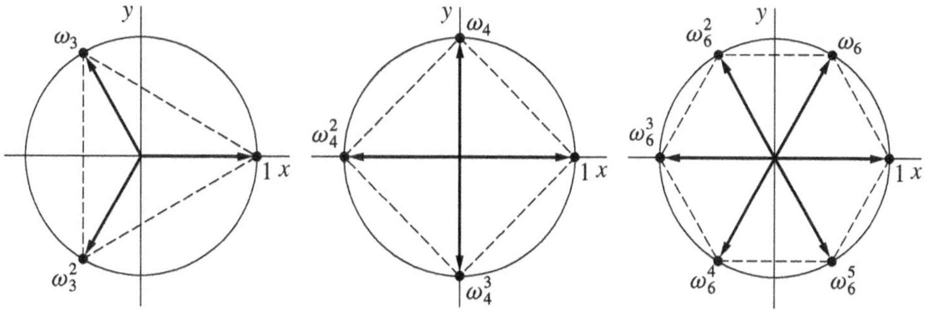

FIGURE 13

EXAMPLE 3. Let a denote any positive real number. In order to find the two square roots of $a + i$, we first write

$$A = |a + i| = \sqrt{a^2 + 1} \qquad \text{and} \qquad \alpha = \operatorname{Arg}(a + i).$$

Since

$$a + i = A \exp[i(\alpha + 2k\pi)] \quad (k = 0, \pm 1, \pm 2, \ldots),$$

the desired square roots are

(3) $$c_k = \sqrt{A} \exp\left[i\left(\frac{\alpha}{2} + k\pi\right)\right] \quad (k = 0, 1).$$

Because $e^{i\pi} = -1$, these two values of $(a + i)^{1/2}$ reduce to

(4) $$c_0 = \sqrt{A}\, e^{i\alpha/2} \quad \text{and} \quad c_1 = -c_0.$$

Euler's formula tells us that

(5) $$c_0 = \sqrt{A}\left(\cos\frac{\alpha}{2} + i \sin\frac{\alpha}{2}\right).$$

Because $a + i$ lies above the real axis, we know that $0 < \alpha < \pi$; and so

$$\cos\frac{\alpha}{2} > 0 \quad \text{and} \quad \sin\frac{\alpha}{2} > 0.$$

Hence, in view of the trigonometric identities

$$\cos^2\frac{\alpha}{2} = \frac{1 + \cos\alpha}{2}, \qquad \sin^2\frac{\alpha}{2} = \frac{1 - \cos\alpha}{2},$$

expression (5) can be put in the form

$$c_0 = \sqrt{A}\left(\sqrt{\frac{1+\cos\alpha}{2}} + i\sqrt{\frac{1-\cos\alpha}{2}}\right). \tag{6}$$

But $\cos\alpha = a/A$, and so

$$\sqrt{\frac{1\pm\cos\alpha}{2}} = \sqrt{\frac{1\pm(a/A)}{2}} = \sqrt{\frac{A\pm a}{2A}}. \tag{7}$$

Consequently, it follows from expression (6) and (7), as well as the relation $c_1 = -c_0$, that the two square roots of $a + i (a > 0)$ are (see Fig. 14)

$$\pm\frac{1}{\sqrt{2}}\left(\sqrt{A+a} + i\sqrt{A-a}\right). \tag{8}$$

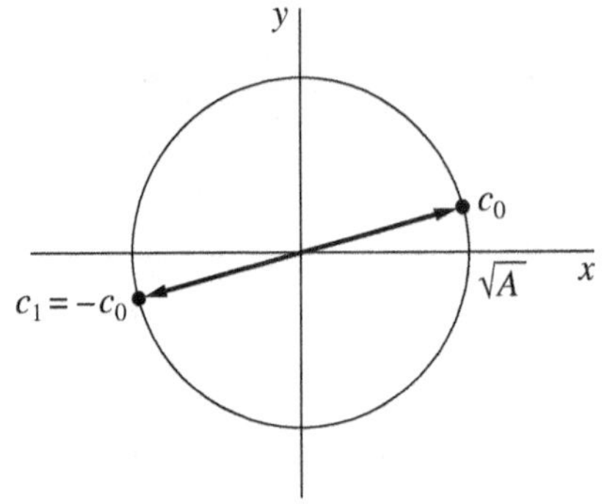

FIGURE 14

EXERCISES

1. Find the square roots of (*a*) $2i$; (*b*) $1 - \sqrt{3}i$ and express them in rectangular coordinates.

   Ans. (*a*) $\pm(1+i)$; (*b*) $\pm\dfrac{\sqrt{3}-i}{\sqrt{2}}$.

2. Find the three cube roots $c_k (k = 0, 1, 2)$ of $-8i$, express them in rectangular coordinates, and point out why they are as shown in Fig. 15.

   Ans. $\pm\sqrt{3} - i, 2i$.

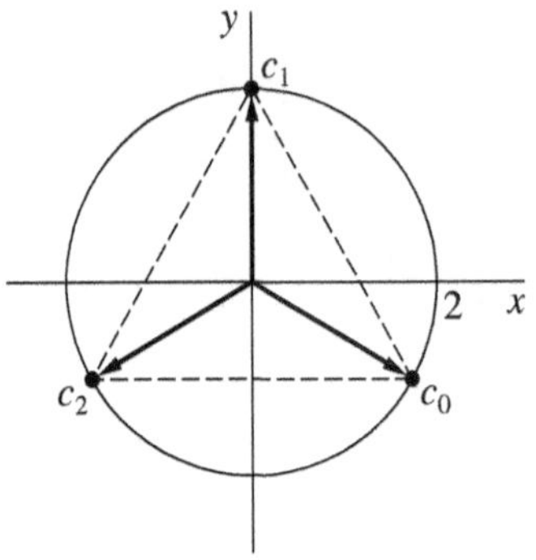

FIGURE 15

3. Find $(-8 - 8\sqrt{3}i)^{1/4}$, express the roots in rectangular coordinates, exhibit them as the vertices of a certain square, and point out which is the principal root.

Ans. $\pm(\sqrt{3} - i),\ \pm(1 + \sqrt{3}i)$.

4. In each case, find all of the roots in rectangular coordinates, exhibit them as vertices of certain regular polygons, and identify the principal root:

(*a*) $(-1)^{1/3}$; (*b*) $8^{1/6}$.

Ans. (*b*) $\pm\sqrt{2},\ \pm\dfrac{1+\sqrt{3}i}{\sqrt{2}},\ \pm\dfrac{1-\sqrt{3}i}{\sqrt{2}}$.

5. According to Sec. 10, the three cube roots of a nonzero complex number z_0 can be written $c_0, c_0\omega_3, c_0\omega_3^2$ where c_0 is the principal cube root of z_0 and

$$\omega_3 = \exp\left(i\frac{2\pi}{3}\right) = \frac{-1+\sqrt{3}i}{2}.$$

Show that if $z_0 = -4\sqrt{2} + 4\sqrt{2}i$, then $c_0 = \sqrt{2}(1+i)$ and the other two cube roots are, in rectangular form, the numbers

$$c_0\omega_3 = \frac{-(\sqrt{3}+1) + (\sqrt{3}-1)i}{\sqrt{2}}, \qquad c_0\omega_3^2 = \frac{(\sqrt{3}-1) - (\sqrt{3}+1)i}{\sqrt{2}}.$$

6. Find the four zeros of the polynomial $z^4 + 4$, one of them being

$$z_0 = \sqrt{2}\,e^{i\pi/4} = 1 + i.$$

Then use those zeros to factor $z^2 + 4$ into quadratic factors with real coefficients.

Ans. $(z^2 + 2z + 2)(z^2 - 2z + 2)$.

7. Show that if c is any nth root of unity other than unity itself, then

$$1 + c + c^2 + \cdots + c^{n-1} = 0.$$

Suggestion: Use the first identity in Exercise 9, Sec. 9.

8. (*a*) Prove that the usual formula solves the quadratic equation

$$az^2 + bz + c = 0 \qquad (a \neq 0)$$

when the coefficients a, b, and c are complex numbers. Specifically, by completing the square on the left-hand side, derive the ***quadratic formula***

$$z = \frac{-b + (b^2 - 4ac)^{1/2}}{2a},$$

where both square roots are to be considered when $b^2 - 4ac \neq 0$,

(*b*) Use the result in part (*a*) to find the roots of the equation $z^2 + 2z + (1 - i) = 0$.

Ans. (*b*) $\left(-1 + \dfrac{1}{\sqrt{2}}\right) + \dfrac{i}{\sqrt{2}},\ \left(-1 - \dfrac{1}{\sqrt{2}}\right) - \dfrac{i}{\sqrt{2}}$.

9. Let $z = re^{i\theta}$ be a nonzero complex number and n a negative integer $(n = -1, -2, \ldots)$. Then define $z^{1/n}$ by means of the equation $z^{1/n} = (z^{-1})^{1/m}$ where $m = -n$. By showing that the m values of $(z^{1/m})^{-1}$ and $(z^{-1})^{1/m}$ are the same, verify that $z^{1/n} = (z^{1/m})^{-1}$. (Compare with Exercise 7, Sec. 9.)

12. REGIONS IN THE COMPLEX PLANE

In this section, we are concerned with sets of complex numbers, or points in the z plane, and their closeness to one another. Our basic tool is the concept of an ε **neighborhood**

$$|z - z_0| < \varepsilon \tag{1}$$

of a given point z_0. It consists of all points z lying inside but not on a circle centered at z_0 and with a specified a positive radius ε (Fig. 16). When the value of ε is understood or immaterial in the discussion, the set (1) is often referred to as just a neighborhood. Occasionally, it is convenient to speak of a ***deleted neighborhood***, or punctured disk,

$$0 < |z - z_0| < \varepsilon \tag{2}$$

consisting of all points z in an ε neighborhood of z_0 except for the point z_0 itself.

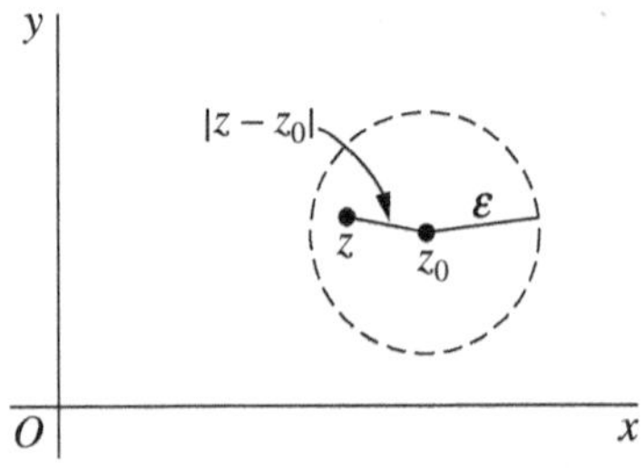

FIGURE 16

A point z_0 is said to be an ***interior point*** of a set S whenever there is some neighborhood of z_0 that contains only points of S; it is called an ***exterior point*** of S when there exists a neighborhood of it containing no points of S. If z_0 is neither of these, it is a ***boundary point*** of S. A boundary point is, therefore, a point all of whose neighborhoods contain at least one point in S and at least one point not in S. The totality of all boundary points is called the ***boundary*** of S. The circle $|z| = 1$, for instance, is the boundary of each of the sets

$$|z| < 1 \quad \text{and} \quad |z| \le 1. \tag{3}$$

A set is ***open*** if it does not contain any of its boundary points. It is left as an exercise to show that a set is open if and only if each of its points is an interior point. A set is ***closed*** if it contains all of its boundary points, and the ***closure*** of a set S is the closed set consisting of all points in S together with the boundary of S. Note that the first of sets (3) is open and that the second is its closure.

Some sets are, of course, neither open nor closed. For a set S to be not open there must be a boundary point that is contained in the set, and for S to be not closed there must be a boundary point not in it. Observe that the punctured disk $0 < |z| \leq 1$ is neither open nor closed. The set of all complex numbers is, on the other hand, both open and closed since it has no boundary points.

An open set S is ***connected*** if each pair of points z_1 and z_2 in it can be joined by a ***polygonal line***, consisting of a finite number of line segments, joined end to end, that lies entirely in S. The open set $|z| < 1$ is connected. The annulus $1 < |z| < 2$ is, of course open and it is also connected (see Fig. 17). A nonempty open set that is connected is called a ***domain***. Note that any neighborhood is a domain. A domain together with some, none, or all of its boundary points is usually referred to as a ***region***.

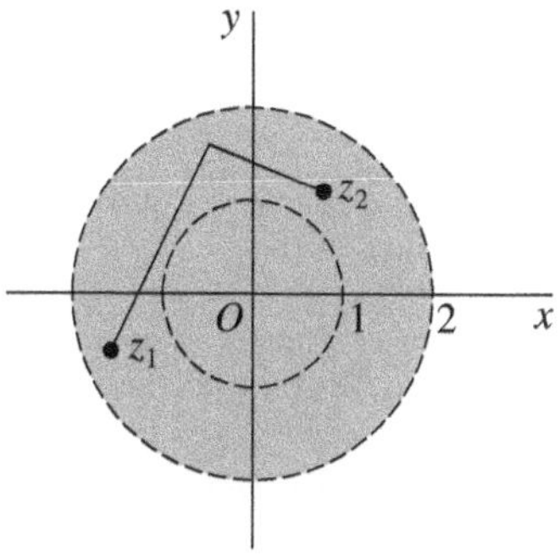

FIGURE 17

A set S is ***bounded*** if every point in S lies inside some circle $|z| = R$; otherwise, it is unbounded. Both of the sets (3) are bounded regions, and the half plane $\text{Re}\, z \geq 0$ is unbounded.

EXAMPLE. Let us sketch the set

$$\text{Im}\left(\frac{1}{z}\right) > 1 \tag{4}$$

and identify a few of the properties just described.

First of all, except when $z = 0$,

$$\frac{1}{z} = \frac{\bar{z}}{z\bar{z}} = \frac{\bar{z}}{|z|^2} = \frac{x - iy}{x^2 + y^2} \qquad (z = x + iy).$$

Inequality (4) then becomes

$$\frac{-y}{x^2 + y^2} > 1,$$

or

$$x^2 + y^2 + y < 0.$$

By completing the square, we arrive at

$$x^2 + \left(y^2 + y + \frac{1}{4}\right) < \frac{1}{4}.$$

So inequality (4) represents the region interior to the circle (Fig. 18)

$$(x-0)^2 + \left(y+\frac{1}{2}\right)^2 = \left(\frac{1}{2}\right)^2,$$

centered at $z = -i/2$ and with radius $1/2$.

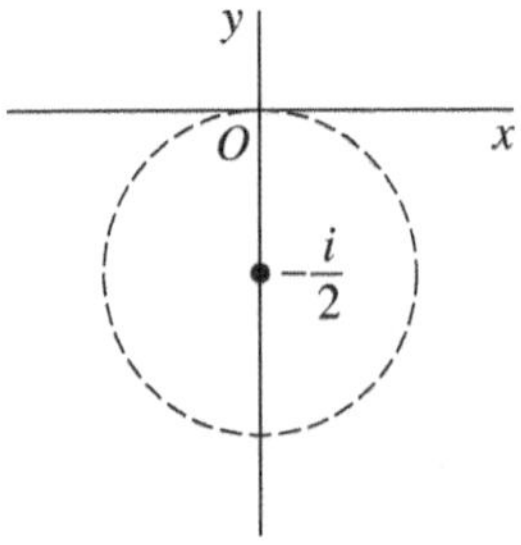

FIGURE 18

A point z_0 is said to be an ***accumulation point***, or limit point, of a set S if each deleted neighborhood of z_0 contains at least one point of S. It follows that if a set S is closed, then it contains each of its accumulation points. For if an accumulation point z_0 were not in S, it would be a boundary point of S; but this contradicts the fact that a closed set contains all of its boundary points. It is left as an exercise to show that the converse is, in fact, true. Thus a set is closed if and only if it contains all of its accumulation points.

Evidently, a point z_0 is *not* an accumulation point of a set S whenever there exists some deleted neighborhood of z_0 that does not contain at least one point in S. Note that the origin is the only accumulation point of the set

$$z_n = \frac{i}{n} \quad (n = 1, 2, \ldots).$$

EXERCISES

1. Sketch the following sets and determine which are domains:

(*a*) $|z - 2 + i| \le 1$; (*b*) $|2z + 3| > 4$;

(*c*) $\operatorname{Im} z > 1$; (*d*) $\operatorname{Im} z = 1$;

(*e*) $0 \le \arg z \le \pi/4$ $(z \ne 0)$; (*f*) $|z - 4| \ge |z|$.

Ans. (*b*), (*c*) are domains.

2. Which sets in Exercise 1 are neither open nor closed?

Ans. (*e*).

3. Which sets in Exercise 1 are bounded?

Ans. (*a*).

4. In each case, sketch the closure of the set:

(*a*) $-\pi < \arg z < \pi \ (z \neq 0)$; (*b*) $|\text{Re}\, z| < |z|$;

(*c*) $\text{Re}\left(\dfrac{1}{z}\right) \leq \dfrac{1}{2}$; (*d*) $\text{Re}(z^2) > 0$.

5. Let S be the open set consisting of all points z such that $|z| < 1$ or $|z - 2| < 1$. State why S is not connected.

6. Show that a set S is open if and only if each point in S is an interior point.

7. Determine the accumulation points of each of the following sets:

(*a*) $z_n = i^n \ (n = 1, 2, \ldots)$; (*b*) $z_n = i^n/n \ (n = 1, 2, \ldots)$;

(*c*) $0 \leq \arg z < \pi/2 \ (z \neq 0)$; (*d*) $z_n = (-1)^n(1+i)\dfrac{n-1}{n} \ (n = 1, 2, \ldots)$.

Ans. (*a*) None; (*b*) 0; (*d*) $\pm(1 + i)$.

8. Prove that if a set contains each of its accumulation points, then it must be a closed set.

9. Show that any point z_0 of a domain is an accumulation point of that domain.

10. Prove that a finite set of points $z_1, z_2, \ldots, z_n$ cannot have any accumulation points.

CHAPTER

2

ANALYTIC FUNCTIONS

We now consider functions of a complex variable and develop a theory of differentiation for them. The main goal of the chapter is to introduce analytic functions, which play a central role in complex analysis.

13. FUNCTIONS AND MAPPINGS

Let S be a set of complex numbers. A ***function*** f defined on S is a rule that assigns to each z in S a complex number w. The number w is called the ***value*** of f at z and is denoted by $f(z)$, so that $w = f(z)$. The set S is called the ***domain of definition*** of f.*

It must be emphasized that both a domain of definition and a rule are needed in order for a function to be well defined. When the domain of definition is not mentioned, we agree that the largest possible set is to be taken. Also, it is not always convenient to use notation that distinguishes between a given function and its values.

EXAMPLE 1. If f is defined on the set $z \neq 0$ by means of the equation $w = 1/z$, it may be referred to only as the function $w = 1/z$, or simply the function $1/z$.

Suppose that $u + iv$ is the value of a function f at $z = x + iy$; that is,

$$u + iv = f(x + iy).$$

*Although the domain of definition is often a domain as defined in Sec. 12, it need not be.

Each of the real numbers u and v depends on the real variables x and y, and it follows that $f(z)$ can be expressed in terms of a pair of real-valued functions of the real variables x and y:

$$f(z) = u(x, y) + iv(x, y). \tag{1}$$

EXAMPLE 2. If $f(z) = z^2$, then

$$f(x + iy) = (x + iy)^2 = x^2 - y^2 + i2xy.$$

Hence

$$u(x, y) = x^2 - y^2 \quad \text{and} \quad v(x, y) = 2xy.$$

If the function v in equation (1) always has value zero, then the value of f is always real. Thus f is a ***real-valued function*** of a complex variable.

EXAMPLE 3. A real-valued function that is used to illustrate some important concepts later in this chapter is

$$f(z) = |z|^2 = x^2 + y^2 + i0.$$

If n is a positive integer and if $a_0, a_1, a_2, \ldots, a_n$ are complex constants, where $a_n \neq 0$, the function

$$P(z) = a_0 + a_1 z + a_2 z^2 + \cdots + a_n z^n$$

is a ***polynomial*** of degree n. Note that the sum here has a finite number of terms and that the domain of definition is the entire z plane. Quotients $P(z)/Q(z)$ of polynomials are called ***rational functions*** and are defined at each point z where $Q(z) \neq 0$. Polynomials and rational functions constitute elementary, but important, classes of functions of a complex variable.

If the polar coordinates r and θ are used instead of x and y, then

$$u + iv = f(re^{i\theta})$$

where $w = u + iv$ and $z = re^{i\theta}$. In that case, we may write

$$f(z) = u(r, \theta) + iv(r, \theta). \tag{2}$$

EXAMPLE 4. Consider the function $w = z^2$ when $z = re^{i\theta}$. Here

$$w = (re^{i\theta})^2 = r^2 e^{i2\theta} = r^2 \cos 2\theta + ir^2 \sin 2\theta.$$

Hence

$$u(r, \theta) = r^2 \cos 2\theta \quad \text{and} \quad v(r, \theta) = r^2 \sin 2\theta.$$

A generalization of the concept of function is a rule that assigns more than one value to a point z in the domain of definition. These ***multiple-valued functions*** occur in the theory of functions of a complex variable, just as they do in the case of a real variable. When multiple-valued functions are studied, usually just one of the possible values assigned at each point is taken, in a systematic manner, and a (single-valued) function is constructed from the multiple-valued one.

EXAMPLE 5. Let z denote any nonzero complex number. We know from Sec. 10 that $z^{1/2}$ has the two values

$$z^{1/2} = \pm\sqrt{r}\exp\left(i\frac{\Theta}{2}\right),$$

where $r = |z|$ and Θ $(-\pi < \Theta \le \pi)$ is the principal value of arg z. But, if we choose only the positive value of $\pm\sqrt{r}$ and write

$$f(z) = \sqrt{r}\exp\left(i\frac{\Theta}{2}\right) \qquad (r > 0, -\pi < \Theta \le \pi), \tag{3}$$

the (single-valued) function (3) is well defined on the set of nonzero numbers in the z plane. Since zero is the only square root of zero, we also write $f(0) = 0$. The function f is then well defined on the entire plane.

Properties of a real-valued function of a real variable are often exhibited by the graph of the function. But when $w = f(z)$, where z and w are complex, no such convenient graphical representation of the function f is available because each of the numbers z and w is located in a plane rather than on a line. One can, however, display some information about the function by indicating pairs of corresponding points $z = (x, y)$ and $w = (u, v)$. To do this, it is generally simpler to draw the z and w planes separately.

When a function f is thought of in this way, it is often referred to as a ***mapping***, or transformation. The ***image*** of a point z in the domain of definition S is the point $w = f(z)$, and the set of images of all points in a set T that is contained in S is called the image of T. The image of the entire domain of definition S is called the ***range*** of f. The ***inverse image*** of a point w is the set of all points z in the domain of definition of f that have w as their image. The inverse image of a point may contain just one point, many points, or none at all. The last case occurs, of course, when w is not in the range of f.

Terms such as ***translation***, ***rotation***, and ***reflection*** are used to convey dominant geometric characteristics of certain mappings. In such cases, it is sometimes convenient to consider the z and w planes to be the same. For example, the mapping

$$w = z + 1 = (x + 1) + iy,$$

where $z = x + iy$, can be thought of as a translation of each point z one unit to the right. Since $i = e^{i\pi/2}$, the mapping

$$w = iz = r\exp\left[i\left(\theta + \frac{\pi}{2}\right)\right],$$

where $z = re^{i\theta}$, rotates the radius vector for each nonzero point z through a right angle about the origin in the counterclockwise direction; and the mapping

$$w = \bar{z} = x - iy$$

transforms each point $z = x + iy$ into its reflection in the real axis.

More information is usually exhibited by sketching images of curves and regions than by simply indicating images of individual points. In the next section, the transformation $w = z^2$ is used to illustrate this.

14. THE MAPPING $w = z^2$

According to Example 2 in Sec. 13, the mapping $w = z^2$ can be thought of as the transformation

$$(1) \qquad u = x^2 - y^2, \quad v = 2xy$$

from the xy plane into the uv plane. This form of the mapping is especially useful in finding the images of certain hyperbolas.

It is easy to show, for instance, that each branch of a hyperbola

$$(2) \qquad x^2 - y^2 = c_1 \qquad (c_1 > 0)$$

is mapped in a one to one manner onto the vertical line $u = c_1$. To do this, we start by noting from the first of equations (1) that $u = c_1$ when (x, y) is a point lying on either branch. When, in particular, it lies on the right-hand branch, the second of equations (1) tells us that $v = 2y\sqrt{y^2 + c_1}$. Thus the image of the right-hand branch can be expressed parametrically as

$$u = c_1, \quad v = 2y\sqrt{y^2 + c_1} \qquad (-\infty < y < \infty);$$

and it is evident that the image of a point (x, y) on that branch moves upward along the entire line as (x, y) traces out the branch in the upward direction (Fig. 19). Likewise, since the pair of equations

$$u = c_1, \quad v = -2y\sqrt{y^2 + c_1} \qquad (-\infty < y < \infty)$$

furnishes a parametric representation for the image of the left-hand branch of the hyperbola, the image of a point going *downward* along the entire left-hand branch is seen to move up the entire line $u = c_1$.

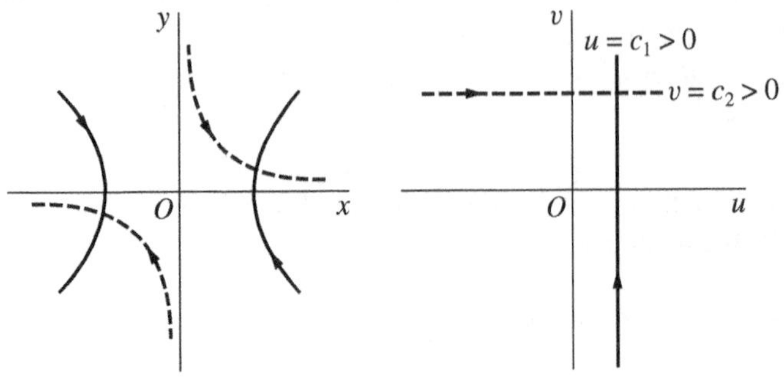

FIGURE 19
$w = z^2$.

On the other hand, each branch of a hyperbola

$$2xy = c_2 \qquad (c_2 > 0) \tag{3}$$

is transformed into the line $v = c_2$, as indicated in Fig. 19. To verify this, we note from the second of equations (1) that $v = c_2$ when (x, y) is a point on either branch. Suppose that (x, y) is on the branch lying in the first quadrant. Then, since $y = c_2/(2x)$, the first of equations (1) reveals that the branch's image has parametric representation

$$u = x^2 - \frac{c_2^2}{4x^2}, \quad v = c_2 \qquad (0 < x < \infty).$$

Observe that

$$\lim_{\substack{x \to 0 \\ x > 0}} u = -\infty \quad \text{and} \quad \lim_{x \to \infty} u = \infty.$$

Since u depends continuously on x, then, it is clear that as (x, y) travels down the entire upper branch of hyperbola (3), its image moves to the right along the entire horizontal line $v = c_2$. Inasmuch as the image of the lower branch has parametric representation

$$u = \frac{c_2^2}{4y^2} - y^2, \quad v = c_2 \qquad (-\infty < y < 0)$$

and since

$$\lim_{y \to -\infty} u = -\infty \quad \text{and} \quad \lim_{\substack{y \to 0 \\ y < 0}} u = \infty,$$

it follows that the image of a point moving *upward* along the entire lower branch also travels to the right along the entire line $v = c_2$ (see Fig. 19).

Let us now illustrate how the form (1) of the mapping $w = z^2$ can be used to find images of certain *regions.*

EXAMPLE 1. The domain $x > 0, y > 0, xy < 1$ consists of all points lying on the upper branches of hyperbolas from the family $2xy = c$, where $0 < c < 2$ (Fig. 20). We have just seen that as a point travels downward along the entirety of such a branch, its image under the transformation $w = z^2$ moves to the right along

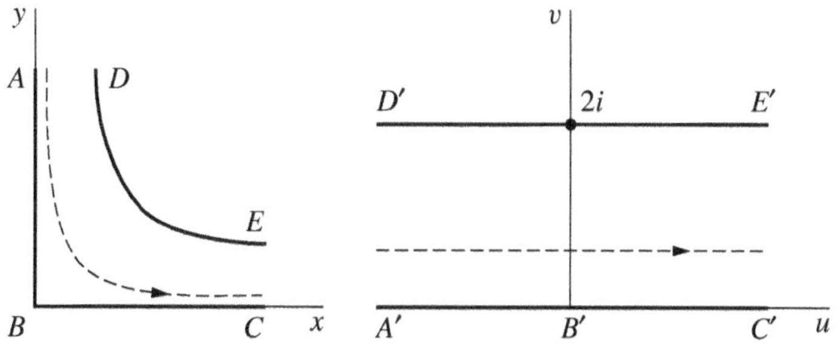

FIGURE 20
$w = z^2$.

the entire line $v = c$. Since, for all values of c between 0 and 2, these upper branches fill out the domain $x > 0, y > 0, xy < 1$, that domain is mapped onto the horizontal strip $0 < v < 2$.

In view of equations (1), the image of a point $(0, y)$ in the z plane is $(-y^2, 0)$. Hence as $(0, y)$ travels downward to the origin along the y axis, its image moves to the right along the negative u axis and reaches the origin in the w plane. Then, since the image of a point $(x, 0)$ is $(x^2, 0)$, that image moves to the right from the origin along the u axis as $(x, 0)$ moves to the right from the origin along the x axis. The image of the upper branch of the hyperbola $xy = 1$ is, of course, the horizontal line $v = 2$. Evidently, then, the closed region $x \geq 0, y \geq 0, xy \leq 1$ is mapped onto the closed strip $0 \leq v \leq 2$, as indicated in Fig. 20.

Our next example illustrates how polar coordinates can be used in analyzing certain mappings.

EXAMPLE 2. The mapping $w = z^2$ becomes

$$w = r^2 e^{i2\theta} \tag{4}$$

when $z = re^{i\theta}$. Evidently, then, the image $w = \rho e^{i\phi}$ of any nonzero point z is found by squaring the modulus $r = |z|$ and doubling the value θ of arg z that is used:

$$\rho = r^2 \quad \text{and} \quad \phi = 2\theta. \tag{5}$$

Observe that points $z = r_0 e^{i\theta}$ on a circle $r = r_0$ are transformed into points $w = r_0^2 e^{i2\theta}$ on the circle $\rho = r_0^2$. As a point on the first circle moves counterclockwise from the positive real axis to the positive imaginary axis, its image on the second circle moves counterclockwise from the positive real axis to the negative real axis (see Fig. 21). So, as all possible positive values of r_0 are chosen, the corresponding arcs in the z and w planes fill out the first quadrant and the upper half plane, respectively. The transformation $w = z^2$ is, then, a one to one mapping of the first quadrant $r \geq 0$, $0 \leq \theta \leq \pi/2$ in the z plane onto the upper half $\rho \geq 0, 0 \leq \phi \leq \pi$ of the w plane, as indicated in Fig. 21. The point $z = 0$ is, of course, mapped onto the point $w = 0$.

This mapping of the first quadrant onto the upper half plane can also be verified using the rays indicated by dashes in Fig. 21. Details of the verification are left to Exercise 7.

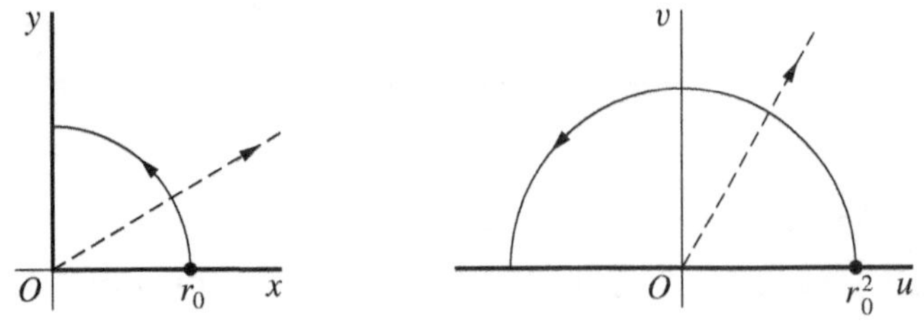

FIGURE 21
$w = z^2$.

The transformation $w = z^2$ also maps the upper half plane $r \geq 0, 0 \leq \theta \leq \pi$ onto the entire w plane. However, in this case, the transformation is not one to one since both the positive and negative real axes in the z plane are mapped onto the positive real axis in the w plane.

When n is a positive integer greater than 2, various mapping properties of the transformation $w = z^n$, or $w = r^n e^{in\theta}$, are similar to those of $w = z^2$. Such a transformation maps the entire z plane onto the entire w plane, where each nonzero point in the w plane is the image of n distinct points in the z plane. The circle $r = r_0$ is mapped onto the circle $\rho = r_0^n$; and the sector $r \leq r_0, 0 \leq \theta \leq 2\pi/n$ is mapped onto the disk $\rho \leq r_0^n$, but not in a one to one manner.

Other, but somewhat more involved, mappings by $w = z^2$ appear in Example 1, Sec. 107, and Exercises 1 through 4 Sec. 108.

EXERCISES

1. For each of the functions below, describe the domain of definition that is understood:

$$(a)\ f(z) = \frac{1}{z^2+1}; \qquad (b)\ f(z) = \operatorname{Arg}\left(\frac{1}{z}\right);$$

$$(c)\ f(z) = \frac{z}{z+\bar{z}}; \qquad (d)\ f(z) = \frac{1}{1-|z|^2}.$$

Ans. (*a*) $z \neq \pm i$; (*b*) $\operatorname{Re} z \neq 0$.

2. In each case, write the function $f(z)$ in the form $f(z) = u(x, y) + iv(x, y)$:

$$(a)\ f(z) = z^3 + z + 1; \qquad (b)\ f(z) = \frac{\bar{z}^2}{z} \quad (z \neq 0).$$

Suggestion: In part (*b*), start by multiplying the numerator and denominator by $\bar{z}$.

Ans. (*a*) $f(z) = (x^3 - 3xy^2 + x + 1) + i(3x^2y - y^3 + y)$;

$$(b)\ f(z) = \frac{x^3 - 3xy^2}{x^2 + y^2} + i\frac{y^3 - 3x^2y}{x^2 + y^2}.$$

3. Suppose that $f(z) = x^2 - y^2 - 2y + i(2x - 2xy)$, where $z = x + iy$. Use the expressions (see Sec. 6)

$$x = \frac{z + \bar{z}}{2} \quad \text{and} \quad y = \frac{z - \bar{z}}{2i}$$

to write $f(z)$ in terms of z, and simplify the result.

Ans. $f(z) = \bar{z}^2 + 2iz$.

4. Write the function

$$f(z) = z + \frac{1}{z} \quad (z \neq 0)$$

in the form $f(z) = u(r,\theta) + iv(r,\theta)$.

$$Ans.\ f(z) = \left(r + \frac{1}{r}\right)\cos\theta + i\left(r - \frac{1}{r}\right)\sin\theta.$$

5. By referring to the discussion in Sec. 14 related to Fig. 19 there, find a domain in the z plane whose image under the transformation $w = z^2$ is the square domain in the w plane bounded by the lines $u = 1$, $u = 2$, $v = 1$, and $v = 2$. (See Fig. 2, Appendix 2.)

6. Find and sketch, showing corresponding orientations, the images of the hyperbolas

$$x^2 - y^2 = c_1\ (c_1 < 0) \quad \text{and} \quad 2xy = c_2\ (c_2 < 0)$$

under the transformation $w = z^2$.

7. Use rays indicated by dashed half lines in Fig. 21 to show that the transformation $w = z^2$ maps the first quadrant onto the upper half plane, as shown in Fig. 21.

8. Sketch the region onto which the sector $r \le 1, 0 \le \theta \le \pi/4$ is mapped by the transformation (*a*) $w = z^2$; (*b*) $w = z^3$; (*c*) $w = z^4$.

9. One interpretation of a function $w = f(z) = u(x,y) + iv(x,y)$ is that of a ***vector field*** in the domain of definition of f. The function assigns a vector w, with components $u(x,y)$ and $v(x,y)$, to each point z at which it is defined. Indicate graphically the vector fields represented by

$$(a)\ w = iz; \qquad (b)\ w = \frac{z}{|z|}.$$

15. LIMITS

Let a function f be defined at all points z in some deleted neighborhood of a point z_0. The statement that $f(z)$ has a ***limit*** w_0 as z approaches z_0, or that

$$\lim_{z \to z_0} f(z) = w_0, \tag{1}$$

means that the point $w = f(z)$ can be made arbitrarily close to w_0 if we choose the point z close enough to z_0 but distinct from it. We now express the definition of limit in a precise and usable form.

Statement (1) means that for each positive number ε, there is a positive number δ such that

$$|f(z) - w_0| < \varepsilon \quad \text{whenever} \quad 0 < |z - z_0| < \delta. \tag{2}$$

Geometrically, this definition says that for each ε neighborhood $|w - w_0| < \varepsilon$ of w_0, there is a deleted δ neighborhood $0 < |z - z_0| < \delta$ of z_0 such that every point z in it has an image w lying in the ε neighborhood (Fig. 22). Note that even though all points in the deleted neighborhood $0 < |z - z_0| < \delta$ are to be considered, their images need not fill up the entire neighborhood $|w - w_0| < \varepsilon$. If f has the constant value w_0, for instance, the image of z is always the center of that neighborhood. Note, too, that once a δ has been found, it can be replaced by any smaller positive number, such as $\delta/2$.

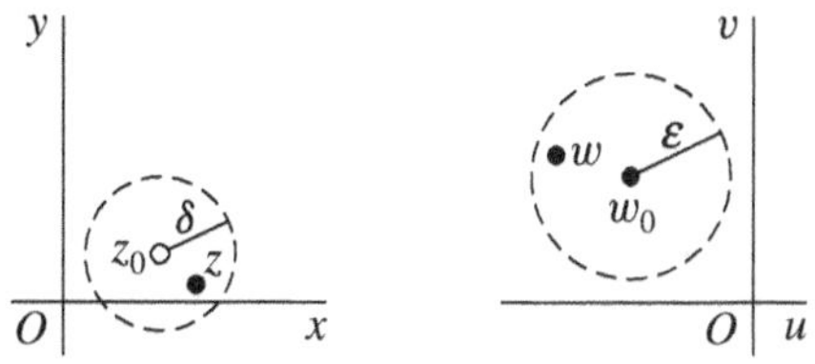

FIGURE 22

The following theorem on uniqueness of limits is central to much of this chapter, especially the material in Sec. 21.

Theorem. *When a limit of a function $f(z)$ exists at a point z_0, it is unique.*

To prove this, we suppose that

$$\lim_{z \to z_0} f(z) = w_0 \quad \text{and} \quad \lim_{z \to z_0} f(z) = w_1.$$

Then, for each positive number ε, there are positive numbers δ_0 and δ_1 such that

$$|f(z) - w_0| < \varepsilon \quad \text{whenever} \quad 0 < |z - z_0| < \delta_0$$

and

$$|f(z) - w_1| < \varepsilon \quad \text{whenever} \quad 0 < |z - z_0| < \delta_1.$$

Since

$$w_1 - w_0 = [f(z) - w_0] + [w_1 - f(z)],$$

the triangle inequality tells us that

$$|w_1 - w_0| \le [f(z) - w_0] + [w_1 - f(z)] = |f(z) - w_0| + |f(z) - w_1|.$$

So if $0 < |z - z_0| < \delta$ where δ is any positive number smaller than δ_0 and δ_1, we find that

$$|w_1 - w_0| < \varepsilon + \varepsilon < 2\varepsilon.$$

But $|w_1 - w_0|$ is a nonnegative constant, and ε can be chosen arbitrarily small. Hence

$$w_1 - w_0 = 0, \quad \text{or} \quad w_1 = w_0.$$

Definition (2) requires that f be defined at all points in some deleted neighborhood of z_0. Such a deleted neighborhood, of course, always exists when z_0 is an interior point of a region on which f is defined. We can extend the definition of limit to the case in which z_0 is a boundary point of the region by agreeing that the first of inequalities (2) need be satisfied by only those points z that lie in both the region *and* the deleted neighborhood.

EXAMPLE 1. Let us show that if $f(z) = i\bar{z}/2$ in the open disk $|z| < 1$, then

$$\lim_{z \to 1} f(z) = \frac{i}{2}, \tag{3}$$

the point 1 being on the boundary of the domain of definition of f. Observe that when z is in the disk $|z| < 1$,

$$\left| f(z) - \frac{i}{2} \right| = \left| \frac{i\bar{z}}{2} - \frac{i}{2} \right| = \frac{|z-1|}{2}.$$

Hence, for any such z and each positive number ε (see Fig. 23),

$$\left| f(z) - \frac{i}{2} \right| < \varepsilon \quad \text{whenever} \quad 0 < |z-1| < 2\varepsilon.$$

Thus condition (2) is satisfied by points in the region $|z| < 1$ when δ is equal to 2ε or any smaller positive number.

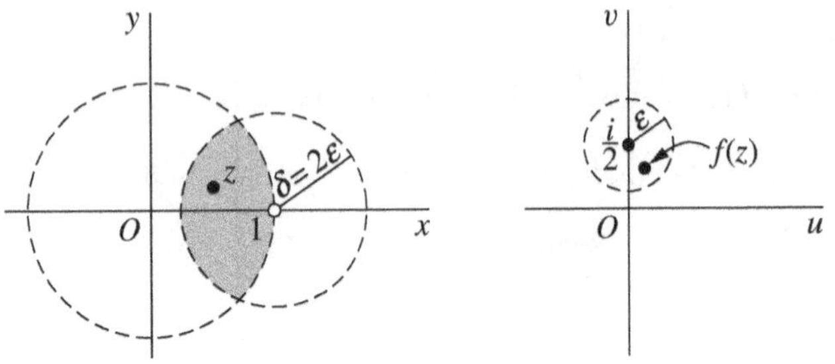

FIGURE 23

If limit (1) exists, the symbol $z \to z_0$ implies that z is allowed to approach z_0 in an arbitrary manner, not just from some particular direction. The next example emphasizes this.

EXAMPLE 2. If

$$f(z) = \frac{z}{\bar{z}}, \tag{4}$$

the limit

$$\lim_{z \to 0} f(z) \tag{5}$$

does not exist. For, if it did exist, it could be found by letting the point $z = (x, y)$ approach the origin in any manner. But when $z = (x, 0)$ is a nonzero point on the real axis (Fig. 24),

$$f(z) = \frac{x + i0}{x - i0} = 1;$$

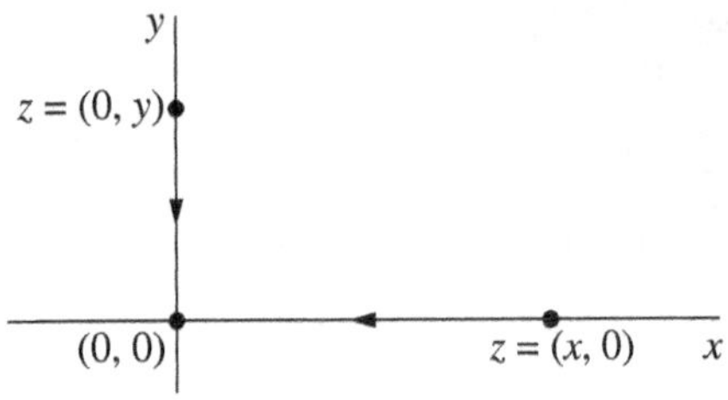

FIGURE 24

and when $z = (0, y)$ is a nonzero point on the imaginary axis,

$$f(z) = \frac{0 + iy}{0 - iy} = -1.$$

Thus, by letting z approach the origin along the real axis, we would find that the desired limit is 1. An approach along the imaginary axis would, on the other hand, yield the limit -1. Since a limit is unique, we must conclude that limit (5) does not exist.

While definition (2) provides a means of testing whether a given point w_0 is a limit, it does not directly provide a method for determining that limit. Theorems on limits, presented in the next section, will enable us to actually find many limits.

16. THEOREMS ON LIMITS

We can expedite our treatment of limits by establishing a connection between limits of functions of a complex variable and limits of real-valued functions of two real variables. Since limits of the latter type are studied in calculus, we may use their definition and properties freely.

Theorem 1. *Suppose that*

$$f(z) = u(x, y) + iv(x, y) \quad (z = x + iy)$$

and

$$z_0 = x_0 + iy_0, \quad w_0 = u_0 + iv_0.$$

If

$$(1) \qquad \lim_{(x,y)\to(x_0,y_0)} u(x, y) = u_0 \quad \textit{and} \quad \lim_{(x,y)\to(x_0,y_0)} v(x, y) = v_0,$$

Then

$$(2) \qquad \lim_{z\to z_0} f(z) = w_0;$$

and, conversely, if statement (2) *is true, then so is statement* (1).

To prove the theorem, we first assume that limits (1) hold and obtain limit (2). Limits (1) tell us that for each positive number ε, there exist positive numbers δ_1 and δ_2 such that

$$(3) \qquad |u - u_0| < \frac{\varepsilon}{2} \quad \text{whenever} \quad 0 < \sqrt{(x - x_0)^2 + (y - y_0)^2} < \delta_1$$

and

$$(4) \qquad |v - v_0| < \frac{\varepsilon}{2} \quad \text{whenever} \quad 0 < \sqrt{(x - x_0)^2 + (y - y_0)^2} < \delta_2.$$

Let δ be any positive number smaller than δ_1 and δ_2. Since

$$|(u + iv) - (u_0 + iv_0)| = |(u - u_0) + i(v - v_0)| \le |u - u_0| + |v - v_0|$$

and

$$\sqrt{(x - x_0)^2 + (y - y_0)^2} = |(x - x_0) + i(y - y_0)| = |(x + iy) - (x_0 + iy_0)|,$$

it follows from statements (3) and (4) that

$$|(u + iv) - (u_0 + iv_0)| < \frac{\varepsilon}{2} + \frac{\varepsilon}{2} = \varepsilon$$

whenever

$$0 < |(x + iy) - (x_0 + iy_0)| < \delta.$$

That is, limit (2) holds.

Let us now start with the assumption that limit (2) holds. With that assumption, we know that for each positive number ε, there is a positive number δ such that

$$|(u + iv) - (u_0 + iv_0)| < \varepsilon \tag{5}$$

whenever

$$0 < |(x + iy) - (x_0 + iy_0)| < \delta. \tag{6}$$

But

$$|u - u_0| \le |(u - u_0) + i(v - v_0)| = |(u + iv) - (u_0 + iv_0)|,$$
$$|v - v_0| \le |(u - u_0) + i(v - v_0)| = |(u + iv) - (u_0 + iv_0)|,$$

and

$$|(x + iy) - (x_0 + iy_0)| = |(x - x_0) + i(y - y_0)| = \sqrt{(x - x_0)^2 + (y - y_0)^2}.$$

Hence it follows from inequalities (5) and (6) that

$$|u - u_0| < \varepsilon \quad \text{and} \quad |v - v_0| < \varepsilon$$

whenever

$$0 < \sqrt{(x - x_0)^2 + (y - y_0)^2} < \delta.$$

This establishes limits (1), and the proof of the theorem is complete.

Theorem 2. *Suppose that*

$$\lim_{z \to z_0} f(z) = w_0 \quad \textit{and} \quad \lim_{z \to z_0} F(z) = W_0. \tag{7}$$

Then

$$\lim_{z \to z_0} [f(z) + F(z)] = w_0 + W_0, \tag{8}$$

$$\lim_{z \to z_0} [f(z)F(z)] = w_0 W_0; \tag{9}$$

and, if $W_0 \neq 0$,

$$\lim_{z \to z_0} \frac{f(z)}{F(z)} = \frac{w_0}{W_0}. \tag{10}$$

This important theorem can be proved directly by using the definition of the limit of a function of a complex variable. But, with the aid of Theorem 1, it follows almost immediately from theorems on limits of real-valued functions of two real variables.

To verify property (9), for example, we write

$$f(z) = u(x, y) + iv(x, y), \quad F(z) = U(x, y) + iV(x, y),$$

$$z_0 = x_0 + iy_0, \quad w_0 = u_0 + iv_0, \quad W_0 = U_0 + iV_0.$$

Then, according to hypotheses (7) and Theorem 1, the limits as (x, y) approaches (x_0, y_0) of the functions u, v, U, and V exist and have the values u_0, v_0, U_0, and V_0, respectively. So the real and imaginary components of the product

$$f(z)F(z) = (uU - vV) + i(vU + uV)$$

have the limits $u_0U_0 - v_0V_0$ and $v_0U_0 + u_0V_0$, respectively, as (x, y) approaches (x_0, y_0). Hence, by Theorem 1 again, $f(z)F(z)$ has the limit

$$(u_0U_0 - v_0V_0) + i(v_0U_0 + u_0V_0)$$

as z approaches z_0; and this is equal to w_0W_0. Property (9) is thus established. Corresponding verifications of properties (8) and (10) can be given.

It is easy to see from definition (2), Sec. 15, of limit that

$$\lim_{z \to z_0} c = c \quad \text{and} \quad \lim_{z \to z_0} z = z_0,$$

where z_0 and c are any complex numbers; and, by property (9) and mathematical induction, it follows that

$$\lim_{z \to z_0} z^n = z_0^n \qquad (n = 1, 2, \ldots).$$

So, in view of properties (8) and (9), the limit of a polynomial

$$P(z) = a_0 + a_1 z + a_2 z^2 + \cdots + a_n z^n$$

as z approaches a point z_0 is the value of the polynomial at that point:

$$\lim_{z \to z_0} P(z) = P(z_0). \tag{11}$$

17. LIMITS INVOLVING THE POINT AT INFINITY

It is sometimes convenient to include with the complex plane the ***point at infinity***, denoted by ∞, and to use limits involving it. The complex plane together with this point is called the ***extended complex plane***. To visualize the point at infinity, one can think of the complex plane as passing through the equator of a unit sphere centered at the origin (Fig. 25). To each point z in the plane there corresponds exactly one point P on the surface of the sphere. The point P is the point where the line through z and the north pole N intersects the sphere. In like manner, to each point P on the surface of the sphere, other than the north pole N, there corresponds exactly one point z in the plane. By letting the point N of the sphere correspond to the point at infinity, we obtain a one to one correspondence between the points on the sphere and the points in the extended complex plane. The sphere is known as the ***Riemann sphere***, and the correspondence is called a ***stereographic projection***.

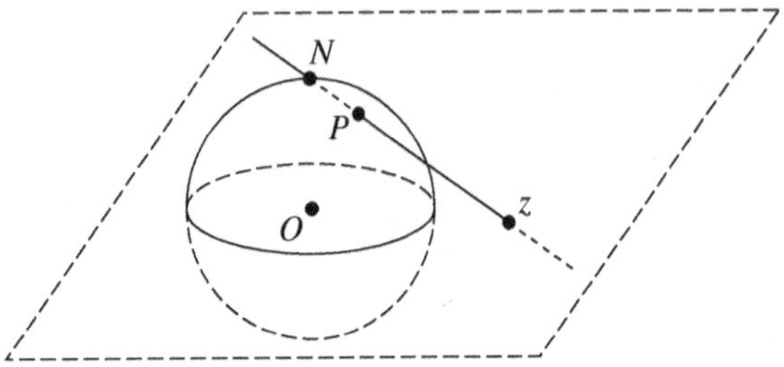

FIGURE 25

Observe that the exterior of the unit circle centered at the origin in the complex plane corresponds to the upper hemisphere with the equator and the point N deleted. Moreover, for each small positive number ε, those points in the complex plane exterior to the circle $|z| = 1/\varepsilon$ correspond to points on the sphere close to N. We thus call the set $|z| > 1/\varepsilon$ a ***neighborhood of*** ∞.

Let us agree that in referring to a point z, we mean a point in the ***finite plane***. Hereafter, when the point at infinity is to be considered, it will be specifically mentioned.

A meaning is now readily given to the statement

$$\lim_{z \to z_0} f(z) = w_0$$

when either z_0 or w_0, or possibly each of these numbers, is replaced by the point at infinity. In the definition of limit in Sec. 15, we simply replace the appropriate neighborhoods of z_0 and w_0 by neighborhoods of ∞. The proof of the following theorem illustrates how this is done.

Theorem. *If z_0 and w_0 are points in the z and w planes, respectively, then*

$$\lim_{z \to z_0} f(z) = \infty \quad \text{if} \quad \lim_{z \to z_0} \frac{1}{f(z)} = 0 \tag{1}$$

and

$$\lim_{z\to\infty} f(z) = w_0 \quad \textit{if} \quad \lim_{z\to 0} f\left(\frac{1}{z}\right) = w_0. \tag{2}$$

Moreover,

$$\lim_{z\to\infty} f(z) = \infty \quad \textit{if} \quad \lim_{z\to 0} \frac{1}{f(1/z)} = 0. \tag{3}$$

We start the proof with the assumption that the second of limits (1) holds. This means that for each positive number ε, there is a positive number δ such that

$$\left|\frac{1}{f(z)} - 0\right| < \varepsilon \quad \text{whenever} \quad 0 < |z - z_0| < \delta.$$

Since this can be written

$$|f(z)| > \frac{1}{\varepsilon} \quad \text{whenever} \quad 0 < |z - z_0| < \delta, \tag{4}$$

we arrive at the first of limits (1).

Suppose now that the second of limits (2) holds. That is,

$$\left|f\left(\frac{1}{z}\right) - w_0\right| < \varepsilon \quad \text{whenever} \quad 0 < |z - 0| < \delta.$$

Replacing z by $1/z$ here, we have the statement

$$|f(z) - w_0| < \varepsilon \quad \text{whenever} \quad |z| > \frac{1}{\delta}, \tag{5}$$

from which the first of limits (2) follows.

Finally, the second of limits (3) means that

$$\left|\frac{1}{f(1/z)} - 0\right| < \varepsilon \quad \text{whenever} \quad 0 < |z - 0| < \delta;$$

and replacement of z by $1/z$ in these inequalities yields the statement

$$|f(z)| > \frac{1}{\varepsilon} \quad \text{whenever} \quad |z| > \frac{1}{\delta}. \tag{6}$$

This is, of course, the definition of the first of limits (3).

EXAMPLES. Observe that

$$\lim_{z\to -1} \frac{iz+3}{z+1} = \infty \quad \text{since} \quad \lim_{z\to -1} \frac{z+1}{iz+3} = 0$$

and

$$\lim_{z\to\infty} \frac{2z+i}{z+1} = 2 \quad \text{since} \quad \lim_{z\to 0} \frac{(2/z)+i}{(1/z)+1} = \lim_{z\to 0} \frac{2+iz}{1+z} = 2.$$

Furthermore,

$$\lim_{z\to\infty} \frac{2z^3 - 1}{z^2 + 1} = \infty \quad \text{since} \quad \lim_{z\to 0} \frac{(1/z^2) + 1}{(2/z^3) - 1} = \lim_{z\to 0} \frac{z + z^3}{2 - z^3} = 0.$$

18. CONTINUITY

A function f is ***continuous*** at a point z_0 if all three of the following conditions are satisfied:

$$\lim_{z\to z_0} f(z) \text{ exists,} \tag{1}$$

$$f(z_0) \text{ exists,} \tag{2}$$

$$\lim_{z\to z_0} f(z) = f(z_0). \tag{3}$$

Observe that statement (3) actually contains statements (1) and (2), since the existence of the quantity on each side of the equation in that statement is needed. Statement (3) says, of course, that for each positive number ε, there is a positive number δ such that

$$|f(z) - f(z_0)| < \varepsilon \quad \text{whenever} \quad |z - z_0| < \delta. \tag{4}$$

A function of a complex variable is said to be continuous in a region R if it is continuous at each point in R.

If two functions are continuous at a point, their sum and product are also continuous at that point; their quotient is continuous at any such point if the denominator is not zero there. These observations are direct consequences of Theorem 2, Sec. 16. Note, too, that a polynomial is continuous in the entire plane because of limit (11) in Sec. 16.

We turn now to two expected properties of continuous functions whose verifications are not so immediate. Our proofs depend on definition (4) of continuity, and we present the results as theorems.

Theorem 1. *A composition of continuous functions is itself continuous.*

A precise statement of this theorem is contained in the proof to follow. We let $w = f(z)$ be a function that is defined for all z in a neighborhood $|z - z_0| < \delta$ of a point z_0, and we let $W = g(w)$ be a function whose domain of definition contains the image (Sec. 13) of that neighborhood under f. The composition $W = g[f(z)]$ is, then, defined for all z in the neighborhood $|z - z_0| < \delta$. Suppose now that f is continuous at z_0 and that g is continuous at the point $f(z_0)$ in the w plane. In view of the continuity of g at $f(z_0)$, there is, for each positive number ε, a positive number γ such that

$$|g[f(z)] - g[f(z_0)]| < \varepsilon \quad \text{whenever} \quad |f(z) - f(z_0)| < \gamma.$$

(See Fig. 26.) But the continuity of f at z_0 ensures that the neighborhood $|z - z_0| < \delta$ can be made small enough that the second of these inequalities holds. The continuity of the composition $g[f(z)]$ is, therefore, established.

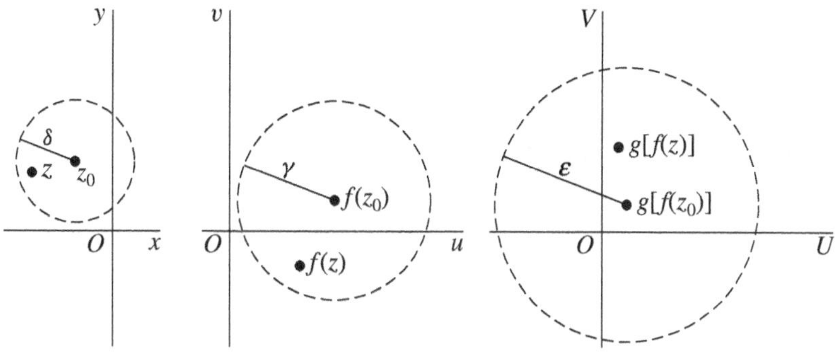

FIGURE 26

Theorem 2. *If a function $f(z)$ is continuous and nonzero at a point z_0, then $f(z) \neq 0$ throughout some neighborhood of that point.*

Assuming that $f(z)$ is, in fact, continuous and nonzero at z_0, we can prove Theorem 2 by assigning the positive value $|f(z_0)|/2$ to the number ε in statement (4). This tells us that there is a positive number δ such that

$$|f(z) - f(z_0)| < \frac{|f(z_0)|}{2} \quad \text{whenever} \quad |z - z_0| < \delta.$$

So if there is a point z in the neighborhood $|z - z_0| < \delta$ at which $f(z) = 0$, we have the contradiction

$$|f(z_0)| < \frac{|f(z_0)|}{2};$$

and the theorem is proved.

The continuity of a function

$$f(z) = u(x, y) + iv(x, y) \tag{5}$$

is closely related to the continuity of its component functions $u(x, y)$ and $v(x, y)$, as the following theorem indicates.

Theorem 3. *If the component functions u and v in expression* (5) *are continuous at a point $z_0 = (x_0, y_0)$, then so is f. Conversely, if f is continuous at z_0, the same is true of u and v at that point.*

The proof follows immediately from Theorem 1 in Sec. 16, regarding the connection between limits of f and limits of u and v.

The next theorem is extremely important and will be used often in later chapters, especially in applications. Before stating the theorem, whose proof is based on Theorem 3, we recall from Sec. 12 that a region R is *closed* if it contains all of its boundary points and that it is *bounded* if it lies inside some circle centered at the origin.

Theorem 4. *If a function f is continuous throughout a region R that is both closed and bounded, there exists a nonnegative real number M such that*

$$|f(z)| \leq M \quad \text{for all points } z \text{ in } R, \tag{6}$$

where equality holds for at least one such z.

To prove this, we assume that the function f in equation (5) is continuous and note how it follows that the function

$$\sqrt{[u(x,y)]^2 + [v(x,y)]^2}$$

is continuous throughout R and thus reaches a maximum value M somewhere in R.* Inequality (6) thus holds, and we say that f is ***bounded on R***.

EXERCISES

1. Use definition (2), Sec. 15, of limit to prove that

(a) $\lim_{z \to z_0} \operatorname{Re} z = \operatorname{Re} z_0$; (b) $\lim_{z \to z_0} \bar{z} = \bar{z}_0$; (c) $\lim_{z \to 0} \dfrac{\bar{z}^2}{z} = 0$.

2. Let a, b, and c denote complex constants. Then use definition (2), Sec. 15, of limit to show that

(a) $\lim_{z \to z_0} (az + b) = az_0 + b$; (b) $\lim_{z \to z_0} (z^2 + c) = z_0^2 + c$;

(c) $\lim_{z \to 1-i} [x + i(2x + y)] = 1 + i \quad (z = x + iy)$.

3. Let n be a positive integer and let $P(z)$ and $Q(z)$ be polynomials, where $Q(z_0) \neq 0$. Use Theorem 2 in Sec. 16, as well as limits appearing in that section, to find

(a) $\lim_{z \to z_0} \dfrac{1}{z^n} \ (z_0 \neq 0)$; (b) $\lim_{z \to i} \dfrac{iz^3 - 1}{z + i}$; (c) $\lim_{z \to z_0} \dfrac{P(z)}{Q(z)}$.

Ans. (a) $1/z_0^n$; (b) 0; (c) $P(z_0)/Q(z_0)$.

4. Use mathematical induction and property (9), Sec. 16, of limits to show that

$$\lim_{z \to z_0} z^n = z_0^n$$

when n is a positive integer $(n = 1, 2, \ldots)$.

5. Show that the function

$$f(z) = \left(\frac{z}{\bar{z}}\right)^2$$

has the value 1 at all nonzero points on the real and imaginary axes, where $z = (x, 0)$ and $z = (0, y)$, respectively, but that it has the value -1 at all nonzero points on the line $y = x$, where $z = (x, x)$. Thus show that the limit of $f(z)$ as z tends to 0 does

*See, for instance, A. E. Taylor and W. R. Mann, "*Advanced Calculus*," 3d ed., pp. 125–126 and p. 529, 1983.

not exist. [Note that it is not sufficient to simply consider nonzero points $z = (x, 0)$ and $z = (0, y)$, as it was in Example 2, Sec. 15.]

6. Prove statement (8) in Theorem 2 of Sec. 16 using

(*a*) Theorem 1 in Sec. 16 and properties of limits of real-valued functions of two real variables;

(*b*) definition (2), Sec. 15, of limit.

7. Use definition (2), Sec. 15, of limit to prove that

$$\text{if} \quad \lim_{z \to z_0} f(z) = w_0, \quad \text{then} \quad \lim_{z \to z_0} |f(z)| = |w_0|.$$

Suggestion: Observe how inequality (2), Sec. 5, enables one to write

$$||f(z)| - |w_0|| \le |f(z) - w_0|.$$

8. Write $\Delta z = z - z_0$ and show that

$$\lim_{z \to z_0} f(z) = w_0 \quad \text{if and only if} \quad \lim_{\Delta z \to 0} f(z_0 + \Delta z) = w_0.$$

9. Show that

$$\lim_{z \to z_0} f(z)g(z) = 0 \quad \text{if} \quad \lim_{z \to z_0} f(z) = 0$$

and if there exists a positive number M such that $|g(z)| \le M$ for all z in some neighborhood of z_0.

10. Use the theorem in Sec. 17 to show that

$$(a)\ \lim_{z \to \infty} \frac{4z^2}{(z-1)^2} = 4; \qquad (b)\ \lim_{z \to 1} \frac{1}{(z-1)^3} = \infty; \qquad (c)\ \lim_{z \to \infty} \frac{z^2+1}{z-1} = \infty.$$

11. With the aid of the theorem in Sec. 17, show that when

$$T(z) = \frac{az+b}{cz+d} \qquad (ad - bc \ne 0),$$

(*a*) $\lim_{z \to \infty} T(z) = \infty \quad \text{if } c = 0;$

(*b*) $\lim_{z \to \infty} T(z) = \dfrac{a}{c}$ and $\lim_{z \to -d/c} T(z) = \infty \quad \text{if } c \ne 0.$

12. State why limits involving the point at infinity are unique.

13. Show that a set S is unbounded (Sec. 12) if and only if every neighborhood of the point at infinity contains at least one point in S.

19. DERIVATIVES

Let f be a function whose domain of definition contains a neighborhood $|z - z_0| < \varepsilon$ of a point z_0. The ***derivative*** of f at z_0 is the limit

$$f'(z_0) = \lim_{z \to z_0} \frac{f(z) - f(z_0)}{z - z_0}, \tag{1}$$

and the function f is said to be ***differentiable*** at z_0 when $f'(z_0)$ exists.

By expressing the variable z in definition (1) in terms of the new complex variable

$$\Delta z = z - z_0 \quad (z \neq z_0),$$

one can write that definition as

$$f'(z_0) = \lim_{\Delta z \to 0} \frac{f(z_0 + \Delta z) - f(z_0)}{\Delta z}. \tag{2}$$

Because f is defined throughout a neighborhood of z_0, the number $f(z_0 + \Delta z)$ is always defined for $|\Delta z|$ sufficiently small (Fig. 27).

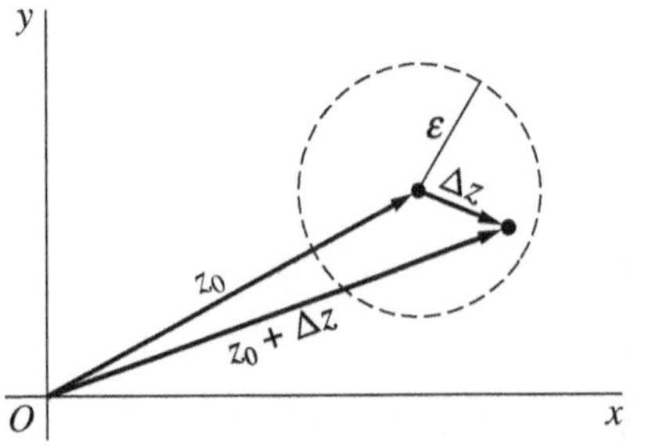

FIGURE 27

When taking form (2) of the definition of derivative, we often drop the subscript on z_0 and introduce the number

$$\Delta w = f(z + \Delta z) - f(z),$$

which denotes the change in the value $w = f(z)$ of f corresponding to a change Δz in the point at which f is evaluated. Then, if we write dw/dz for $f'(z)$, equation (2) becomes

$$\frac{dw}{dz} = \lim_{\Delta z \to 0} \frac{\Delta w}{\Delta z}. \tag{3}$$

EXAMPLE 1. Suppose that $f(z) = 1/z$. At each nonzero point z,

$$\lim_{\Delta z \to 0} \frac{\Delta w}{\Delta z} = \lim_{\Delta z \to 0} \left(\frac{1}{z + \Delta z} - \frac{1}{z} \right) \frac{1}{\Delta z} = \lim_{\Delta z \to 0} \frac{-1}{(z + \Delta z)\, z},$$

provided these limits exist; and properties of limits in Sec. 16 tell us that

$$\frac{dw}{dz} = -\frac{1}{z^2}, \quad \text{or} \quad f'(z) = -\frac{1}{z^2},$$

when $z \neq 0$.

EXAMPLE 2. If $f(z) = \overline{z}$, then

$$\frac{\Delta w}{\Delta z} = \frac{\overline{z + \Delta z} - \overline{z}}{\Delta z} = \frac{\overline{z} + \overline{\Delta z} - \overline{z}}{\Delta z} = \frac{\overline{\Delta z}}{\Delta z}. \tag{4}$$

If the limit of $\Delta w/\Delta z$ exists, it can be found by letting the point $\Delta z = (\Delta x, \Delta y)$ approach the origin $(0, 0)$ in the Δz plane in any manner. In particular, as Δz approaches

(0, 0) horizontally through the points $(\Delta x, 0)$ on the real axis (Fig. 28),

$$\overline{\Delta z} = \overline{\Delta x + i0} = \Delta x - i0 = \Delta x + i0 = \Delta z.$$

In that case, expression (4) tells us that

$$\frac{\Delta w}{\Delta z} = \frac{\Delta z}{\Delta z} = 1.$$

Hence if the limit of $\Delta w/\Delta z$ exists, its value must be unity. However, when Δz approaches (0, 0) vertically through the points $(0, \Delta y)$ on the imaginary axis, so that

$$\overline{\Delta z} = \overline{0 + i\Delta y} = 0 - i\Delta y = -(0 + i\Delta y) = -\Delta z,$$

we find from expression (4) that

$$\frac{\Delta w}{\Delta z} = \frac{-\Delta z}{\Delta z} = -1.$$

Hence the limit must be -1 if it exists. Since limits are unique (Sec. 15), it follows that dw/dz does not exist anywhere.

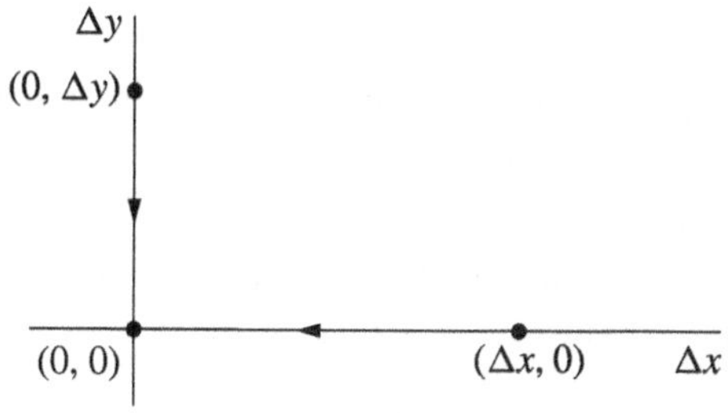

FIGURE 28

EXAMPLE 3. Consider the real-valued function $f(z) = |z|^2$. Here

$$\frac{\Delta w}{\Delta z} = \frac{|z + \Delta z|^2 - |z|^2}{\Delta z} = \frac{(z + \Delta z)(\overline{z + \Delta z}) - z\overline{z}}{\Delta z};$$

and since $\overline{z + \Delta z} = \overline{z} + \overline{\Delta z}$, this becomes

$$\frac{\Delta w}{\Delta z} = \overline{z} + \overline{\Delta z} + z\frac{\overline{\Delta z}}{\Delta z}. \tag{5}$$

Proceeding as in Example 2, where horizontal and vertical approaches of Δz toward the origin gave us

$$\overline{\Delta z} = \Delta z \quad \text{and} \quad \overline{\Delta z} = -\Delta z,$$

respectively, we have the expressions

$$\frac{\Delta w}{\Delta z} = \overline{z} + \Delta z + z \quad \text{when} \quad \Delta z = (\Delta x, 0)$$

and

$$\frac{\Delta w}{\Delta z} = \overline{z} - \Delta z - z \quad \text{when} \quad \Delta z = (0, \Delta y).$$

Hence if the limit of $\Delta w/\Delta z$ exists as Δz tends to zero, the uniqueness of limits, used in Example 2, tells us that

$$\overline{z} + z = \overline{z} - z,$$

or that $z = 0$. Evidently, then, dw/dz cannot exist if $z \neq 0$.

To show that dw/dz does, in fact, exist at $z = 0$, we need only observe that expression (5) reduces to

$$\frac{\Delta w}{\Delta z} = \overline{\Delta z}$$

when $z = 0$. We conclude, therefore, that dw/dz exists *only* at $z = 0$, its value there being 0.

Example 3 illustrates the following three facts, the first two of which may be surprising.

(*a*) A function $f(z) = u(x, y) + iv(x, y)$ can be differentiable at a point $z = (x, y)$ but nowhere else in any neighborhood of that point.

(*b*) Since $u(x, y) = x^2 + y^2$ and $v(x, y) = 0$ when $f(z) = |z|^2$, one can see that the real and imaginary components of a function of a complex variable can have continuous partial derivatives of all orders at a point $z = (x, y)$ and yet the function of z may not be differentiable there.

(*c*) Because the component functions $u(x, y) = x^2 + y^2$ and $v(x, y) = 0$ of the function $f(z) = |z|^2$ are continuous everywhere in the plane, it is also evident that the continuity of a function of a complex variable at a point does not imply the existence of its derivative there. More precisely, the components

$$u(x, y) = x^2 + y^2 \quad \text{and} \quad v(x, y) = 0$$

of $f(z) = |z|^2$ are continuous at each nonzero point $z = (x, y)$ but $f'(z)$ does not exist there. It is, however, true that *the existence of the derivative of a function at a point implies the continuity of the function at that point.* To see this, we assume that $f'(z_0)$ exists and write

$$\lim_{z \to z_0} [f(z) - f(z_0)] = \lim_{z \to z_0} \frac{f(z) - f(z_0)}{z - z_0} \lim_{z \to z_0} (z - z_0) = f'(z_0) \cdot 0 = 0,$$

from which it follows that

$$\lim_{z \to z_0} f(z) = f(z_0).$$

This is the statement of continuity of f at z_0 (Sec. 18).

Geometric interpretations of derivatives of functions of a complex variable are not as immediate as they are for derivatives of functions of a real variable. We defer the development of such interpretations until Chap. 9.

20. RULES FOR DIFFERENTIATION

The definition of derivative in Sec. 19 is formally the same as the definition in calculus when z is substituted for x. Hence the basic differentiation rules given below can be derived from the definition in Sec. 19 by the same steps as the ones used in calculus. In stating such rules, we shall use either

$$\frac{d}{dz}f(z) \quad \text{or} \quad f'(z),$$

depending on which notation is more convenient.

Let c be a complex constant, and let f be a function whose derivative exists at a point z. It is easy to show that

$$\frac{d}{dz}c = 0, \quad \frac{d}{dz}z = 1, \quad \frac{d}{dz}[cf(z)] = cf'(z). \tag{1}$$

Also, if n is a positive integer,

$$\frac{d}{dz}z^n = nz^{n-1}. \tag{2}$$

This rule remains valid when n is a negative integer, provided that $z \neq 0$.

If the derivatives of two functions f and g exist at a point z, then

$$\frac{d}{dz}[f(z) + g(z)] = f'(z) + g'(z), \tag{3}$$

$$\frac{d}{dz}[f(z)g(z)] = f(z)g'(z) + f'(z)g(z); \tag{4}$$

and, when $g(z) \neq 0$,

$$\frac{d}{dz}\left[\frac{f(z)}{g(z)}\right] = \frac{g(z)f'(z) - f(z)g'(z)}{[g(z)]^2}. \tag{5}$$

Let us derive rule (4). To do this, we write the following expression for the change in the product $w = f(z)g(z)$:

$$\begin{aligned}\Delta w &= f(z+\Delta z)g(z+\Delta z) - f(z)g(z)\\ &= f(z)[g(z+\Delta z) - g(z)] + [f(z+\Delta z) - f(z)]g(z+\Delta z).\end{aligned}$$

Thus

$$\frac{\Delta w}{\Delta z} = f(z)\frac{g(z+\Delta z) - g(z)}{\Delta z} + \frac{f(z+\Delta z) - f(z)}{\Delta z}g(z+\Delta z);$$

and, letting Δz tend to zero, we arrive at the desired rule for the derivative of $f(z)g(z)$. Here we have used the fact that g is continuous at the point z, since $g'(z)$ exists; thus $g(z+\Delta z)$ tends to $g(z)$ as Δz tends to zero (see Exercise 8, Sec. 18).

There is also a chain rule for differentiating composite functions. Suppose that f has a derivative at z_0 and that g has a derivative at the point $f(z_0)$. Then the function $F(z) = g[f(z)]$ has a derivative at z_0, and

$$F'(z_0) = g'[f(z_0)]f'(z_0). \tag{6}$$

If we write $w = f(z)$ and $W = g(w)$, so that $W = F(z)$, the chain rule becomes

$$\frac{dW}{dz} = \frac{dW}{dw}\frac{dw}{dz}.$$

EXAMPLE. To find the derivative of $(1-4z^2)^3$, one can write $w = 1-4z^2$ and $W = w^3$. Then

$$\frac{d}{dz}(1-4z^2)^3 = 3w^2(-8z) = -24z(1-4z^2)^2.$$

To start the derivation of rule (6), choose a specific point z_0 at which $f'(z_0)$ exists. Write $w_0 = f(z_0)$ and also assume that $g'(w_0)$ exists. There is, then, some ε neighborhood $|w - w_0| < \varepsilon$ of w_0 such that for all points w in that neighborhood, we can define a function Φ having the values $\Phi(w_0) = 0$ and

$$\Phi(w) = \frac{g(w) - g(w_0)}{w - w_0} - g'(w_0) \quad \text{when} \quad w \neq w_0. \tag{7}$$

Note that in view of the definition of derivative,

$$\lim_{w \to w_0} \Phi(w) = 0. \tag{8}$$

Hence Φ is continuous at w_0.

Now expression (7) can be put in the form

$$g(w) - g(w_0) = [g'(w_0) + \Phi(w)](w - w_0) \qquad (|w - w_0| < \varepsilon), \tag{9}$$

which is valid even when $w = w_0$; and since $f'(z_0)$ exists and f is therefore continuous at z_0, we can choose a positive number δ such that the point $f(z)$ lies in the ε neighborhood $|w - w_0| < \varepsilon$ of w_0 if z lies in the δ neighborhood $|z - z_0| < \delta$ of z_0. Thus it is legitimate to replace the variable w in equation (9) by $f(z)$ when z is any point in the neighborhood $|z - z_0| < \delta$. With that substitution, and with $w_0 = f(z_0)$, equation (9) becomes

$$\frac{g[f(z)] - g[f(z_0)]}{z - z_0} = \{g'[f(z_0)] + \Phi[f(z)]\}\frac{f(z) - f(z_0)}{z - z_0} \qquad (0 < |z - z_0| < \delta), \tag{10}$$

where we must stipulate that $z \neq z_0$ so that we are not dividing by zero. As already noted, f is continuous at z_0 and Φ is continuous at the point $w_0 = f(z_0)$. Hence the composition $\Phi[f(z)]$ is continuous at z_0; and since $\Phi(w_0) = 0$,

$$\lim_{z \to z_0} \Phi[f(z)] = 0.$$

So equation (10) becomes equation (6) in the limit as z approaches z_0.

EXERCISES

1. Use definition (3), Sec. 19, to give a direct proof that

$$\frac{dw}{dz} = 2z \quad \text{when} \quad w = z^2.$$

2. Use results in Sec. 20 to find $f'(z)$ when

(*a*) $f(z) = 3z^2 - 2z + 4$; (*b*) $f(z) = (2z^2 + i)^5$;

(*c*) $f(z) = \dfrac{z-1}{2z+1} \quad \left(z \neq -\dfrac{1}{2}\right)$; (*d*) $f(z) = \dfrac{(1+z^2)^4}{z^2} \quad (z \neq 0)$.

3. Using results in Sec. 20, show that

(*a*) a polynomial

$$P(z) = a_0 + a_1 z + a_2 z^2 + \cdots + a_n z^n \qquad (a_n \neq 0)$$

of degree n ($n \geq 1$) is differentiable everywhere, with derivative

$$P'(z) = a_1 + 2a_2 z + \cdots + n a_n z^{n-1};$$

(*b*) the coefficients in the polynomial $P(z)$ in part (*a*) can be written

$$a_0 = P(0), \quad a_1 = \frac{P'(0)}{1!}, \quad a_2 = \frac{P''(0)}{2!}, \quad \ldots, \quad a_n = \frac{P^{(n)}(0)}{n!}.$$

4. Suppose that $f(z_0) = g(z_0) = 0$ and that $f'(z_0)$ and $g'(z_0)$ exist, where $g'(z_0) \neq 0$. Use definition (1), Sec. 19, of derivative to show that

$$\lim_{z \to z_0} \frac{f(z)}{g(z)} = \frac{f'(z_0)}{g'(z_0)}.$$

5. Derive expression (3), Sec. 20, for the derivative of the sum of two functions.

6. Derive expression (2), Sec. 20, for the derivative of z^n when n is a positive integer by using

(*a*) mathematical induction and expression (4), Sec. 20, for the derivative of the product of two functions;

(*b*) definition (3), Sec. 19, of derivative and the binomial formula (Sec. 3).

7. Prove that expression (2), Sec. 20, for the derivative of z^n remains valid when n is a negative integer ($n = -1, -2, \ldots$), provided that $z \neq 0$.

Suggestion: Write $m = -n$ and use the rule for the derivative of a quotient of two functions.

8. Use the method in Example 2, Sec. 19, to show that $f'(z)$ does not exist at any point z when

(*a*) $f(z) = \text{Re}\, z$; (*b*) $f(z) = \text{Im}\, z$.

9. Let f denote the function whose values are

$$f(z) = \begin{cases} \overline{z}^2/z & \text{when} \quad z \neq 0, \\ 0 & \text{when} \quad z = 0. \end{cases}$$

Show that if $z = 0$, then $\Delta w/\Delta z = 1$ at each nonzero point on the real and imaginary axes in the Δz, or $\Delta x\, \Delta y$, plane. Then show that $\Delta w/\Delta z = -1$ at each nonzero point $(\Delta x, \Delta x)$ on the line $\Delta y = \Delta x$ in that plane (Fig. 29). Conclude from these observations that $f'(0)$ does not exist. Note that to obtain this result, it is not sufficient to consider only horizontal and vertical approaches to the origin in the Δz plane. (Compare with Exercise 5, Sec. 18, as well as Example 2, Sec. 19.)

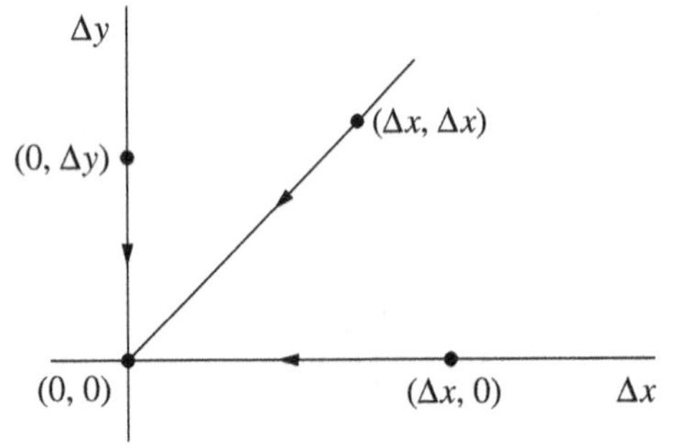

FIGURE 29

10. With the aid of the binomial formula (13) in Sec. 3, point out why each of the functions

$$P_n(z) = \frac{1}{n!2^n} \frac{d^n}{dz^n}(z^2 - 1)^n \qquad (n = 0, 1, 2, \ldots)$$

is a polynomial (Sec. 13) of degree n*. (We use the convention that the derivative of order zero of a function is the function itself.)

21. CAUCHY–RIEMANN EQUATIONS

In this section, we obtain a pair of equations that the first-order partial derivatives of the component functions u and v of a function

$$(1) \qquad f(z) = u(x, y) + iv(x, y)$$

must satisfy at a point $z_0 = (x_0, y_0)$ when the derivative of f exists there. We also show how to express $f'(z_0)$ in terms of those partial derivatives.

Starting with the assumption that $f'(z_0)$ exists, we write

$$z_0 = x_0 + iy_0, \quad \Delta z = \Delta x + i\Delta y,$$

*These are called ***Legendre polynomials*** and are important in applied mathematics. See, for instance, Chap. 10 of the authors' book (2012), listed in the Bibliography.

and

$$\Delta w = f(z_0 + \Delta z) - f(z_0),$$

which is the same as

$$\Delta w = [u(x_0 + \Delta x, y_0 + \Delta y) + iv(x_0 + \Delta x, y_0 + \Delta y)] - [u(x_0, y_0) + iv(x_0, y_0)].$$

This last equation enables us to write

$$(2)\quad \frac{\Delta w}{\Delta z} = \frac{u(x_0 + \Delta x, y_0 + \Delta y) - u(x_0 y_0)}{\Delta x + i\Delta y} + i\frac{v(x_0 + \Delta x, y_0 + \Delta y) - v(x_0 y_0)}{\Delta x + i\Delta y}.$$

Now it is important to keep in mind that expression (2) remains valid as $(\Delta x, \Delta y)$ tends to $(0, 0)$ in any manner that we may choose.

Horizontal approach

In particular, write $\Delta y = 0$ and let $(\Delta x,\ 0)$ tend to $(0,\ 0)$ horizontally. Then, in view of Theorem 1 in Sec. 16, equation (2) tells us that

$$f'(z_0) = \lim_{\Delta x \to 0} \frac{u(x_0 + \Delta x, y_0) - u(x_0 y_0)}{\Delta x} + i \lim_{\Delta x \to 0} \frac{v(x_0 + \Delta x, y_0) - v(x_0 y_0)}{\Delta x}.$$

That is,

$$(3)\quad f'(z_0) = u_x(x_0, y_0) + iv_x(x_0, y_0).$$

Vertical approach

We might have set $\Delta x = 0$ in equation (2) and taken a vertical approach. In that case, we find from Theorem 1 in Sec. 16 and equation (2) that

$$f'(z_0) = \lim_{\Delta y \to 0} \frac{u(x_0, y_0 + \Delta y) - u(x_0 y_0)}{i\Delta y} + i \lim_{\Delta y \to 0} \frac{v(x_0, y_0 + \Delta y) - v(x_0 y_0)}{i\Delta y},$$

or, because $1/i = -i$,

$$f'(z_0) = \lim_{\Delta y \to 0} \frac{v(x_0, y_0 + \Delta y) - v(x_0 y_0)}{\Delta y} - i \lim_{\Delta y \to 0} \frac{u(x_0, y_0 + \Delta y) - u(x_0 y_0)}{\Delta y}.$$

It now follows that

$$(4)\quad f'(z_0) = v_y(x_0, y_0) - iu_y(x_0, y_0),$$

where the partial derivatives of u and v are, this time, with respect to y. Note that equation (4) can also be written in the form

$$(5)\quad f'(z_0) = -i[u_y(x_0, y_0) + iv_y(x_0, y_0)].$$

Expressions (3) and (4) not only give $f'(z_0)$ in terms of partial derivatives of the component functions u and v but, in view of the uniqueness of limits (Sec. 15), they also provide necessary conditions for the existence of $f'(z_0)$. To obtain those conditions, we need only equate the real parts and then the imaginary parts in expressions

(3) and (4) to see that the existence of $f'(z_0)$ requires that

$$u_x(x_0, y_0) = v_y(x_0, y_0) \quad \text{and} \quad u_y(x_0, y_0) = -\,v_x(x_0, y_0). \tag{6}$$

Equations (6) are the ***Cauchy–Riemann equations***, so named in honor of the French mathematician A. L. Cauchy (1789–1857), who discovered and used them, and in honor of the German mathematician G. F. B. Riemann (1826–1866), who made them fundamental in his development of the theory of functions of a complex variable.

We summarize the above results as follows.

Theorem. *Suppose that*

$$f(z) = u(x, y) + iv(x, y)$$

and that $f'(z)$ exists at a point $z_0 = x_0 + iy_0$. Then the first-order partial derivatives of u and v must exist at (x_0, y_0), and they must satisfy the Cauchy–Riemann equations

$$u_x = v_y, \quad u_y = -v_x \tag{7}$$

there. Also, $f'(z_0)$ can be written

$$f'(z_0) = u_x + iv_x, \tag{8}$$

where these partial derivatives are to be evaluated at (x_0, y_0).

22. EXAMPLES

Before we continue our discussion of the Cauchy–Riemann equations, we pause here to illustrate their use and to motivate further discussion of them.

EXAMPLE 1. In Exercise 1, Sec. 20, we showed that the function

$$f(z) = z^2 = x^2 - y^2 + i2xy$$

is differentiable everywhere and that $f'(z) = 2z$. To verify that the Cauchy–Riemann equations are satisfied everywhere, write

$$u(x, y) = x^2 - y^2 \quad \text{and} \quad v(x, y) = 2xy.$$

Thus

$$u_x = 2x = v_y, \quad u_y = -2y = -v_x.$$

Moreover, according to equation (8) in Sec. 21,

$$f'(z) = 2x + i2y = 2(x + iy) = 2z.$$

Since the Cauchy–Riemann equations are necessary conditions for the existence of the derivative of a function f at a point z_0, they can often be used to locate points at which f does *not* have a derivative.

EXAMPLE 2. When $f(z) = |z|^2$, we have

$$u(x, y) = x^2 + y^2 \quad \text{and} \quad v(x, y) = 0.$$

If the Cauchy–Riemann equations are to hold at a point (x, y), it follows that $2x = 0$ and $2y = 0$, or that $x = y = 0$. Consequently, $f'(z)$ does not exist at any nonzero point, as we already know from Example 3 in Sec. 19. Note that the theorem just proved does not ensure the existence of $f'(0)$. The theorem in the next section will, however, do this.

In Example 2, we considered a function $f(z)$ whose component functions $u(x, y)$ and $v(x, y)$ satisfy the Cauchy–Riemann equations at the origin and whose derivative $f'(0)$ exists there. It is possible, however, to have a function $f(z)$ whose component functions satisfy the Cauchy–Riemann equations at the origin but whose derivative $f'(0)$ does *not* exist. This is illustrated in our next example.

EXAMPLE 3. If the function $f(z) = u(x, y) + iv(x, y)$ is defined by means of the equations

$$f(z) = \begin{cases} \bar{z}^2/z & \text{when } z \neq 0, \\ 0 & \text{when } z = 0, \end{cases}$$

its real and imaginary components are [see Exercise 2(*b*), Sec. 14]

$$u(x, y) = \frac{x^3 - 3xy^2}{x^2 + y^2} \quad \text{and} \quad v(x, y) = \frac{y^3 - 3x^2y}{x^2 + y^2}$$

when $(x, y) \neq (0, 0)$. Also, $u(0, 0) = 0$ and $v(0, 0) = 0$.

Because

$$u_x(0, 0) = \lim_{\Delta x \to 0} \frac{u(0 + \Delta x, 0) - u(0, 0)}{\Delta x} = \lim_{\Delta x \to 0} \frac{\Delta x}{\Delta x} = 1$$

and

$$v_y(0, 0) = \lim_{\Delta y \to 0} \frac{v(0, 0 + \Delta y) - v(0, 0)}{\Delta y} = \lim_{\Delta y \to 0} \frac{\Delta y}{\Delta y} = 1,$$

we find that the first Cauchy–Riemann equation $u_x = v_y$ is satisfied at $z = 0$. Likewise, it is easy to show that $u_y = 0 = -v_x$ when $z = 0$. But, as was shown in Exercise 9, Sec. 20, $f'(0)$ fails to exist.

23. SUFFICIENT CONDITIONS FOR DIFFERENTIABILITY

As pointed out in Example 3, Sec. 22, satisfaction of the Cauchy–Riemann equations at a point $z_0 = (x_0, y_0)$ is not sufficient to ensure the existence of the derivative of a function $f(z)$ at that point. But, with certain continuity conditions, we have the following useful theorem.

Theorem. *Let the function*

$$f(z) = u(x, y) + iv(x, y)$$

be defined throughout some ε *neighborhood of a point* $z_0 = x_0 + iy_0$, *and suppose that*

(*a*) *the first-order partial derivatives of the functions* u *and* v *with respect to* x *and* y *exist everywhere in the neighborhood;*

(*b*) *those partial derivatives are continuous at* (x_0, y_0) *and satisfy the Cauchy–Riemann equations*

$$u_x = v_y, \quad u_y = -v_x$$

at (x_0, y_0).

Then $f'(z_0)$ *exists, its value being*

$$f'(z_0) = u_x + iv_x$$

where the right-hand side is to be evaluated at (x_0, y_0).

To prove the theorem, we assume that conditions (*a*) and (*b*) in its hypothesis are satisfied and write $\Delta z = \Delta x + i\Delta y$, where $0 < |\Delta z| < \varepsilon$, as well as

$$\Delta w = f(z_0 + \Delta z) - f(z_0).$$

Thus

$$\Delta w = \Delta u + i\Delta v, \tag{1}$$

where

$$\Delta u = u(x_0 + \Delta x, y_0 + \Delta y) - u(x_0, y_0)$$

and

$$\Delta v = v(x_0 + \Delta x, y_0 + \Delta y) - v(x_0, y_0).$$

The assumption that the first-order partial derivatives of u and v are continuous at the point (x_0, y_0) enables us to write*

$$\Delta u = u_x(x_0, y_0)\Delta x + u_y(x_0, y_0)\Delta y + \varepsilon_1\Delta x + \varepsilon_2\Delta y \tag{2}$$

and

$$\Delta v = v_x(x_0, y_0)\Delta x + v_y(x_0, y_0)\Delta y + \varepsilon_3\Delta x + \varepsilon_4\Delta y, \tag{3}$$

*See, for instance, W. Kaplan, "*Advanced Calculus*," 5th ed., pp. 86ff, 2003.

where ε_1, ε_2, ε_3, and ε_4 tend to zero as $(\Delta x, \Delta y)$ approaches $(0, 0)$ in the Δz plane. Substitution of expressions (2) and (3) into equation (1) now tells us that

$$(4)\qquad \Delta w = u_x(x_0, y_0)\Delta x + u_y(x_0, y_0)\Delta y + \varepsilon_1\Delta x + \varepsilon_2\Delta y + i[v_x(x_0, y_0)\Delta x + v_y(x_0, y_0)\Delta y + \varepsilon_3\Delta x + \varepsilon_4\Delta y].$$

Because the Cauchy–Riemann equations are assumed to be satisfied at (x_0, y_0), one can replace $u_y(x_0, y_0)$ by $-v_x(x_0, y_0)$ and $v_y(x_0, y_0)$ by $u_x(x_0, y_0)$ in equation (4) and then divide through by the quantity $\Delta z = \Delta x + i\Delta y$ to get

$$(5)\qquad \frac{\Delta w}{\Delta z} = u_x(x_0, y_0) + iv_x(x_0, y_0) + (\varepsilon_1 + i\varepsilon_3)\frac{\Delta x}{\Delta z} + (\varepsilon_2 + i\varepsilon_4)\frac{\Delta y}{\Delta z}.$$

But $|\Delta x| \le |\Delta z|$ and $|\Delta y| \le |\Delta z|$, according to inequalities (3) in Sec. 4, and so

$$\left|\frac{\Delta x}{\Delta z}\right| \le 1 \quad \text{and} \quad \left|\frac{\Delta y}{\Delta z}\right| \le 1.$$

Consequently,

$$\left|(\varepsilon_1 + i\varepsilon_3)\frac{\Delta x}{\Delta z}\right| \le |\varepsilon_1 + i\varepsilon_3| \le |\varepsilon_1| + |\varepsilon_3|$$

and

$$\left|(\varepsilon_2 + i\varepsilon_4)\frac{\Delta y}{\Delta z}\right| \le |\varepsilon_2 + i\varepsilon_4| \le |\varepsilon_2| + |\varepsilon_4|;$$

and this means that the last two terms on the right in equation (5) tend to zero as the variable $\Delta z = \Delta x + i\Delta y$ approaches zero. The expression for $f'(z_0)$ in the statement of the theorem is now established.

EXAMPLE 1. Consider the function

$$f(z) = e^x e^{iy} = e^x \cos y + ie^x \sin y,$$

where $z = x + iy$ and y is to be taken in radians when $\cos y$ and $\sin y$ are evaluated. Here

$$u(x, y) = e^x \cos y \quad \text{and} \quad v(x, y) = e^x \sin y.$$

Since $u_x = v_y$ and $u_y = -v_x$ everywhere and since these derivatives are everywhere continuous, the conditions in the above theorem are satisfied at all points in the complex plane. Thus $f'(z)$ exists everywhere, and

$$f'(z) = u_x + iv_x = e^x \cos y + ie^x \sin y.$$

Note that $f'(z) = f(z)$ for all z.

EXAMPLE 2. It also follows from our theorem that the function $f(z) = |z|^2$, whose components are

$$u(x, y) = x^2 + y^2 \quad \text{and} \quad v(x, y) = 0,$$

has a derivative at $z = 0$. In fact, $f'(0) = 0 + i0 = 0$. We saw in Example 2, Sec. 22, that this function *cannot* have a derivative at any nonzero point since the Cauchy–Riemann equations are not satisfied at such points. (See also Example 3, Sec. 19.)

EXAMPLE 3. When using the theorem in this section to find a derivative at a point z_0, one must be careful not to use the expression for $f'(z)$ in the statement of the theorem before the *existence* of $f'(z)$ at z_0 is established.

Consider, for instance, the function

$$f(z) = x^3 + i(1-y)^3.$$

Here

$$u(x, y) = x^3 \quad \text{and} \quad v(x, y) = (1-y)^3,$$

and it would be a mistake to say that $f'(z)$ exists everywhere and that

$$f'(z) = u_x + iv_x = 3x^2. \tag{6}$$

To see this, we observe that the first Cauchy–Riemann equation $u_x = v_y$ can hold only if

$$x^2 + (1-y)^2 = 0 \tag{7}$$

and that the second equation $u_y = -v_x$ is always satisfied. Condition (7) thus tells us that $f'(z)$ can exist only when $x = 0$ and $y = 1$. In view of equation (6), then, our theorem tells us that $f'(z)$ exists *only* when $z = i$, in which case $f'(i) = 0$.

24. POLAR COORDINATES

Assuming that $z_0 \neq 0$, we shall in this section use the coordinate transformation

$$x = r\cos\theta, \quad y = r\sin\theta \tag{1}$$

to restate the theorem in Sec. 23 in polar coordinates.

Depending on whether we write

$$z = x + iy \quad \text{or} \quad z = re^{i\theta} \qquad (z \neq 0)$$

when $w = f(z)$, the real and imaginary components of $w = u + iv$ are expressed in terms of either the variables x and y or r and θ. Suppose that the first-order partial derivatives of u and v with respect to x and y exist everywhere in some neighborhood of a given nonzero point z_0 and are continuous at z_0. The first-order partial derivatives of u and v with respect to r and θ also have those properties, and the chain rule for differentiating real-valued functions of two real variables can be used to write them in terms of the ones with respect to x and y. More precisely, since

$$\frac{\partial u}{\partial r} = \frac{\partial u}{\partial x}\frac{\partial x}{\partial r} + \frac{\partial u}{\partial y}\frac{\partial y}{\partial r}, \quad \frac{\partial u}{\partial \theta} = \frac{\partial u}{\partial x}\frac{\partial x}{\partial \theta} + \frac{\partial u}{\partial y}\frac{\partial y}{\partial \theta},$$

one can write

(2) $$u_r = u_x \cos\theta + u_y \sin\theta, \quad u_\theta = -u_x r \sin\theta + u_y r \cos\theta.$$

Likewise,

(3) $$v_r = v_x \cos\theta + v_y \sin\theta, \quad v_\theta = -v_x r \sin\theta + v_y r \cos\theta.$$

If the partial derivatives of u and v with respect to x and y also satisfy the Cauchy–Riemann equations

(4) $$u_x = v_y, \quad u_y = -v_x$$

at z_0, equations (3) become

(5) $$v_r = -u_y \cos\theta + u_x \sin\theta, \quad v_\theta = u_y r \sin\theta + u_x r \cos\theta$$

at that point. It is then clear from equations (2) and (5) that

(6) $$r u_r = v_\theta, \quad u_\theta = -r v_r$$

at z_0.

If, on the other hand, equations (6) are known to hold at z_0, it is straightforward to show (Exercise 7) that equations (4) must hold there. Equations (6) are, therefore, an alternative form of the Cauchy–Riemann equations (4).

In view of equations (6) and the expression for $f'(z_0)$ that is found in Exercise 8, we are now able to restate the theorem in Sec. 23 using r and θ.

Theorem. *Let the function*

$$f(z) = u(r,\theta) + iv(r,\theta)$$

be defined throughout some ε *neighborhood of a nonzero point* $z_0 = r_0 \exp(i\theta_0)$, *and suppose that*

(*a*) *the first-order partial derivatives of the functions* u *and* v *with respect to* r *and* θ *exist everywhere in the neighborhood;*

(*b*) *those partial derivatives are continuous at* (r_0, θ_0) *and satisfy the polar form*

$$r u_r = v_\theta, \quad u_\theta = -r v_r$$

of the Cauchy–Riemann equations at (r_0, θ_0).

Then $f'(z_0)$ *exists, its value being*

$$f'(z_0) = e^{-i\theta}(u_r + i v_r),$$

where the right-hand side is to be evaluated at (r_0, θ_0).

EXAMPLE 1. If

$$f(z) = \frac{1}{z^2} = \frac{1}{(re^{i\theta})^2} = \frac{1}{r^2}e^{-i2\theta} = \frac{1}{r^2}(\cos 2\theta - i \sin 2\theta),$$

where $z \neq 0$, the component functions are

$$u = \frac{\cos 2\theta}{r^2} \quad \text{and} \quad v = -\frac{\sin 2\theta}{r^2}.$$

Since

$$r u_r = -\frac{2\cos 2\theta}{r^2} = v_\theta, \qquad u_\theta = -\frac{2\sin 2\theta}{r^2} = -r\,v_r$$

and since the other conditions in the theorem are satisfied at every nonzero point $z = re^{i\theta}$, the derivative of f exists when $z \neq 0$. Moreover, according to the theorem,

$$f'(z) = e^{-i\theta}\left(-\frac{2\cos 2\theta}{r^3} + i\frac{2\sin 2\theta}{r^3}\right) = -2e^{-i\theta}\frac{e^{-i2\theta}}{r^3} = -\frac{2}{(re^{i\theta})^3} = -\frac{2}{z^3}.$$

EXAMPLE 2. The theorem can be used to show that any branch

$$f(z) = \sqrt{r}\,e^{i\theta/2} \quad (r > 0,\ \alpha < \theta < \alpha + 2\pi)$$

of the square root function $z^{1/2}$ has a derivative everywhere in its domain of definition. Here

$$u(r,\theta) = \sqrt{r}\cos\frac{\theta}{2} \quad \text{and} \quad v(r,\theta) = \sqrt{r}\sin\frac{\theta}{2}.$$

Inasmuch as

$$r u_r = \frac{\sqrt{r}}{2}\cos\frac{\theta}{2} = v_\theta \quad \text{and} \quad u_\theta = -\frac{\sqrt{r}}{2}\sin\frac{\theta}{2} = -r v_r$$

and since the remaining conditions in the theorem are satisfied, the derivative $f'(z)$ exists at each point where $f(z)$ is defined. The theorem also tells us that

$$f'(z) = e^{-i\theta}\left(\frac{1}{2\sqrt{r}}\cos\frac{\theta}{2} + i\frac{1}{2\sqrt{r}}\sin\frac{\theta}{2}\right);$$

and this reduces to

$$f'(z) = \frac{1}{2\sqrt{r}}e^{-i\theta}\left(\cos\frac{\theta}{2} + i\sin\frac{\theta}{2}\right) = \frac{1}{2\sqrt{r}\,e^{i\theta/2}} = \frac{1}{2f(z)}.$$

EXERCISES

1. Use the theorem in Sec. 21 to show that $f'(z)$ does not exist at any point if

(a) $f(z) = \bar{z}$; (b) $f(z) = z - \bar{z}$;

(c) $f(z) = 2x + ixy^2$; (d) $f(z) = e^x e^{-iy}$.

2. Use the theorem in Sec. 23 to show that $f'(z)$ and its derivative $f''(z)$ exist everywhere, and find $f''(z)$ when

(a) $f(z) = iz + 2$; (b) $f(z) = e^{-x}e^{-iy}$;

(c) $f(z) = z^3$; (d) $f(z) = \cos x \cosh y - i \sin x \sinh y$.

Ans. (b) $f''(z) = f(z)$; (d) $f''(z) = -f(z)$.

3. From results obtained in Secs. 21 and 23, determine where $f'(z)$ exists and find its value when

(*a*) $f(z) = 1/z$; (*b*) $f(z) = x^2 + iy^2$; (*c*) $f(z) = z \operatorname{Im} z$.

Ans. (*a*) $f'(z) = -1/z^2$ $(z \neq 0)$; (*b*) $f'(x + ix) = 2x$; (*c*) $f'(0) = 0$.

4. Use the theorem in Sec. 24 to show that each of these functions is differentiable in the indicated domain of definition, and also to find $f'(z)$:

(*a*) $f(z) = 1/z^4$ $(z \neq 0)$;
(*b*) $f(z) = e^{-\theta} \cos(\ln r) + i\, e^{-\theta} \sin(\ln r)$ $(r > 0, 0 < \theta < 2\pi)$.

Ans. (*b*) $f'(z) = i\,\dfrac{f(z)}{z}$.

5. Solve equations (2), Sec. 24 for u_x and u_y to show that

$$u_x = u_r \cos\theta - u_\theta \frac{\sin\theta}{r}, \qquad u_y = u_r \sin\theta + u_\theta \frac{\cos\theta}{r}.$$

Then use these equations and similar ones for v_x and v_y to show that in Sec. 24 equations (4) are satisfied at a point z_0 if equations (6) are satisfied there. Thus complete the verification that equations (6), Sec. 24, are the Cauchy–Riemann equations in polar form.

6. Let a function $f(z) = u + iv$ be differentiable at a nonzero point $z_0 = r_0 \exp(i\theta_0)$. Use the expressions for u_x and v_x found in Exercise 5, together with the polar form (6), Sec. 24, of the Cauchy–Riemann equations, to rewrite the expression

$$f'(z_0) = u_x + i v_x$$

in Sec. 23 as

$$f'(z_0) = e^{-i\theta}(u_r + i v_r),$$

where u_r and v_r are to be evaluated at (r_0, θ_0).

7. (*a*) With the aid of the polar form (6), Sec. 24, of the Cauchy–Riemann equations, derive the alternative form

$$f'(z_0) = \frac{-i}{z_0}(u_\theta + i v_\theta)$$

of the expression for $f'(z_0)$ found in Exercise 6.

(*b*) Use the expression for $f'(z_0)$ in part (*a*) to show that the derivative of the function $f(z) = 1/z$ $(z \neq 0)$ in Exercise 3(*a*) is $f'(z) = -1/z^2$.

8. (*a*) Recall (Sec. 6) that if $z = x + iy$, then

$$x = \frac{z + \overline{z}}{2} \quad \text{and} \quad y = \frac{z - \overline{z}}{2i}.$$

By *formally* applying the chain rule in calculus to a function $F(x, y)$ of two real variables, derive the expression

$$\frac{\partial F}{\partial \overline{z}} = \frac{\partial F}{\partial x}\frac{\partial x}{\partial \overline{z}} + \frac{\partial F}{\partial y}\frac{\partial y}{\partial \overline{z}} = \frac{1}{2}\left(\frac{\partial F}{\partial x} + i\frac{\partial F}{\partial y}\right).$$

(*b*) Define the operator

$$\frac{\partial}{\partial \bar{z}} = \frac{1}{2}\left(\frac{\partial}{\partial x} + i\frac{\partial}{\partial y}\right),$$

suggested by part (*a*), to show that if the first-order partial derivatives of the real and imaginary components of a function $f(z) = u(x, y) + iv(x, y)$ satisfy the Cauchy–Riemann equations, then

$$\frac{\partial f}{\partial \bar{z}} = \frac{1}{2}[(u_x - v_y) + i(v_x + u_y)] = 0.$$

Thus derive the ***complex form*** $\partial f/\partial \bar{z} = 0$ of the Cauchy–Riemann equations.

25. ANALYTIC FUNCTIONS

We are now ready to introduce the concept of an analytic function. A function f of the complex variable z is ***analytic in an open set*** S if it has a derivative everywhere in that set. It is ***analytic at a point*** z_0 if it is analytic in some neighborhood of z_0.*

Note how it follows that if f is analytic at a point z_0, it must be analytic at *each* point in some neighborhood of z_0. If we should speak of a function that is analytic in a set S that is not open, it is to be understood that f is analytic in an open set containing S.

An ***entire*** function is a function that is analytic at each point in the entire plane.

EXAMPLES. The function $f(z) = 1/z$ is analytic at each nonzero point in the finite plane since its derivative $f'(z) = -1/z^2$ exists at such a point. But the function $f(z) = |z|^2$ is not analytic anywhere since its derivative exists only at $z = 0$ and not throughout any neighborhood. (See Example 3, Sec. 19.) Finally, since the derivative of a polynomial exists everywhere, it follows that *every polynomial is an entire function.*

A necessary, but by no means sufficient, condition for a function to be analytic in a domain D is clearly the continuity of f throughout D. (See the statement in italics near the end of Sec. 19.) Satisfaction of the Cauchy–Riemann equations is also necessary, but not sufficient. Sufficient conditions for analyticity in D are provided by the theorems in Secs. 23 and 24.

Other useful sufficient conditions are obtained from the rules for differentiation in Sec. 20. The derivatives of the sum and product of two functions exist wherever the functions themselves have derivatives. Thus, *if two functions are analytic in a domain D, their sum and their product are both analytic in D.* Similarly, *their quotient is analytic in D provided the function in the denominator does not vanish at any point in D.* In particular, the quotient $P(z)/Q(z)$ of two polynomials is analytic in any domain throughout which $Q(z) \neq 0$.

*The terms *regular* and *holomorphic* are also used in the literature to denote analyticity.

From the chain rule for the derivative of a composite function, we find that *a composition of two analytic functions is analytic.* More precisely, suppose that a function $f(z)$ is analytic in a domain D and that the image (Sec. 13) of D under the transformation $w = f(z)$ is contained in the domain of definition of a function $g(w)$. Then the composition $g[f(z)]$ is analytic in D, with derivative

$$\frac{d}{dz}g[f(z)] = g'[f(z)]f'(z).$$

The following property of analytic functions is especially useful, in addition to being expected.

Theorem. *If $f'(z) = 0$ everywhere in a domain D, then $f(z)$ must be constant throughout D.*

We start the proof by writing $f(z) = u(x, y) + iv(x, y)$. Assuming that $f'(z) = 0$ in D, we note that $u_x + iv_x = 0$; and, in view of the Cauchy–Riemann equations, $v_y - iu_y = 0$. Consequently,

$$u_x = u_y = 0 \quad \text{and} \quad v_x = v_y = 0$$

at each point in D.

Next, we show that $u(x, y)$ is constant along any line segment L extending from a point P to a point P' and lying entirely in D. We let s denote the distance along L from the point P and let $\mathbf{U}$ denote the unit vector along L in the direction of increasing s (see Fig. 30). We know from calculus that the directional derivative du/ds can be written as the dot product

$$\frac{du}{ds} = (\text{grad } u) \cdot \mathbf{U}, \tag{1}$$

where grad u is the gradient vector

$$\text{grad } u = u_x\mathbf{i} + u_y\mathbf{j}. \tag{2}$$

Because u_x and u_y are zero everywhere in D, grad u is evidently the zero vector at all points on L. Hence it follows from equation (1) that the derivative du/ds is zero along L; and this means that u is constant on L.

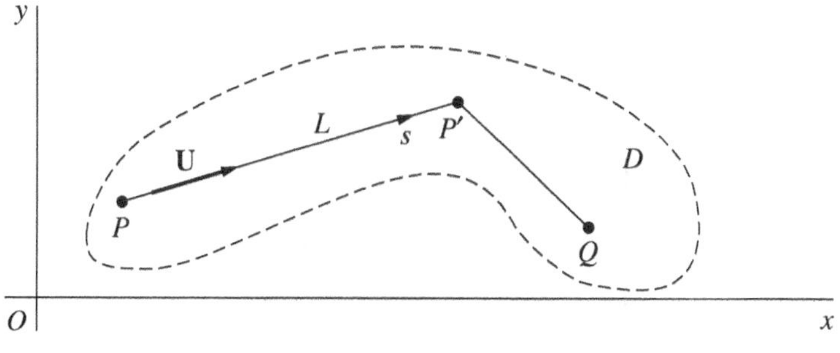

FIGURE 30

Finally, since there is always a finite number of such line segments, joined end to end, connecting any two points P and Q in D (Sec. 12), the values of u at P and Q must be the same. We may conclude, then, that there is a real constant a such that $u(x, y) = a$ throughout D. Similarly, $v(x, y) = b$; and we find that $f(z) = a + bi$ at each point in D. That is, $f(z) = c$ where c is the constant $c = a + bi$.

If a function f fails to be analytic at a point z_0 but is analytic at some point in every neighborhood of z_0, then z_0 is called a ***singular point,*** or singularity, of f. The point $z = 0$ is evidently a singular point of the function $f(z) = 1/z$. The function $f(z) = |z|^2$, on the other hand, has no singular points since it is nowhere analytic. Singular points will play an important role in our development of complex analysis in chapters to follow.

26. FURTHER EXAMPLES

As pointed out in Sec. 25, it is often possible to determine where a given function $f(z)$ is analytic by simply recalling various differentiation rules in Sec. 20.

EXAMPLE 1. The quotient

$$f(z) = \frac{z^2 + 3}{(z + 1)(z^2 + 5)}$$

is evidently analytic throughout the z plane except for the singular points $z = -1$ and $z = \pm\sqrt{5}\,i$. The analyticity is due to the existence of familiar differentiation rules, which need to be applied only if an expression for $f'(z)$ is actually wanted.

When a function is given in terms of its component functions u and v, its analyticity can be determined by direct application of the Cauchy–Riemann equations.

EXAMPLE 2. If $f(z) = \sin x \cosh y + i \cos x \sinh y$, the component functions are

$$u(x, y) = \sin x \cosh y \quad \text{and} \quad v(x, y) = \cos x \sinh y.$$

Because

$$u_x = \cos x \cosh y = v_y \quad \text{and} \quad u_y = \sin x \sinh y = -v_x$$

everywhere, it is clear from the theorem in Sec. 23 that f is entire. In fact, according to that theorem,

$$f'(z) = u_x + iv_x = \cos x \cosh y - i \sin x \sinh y. \tag{1}$$

It is straightforward to show that $f'(z)$ is also entire by writing expression (1) as

$$f'(z) = U(x, y) + iV(x, y)$$

where

$$U(x, y) = \cos x \cosh y \quad \text{and} \quad V(x, y) = -\sin x \sinh y.$$

For then

$$U_x = -\sin x \cosh y = V_y \quad \text{and} \quad U_y = \cos x \sinh y = -V_x.$$

Furthermore,

$$f''(z) = U_x + iV_x = -(\sin x \cosh y + i \cos x \sinh y) = -f(z).$$

The next two examples serve to illustrate how the Cauchy–Riemann equations can be used to obtain various properties of analytic functions.

EXAMPLE 3. Suppose that a function $f(z) = u(x, y) + iv(x, y)$ and its conjugate $\overline{f(z)} = u(x, y) - iv(x, y)$ are *both* analytic in a domain D. Let us show that $f(z)$ must, then, be constant throughout D.

To do this, we write $\overline{f(z)} = U(x, y) + V(x, y)$ where

$$U(x, y) = u(x, y) \quad \text{and} \quad V(x, y) = -v(x, y). \tag{2}$$

Because of the analyticity of $f(z)$, the Cauchy–Riemann equations

$$u_x = v_y, \quad u_y = -v_x \tag{3}$$

hold in D; and the analyticity of $\overline{f(z)}$ in D tells us that

$$U_x = V_y, \quad U_y = -V_x. \tag{4}$$

In view of relations (2), equations (4) can also be written

$$u_x = -v_y, \quad u_y = v_x. \tag{5}$$

By adding corresponding sides of the first of equations (3) and (5), we find that $u_x = 0$ in D. Similarly, subtraction involving corresponding sides of the second of equations (3) and (5) reveals that $v_x = 0$. According to expression (8) in Sec. 25, then,

$$f'(z) = u_x + iv_x = 0 + i0 = 0;$$

and it follows from the theorem in Sec. 25 that $f(z)$ is constant throughout D.

EXAMPLE 4. As in Example 3, we consider a function f that is analytic throughout a given domain D. Assuming further that the modulus $|f(z)|$ is constant throughout D, one can prove that $f(z)$ must be constant there too. This result is needed to obtain an important result later on in Chap. 4 (Sec. 59).

The proof is accomplished by writing

$$|f(z)| = c \quad \text{for all } z \text{ in } D, \tag{6}$$

where c is a real constant. If $c = 0$, it follows that $f(z) = 0$ everywhere in D. If $c \neq 0$, the property $z\bar{z} = |z|^2$ of complex numbers tells us that

$$f(z)\overline{f(z)} = c^2 \neq 0$$

and hence that $f(z)$ is never zero in D. So

$$\overline{f(z)} = \frac{c^2}{f(z)} \qquad \text{for all } z \text{ in } D,$$

and it follows from this that $\overline{f(z)}$ is analytic everywhere in D. The main result in Example 3 just above thus ensures that $f(z)$ is constant throughout D.

EXERCISES

1. Apply the theorem in Sec. 23 to verify that each of these functions is entire:

(*a*) $f(z) = 3x + y + i(3y - x)$; (*b*) $f(z) = \cosh x \cos y + i \sinh x \sin y$;

(*c*) $f(z) = e^{-y}\sin x - ie^{-y}\cos x$; (*d*) $f(z) = (z^2 - 2)e^{-x}e^{-iy}$.

2. With the aid of the theorem in Sec. 21, show that each of these functions is nowhere analytic:

(*a*) $f(z) = xy + iy$; (*b*) $f(z) = 2xy + i(x^2 - y^2)$;

(*c*) $f(z) = e^y e^{ix}$.

3. State why a composition of two entire functions is entire. Also, state why any *linear combination* $c_1 f_1(z) + c_2 f_2(z)$ of two entire functions, where c_1 and c_2 are complex constants, is entire.

4. In each case, determine the singular points of the function and state why the function is analytic everywhere else:

(*a*) $f(z) = \dfrac{2z + 1}{z(z^2 + 1)}$; (*b*) $f(z) = \dfrac{z^3 + i}{z^2 - 3z + 2}$;

(*c*) $f(z) = \dfrac{z^2 + 1}{(z + 2)(z^2 + 2z + 2)}$.

Ans. (*a*) $z = 0, \pm i$; (*b*) $z = 1, 2$; (*c*) $z = -2, -1 \pm i$.

5. According to Example 2, Sec. 24, the function

$$g(z) = \sqrt{r}e^{i\theta/2} \qquad (r > 0, -\pi < \theta < \pi)$$

is analytic in its domain of definition, with derivative

$$g'(z) = \frac{1}{2\,g(z)}.$$

Show that the composite function $G(z) = g(2z - 2 + i)$ is analytic in the half plane $x > 1$, with derivative

$$G'(z) = \frac{1}{g(2z - 2 + i)}.$$

Suggestion: Observe that $\text{Re}(2z - 2 + i) > 0$ when $x > 1$.

6. Use results in Sec. 24 to verify that the function

$$g(z) = \ln r + i\theta \qquad (r > 0, 0 < \theta < 2\pi)$$

is analytic in the indicated domain of definition, with derivative $g'(z) = 1/z$. Then show that the composite function $G(z) = g(z^2 + 1)$ is analytic in the quadrant $x > 0, y > 0$, with derivative

$$G'(z) = \frac{2z}{z^2 + 1}.$$

Suggestion: Observe that $\text{Im}(z^2 + 1) > 0$ when $x > 0, y > 0$.

7. Let a function f be analytic everywhere in a domain D. Prove that if $f(z)$ is real-valued for all z in D, then $f(z)$ must be constant throughout D.

27. HARMONIC FUNCTIONS

A real-valued function H of two real variables x and y is said to be ***harmonic*** in a given domain of the xy plane if, throughout that domain, it has continuous partial derivatives of the first and second order and satisfies the partial differential equation

$$H_{xx}(x, y) + H_{yy}(x, y) = 0, \tag{1}$$

known as ***Laplace's equation***.

Harmonic functions play an important role in applied mathematics. For example, the temperatures $T(x, y)$ in thin plates lying in the xy plane are often harmonic. A function $V(x, y)$ is harmonic when it denotes an electrostatic potential that varies only with x and y in the interior of a region of three-dimensional space that is free of charges.

EXAMPLE 1. It is easy to verify that the function $T(x, y) = e^{-y} \sin x$ is harmonic in any domain of the xy plane and, in particular, in the semi-infinite vertical strip $0 < x < \pi, y > 0$. It also assumes the values on the edges of the strip that are indicated in Fig. 31. More precisely, it satisfies all of the conditions

$$T_{xx}(x, y) + T_{yy}(x, y) = 0,$$

$$T(0, y) = 0, \quad T(\pi, y) = 0,$$

$$T(x, 0) = \sin x, \quad \lim_{y \to \infty} T(x, y) = 0,$$

which describe steady temperatures $T(x, y)$ in a thin homogeneous plate in the xy plane that has no heat sources or sinks and is insulated except for the stated conditions along the edges.

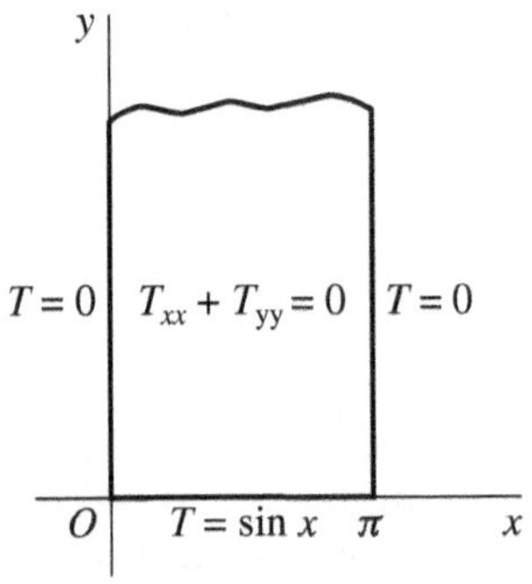

FIGURE 31

The use of the theory of functions of a complex variable in discovering solutions, such as the one in Example 1, of temperature and other problems is described in considerable detail later on in Chap. 10 and in parts of chapters following it.* That theory is based on the theorem below, which provides a source of harmonic functions.

Theorem. *If a function $f(z) = u(x, y) + iv(x, y)$ is analytic in a domain D, then its component functions u and v are harmonic in D.*

To show this, we need a result that is to be proved in Chap. 4 (Sec. 57). Namely, if a function of a complex variable is analytic at a point, then its real and imaginary components have continuous partial derivatives of all orders at that point.

Assuming that f is analytic in D, we start with the observation that the first-order partial derivatives of its component functions must satisfy the Cauchy–Riemann equations throughout D:

$$u_x = v_y, \quad u_y = -v_x. \tag{2}$$

Differentiating both sides of these equations with respect to x, we have

$$u_{xx} = v_{yx}, \quad u_{yx} = -v_{xx}. \tag{3}$$

Likewise, differentiation with respect to y yields

$$u_{xy} = v_{yy}, \quad u_{yy} = -v_{xy}. \tag{4}$$

Now, by a theorem in advanced calculus,† the continuity of the partial derivatives of u and v ensures that $u_{yx} = u_{xy}$ and $v_{yx} = v_{xy}$. It then follows from equations (3) and (4) that

$$u_{xx} + u_{yy} = 0 \quad \text{and} \quad v_{xx} + v_{yy} = 0.$$

That is, u and v are harmonic in D.

*Another important method is developed in the authors' "*Fourier Series and Boundary Value Problems*," 8th ed., 2012.

†See, for instance, A. E. Taylor and W. R. Mann, "*Advanced Calculus*," 3d ed., pp. 199–201, 1983.

EXAMPLE 2. The function $f(z) = e^{-y}\sin x - ie^{-y}\cos x$ is entire, as is shown in Exercise 1(*c*), Sec. 26. Hence its real component, which is the temperature function $T(x, y) = e^{-y}\sin x$ in Example 1, must be harmonic in every domain of the xy plane.

EXAMPLE 3. Since the function $f(z) = 1/z^2$ is analytic at every nonzero point z and since

$$\frac{1}{z^2} = \frac{1}{z^2}\cdot\frac{\bar{z}^2}{\bar{z}^2} = \frac{\bar{z}^2}{(z\,\bar{z})^2} = \frac{\bar{z}^2}{|z^2|^2} = \frac{(x^2-y^2)-i2xy}{(x^2+y^2)^2},$$

the two functions

$$u(x, y) = \frac{x^2-y^2}{(x^2+y^2)^2} \quad \text{and} \quad v(x, y) = -\frac{2xy}{(x^2+y^2)^2}$$

are harmonic throughout any domain in the xy plane that does not contain the origin.

Further discussion of harmonic functions related to the theory of functions of a complex variable appears in Chaps. 9 and 10, where they are needed in solving physical problems, such as in Example 1 here.

EXERCISES

1. Let the function $f(z) = u(r, \theta) + iv(r, \theta)$ be analytic in a domain D that does not include the origin. Using the Cauchy–Riemann equations in polar coordinates (Sec. 24) and assuming continuity of partial derivatives, show that throughout D the function $u(r, \theta)$ satisfies the partial differential equation

$$r^2 u_{rr}(r, \theta) + r u_r(r, \theta) + u_{\theta\theta}(r, \theta) = 0,$$

which is the ***polar form of Laplace's equation***. Show that the same is true of the function $v(r, \theta)$.

2. Let the function $f(z) = u(x, y) + iv(x, y)$ be analytic in a domain D, and consider the families of ***level curves*** $u(x, y) = c_1$ and $v(x, y) = c_2$, where c_1 and c_2 are arbitrary real constants. Prove that these families are orthogonal. More precisely, show that if $z_0 = (x_0, y_0)$ is a point in D which is common to two particular curves $u(x, y) = c_1$ and $v(x, y) = c_2$ and if $f'(z_0) \neq 0$, then the lines tangent to those curves at (x_0, y_0) are perpendicular.

Suggestion: Note how it follows from the pair of equations $u(x, y) = c_1$ and $v(x, y) = c_2$ that

$$\frac{\partial u}{\partial x} + \frac{\partial u}{\partial y}\frac{dy}{dx} = 0 \quad \text{and} \quad \frac{\partial v}{\partial x} + \frac{\partial v}{\partial y}\frac{dy}{dx} = 0.$$

3. Show that when $f(z) = z^2$, the level curves $u(x, y) = c_1$ and $v(x, y) = c_2$ of the component functions are the hyperbolas indicated in Fig. 32. Note the orthogonality of the two families, described in Exercise 2. Observe that the curves $u(x, y) = 0$ and $v(x, y) = 0$ intersect at the origin but are not, however, orthogonal to each other. Why is this fact in agreement with the result in Exercise 2?

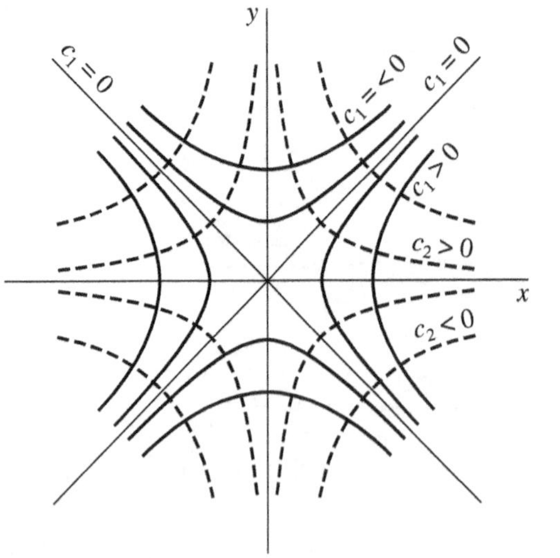

FIGURE 32

4. Sketch the families of level curves of the component functions u and v when $f(z) = 1/z$, and note the orthogonality described in Exercise 2.

5. Do Exercise 4 using polar coordinates.

6. Sketch the families of level curves of the component functions u and v when

$$f(z) = \frac{z-1}{z+1},$$

and note how the result in Exercise 2 is illustrated here.

28. UNIQUELY DETERMINED ANALYTIC FUNCTIONS

We conclude this chapter with two sections dealing with how the values of an analytic function in a domain D are affected by its values in a subdomain of D or on a line segment lying in D. While these sections are of considerable theoretical interest, they are not central to our development of analytic functions in later chapters. The reader may pass directly to Chap. 3 at this time and refer back when necessary.

Lemma. *Suppose that*

(*a*) *a function f is analytic throughout a domain D;*

(*b*) *$f(z) = 0$ at each point z of a domain or line segment contained in D.*

Then $f(z) \equiv 0$ in D; that is, $f(z)$ is identically equal to zero throughout D.

To prove this lemma, we let f be as stated in its hypothesis and let z_0 be any point of the subdomain or line segment where $f(z) = 0$. Since D is a *connected* open set (Sec. 12), there is a polygonal line L, consisting of a finite number of line segments joined end to end and lying entirely in D, that extends from z_0 to any other point P in D. We let d be the shortest distance from points on L to the boundary of D, unless D is the entire plane; in that case, d may be any positive number. We then form a finite sequence of points

$$z_0, z_1, z_2, \ldots, z_{n-1}, z_n$$

along L, where the point z_n coincides with P (Fig. 33) and where each point is sufficiently close to adjacent ones that

$$|z_k - z_{k-1}| < d \qquad (k = 1, 2, \ldots, n).$$

Finally, we construct a finite sequence of neighborhoods

$$N_0, N_1, N_2, \ldots, N_{n-1}, N_n,$$

where each neighborhood N_k is centered at z_k and has radius d. Note that these neighborhoods are all contained in D and that the center z_k of any neighborhood N_k $(k = 1, 2, \ldots, n)$ lies in the preceding neighborhood N_{k-1}.

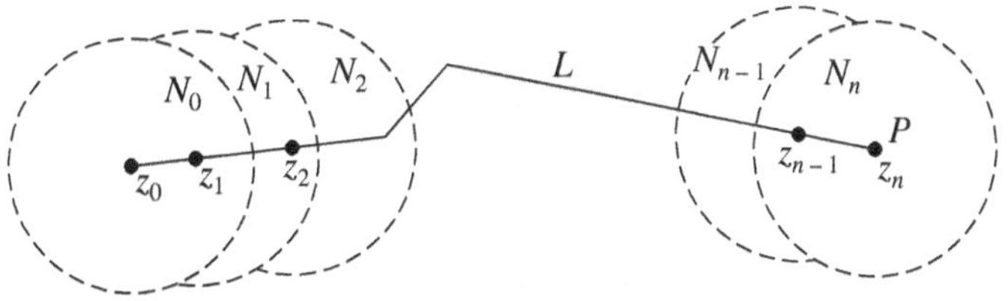

FIGURE 33

At this point, we need to use a result that is proved later on in Chap. 6. Namely, Theorem 3 in Sec. 82 tells us that since f is analytic in N_0 and since $f(z) = 0$ in a domain or on a line segment containing z_0, then $f(z) \equiv 0$ in N_0. But the point z_1 lies in N_0. Hence a second application of the same theorem reveals that $f(z) \equiv 0$ in N_1; and, by continuing in this manner, we arrive at the fact that $f(z) \equiv 0$ in N_n. Since N_n is centered at the point P and since P was arbitrarily selected in D, we may conclude that $f(z) \equiv 0$ in D. This completes the proof of the lemma.

Suppose now that two functions f and g are analytic in the same domain D and that $f(z) = g(z)$ at each point z of some domain or line segment contained in D. The difference

$$h(z) = f(z) - g(z)$$

is also analytic in D, and $h(z) = 0$ throughout the subdomain or along the line segment. According to the lemma, then, $h(z) \equiv 0$ throughout D; that is, $f(z) = g(z)$ at each point in D. We thus arrive at the following important theorem.

Theorem. *A function that is analytic in a domain D is uniquely determined over D by its values in a domain, or along a line segment, contained in D.*

A more general result, sometimes called the ***coincidence principle***, is straightforward to prove. Namely, *if two functions f and g are analytic in the same domain D and if $f(z) = g(z)$ on a subset of D that has a limit point z_0 in D, then $f(z) = g(z)$ everywhere in D.** We do not, however, have need for such a generalization.

*See, for example, pp. 56–57 of the book by Boas, pp. 142–144 of the book by Silverman, or pp. 369–370 in Vol. I of the book by Markushevich, all of which are listed in Appendix 1.

The theorem just proved is useful in studying the question of extending the domain of definition of an analytic function. More precisely, given two domains D_1 and D_2, consider the *intersection* $D_1 \cap D_2$, consisting of all points that lie in both D_1 and D_2. If D_1 and D_2 have points in common (see Fig. 34) and a function f_1 is analytic in D_1, there *may* exist a function f_2, which is analytic in D_2, such that $f_2(z) = f_1(z)$ for each z in the intersection $D_1 \cap D_2$. If so, we call f_2 an ***analytic continuation*** of f_1 into the second domain D_2.

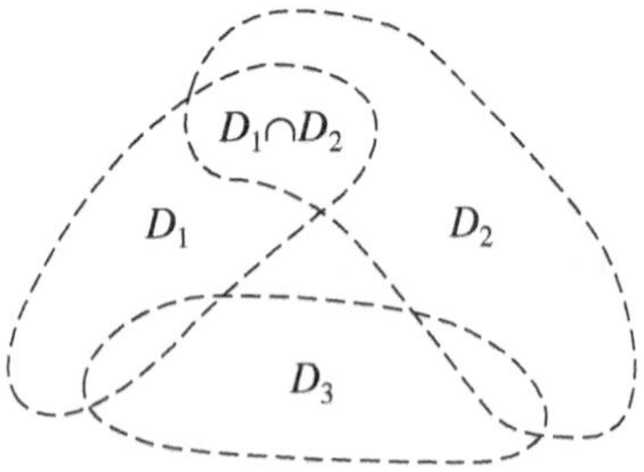

FIGURE 34

Whenever that analytic continuation exists, it is unique, according to the theorem just proved. That is, not more than one function can be analytic in D_2 and assume the value $f_1(z)$ at each point z of the domain $D_1 \cap D_2$ interior to D_2. However, if there is an analytic continuation f_3 of f_2 from D_2 into a domain D_3 which intersects D_1, as indicated in Fig. 34, it is not necessarily true that $f_3(z) = f_1(z)$ for each z in $D_1 \cap D_3$. Exercise 2, Sec. 29, illustrates this.

If f_2 is the analytic continuation of f_1 from a domain D_1 into a domain D_2, then the function F defined by means of the equations

$$F(z) = \begin{cases} f_1(z) & \text{when } z \text{ is in } D_1, \\ f_2(z) & \text{when } z \text{ is in } D_2 \end{cases}$$

is analytic in the *union* $D_1 \cup D_2$, which is the domain consisting of all points that lie in either D_1 or D_2. The function F is the analytic continuation into $D_1 \cup D_2$ of either f_1 or f_2; and f_1 and f_2 are called ***elements*** of F.

29. REFLECTION PRINCIPLE

The theorem in this section concerns the fact that some analytic functions possess the property that $\overline{f(z)} = f(\overline{z})$ for all points z in certain domains, while others do not. We note, for example, that the functions $z + 1$ and z^2 have that property when D is the entire finite plane; but the same is not true of $z + i$ and iz^2. The theorem here, which is known as the ***reflection principle,*** provides a way of predicting when $\overline{f(z)} = f(\overline{z})$.

Theorem. *Suppose that a function f is analytic in some domain D which contains a segment of the x axis and whose lower half is the reflection of the upper half with respect to that axis. Then*

$$\overline{f(z)} = f(\overline{z}) \tag{1}$$

for each point z in the domain if and only if $f(x)$ is real for each point x on the segment.

We start the proof by assuming that $f(x)$ is real at each point x on the segment. Once we show that the function

$$F(z) = \overline{f(\overline{z})} \tag{2}$$

is analytic in D, we shall use it to obtain equation (1). To establish the analyticity of $F(z)$, we write

$$f(z) = u(x, y) + iv(x, y), \quad F(z) = U(x, y) + iV(x, y)$$

and observe how it follows from equation (2) that since

$$\overline{f(\overline{z})} = u(x, -y) - iv(x, -y), \tag{3}$$

the components of $F(z)$ and $f(z)$ are related by the equations

$$U(x, y) = u(x, t) \quad \text{and} \quad V(x, y) = -v(x, t), \tag{4}$$

where $t = -y$. Now, because $f(x + it)$ is an analytic function of $x + it$, the first-order partial derivatives of the functions $u(x, t)$ and $v(x, t)$ are continuous throughout D and satisfy the Cauchy–Riemann equations*

$$u_x = v_t, \quad u_t = -v_x. \tag{5}$$

Furthermore, in view of equations (4),

$$U_x = u_x, \quad V_y = -v_t \frac{dt}{dy} = v_t;$$

and it follows from these and the first of equations (5) that $U_x = V_y$. Similarly,

$$U_y = u_t \frac{dt}{dy} = -u_t, \quad V_x = -v_x;$$

and the second of equations (5) tells us that $U_y = -V_x$. Inasmuch as the first-order partial derivatives of $U(x, y)$ and $V(x, y)$ are now shown to satisfy the Cauchy–Riemann equations and since those derivatives are continuous, we find that the function $F(z)$ is analytic in D. Moreover, since $f(x)$ is real on the segment of the real axis lying in D, we know that $v(x, 0) = 0$ on the segment; and, in view of equations (4), this means that

$$F(x) = U(x, 0) + iV(x, 0) = u(x, 0) - iv(x, 0) = u(x, 0).$$

That is,

$$F(z) = f(z) \tag{6}$$

*See the paragraph immediately following Theorem 1 in Sec. 26.

at each point on the segment. According to the theorem in Sec. 28, which tells us that an analytic function defined on a domain D is uniquely determined by its values along any line segment lying in D, it follows that equation (6) actually holds throughout D. Because of definition (2) of the function $F(z)$, then,

$$\overline{f(\overline{z})} = f(z); \tag{7}$$

and this is the same as equation (1).

To prove the converse in the theorem, we assume that equation (1) holds and note that in view of expression (3), the form (7) of equation (1) can be written

$$u(x, -y) - iv(x, -y) = u(x, y) + iv(x, y).$$

In particular, if $(x, 0)$ is a point on the segment of the real axis that lies in D,

$$u(x, 0) - iv(x, 0) = u(x, 0) + iv(x, 0);$$

and, by equating imaginary parts here, we see that $v(x, 0) = 0$. Hence $f(x)$ is real on the segment of the real axis lying in D.

EXAMPLES. Just prior to the statement of the theorem, we noted that

$$\overline{z+1} = \overline{z} + 1 \quad \text{and} \quad \overline{z^2} = \overline{z}^2$$

for all z in the finite plane. The theorem tells us, of course, that this is true, since $x + 1$ and x^2 are real when x is real. We also noted that $z+i$ and iz^2 do not have the reflection property throughout the plane, and we now know that this is because $x + i$ and ix^2 are *not* real when x is real.

EXERCISES

1. Use the theorem in Sec. 28 to show that if $f(z)$ is analytic and not constant throughout a domain D, then it cannot be constant throughout any neighborhood lying in D.

Suggestion: Suppose that $f(z)$ does have a constant value w_0 throughout some neighborhood in D.

2. Starting with the function

$$f_1(z) = \sqrt{r}e^{i\theta/2} \qquad (r > 0, 0 < \theta < \pi)$$

and referring to Example 2, Sec. 24, point out why

$$f_2(z) = \sqrt{r}e^{i\theta/2} \qquad \left(r > 0, \frac{\pi}{2} < \theta < 2\pi\right)$$

is an analytic continuation of f_1 across the negative real axis into the lower half plane. Then show that the function

$$f_3(z) = \sqrt{r}e^{i\theta/2} \qquad \left(r > 0, \pi < \theta < \frac{5\pi}{2}\right)$$

is an analytic continuation of f_2 across the positive real axis into the first quadrant but that $f_3(z) = -f_1(z)$ there.

3. State why the function

$$f_4(z) = \sqrt{r}e^{i\theta/2} \qquad (r > 0, -\pi < \theta < \pi)$$

is the analytic continuation of the function $f_1(z)$ in Exercise 2 across the positive real axis into the lower half plane.

4. We know from Example 1, Sec. 23, that the function

$$f(z) = e^x \cos y + ie^x \sin y$$

has a derivative everywhere in the finite plane. Point out how it follows from the reflection principle (Sec. 29) that

$$\overline{f(z)} = f(\overline{z})$$

for each z. Then verify this directly.

5. Show that if the condition that $f(x)$ is real in the reflection principle (Sec. 29) is replaced by the condition that $f(x)$ is pure imaginary, then equation (1) in the statement of the principle is changed to

$$\overline{f(z)} = -f(\overline{z}).$$

CHAPTER 3

ELEMENTARY FUNCTIONS

We consider here various elementary functions studied in calculus and define corresponding functions of a complex variable. To be specific, we define analytic functions of a complex variable z that reduce to the elementary functions in calculus when $z = x + i0$. We start by defining the complex exponential function and then use it to develop the others.

30. THE EXPONENTIAL FUNCTION

The exponential function can be defined by writing

$$e^z = e^x e^{iy} \qquad (z = x + iy), \tag{1}$$

where Euler's formula (see Sec. 7)

$$e^{iy} = \cos y + i \sin y \tag{2}$$

is used and y is to be taken in radians. We see from this definition that e^z reduces to the usual exponential function in calculus when $y = 0$; and, following the convention used in calculus, we often write $\exp z$ for e^z.

Note that since the *positive* nth root $\sqrt[n]{e}$ of e is assigned to e^x when $x = 1/n$ $(n = 2, 3, \ldots)$, expression (1) tells us that the complex exponential function e^z is also $\sqrt[n]{e}$ when $z = 1/n$ $(n = 2, 3, \ldots)$. This is an exception to the convention (Sec. 10) that would ordinarily require us to interpret $e^{1/n}$ as the *set* of nth roots of e.

Note, too, that when definition (1) is written in the form

$$e^z = \rho e^{i\phi} \qquad \text{where} \qquad \rho = e^x \text{ and } \phi = y,$$

it becomes clear that

$$(3) \qquad |e^z| = e^x \qquad \text{and} \qquad \arg(e^z) = y + 2n\pi \quad (n = 0, \pm 1, \pm 2, \ldots).$$

Moreover, since e^x is never zero,

$$(4) \qquad e^z \neq 0 \qquad \text{for any complex number } z.$$

In addition to property (4), there are a number of other properties that carry over from e^x to e^z, and we mention a few of them here.

According to definition (1), $e^x e^{iy} = e^{x+iy}$; and this is consistent with the additive property $e^{x_1} e^{x_2} = e^{x_1+x_2}$ of the exponential function in calculus. The extension

$$(5) \qquad e^{z_1} e^{z_2} = e^{z_1+z_2}$$

to complex analysis is easy to verify. To do this, we write

$$z_1 = x_1 + iy_1 \quad \text{and} \quad z_2 = x_2 + iy_2.$$

Then

$$e^{z_1} e^{z_2} = (e^{x_1} e^{iy_1})(e^{x_2} e^{iy_2}) = (e^{x_1} e^{x_2})(e^{iy_1} e^{iy_2}).$$

But x_1 and x_2 are both real, and we know from Sec. 8 that

$$e^{iy_1} e^{iy_2} = e^{i(y_1+y_2)}.$$

Hence

$$e^{z_1} e^{z_2} = e^{(x_1+x_2)} e^{i(y_1+y_2)};$$

and, since

$$(x_1 + x_2) + i(y_1 + y_2) = (x_1 + iy_1) + (x_2 + iy_2) = z_1 + z_2,$$

the right-hand side of this last equation becomes $e^{z_1+z_2}$. Property (5) is now established.

Observe how property (5) enables us to write $e^{z_1-z_2} e^{z_2} = e^{z_1}$, or

$$(6) \qquad \frac{e^{z_1}}{e^{z_2}} = e^{z_1-z_2}.$$

From this and the fact that $e^0 = 1$, it follows that $1/e^z = e^{-z}$.

There are a number of other important properties of e^z that are expected. According to Example 1 in Sec. 23, for instance,

$$(7) \qquad \frac{d}{dz} e^z = e^z$$

everywhere in the z plane. Note that the differentiability of e^z for all z tells us that e^z *is entire* (Sec. 25).

Some properties of e^z are, on the other hand, *not* expected. For example, since

$$e^{z+2\pi i} = e^z e^{2\pi i} \quad \text{and} \quad e^{2\pi i} = 1,$$

we find that e^z *is periodic,* with a pure imaginary period of $2\pi i$:

$$e^{z+2\pi i} = e^z. \tag{8}$$

For another property of e^z that e^x does not have, we note that while e^x is always positive, e^z can be negative. We recall (Sec. 6), for instance, that $e^{i\pi} = -1$. In fact,

$$e^{i(2n+1)\pi} = e^{i2n\pi + i\pi} = e^{i2n\pi} e^{i\pi} = (1)(-1) = -1 \qquad (n = 0, \pm 1, \pm 2, \ldots).$$

There are, moreover, values of z such that e^z is *any* given nonzero complex number. This is shown in the next section, where the logarithmic function is developed, and is illustrated in the following example.

EXAMPLE. In order to find numbers $z = x + iy$ such that

$$e^z = 1 + \sqrt{3}i, \tag{9}$$

we write equation (9) as

$$e^x e^{iy} = 2\, e^{i\pi/3}.$$

Then, in view of the statement in italics at the beginning of Sec. 10, regarding the equality of two nonzero complex numbers in exponential form,

$$e^x = 2 \quad \text{and} \quad y = \frac{\pi}{3} + 2n\pi \qquad (n = 0, \pm 1, \pm 2, \ldots).$$

Because $\ln(e^x) = x$, it follows that

$$x = \ln 2 \quad \text{and} \quad y = \frac{\pi}{3} + 2n\pi \qquad (n = 0, \pm 1, \pm 2, \ldots);$$

and so

$$z = \ln 2 + \left(2n + \frac{1}{3}\right)\pi i \qquad (n = 0, \pm 1, \pm 2, \ldots). \tag{10}$$

EXERCISES

1. Show that

   (*a*) $\exp(2 \pm 3\pi i) = -e^2$; (*b*) $\exp\left(\dfrac{2 + \pi i}{4}\right) = \sqrt{\dfrac{e}{2}}\,(1 + i)$;

   (*c*) $\exp(z + \pi i) = -\exp z$.

2. State why the function $f(z) = 2z^2 - 3 - ze^z + e^{-z}$ is entire.

3. Use the Cauchy–Riemann equations and the theorem in Sec. 21 to show that the function $f(z) = \exp \bar{z}$ is not analytic anywhere.

4. Show in two ways that the function $f(z) = \exp(z^2)$ is entire. What is its derivative?

   Ans. $f'(z) = 2z \exp(z^2)$.

5. Write $|\exp(2z+i)|$ and $|\exp(iz^2)|$ in terms of x and y. Then show that

$$|\exp(2z+i)+\exp(iz^2)| \le e^{2x}+e^{-2xy}.$$

6. Show that $|\exp(z^2)| \le \exp(|z|^2)$.

7. Prove that $|\exp(-2z)| < 1$ if and only if $\operatorname{Re} z > 0$.

8. Find all values of z such that

(*a*) $e^z = -2$; (*b*) $e^z = 1+i$; (*c*) $\exp(2z-1) = 1$.

Ans. (*a*) $z = \ln 2 + (2n+1)\pi i \ (n = 0, \pm1, \pm2, \ldots)$;

(*b*) $z = \frac{1}{2}\ln 2 + \left(2n + \frac{1}{4}\right)\pi i \ (n = 0, \pm1, \pm2, \ldots)$;

(*c*) $z = \frac{1}{2} + n\pi i \ (n = 0, \pm1, \pm2, \ldots)$.

9. Show that $\overline{\exp(iz)} = \exp(i\bar{z})$ if and only if $z = n\pi \ (n = 0, \pm1, \pm2, \ldots)$. (Compare with Exercise 4, Sec. 29.)

10. (*a*) Show that if e^z is real, then $\operatorname{Im} z = n\pi \ (n = 0, \pm1, \pm2, \ldots)$.

(*b*) If e^z is pure imaginary, what restriction is placed on z?

11. Describe the behavior of $e^z = e^x e^{iy}$ as (*a*) x tends to $-\infty$; (*b*) y tends to ∞.

12. Write $\operatorname{Re}(e^{1/z})$ in terms of x and y. Why is this function harmonic in every domain that does not contain the origin?

13. Let the function $f(z) = u(x,y) + iv(x,y)$ be analytic in some domain D. State why the functions

$$U(x,y) = e^{u(x,y)}\cos v(x,y), \quad V(x,y) = e^{u(x,y)}\sin v(x,y)$$

are harmonic in D.

14. Establish the identity

$$(e^z)^n = e^{nz} \qquad (n = 0, \pm1, \pm2, \ldots)$$

in the following way.

(*a*) Use mathematical induction to show that it is valid when $n = 0, 1, 2, \ldots$.

(*b*) Verify it for negative integers n by first recalling from Sec. 8 that

$$z^n = (z^{-1})^m \qquad (m = -n = 1, 2, \ldots)$$

when $z \ne 0$ and writing $(e^z)^n = (1/e^z)^m$. Then use the result in part (*a*), together with the property $1/e^z = e^{-z}$ (Sec. 30) of the exponential function.

31. THE LOGARITHMIC FUNCTION

Our motivation for the definition of the logarithmic function is based on solving the equation

$$e^w = z \tag{1}$$

for w, where z is any *nonzero* complex number. To do this, we note that when z and w are written $z = re^{i\Theta}$ $(-\pi < \Theta \leq \pi)$ and $w = u + iv$, equation (1) becomes

$$e^u e^{iv} = re^{i\Theta}.$$

According to the statement in italics at the beginning of Sec. 10 about the equality of two nonzero complex numbers expressed in exponential form, this tells us that

$$e^u = r \quad \text{and} \quad v = \Theta + 2n\pi$$

where n is any integer. Since the equation $e^u = r$ is the same as $u = \ln r$, it follows that equation (1) is satisfied if and only if w has one of the values

$$w = \ln r + i(\Theta + 2n\pi) \qquad (n = 0, \pm 1, \pm 2, \ldots).$$

Thus, if we write

$$\log z = \ln r + i(\Theta + 2n\pi) \qquad (n = 0, \pm 1, \pm 2, \ldots), \tag{2}$$

equation (1) tells us that

$$e^{\log z} = z \qquad (z \neq 0), \tag{3}$$

Inasmuch as equation (2) becomes

$$\log x = \ln x + 2n\pi i \qquad (n = 0, \pm 1, \pm 2, \ldots)$$

when $z = x > 0$ and since equation (3) then reduces to the familiar identity

$$e^{\ln x} = x \qquad (x > 0) \tag{4}$$

in calculus, equation (4) suggests that we use expression (2) as the definition of the (multiple-valued) ***logarithmic function*** of a nonzero complex variable $z = re^{i\theta}$.

It should be emphasized that it is *not* true that the left-hand side of equation (3) with the order of the exponential and logarithmic functions reversed reduces to just z. More precisely, since expression (2) can be written

$$\log z = \ln |z| + i \arg z$$

and since (Sec. 30)

$$|e^z| = e^x \quad \text{and} \quad \arg(e^z) = y + 2n\pi \qquad (n = 0, \pm 1, \pm 2, \ldots)$$

when $z = x + iy$, we know that

$$\log(e^z) = \ln |e^z| + i \arg(e^z) = \ln(e^x) + i(y + 2n\pi) = (x + iy) + 2n\pi i$$
$$(n = 0, \pm 1, \pm 2, \ldots).$$

That is,

$$\log(e^z) = z + 2n\pi i \qquad (n = 0, \pm 1, \pm 2, \ldots). \tag{5}$$

The ***principal value*** of $\log z$ is the value obtained from equation (2) when $n = 0$ there and is denoted by Log z. Thus

$$\text{Log}\, z = \ln r + i\Theta. \tag{6}$$

Note that Log z is well defined and single-valued when $z \neq 0$ and that

$$\log z = \operatorname{Log} z + 2n\pi i \qquad (n = 0, \pm 1, \pm 2, \ldots). \tag{7}$$

It reduces to the usual logarithm in calculus when z is a positive real number. To see this, one need only write $z = x$ $(x > 0)$, in which case equation (6) becomes $\operatorname{Log} z = \ln x$.

32. EXAMPLES

In this section we illustrate material in Sec. 31.

EXAMPLE 1. If $z = -1 - \sqrt{3}i$, then $r = 2$ and $\Theta = -2\pi/3$. Hence

$$\log(-1 - \sqrt{3}i) = \ln 2 + i\left(-\frac{2\pi}{3} + 2n\pi\right) = \ln 2 + 2\left(n - \frac{1}{3}\right)\pi i$$
$$(n = 0, \pm 1, \pm 2, \ldots).$$

EXAMPLE 2. From expression (2) in Sec. 31, we find that

$$\log 1 = \ln 1 + i(0 + 2n\pi) = 2n\pi i \qquad (n = 0, \pm 1, \pm 2, \ldots).$$

As anticipated, $\operatorname{Log} 1 = 0$.

The next example reminds us that although we were unable to find logarithms of *negative* real numbers in calculus, it is now possible.

EXAMPLE 3. Observe that

$$\log(-1) = \ln 1 + i(\pi + 2n\pi) = (2n + 1)\pi i \qquad (n = 0, \pm 1, \pm 2, \ldots)$$

and that $\operatorname{Log}(-1) = \pi i$.

Special care must be taken in anticipating that familiar properties of $\ln x$ in calculus carry over to be properties of $\log z$ and $\operatorname{Log} z$.

EXAMPLE 4. The identity

$$\operatorname{Log}[(1 + i)^2] = 2\operatorname{Log}(1 + i) \tag{1}$$

is valid since

$$\operatorname{Log}[(1 + i)^2] = \operatorname{Log}(2i) = \ln 2 + i\frac{\pi}{2}$$

and

$$2\operatorname{Log}(1 + i) = 2\left(\ln\sqrt{2} + i\frac{\pi}{4}\right) = \ln 2 + i\frac{\pi}{2}.$$

On the other hand,

$$\text{Log}[(-1+i)^2] \neq 2\,\text{Log}(-1+i) \tag{2}$$

because

$$\text{Log}[(-1+i)^2] = \text{Log}(-2i) = \ln 2 - i\frac{\pi}{2}$$

and

$$2\,\text{Log}(-1+i) = 2\left(\ln\sqrt{2} + i\frac{3\pi}{4}\right) = \ln 2 + i\frac{3\pi}{2}.$$

While statement (1) might be expected, we see that statement (2) would not be true as an equality.

EXAMPLE 5. It is shown in Exercise 5, Sec. 33, that

$$\log(i^{1/2}) = \frac{1}{2}\log i \tag{3}$$

in the sense that the set of values on the left is the same as the set of values on the right. But

$$\log(i^2) \neq 2\log i \tag{4}$$

because

$$\ln(i^2) = \log(-1) = (2n+1)\pi i \qquad (n = 0, \pm 1, \pm 2, \ldots),$$

according to Example 3, and since

$$2\log i = 2\left[\ln 1 + i\left(\frac{\pi}{2} + 2n\pi\right)\right] = (4n+1)\pi i \qquad (n = 0, \pm 1, \pm 2, \ldots).$$

Upon comparing statements (3) and (4), we find that familiar properties of logarithms in calculus are sometimes but not always true in complex analysis.

33. BRANCHES AND DERIVATIVES OF LOGARITHMS

If $z = re^{i\theta}$ is a nonzero complex number, the argument θ has any one of the values $\theta = \Theta + 2n\pi$ $(n = 0, \pm 1, \pm 2, \ldots)$, where $\Theta = \text{Arg}\, z$. Hence the definition

$$\log z = \ln r + i(\Theta + 2n\pi) \qquad (n = 0, \pm 1, \pm 2, \ldots)$$

of the multiple-valued logarithmic function in Sec. 31 can be written

$$\log z = \ln r + i\theta. \tag{1}$$

If we let α denote any real number and restrict the value of θ in expression (1) so that $\alpha < \theta < \alpha + 2\pi$, the function

$$\log z = \ln r + i\theta \qquad (r > 0, \alpha < \theta < \alpha + 2\pi), \tag{2}$$

with components

$$u(r, \theta) = \ln r \quad \text{and} \quad v(r, \theta) = \theta, \tag{3}$$

is *single-valued* and continuous in the stated domain (Fig. 35). Note that if the function (2) were to be defined on the ray $\theta = \alpha$, it would not be continuous there. For if z is a point on that ray, there are points arbitrarily close to z at which the values of v are near α and also points such that the values of v are near $\alpha + 2\pi$.

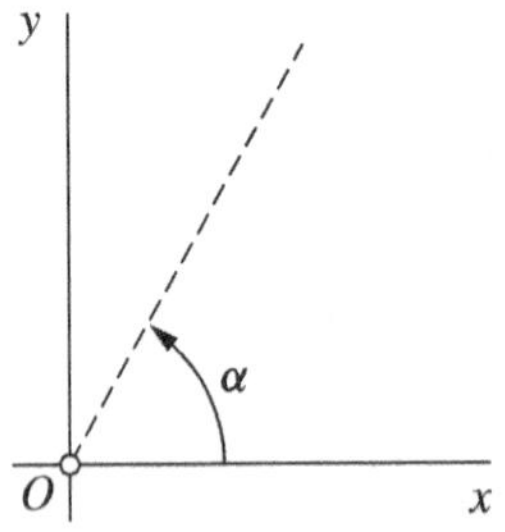

FIGURE 35

The function (2) is not only continuous but also analytic throughout the domain $r > 0$, $\alpha < \theta < \alpha + 2\pi$ since the first-order partial derivatives of u and v are continuous there and satisfy the polar form (Sec. 24)

$$ru_r = v_\theta, \quad u_\theta = -rv_r$$

of the Cauchy–Riemann equations. Furthermore, according to Sec. 24,

$$\frac{d}{dz}\log z = e^{-i\theta}(u_r + iv_r) = e^{-i\theta}\left(\frac{1}{r} + i0\right) = \frac{1}{re^{i\theta}};$$

that is,

$$\frac{d}{dz}\log z = \frac{1}{z} \qquad (|z| > 0, \alpha < \arg z < \alpha + 2\pi). \tag{4}$$

In particular,

$$\frac{d}{dz}\,\text{Log}\, z = \frac{1}{z} \qquad (|z| > 0, -\pi < \text{Arg}\, z < \pi). \tag{5}$$

A ***branch*** of a multiple-valued function f is any single-valued function F that is analytic in some domain at each point z of which the value $F(z)$ is one of the values of f. The requirement of analyticity, of course, prevents F from taking on a random selection of the values of f. Observe that for each fixed α, the single-valued function (2) is a branch of the multiple-valued function (1). The function

$$\text{Log}\, z = \ln r + i\Theta \qquad (r > 0, -\pi < \Theta < \pi) \tag{6}$$

is called the ***principal branch.***

A ***branch cut*** is a portion of a line or curve that is introduced in order to define a branch F of a multiple-valued function f. Points on the branch cut for F are singular points (Sec. 25) of F, and any point that is common to all branch cuts of f is called a ***branch point.*** The origin and the ray $\theta = \alpha$ make up the branch cut for the branch (2) of the logarithmic function. The branch cut for the principal branch (6) consists of the origin and the ray $\Theta = \pi$. The origin is evidently a branch point for branches of the multiple-valued logarithmic function.

We saw in Example 5, Sec. 32, that the set of values of $\log(i^2)$ is not the set of values of $2\log i$. The following example does show, however, that equality can occur when a specific branch of the logarithm is used. In that case, of course, there is only one value of $\log(i^2)$ that is to be taken, and the same is true of $2\log i$.

EXAMPLE. In order to show that

$$\log(i^2) = 2\log i \tag{7}$$

when the branch

$$\log z = \ln r + i\theta \qquad \left(r > 0, \frac{\pi}{4} < \theta < \frac{9\pi}{4}\right)$$

is used, write

$$\log(i^2) = \log(-1) = \ln 1 + i\pi = \pi i$$

and then observe that

$$2\log i = 2\left(\ln 1 + i\frac{\pi}{2}\right) = \pi i.$$

It is interesting to contrast equality (7) with the result $\log(i^2) \neq 2\log i$ in Exercise 4, where a different branch of $\log z$ is used.

In Sec. 34, we shall consider other identities involving logarithms, sometimes with qualifications as to how they are to be interpreted. A reader who wishes to pass to Sec. 35 can simply refer to results in Sec. 34 when needed.

EXERCISES

1. Show that

(*a*) $\text{Log}(-ei) = 1 - \frac{\pi}{2}i$; (*b*) $\text{Log}(1 - i) = \frac{1}{2}\ln 2 - \frac{\pi}{4}i$.

2. Show that

(*a*) $\log e = 1 + 2n\pi i \quad (n = 0, \pm 1, \pm 2, \ldots)$;

(*b*) $\log i = \left(2n + \frac{1}{2}\right)\pi i \quad (n = 0, \pm 1, \pm 2, \ldots)$;

(*c*) $\log(-1 + \sqrt{3}i) = \ln 2 + 2\left(n + \frac{1}{3}\right)\pi i \quad (n = 0, \pm 1, \pm 2, \ldots)$.

3. Show that $\text{Log}(i^3) \neq 3\,\text{Log}\, i$.

4. Show that $\log(i^2) \neq 2\log i$ when the branch

$$\log z = \ln r + i\theta \qquad \left(r > 0, \frac{3\pi}{4} < \theta < \frac{11\pi}{4}\right)$$

is used. (Compare this with the example in Sec. 33.)

5. (*a*) Show that the two square roots of i are

$$e^{i\pi/4} \quad \text{and} \quad e^{i5\pi/4}.$$

Then show that

$$\log(e^{i\pi/4}) = \left(2n + \frac{1}{4}\right)\pi i \qquad (n = 0, \pm 1, \pm 2, \ldots)$$

and

$$\log(e^{i5\pi/4}) = \left[(2n+1) + \frac{1}{4}\right]\pi i \qquad (n = 0, \pm 1, \pm 2, \ldots).$$

Conclude that

$$\log(i^{1/2}) = \left(n + \frac{1}{4}\right)\pi i \qquad (n = 0, \pm 1, \pm 2, \ldots).$$

(*b*) Show that

$$\log(i^{1/2}) = \frac{1}{2}\log i,$$

as stated in Example 5, Sec. 32, by finding the values on the right-hand side of this equation and then comparing them with the final result in part (*a*).

6. Given that the branch $\log z = \ln r + i\theta$ $(r > 0, \alpha < \theta < \alpha + 2\pi)$ of the logarithmic function is analytic at each point z in the stated domain, obtain its derivative by differentiating each side of the identity (Sec. 31)

$$e^{\log z} = z \qquad (|z| > 0, \alpha < \arg z < \alpha + 2\pi)$$

and using the chain rule.

7. Show that a branch (Sec. 33)

$$\log z = \ln r + i\theta \qquad (r > 0, \alpha < \theta < \alpha + 2\pi)$$

of the logarithmic function can be written

$$\log z = \frac{1}{2}\ln(x^2 + y^2) + i\tan^{-1}\left(\frac{y}{x}\right)$$

in rectangular coordinates. Then, using the theorem in Sec. 23, show that the given branch is analytic in its domain of definition and that

$$\frac{d}{dz}\log z = \frac{1}{z}$$

there.

8. Find all roots of the equation $\log z = i\pi/2$.

Ans. $z = i$.

9. Suppose that the point $z = x + iy$ lies in the horizontal strip $\alpha < y < \alpha + 2\pi$. Show that when the branch $\log z = \ln r + i\theta$ $(r > 0, \alpha < \theta < \alpha + 2\pi)$ of the logarithmic function is used, $\log(e^z) = z$. [Compare with equation (5), Sec. 31.]

10. Show that

(*a*) the function $f(z) = \text{Log}(z - i)$ is analytic everywhere except on the portion $x \leq 0$ of the line $y = 1$;

(*b*) the function

$$f(z) = \frac{\text{Log}(z + 4)}{z^2 + i}$$

is analytic everywhere except at the points $\pm(1 - i)/\sqrt{2}$ and on the portion $x \leq -4$ of the real axis.

11. Show in two ways that the function $\ln(x^2 + y^2)$ is harmonic in every domain that does not contain the origin.

12. Show that

$$\text{Re}\,[\log(z - 1)] = \frac{1}{2}\ln[(x - 1)^2 + y^2] \qquad (z \neq 1).$$

Why must this function satisfy Laplace's equation when $z \neq 1$?

34. SOME IDENTITIES INVOLVING LOGARITHMS

If z_1 and z_2 denote any two nonzero complex numbers, it is straightforward to show that

$$\log(z_1 z_2) = \log z_1 + \log z_2. \tag{1}$$

This statement, involving a multiple-valued function, is to be interpreted in the same way that the statement

$$\arg(z_1 z_2) = \arg z_1 + \arg z_2 \tag{2}$$

was in Sec. 9. That is, if values of two of the three logarithms are specified, then there is a value of the third such that equation (1) holds.

The verification of statement (1) can be based on statement (2) in the following way. Since $|z_1 z_2| = |z_1||z_2|$ and since these moduli are all positive real numbers, we know from experience with logarithms of such numbers in calculus that

$$\ln|z_1 z_2| = \ln|z_1| + \ln|z_2|.$$

So it follows from this and equation (2) that

$$\ln|z_1 z_2| + i\arg(z_1 z_2) = (\ln|z_1| + i\arg z_1) + (\ln|z_2| + i\arg z_2). \tag{3}$$

Finally, because of the way in which equations (1) and (2) are to be interpreted, equation (3) is the same as equation (1).

EXAMPLE 1. To illustrate statement (1), write $z_1 = z_2 = -1$ and recall from Examples 2 and 3 in Sec. 32 that

$$\log 1 = 2n\pi i \quad \text{and} \quad \log(-1) = (2n + 1)\pi i,$$

where $n = 0, \pm 1, \pm 2, \ldots$. Noting that $z_1 z_2 = 1$ and using the values

$$\log(z_1 z_2) = 0 \quad \text{and} \quad \log z_1 = \pi i,$$

we find that equation (1) is satisfied when the value $\log z_2 = -\pi i$ is chosen.

If, on the other hand, principal values are used when $z_1 = z_2 = -1$,

$$\text{Log}(z_1 z_2) = 0 \quad \text{and} \quad \text{Log}\, z_1 + \text{Log}\, z_2 = 2\pi i.$$

Thus statement (1) is not always true when principal values are used in all three terms. In our next example, however, principal values can be used everywhere in equation (1) when certain restrictions are placed on the nonzero numbers z_1 and z_2.

EXAMPLE 2. Let z_1 and z_2 denote nonzero complex numbers lying to the right of the imaginary axis, so that

$$\text{Re}\, z_1 > 0 \quad \text{and} \quad \text{Re}\, z_2 > 0.$$

Thus

$$z_1 = r_1 \exp(i\Theta_1) \quad \text{and} \quad z_2 = r_2 \exp(i\Theta_2),$$

where

$$-\frac{\pi}{2} < \Theta_1 < \frac{\pi}{2} \quad \text{and} \quad -\frac{\pi}{2} < \Theta_2 < \frac{\pi}{2}.$$

Now it is important to notice that $-\pi < \Theta_1 + \Theta_2 < \pi$ since this means that

$$\text{Arg}\,(z_1 z_2) = \Theta_1 + \Theta_2.$$

Consequently,

$$\begin{aligned} \text{Log}(z_1 z_2) &= \ln |z_1 z_2| + i\,\text{Arg}\,(z_1 z_2) \\ &= \ln(r_1 r_2) + i(\Theta_1 + \Theta_2) \\ &= (\ln r_1 + i\Theta_1) + (\ln r_2 + i\Theta_2). \end{aligned}$$

That is,

$$\text{Log}(z_1 z) = \text{Log}\, z_1 + \text{Log}\, z_2.$$

(Compare this result with the one in Exercise 6, Sec. 9.)

Verification of the statement

$$\log\left(\frac{z_1}{z_2}\right) = \log z_1 - \log z_2, \tag{4}$$

which is to be interpreted in the same way as statement (1), is left to the exercises.

We include here two other properties of $\log z$ that will be of special interest in Sec. 35. If z is a nonzero complex number, then

$$z^n = e^{n \log z} \qquad (n = 0 \pm 1, \pm 2, \ldots) \tag{5}$$

for any value of $\log z$ that is taken. When $n = 1$, this reduces, of course, to relation (3), Sec. 31. Equation (5) is readily verified by writing $z = re^{i\theta}$ and noting that each side becomes $r^n e^{in\theta}$.

It is also true that when $z \neq 0$,

$$z^{1/n} = \exp\left(\frac{1}{n}\log z\right) \qquad (n = 1, 2, \ldots). \tag{6}$$

That is, the term on the right here has n distinct values, and those values are the nth roots of z. To prove this, we write $z = r\exp(i\Theta)$, where Θ is the principal value of $\arg z$. Then, in view of definition (2), Sec. 31, of $\log z$,

$$\exp\left(\frac{1}{n}\log z\right) = \exp\left[\frac{1}{n}\ln r + \frac{i(\Theta + 2k\pi)}{n}\right]$$

where $k = 0, \pm1, \pm2, \ldots$. Thus

$$\exp\left(\frac{1}{n}\log z\right) = \sqrt[n]{r}\exp\left[i\left(\frac{\Theta}{n} + \frac{2k\pi}{n}\right)\right] \qquad (k = 0, \pm1, \pm2, \ldots). \tag{7}$$

Because $\exp(i2k\pi/n)$ has distinct values only when $k = 0, 1, \ldots, n-1$, the right-hand side of equation (7) has only n values. That right-hand side is, in fact, an expression for the nth roots of z (Sec. 10), and so it can be written $z^{1/n}$. This establishes property (6), which is actually valid when n is a negative integer too (see Exercise 4).

EXERCISES

1. Show that for any two nonzero complex numbers z_1 and z_2,

$$\text{Log}(z_1 z_2) = \text{Log}\, z_1 + \text{Log}\, z_2 + 2N\pi i$$

where N has one of the values $0, \pm1$. (Compare with Example 2 in Sec. 34.)

2. Verify expression (4), Sec. 34, for $\log(z_1/z_2)$ by

(*a*) using the fact that $\arg(z_1/z_2) = \arg z_1 - \arg z_2$ (Sec. 9);

(*b*) showing that $\log(1/z) = -\log z$ $(z \neq 0)$, in the sense that $\log(1/z)$ and $-\log z$ have the same set of values, and then referring to expression (1), Sec. 34, for $\log(z_1 z_2)$.

3. By choosing specific nonzero values of z_1 and z_2, show that expression (4), Sec. 34, for $\log(z_1/z_2)$ is not always valid when *log* is replaced by *Log*.

4. Show that property (6), Sec. 34, also holds when n is a negative integer. Do this by writing $z^{1/n} = (z^{1/m})^{-1}$ $(m = -n)$, where n has any one of the negative values $n = -1, -2, \ldots$ (see Exercise 9, Sec. 11), and using the fact that the property is already known to be valid for positive integers.

5. Let z denote any nonzero complex number, written $z = re^{i\Theta}$ $(-\pi < \Theta \leq \pi)$, and let n denote any fixed positive integer $(n = 1, 2, \ldots)$. Show that all of the values of $\log(z^{1/n})$ are given by the equation

$$\log(z^{1/n}) = \frac{1}{n}\ln r + i\frac{\Theta + 2(pn + k)\pi}{n},$$

where $p = 0, \pm1, \pm2, \ldots$ and $k = 0, 1, 2, \ldots, n-1$. Then, after writing

$$\frac{1}{n}\log z = \frac{1}{n}\ln r + i\frac{\Theta + 2q\pi}{n},$$

where $q = 0, \pm1, \pm2, \ldots$, show that the set of values of $\log(z^{1/n})$ is the same as the set of values of $(1/n)\log z$. Thus show that $\log(z^{1/n}) = (1/n)\log z$ where, corresponding to a value of $\log(z^{1/n})$ taken on the left, the appropriate value of $\log z$ is to be selected on the right, and conversely. [The result in Exercise 5, Sec. 33, is a special case of this one.]

Suggestion: Use the fact that the remainder upon dividing an integer by a positive integer n is always an integer between 0 and $n-1$, inclusive; that is, when a positive integer n is specified, any integer q can be written $q = pn + k$, where p is an integer and k has one of the values $k = 0, 1, 2, \ldots, n-1$.

35. THE POWER FUNCTION

When $z \neq 0$ and the exponent c is any complex number, the ***power function*** z^c is defined by means of the equation

$$z^c = e^{c\log z} \qquad (z \neq 0). \tag{1}$$

Because of the logarithm, z^c is, in general, multiple-valued. This will be illustrated in the next section. Equation (1) provides a consistent definition of z^c in the sense that it is already known to be valid (see Sec. 32) when $c = n$ $(n = 0, \pm1, \pm2, \ldots)$ and $c = 1/n$ $(n = \pm1, \pm2, \ldots)$. Definition (1) is, in fact, suggested by those particular choices of c.

We mention here two other expected properties of the power function z^c.

One such property follows from the expression $1/e^z = e^{-z}$ (Sec. 30) of the exponential function. Namely,

$$\frac{1}{z^c} = \frac{1}{\exp(c\log z)} = \exp(-c\log z) = z^{-c}.$$

The other property is a differentiation rule for z^c. When a specific branch (Sec. 33)

$$\log z = \ln r + i\theta \qquad (r > 0, \alpha < \theta < \alpha + 2\pi)$$

of the logarithmic function is used, $\log z$ is single-valued and analytic in the indicated domain. When that branch is used, the function (1) is single-valued and analytic in the same domain. The derivative of such a ***branch*** of z^c is found by first using the chain rule to write

$$\frac{d}{dz}z^c = \frac{d}{dz}\exp(c\log z) = \frac{c}{z}\exp(c\log z)$$

and then recalling (Sec. 31) the identity $z = \exp(\log z)$. That yields the result

$$\frac{d}{dz}z^c = c\frac{\exp(c\log z)}{\exp(\log z)} = c\exp[(c-1)\log z],$$

or

$$\frac{d}{dz}z^c = cz^{c-1} \qquad (|z| > 0, \alpha < \arg z < \alpha + 2\pi). \tag{2}$$

The ***principal value*** of z^c occurs when $\log z$ is replaced by $\text{Log}\, z$ in definition (1):

$$\text{P.V. } z^c = e^{c \,\text{Log}\, z}. \tag{3}$$

Equation (3) also serves to define the ***principal branch*** of the function z^c on the domain $|z| > 0, -\pi < \text{Arg}\, z < \pi$.

According to definition (1), the ***exponential function with base c***, where c is any nonzero complex constant, is written

$$c^z = e^{z \log c}. \tag{4}$$

Note that although e^z is, in general, multiple-valued according to definition (4), the usual interpretation of e^z occurs when the principal value of the logarithm is taken. This is because the principal value of $\log e$ is unity.

When a value of $\log c$ is specified, c^z is an entire function of z. In fact,

$$\frac{d}{dz}c^z = \frac{d}{dz}e^{z \log c} = e^{z \log c} \log c;$$

and this shows that

$$\frac{d}{dz}c^z = c^z \log c. \tag{5}$$

36. EXAMPLES

The examples here are intended to illustrate the material in Sec. 35.

EXAMPLE 1. Consider the power function

$$i^i = e^{i \log i}.$$

Inasmuch as

$$\log i = \ln 1 + i\left(\frac{\pi}{2} + 2n\pi\right) = \left(2n + \frac{1}{2}\right)\pi i \qquad (n = 0, \pm 1, \pm 2, \ldots),$$

we are able to write

$$i^i = \exp\left[i\left(2n + \frac{1}{2}\right)\pi i\right] = \exp\left[-\left(2n + \frac{1}{2}\right)\pi\right] \qquad (n = 0, \pm 1, \pm 2, \ldots)$$

and

$$\text{P.V. } i^i = \exp\left(-\frac{\pi}{2}\right).$$

Note that the values of i^i are all *real numbers*.

EXAMPLE 2. Because

$$\log(-1) = \ln 1 + i(\pi + 2n\pi) = (2n+1)\pi i \qquad (n = 0, \pm 1, \pm 2, \ldots),$$

it is easy to see that

$$(-1)^{1/\pi} = \exp\left[\frac{1}{\pi}\log(-1)\right] = \exp[(2n+1)i] \qquad (n = 0, \pm 1, \pm 2, \ldots).$$

EXAMPLE 3. The principal branch of $z^{2/3}$ can be written

$$\exp\left(\frac{2}{3}\operatorname{Log} z\right) = \exp\left(\frac{2}{3}\ln r + \frac{2}{3}i\Theta\right) = \sqrt[3]{r^2}\exp\left(i\frac{2\Theta}{3}\right).$$

Thus

$$\text{P.V. } z^{2/3} = \sqrt[3]{r^2}\cos\frac{2\Theta}{3} + i\sqrt[3]{r^2}\sin\frac{2\Theta}{3}.$$

This function is analytic in the domain $r > 0, -\pi < \Theta < \pi$, as one can see directly from the theorem in Sec. 24.

While familiar laws of exponents used in calculus often carry over to complex analysis, there are exceptions when certain numbers are involved.

EXAMPLE 4. Consider the nonzero complex numbers

$$z_1 = 1 + i, \quad z_2 = 1 - i, \quad \text{and} \quad z_3 = -1 - i.$$

When principal values of the powers are taken,

$$(z_1 z_2)^i = 2^i = e^{i\operatorname{Log} 2} = e^{i(\ln 2 + i0)} = e^{i \ln 2}$$

and

$$z_1^i = e^{i\operatorname{Log}(1+i)} = e^{i(\ln\sqrt{2} + i\pi/4)} = e^{-\pi/4}e^{i(\ln 2)/2},$$

$$z_2^i = e^{i\operatorname{Log}(1-i)} = e^{i(\ln\sqrt{2} - i\pi/4)} = e^{\pi/4}e^{i(\ln 2)/2}.$$

Thus

$$(1) \qquad (z_1 z_2)^i = z_1^i z_2^i,$$

as might be expected.

On the other hand, continuing to use principal values, we see that

$$(z_2 z_3)^i = (-2)^i = e^{i\operatorname{Log}(-2)} = e^{i(\ln 2 + i\pi)} = e^{-\pi}e^{i \ln 2}$$

and

$$z_3^i = e^{i\operatorname{Log}(-1-i)} = e^{i(\ln\sqrt{2} - i3\pi/4)} = e^{3\pi/4}e^{i(\ln 2)/2}.$$

Hence

$$(z_2 z_3)^i = \left[e^{\pi/4} e^{i(\ln 2)/2}\right]\left[e^{3\pi/4} e^{i(\ln 2)/2}\right] e^{-2\pi},$$

or

$$(z_2 z_3)^i = z_2^i z_3^i \, e^{-2\pi}. \tag{2}$$

EXERCISES

1. Show that

(*a*) $(1+i)^i = \exp\left(-\frac{\pi}{4} + 2n\pi\right)\exp\left(i\frac{\ln 2}{2}\right) \quad (n = 0, \pm 1, \pm 2, \ldots);$

(*b*) $\frac{1}{i^{2i}} = \exp[(4n+1)\pi] \quad (n = 0, \pm 1, \pm 2, \ldots).$

2. Find the principal value of

(*a*) $(-i)^i$; (*b*) $\left[\frac{e}{2}(-1-\sqrt{3}i)\right]^{3\pi i}$; (*c*) $(1-i)^{4i}$.

Ans. (*a*) $\exp(\pi/2)$; (*b*) $-\exp(2\pi^2)$; (*c*) $e^{\pi}[\cos(2\ln 2) + i\sin(2\ln 2)]$.

3. Use definition (1), Sec. 35, of z^c to show that $(-1+\sqrt{3}i)^{3/2} = \pm 2\sqrt{2}$.

4. Show that the result in Exercise 3 could have been obtained by writing

(*a*) $(-1+\sqrt{3}i)^{3/2} = [(-1+\sqrt{3}i)^{1/2}]^3$ and first finding the square roots of $-1+\sqrt{3}i$;

(*b*) $(-1+\sqrt{3}i)^{3/2} = [(-1+\sqrt{3}i)^3]^{1/2}$ and first cubing $-1+\sqrt{3}i$.

5. Show that the *principal* nth root of a nonzero complex number z_0 that was defined in Sec. 10 is the same as the principal value of $z_0^{1/n}$ defined by equation (3), Sec. 35.

6. Show that if $z \neq 0$ and a is a real number, then $|z^a| = \exp(a \ln|z|) = |z|^a$, where the principal value of $|z|^a$ is to be taken.

7. Let $c = a + bi$ be a fixed complex number, where $c \neq 0, \pm 1, \pm 2, \ldots$, and note that i^c is multiple-valued. What additional restriction must be placed on the constant c so that the values of $|i^c|$ are all the same?

Ans. c is real.

8. Let c, c_1, c_2, and z denote complex numbers, where $z \neq 0$. Prove that if all of the powers involved are principal values, then

(*a*) $z^{c_1} z^{c_2} = z^{c_1+c_2}$; (*b*) $\frac{z^{c_1}}{z^{c_2}} = z^{c_1-c_2}$;

(*c*) $(z^c)^n = z^{cn} \quad (n = 1, 2, \ldots).$

9. Assuming that $f'(z)$ exists, state the formula for the derivative of $c^{f(z)}$.

37. THE TRIGONOMETRIC FUNCTIONS sin z AND cos z

Euler's formula (Sec. 7) tells us that

$$e^{ix} = \cos x + i\sin x \quad \text{and} \quad e^{-ix} = \cos x - i\sin x$$

for every real number x. Hence

$$e^{ix} - e^{-ix} = 2i \sin x \quad \text{and} \quad e^{ix} + e^{-ix} = 2\cos x.$$

That is,

$$\sin x = \frac{e^{ix} - e^{-ix}}{2i} \quad \text{and} \quad \cos x = \frac{e^{ix} + e^{-ix}}{2}.$$

It is, therefore, natural to define ***the sine and cosine functions*** of a complex variable z as follows:

$$\sin z = \frac{e^{iz} - e^{-iz}}{2i} \quad \text{and} \quad \cos z = \frac{e^{iz} + e^{-iz}}{2}. \tag{1}$$

These functions are entire since they are linear combinations (Exercise 3, Sec. 26) of the entire functions e^{iz} and e^{-iz}. Knowing the derivatives

$$\frac{d}{dz} e^{iz} = ie^{iz} \quad \text{and} \quad \frac{d}{dz} e^{-iz} = -ie^{-iz}$$

of those exponential functions, we find from equations (1) that

$$\frac{d}{dz} \sin z = \cos z \quad \text{and} \quad \frac{d}{dz} \cos z = -\sin z. \tag{2}$$

It is easy to see from definitions (1) that the sine and cosine functions remain odd and even, respectively:

$$\sin(-z) = -\sin z, \quad \cos(-z) = \cos z. \tag{3}$$

Also,

$$e^{iz} = \cos z + i \sin z. \tag{4}$$

This is, of course, Euler's formula (Sec. 7) when z is real.

A variety of identities carry over from trigonometry. For instance (see Exercises 2 and 3),

$$\sin(z_1 + z_2) = \sin z_1 \cos z_2 + \cos z_1 \sin z_2, \tag{5}$$

$$\cos(z_1 + z_2) = \cos z_1 \cos z_2 - \sin z_1 \sin z_2. \tag{6}$$

From these, it follows readily that

$$\sin 2z = 2 \sin z \cos z, \quad \cos 2z = \cos^2 z - \sin^2 z, \tag{7}$$

$$\sin\left(z + \frac{\pi}{2}\right) = \cos z, \quad \sin\left(z - \frac{\pi}{2}\right) = -\cos z, \tag{8}$$

and [Exercise 4(a)]

$$\sin^2 z + \cos^2 z = 1. \tag{9}$$

The periodic character of sin z and cos z is also evident:

$$\sin(z + 2\pi) = \sin z, \quad \sin(z + \pi) = -\sin z, \tag{10}$$

$$\cos(z + 2\pi) = \cos z, \quad \cos(z + \pi) = -\cos z. \tag{11}$$

When y is any real number, definitions (1) and the hyperbolic functions

$$\sinh y = \frac{e^y - e^{-y}}{2} \quad \text{and} \quad \cosh y = \frac{e^y + e^{-y}}{2}$$

from calculus can be used to write

$$\sin(iy) = i \sinh y \quad \text{and} \quad \cos(iy) = \cosh y. \tag{12}$$

Also, the real and imaginary components of $\sin z$ and $\cos z$ can be displayed in terms of those hyperbolic functions:

$$\sin z = \sin x \cosh y + i \cos x \sinh y, \tag{13}$$

$$\cos z = \cos x \cosh y - i \sin x \sinh y, \tag{14}$$

where $z = x + iy$. To obtain expressions (13) and (14), we write

$$z_1 = x \quad \text{and} \quad z_2 = iy$$

in identities (5) and (6) and then refer to relations (12). Observe that once expression (13) is obtained, relation (14) also follows from the fact (Sec. 21) that if the derivative of a function

$$f(z) = u(x, y) + iv(x, y)$$

exists at a point $z = (x, y)$, then

$$f'(z) = u_x(x, y) + iv_x(x, y).$$

Expressions (13) and (14) can be used (Exercise 7, Sec. 38), to show that

$$|\sin z|^2 = \sin^2 x + \sinh^2 y, \tag{15}$$

$$|\cos z|^2 = \cos^2 x + \sinh^2 y. \tag{16}$$

Inasmuch as $\sinh y$ tends to infinity as y tends to infinity, it is clear from these two equations that $\sin z$ and $\cos z$ are *not bounded* on the complex plane, whereas the absolute values of $\sin x$ and $\cos x$ are less than or equal to unity for all values of x. (See the definition of a bounded function at the end of Sec. 18.)

38. ZEROS AND SINGULARITIES OF TRIGONOMETRIC FUNCTIONS

A ***zero*** of a given function f is a number z_0 such that $f(z_0) = 0$. It is possible that a function of a real variable can have more zeros when the domain of definition is enlarged.

EXAMPLE. The function $f(x) = x^2 + 1$, defined on the real line, has no zeros. But the function $f(z) = z^2 + 1$, defined on the complex plane, has the zeros $z = \pm i$.

Consider now the sine function $f(z) = \sin z$ that was introduced in Sec. 37. Since $\sin z$ becomes the usual sine function $\sin x$ in calculus when z is real, we know that the real numbers

$$z = n\pi \qquad (n = 0, \pm 1, 2, \ldots)$$

are zeros of $\sin z$. One might ask if there are other zeros in the entire plane, and a similar question can be asked regarding the cosine function.

Theorem. *The zeros of* $\sin z$ *and* $\cos z$ *in the complex plane are the same as the zeros of* $\sin x$ *and* $\cos x$ *on the real line. That is,*

$$\sin z = 0 \qquad \textit{if and only if} \qquad z = n\pi \quad (n = 0, \pm 1, 2, \ldots)$$

and

$$\cos z = 0 \qquad \textit{if and only if} \qquad z = \frac{\pi}{2} + n\pi \quad (n = 0, \pm 1, \pm 2, \ldots).$$

In order to prove this theorem, we consider first the sine function and assume that $\sin z = 0$. Since $\sin z$ becomes the usual sine function in calculus when z is real, we know that the real numbers $z = n\pi$ $(n = 0, \pm 1, \pm 2, \ldots)$ are all zeros of $\sin z$. To show that *there are no other zeros,* we assume that $\sin z = 0$ and note how it follows from equation (15), Sec. 37, that

$$\sin^2 x + \sinh^2 y = 0.$$

This sum of two squares reveals that

$$\sin x = 0 \quad \text{and} \quad \sinh y = 0.$$

Evidently, then, $x = n\pi$ $(n = 0, \pm 1, 2, \ldots)$ and $y = 0$. Hence the zeros of $\sin z$ are as stated in the theorem.

As for the cosine function, the second of relations (8) in Sec. 37 tells us that

$$\cos z = -\sin\left(z - \frac{\pi}{2}\right);$$

and it follows that the zeros of $\cos z$ are also the ones in the statement of the theorem.

The other four trigonometric functions are defined in terms of the sine and cosine functions by the expected relations:

$$\tan z = \frac{\sin z}{\cos z}, \qquad \cot z = \frac{\cos z}{\sin z}, \tag{1}$$

$$\sec z = \frac{1}{\cos z}, \qquad \csc z = \frac{1}{\sin z}. \tag{2}$$

Observe that the quotients $\tan z$ and $\sec z$ are analytic everywhere except at the singularities (Sec. 25)

$$z = \frac{\pi}{2} + n\pi \qquad (n = 0, \pm 1, \pm 2, \ldots),$$

which are the zeros of $\cos z$. Likewise, $\cot z$ and $\csc z$ have singularities at the zeros of $\sin z$, namely

$$z = n\pi \qquad (n = 0, \pm 1, \pm 2, \ldots).$$

By differentiating the right-hand sides of equations (1) and (2), we obtain the anticipated differentiation formulas

$$\frac{d}{dz}\tan z = \sec^2 z, \qquad \frac{d}{dz}\cot z = -\csc^2 z, \tag{3}$$

$$\frac{d}{dz}\sec z = \sec z \tan z, \quad \frac{d}{dz}\csc z = -\csc z \cot z. \tag{4}$$

The periodicity of each of the trigonometric functions defined by equations (1) and (2) follows readily from equations (10) and (11) in Sec. 37. For example,

$$\tan(z + \pi) = \tan z. \tag{5}$$

Mapping properties of the transformation $w = \sin z$ are especially important in the applications later on. A reader who wishes at this time to learn some of those properties is sufficiently prepared to read Secs. 104 and 105 (Chap. 8), where they are discussed.

EXERCISES

1. Give details in the derivation of expressions (2), Sec. 37, for the derivatives of $\sin z$ and $\cos z$.

2. (*a*) With the aid of expression (4), Sec. 37, show that

$$e^{iz_1}e^{iz_2} = \cos z_1 \cos z_2 - \sin z_1 \sin z_2 + i(\sin z_1 \cos z_2 + \cos z_1 \sin z_2).$$

Then use relations (3), Sec. 37, to show how it follows that

$$e^{-iz_1}e^{-iz_2} = \cos z_1 \cos z_2 - \sin z_1 \sin z_2 - i(\sin z_1 \cos z_2 + \cos z_1 \sin z_2).$$

(*b*) Use the results in part (*a*) and the fact that

$$\sin(z_1 + z_2) = \frac{1}{2i}\left[e^{i(z_1+z_2)} - e^{-i(z_1+z_2)}\right] = \frac{1}{2i}\left(e^{iz_1}e^{iz_2} - e^{-iz_1}e^{-iz_2}\right)$$

to obtain the identity

$$\sin(z_1 + z_2) = \sin z_1 \cos z_2 + \cos z_1 \sin z_2$$

in Sec. 37.

3. According to the final result in Exercise 2(*b*),

$$\sin(z + z_2) = \sin z \cos z_2 + \cos z \sin z_2.$$

By differentiating each side here with respect to z and then setting $z = z_1$, derive the expression

$$\cos(z_1 + z_2) = \cos z_1 \cos z_2 - \sin z_1 \sin z_2$$

that was stated in Sec. 37.

4. Verify identity (9) in Sec. 37 using

(*a*) identity (6) and relations (3) in that section;

(*b*) the lemma in Sec. 28 and the fact that the entire function

$$f(z) = \sin^2 z + \cos^2 z - 1$$

has zero values along the x axis.

5. Use identity (9) in Sec. 37 to show that

(*a*) $1 + \tan^2 z = \sec^2 z$; (*b*) $1 + \cot^2 z = \csc^2 z$.

6. Establish differentiation formulas (3) and (4) in Sec. 38.

7. In Sec. 37, use expressions (13) and (14) to derive expressions (15) and (16) for $|\sin z|^2$ and $|\cos z|^2$.

Suggestion: Recall the identities $\sin^2 x + \cos^2 x = 1$ and $\cosh^2 y - \sinh^2 y = 1$.

8. Point out how it follows from expressions (15) and (16) in Sec. 37 for $|\sin z|^2$ and $|\cos z|^2$ that

(*a*) $|\sin z| \geq |\sin x|$; (*b*) $|\cos z| \geq |\cos x|$.

9. With the aid of expressions (15) and (16) in Sec. 37 for $|\sin z|^2$ and $|\cos z|^2$, show that

(*a*) $|\sinh y| \leq |\sin z| \leq \cosh y$; (*b*) $|\sinh y| \leq |\cos z| \leq \cosh y$.

10. (*a*) Use definitions (1), Sec. 37, of $\sin z$ and $\cos z$ to show that

$$2\sin(z_1 + z_2)\sin(z_1 - z_2) = \cos 2z_2 - \cos 2z_1.$$

(*b*) With the aid of the identity obtained in part (*a*), show that if $\cos z_1 = \cos z_2$, then at least one of the numbers $z_1 + z_2$ and $z_1 - z_2$ is an integral multiple of 2π.

11. Use the Cauchy–Riemann equations and the theorem in Sec. 21 to show that neither $\sin \overline{z}$ nor $\cos \overline{z}$ is an analytic function of z anywhere.

12. Use the reflection principle (Sec. 29) to show that for all z,

(*a*) $\overline{\sin z} = \sin \overline{z}$; (*b*) $\overline{\cos z} = \cos \overline{z}$.

13. With the aid of expressions (13) and (14) in Sec. 37, give direct verifications of the relations obtained in Exercise 12.

14. Show that

(*a*) $\overline{\cos(iz)} = \cos(i\overline{z})$ for all z;

(*b*) $\overline{\sin(iz)} = \sin(i\overline{z})$ if and only if $z = n\pi i \ (n = 0, \pm 1, \pm 2, \ldots)$.

15. Find all roots of the equation $\sin z = \cosh 4$ by equating the real parts and then the imaginary parts of $\sin z$ and $\cosh 4$.

Ans. $\left(\dfrac{\pi}{2} + 2n\pi\right) \pm 4i \quad (n = 0, \pm 1, \pm 2, \ldots)$.

16. With the aid of expression (14), Sec. 37, show that the roots of the equation $\cos z = 2$ are

$$z = 2n\pi + i\cosh^{-1} 2 \qquad (n = 0, \pm 1, \pm 2, \ldots).$$

Then express them in the form

$$z = 2n\pi \pm i\ln(2 + \sqrt{3}) \qquad (n = 0, \pm 1, \pm 2, \ldots).$$

39. HYPERBOLIC FUNCTIONS

The ***hyperbolic sine and cosine functions*** of a complex variable z are defined as they are with a real variable:

$$\sinh z = \frac{e^z - e^{-z}}{2}, \quad \cosh z = \frac{e^z + e^{-z}}{2}. \tag{1}$$

Since e^z and e^{-z} are entire, it follows from definitions (1) that $\sinh z$ and $\cosh z$ are entire. Furthermore,

$$\frac{d}{dz}\sinh z = \cosh z, \quad \frac{d}{dz}\cosh z = \sinh z. \tag{2}$$

Because of the way in which the exponential function appears in definitions (1) and in the definitions (Sec. 37)

$$\sin z = \frac{e^{iz} - e^{-iz}}{2i}, \quad \cos z = \frac{e^{iz} + e^{-iz}}{2}$$

of $\sin z$ and $\cos z$, the hyperbolic sine and cosine functions are closely related to those trigonometric functions:

$$-i\sinh(iz) = \sin z, \quad \cosh(iz) = \cos z, \tag{3}$$

$$-i\sin(iz) = \sinh z, \quad \cos(iz) = \cosh z. \tag{4}$$

Note how it follows readily from relations (4) and the periodicity of $\sin z$ and $\cos z$ that $\sinh z$ and $\cosh z$ are *periodic with period* $2\pi i$.

Some of the most frequently used identities involving hyperbolic sine and cosine functions are

$$\sinh(-z) = -\sinh z, \quad \cosh(-z) = \cosh z, \tag{5}$$

$$\cosh^2 z - \sinh^2 z = 1, \tag{6}$$

$$\sinh(z_1 + z_2) = \sinh z_1 \cosh z_2 + \cosh z_1 \sinh z_2, \tag{7}$$

$$\cosh(z_1 + z_2) = \cosh z_1 \cosh z_2 + \sinh z_1 \sinh z_2 \tag{8}$$

and

$$\sinh z = \sinh x \cos y + i \cosh x \sin y, \tag{9}$$

$$\cosh z = \cosh x \cos y + i \sinh x \sin y, \tag{10}$$

$$|\sinh z|^2 = \sinh^2 x + \sin^2 y, \tag{11}$$

$$|\cosh z|^2 = \sinh^2 x + \cos^2 y, \tag{12}$$

where $z = x + iy$. While these identities follow directly from definitions (1), they are often more easily obtained from related trigonometric identities, with the aid of relations (3) and (4).

EXAMPLE 1. To illustrate the method of proof just suggested, let us verify identity (6), starting with the relation

$$\sin^2 z + \cos^2 z = 1 \tag{13}$$

in Sec. 37. Using relations (3) to replace $\sin z$ and $\cos z$ in relation (13) here, we have

$$-\sinh^2(iz) + \cosh^2(iz) = 1.$$

Then, replacing z by $-iz$ in this last equation, we arrive at identity (6).

EXAMPLE 2. Let us verify expression (12) using the second of relations (4). We begin by writing

$$|\cosh z|^2 = |\cos(iz)|^2 = |\cos(-y + ix)|^2. \tag{14}$$

Now we already know from relation (16) in Sec. 37 that

$$|\cos(x + iy)|^2 = \cos^2 x + \sinh^2 y,$$

and this tells us that

$$|\cos(-y + ix)|^2 = \cos^2 y + \sinh^2 x. \tag{15}$$

Expressions (14) and (15) now combine to yield relation (12).

We turn now to the zeros of $\sinh z$ and $\cosh z$. We present the results as a theorem in order to emphasize their importance in later chapters and in order to provide easy comparison with the theorem in Sec. 38, regarding the zeros of $\sin z$ and $\cos z$. In fact, the theorem here is an immediate consequence of relations (4) and that earlier theorem.

Theorem. *The zeros of* $\sinh z$ *and* $\cosh z$ *in the complex plane all lie on the imaginary axis. To be specific,*

$$\sinh z = 0 \quad \textit{if and only if} \quad z = n\pi i \quad (n = 0, \pm 1, 2, \ldots)$$

and

$$\cosh z = 0 \quad \textit{if and only if} \quad z = \left(\frac{\pi}{2} + n\pi\right) i \quad (n = 0, \pm 1, \pm 2, \ldots).$$

The ***hyperbolic tangent*** of z is defined by means of the equation

$$\tanh z = \frac{\sinh z}{\cosh z} \tag{16}$$

and is analytic in every domain in which $\cosh z \neq 0$. The functions $\coth z$, $\operatorname{sech} z$, and $\operatorname{csch} z$ are the reciprocals of $\tanh z$, $\cosh z$, and $\sinh z$, respectively. It is straightforward to verify the following differentiation formulas, which are the same as those established in calculus for the corresponding functions of a real variable:

$$\frac{d}{dz}\tanh z = \operatorname{sech}^2 z, \qquad \frac{d}{dz}\coth z = -\operatorname{csch}^2 z, \tag{17}$$

$$\frac{d}{dz}\operatorname{sech} z = -\operatorname{sech} z \tanh z, \qquad \frac{d}{dz}\operatorname{csch} z = -\operatorname{csch} z \coth z. \tag{18}$$

EXERCISES

1. Verify that the derivatives of $\sinh z$ and $\cosh z$ are as stated in equations (2), Sec. 39.

2. Prove that $\sinh 2z = 2 \sinh z \cosh z$ by starting with

(*a*) definitions (1), Sec. 39, of $\sinh z$ and $\cosh z$;

(*b*) the identity $\sin 2z = 2 \sin z \cos z$ (Sec. 37) and using relations (3) in Sec. 39.

3. Show how identities (6) and (8) in Sec. 39 follow from identities (9) and (6), respectively, in Sec. 37.

4. Write $\sinh z = \sinh(x + iy)$ and $\cosh z = \cosh(x + iy)$, and then show how expressions (9) and (10) in Sec. 39 follow from identities (7) and (8), respectively, in that section.

5. Derive expression (11) in Sec. 39 for $|\sinh z|^2$.

6. Show that $|\sinh x| \leq |\cosh z| \leq \cosh x$ by using

(*a*) identity (12), Sec. 39;

(*b*) the inequalities $|\sinh y| \leq |\cos z| \leq \cosh y$, obtained in Exercise 9(*b*), Sec. 38.

7. Show that

(*a*) $\sinh(z + \pi i) = -\sinh z$; (*b*) $\cosh(z + \pi i) - \cosh z$;

(*c*) $\tanh(z + \pi i) = \tanh z$.

8. Give details showing that the zeros of $\sinh z$ and $\cosh z$ are as in the theorem in Sec. 39.

9. Using the results proved in Exercise 8, locate all zeros and singularities of the hyperbolic tangent function.

10. Show that $\tanh z = -i \tan(iz)$.

Suggestion: Use identities (4) in Sec. 39.

11. Derive differentiation formulas (17), Sec. 39.

12. Use the reflection principle (Sec. 29) to show that for all z,

(*a*) $\overline{\sinh z} = \sinh \bar{z}$; (*b*) $\overline{\cosh z} = \cosh \bar{z}$.

13. Use the results in Exercise 12 to show that $\overline{\tanh z} = \tanh \bar{z}$ at points where $\cosh z \neq 0$.

14. By accepting that the stated identity is valid when z is replaced by the real variable x and using the lemma in Sec. 28, verify that

(*a*) $\cosh^2 z - \sinh^2 z = 1$; (*b*) $\sinh z + \cosh z = e^z$.

[Compare with Exercise 4(*b*), Sec. 38.]

15. Why is the function $\sinh(e^z)$ entire? Write its real component as a function of x and y, and state why that function must be harmonic everywhere.

16. By using one of the identities (9) and (10) in Sec. 39 and then proceeding as in Exercise 15, Sec. 38, find all roots of the equation

(*a*) $\sinh z = i$; (*b*) $\cosh z = \dfrac{1}{2}$.

Ans. (*a*) $z = \left(2n + \dfrac{1}{2}\right)\pi i \quad (n = 0, \pm 1, \pm 2, \ldots)$;

(*b*) $z = \left(2n \pm \dfrac{1}{3}\right)\pi i \quad (n = 0, \pm 1, \pm 2, \ldots)$.

17. Find all roots of the equation $\cosh z = -2$. (Compare this exercise with Exercise 16, Sec. 38.)

Ans. $z = \pm \ln(2 + \sqrt{3}) + (2n + 1)\pi i \ (n = 0, \pm 1, \pm 2, \ldots)$.

40. INVERSE TRIGONOMETRIC AND HYPERBOLIC FUNCTIONS

Inverses of the trigonometric and hyperbolic functions can be described in terms of logarithms.

In order to define the inverse sine function $\sin^{-1} z$, we write

$$w = \sin^{-1} z \quad \text{when} \quad z = \sin w.$$

That is, $w = \sin^{-1} z$ when

$$z = \frac{e^{iw} - e^{-iw}}{2i}.$$

If we put this equation in the form

$$(e^{iw})^2 - 2iz(e^{iw}) - 1 = 0,$$

which is quadratic in e^{iw}, and solve for e^{iw} [see Exercise 8(*a*), Sec. 11], we find that

$$(1) \qquad e^{iw} = iz + (1 - z^2)^{1/2}$$

where $(1 - z^2)^{1/2}$ is, of course, a double-valued function of z. Taking logarithms of each side of equation (1) and recalling that $w = \sin^{-1} z$, we arrive at the expression

$$(2) \qquad \sin^{-1} z = -i \log[iz + (1 - z^2)^{1/2}].$$

The following example emphasizes the fact that $\sin^{-1} z$ is a multiple-valued function, with infinitely many values at each point z.

EXAMPLE. Expression (2) tells us that

$$\sin^{-1}(-i) = -i\log(1 \pm \sqrt{2}).$$

But

$$\log(1+\sqrt{2}) = \ln(1+\sqrt{2}) + 2n\pi i \qquad (n = 0, \pm 1, \pm 2, \ldots)$$

and

$$\log(1-\sqrt{2}) = \ln(\sqrt{2}-1) + (2n+1)\pi i \qquad (n = 0, \pm 1, \pm 2, \ldots).$$

Since

$$\ln(\sqrt{2}-1) = \ln\frac{1}{1+\sqrt{2}} = -\ln(1+\sqrt{2}),$$

then, the numbers

$$(-1)^n \ln(1+\sqrt{2}) + n\pi i \qquad (n = 0, \pm 1, \pm 2, \ldots)$$

constitute the set of values of $\log(1 \pm \sqrt{2})$. Thus, in rectangular form,

$$\sin^{-1}(-i) = n\pi + i(-1)^{n+1}\ln(1+\sqrt{2}) \qquad (n = 0, \pm 1, \pm 2, \ldots).$$

One can apply the technique used to derive expression (2) for $\sin^{-1} z$ to show that

$$\cos^{-1} z = -i\log\left[z + i(1-z^2)^{1/2}\right] \tag{3}$$

and that

$$\tan^{-1} z = \frac{i}{2}\log\frac{i+z}{i-z}. \tag{4}$$

The functions $\cos^{-1} z$ and $\tan^{-1} z$ are also multiple-valued. When specific branches of the square root and logarithmic functions are used, all three inverse functions become single-valued and analytic because they are then compositions of analytic functions.

The derivatives of these three functions are readily obtained from their logarithmic expressions. The derivatives of the first two depend on the values chosen for the square roots:

$$\frac{d}{dz}\sin^{-1} z = \frac{1}{(1-z^2)^{1/2}}, \tag{5}$$

$$\frac{d}{dz}\cos^{-1} z = \frac{-1}{(1-z^2)^{1/2}}. \tag{6}$$

The derivative of the last one,

$$\frac{d}{dz}\tan^{-1} z = \frac{1}{1+z^2}, \tag{7}$$

does not, however, depend on the manner in which the function is made single-valued.

Inverse hyperbolic functions can be treated in a corresponding manner. It turns out that

$$\sinh^{-1} z = \log\left[z + (z^2 + 1)^{1/2}\right], \tag{8}$$

$$\cosh^{-1} z = \log\left[z + (z^2 - 1)^{1/2}\right], \tag{9}$$

and

$$\tanh^{-1} z = \frac{1}{2} \log \frac{1+z}{1-z}. \tag{10}$$

Finally, we remark that common alternative notation for all of these inverse functions is arcsin z, etc.

EXERCISES

1. Find all the values of

(*a*) $\tan^{-1}(2i)$; (*b*) $\tan^{-1}(1+i)$; (*c*) $\cosh^{-1}(-1)$; (*d*) $\tanh^{-1} 0$.

Ans. (*a*) $\left(n + \frac{1}{2}\right)\pi + \frac{i}{2} \ln 3 \, (n = 0, \pm 1, \pm 2, \ldots)$;

(*d*) $n\pi i \, (n = 0, \pm 1, \pm 2, \ldots)$.

2. Solve the equation $\sin z = 2$ for z by

(*a*) equating real parts and then imaginary parts in that equation;

(*b*) using expression (2), Sec. 40, for $\sin^{-1} z$.

Ans. $z = \left(2n + \frac{1}{2}\right)\pi \pm i \ln(2 + \sqrt{3}) \, (n = 0, \pm 1, \pm 2, \ldots)$.

3. Solve the equation $\cos z = \sqrt{2}$ for z.

4. Derive expression (5), Sec. 40, for the derivative of $\sin^{-1} z$.

5. Derive expression (4), Sec. 40, for $\tan^{-1} z$.

6. Derive expression (7), Sec. 40, for the derivative of $\tan^{-1} z$.

7. Derive expression (9), Sec. 40, for $\cosh^{-1} z$.

CHAPTER 4

INTEGRALS

Integrals are extremely important in the study of functions of a complex variable. The theory of integration, to be developed in this chapter, is noted for its mathematical elegance. The theorems are generally concise and powerful, and many of the proofs are short.

41. DERIVATIVES OF FUNCTIONS $w(t)$

In order to introduce integrals of $f(z)$ in a fairly simple way, we need to first consider derivatives of complex-valued functions w of a *real* variable t. We write

$$w(t) = u(t) + iv(t), \tag{1}$$

where the functions u and v are *real-valued* functions of t. The derivative

$$w'(t), \text{ or } \frac{d}{dt}w(t),$$

of the function (1) at a point t is defined as

$$w'(t) = u'(t) + iv'(t), \tag{2}$$

provided each of the derivatives u' and v' exists at t.

Various rules learned in calculus, such as the ones for differentiating sums and products, apply just as they do for real-valued functions of a real variable t. Verifications can often be based on corresponding rules in calculus.

EXAMPLE 1. Assuming that the functions $u(t)$ and $v(t)$ in expression (1) are differentiable at t, let us prove that

$$\frac{d}{dt}[w(t)]^2 = 2w(t)w'(t). \tag{3}$$

To do this, we begin by writing

$$[w(t)]^2 = (u + iv)^2 = u^2 - v^2 + i2uv.$$

Then

$$\begin{aligned}\frac{d}{dt}[w(t)]^2 &= (u^2 - v^2)' + i(2uv)' \\ &= 2uu' - 2vv' + i2(uv' + u'v) \\ &= 2(u + iv)(u' + iv'),\end{aligned}$$

and we arrive at expression (3).

EXAMPLE 2. Another expected rule for differentiation that we shall often use is

$$\frac{d}{dt}e^{z_0 t} = z_0 e^{z_0 t}, \tag{4}$$

where $z_0 = x_0 + iy_0$. To verify this, we write

$$e^{z_0 t} = e^{x_0 t}e^{iy_0 t} = e^{x_0 t}\cos y_0 t + ie^{x_0 t}\sin y_0 t$$

and refer to definition (2) to see that

$$\frac{d}{dt}e^{z_0 t} = (e^{x_0 t}\cos y_0 t)' + i(e^{x_0 t}\sin y_0 t)'.$$

Familiar rules from calculus and some simple algebra then lead us to the expression

$$\frac{d}{dt}e^{z_0 t} = (x_0 + iy_0)(e^{x_0 t}\cos y_0 t + ie^{x_0 t}\sin y_0 t),$$

or

$$\frac{d}{dt}e^{z_0 t} = (x_0 + iy_0)e^{x_0 t}e^{iy_0 t}.$$

This is, of course, the same as equation (4).

While many rules in calculus carry over to functions of the type (1), not all of them do. The following example illustrates this.

EXAMPLE 3. Suppose that $w(t)$ is continuous on an interval $a \le t \le b$; that is, its component functions $u(t)$ and $v(t)$ are continuous there. Even if $w'(t)$ exists when $a < t < b$, the mean value theorem for derivatives no longer applies. To be precise, it is not necessarily true that there is a number c in the interval $a < t < b$ such that

$$w'(c) = \frac{w(b) - w(a)}{b - a}. \tag{5}$$

To see this, consider the function $w(t) = e^{it}$ on the interval $0 \leq t \leq 2\pi$. When that function is used, $|w'(t)| = |ie^{it}| = 1$ (see Example 2); and this means that the derivative $w'(c)$ on the left in equation (5) is never zero. As for the quotient on the right in equation (5),

$$\frac{w(b) - w(a)}{b - a} = \frac{w(2\pi) - w(0)}{2\pi - 0} = \frac{e^{i2\pi} - e^{i0}}{2\pi} = \frac{1 - 1}{2\pi} = 0.$$

So there is no number c such that equation (5) holds.

42. DEFINITE INTEGRALS OF FUNCTIONS $w(t)$

When $w(t)$ is a complex-valued function of a real variable t and is written

$$w(t) = u(t) + iv(t), \tag{1}$$

where u and v are real-valued, the ***definite integral*** of $w(t)$ over an interval $a \leq t \leq b$ is defined as

$$\int_a^b w(t)\,dt = \int_a^b u(t)\,dt + i\int_a^b v(t)\,dt, \tag{2}$$

provided the individual integrals on the right exist. Thus

$$\operatorname{Re}\int_a^b w(t)\,dt = \int_a^b \operatorname{Re}[w(t)]\,dt \quad \text{and} \quad \operatorname{Im}\int_a^b w(t)\,dt = \int_a^b \operatorname{Im}[w(t)]\,dt. \tag{3}$$

EXAMPLE 1. For an illustration of definition (2),

$$\int_0^{\pi/4} e^{it}\,dt = \int_0^{\pi/4} (\cos t + i\sin t)\,dt = \int_0^{\pi/4} \cos t dt + i\int_0^{\pi/4} \sin t\,dt$$
$$= [\sin t]_0^{\pi/4} + i[-\cos t]_0^{\pi/4} = \frac{1}{\sqrt{2}} + i\left(-\frac{1}{\sqrt{2}} + 1\right).$$

Improper integrals of $w(t)$ over unbounded intervals are defined in a similar way. [See Exercise 2(*d*).]

The existence of the integrals of u and v in definition (2) is ensured if those functions are ***piecewise continuous*** on the interval $a \leq t \leq b$. Such a function is continuous everywhere in the stated interval except possibly for a finite number of points where, although discontinuous, it has one-sided limits. Of course, only the right-hand limit is required at a; and only the left-hand limit is required at b. When both u and v are piecewise continuous, the function w is said to have that property.

Anticipated rules for integrating a complex constant times a function $w(t)$, for integrating sums of such functions, and for interchanging limits of integration are all valid. Those rules, as well as the property

$$\int_a^b w(t)\,dt = \int_a^c w(t)\,dt + \int_c^b w(t)\,dt,$$

are easy to verify by recalling corresponding results in calculus.

The *fundamental theorem of calculus,* involving antiderivatives, can, moreover, be extended so as to apply to integrals of the type (2). To be specific, suppose that the functions

$$w(t) = u(t) + iv(t) \quad \text{and} \quad W(t) = U(t) + iV(t)$$

are continuous on the interval $a \leq t \leq b$. If $W'(t) = w(t)$ when $a \leq t \leq b$, then $U'(t) = u(t)$ and $V'(t) = v(t)$. Hence, in view of definition (2),

$$\int_a^b w(t)\,dt = [U(t)]_a^b + i[V(t)]_a^b = [U(b) + iV(b)] - [U(a) + iV(a)].$$

That is,

$$\int_a^b w(t)\,dt = W(b) - W(a) = W(t)\Big]_a^b. \tag{4}$$

We now have another way to evaluate the integral of e^{it} in Example 1.

EXAMPLE 2. Since (see Example 2 in Sec. 41)

$$\frac{d}{dt}\left(\frac{e^{it}}{i}\right) = \frac{1}{i}\frac{d}{dt}e^{it} = \frac{1}{i}ie^{it} = e^{it},$$

one can see that

$$\int_0^{\pi/4} e^{it}\,dt = \frac{e^{it}}{i}\Big]_0^{\pi/4} = \frac{e^{i\pi/4}}{i} - \frac{1}{i} = \frac{1}{i}\left(\cos\frac{\pi}{4} + i\sin\frac{\pi}{4} - 1\right)$$
$$= \frac{1}{i}\left(\frac{1}{\sqrt{2}} + \frac{i}{\sqrt{2}} - 1\right) = \frac{1}{\sqrt{2}} + \frac{1}{i}\left(\frac{1}{\sqrt{2}} - 1\right).$$

Then, because $1/i = -i$,

$$\int_0^{\pi/4} e^{it}\,dt = \frac{1}{\sqrt{2}} + i\left(-\frac{1}{\sqrt{2}} + 1\right).$$

We recall from Example 3 in Sec. 41 how the mean value theorem for derivatives in calculus does not carry over to complex-valued functions $w(t)$. Our final example here shows that the mean value theorem for *integrals* does not carry over either. Thus special care must continue to be used in applying rules from calculus.

EXAMPLE 3. Let $w(t)$ be a continuous complex-valued function of t defined on an interval $a \leq t \leq b$. In order to show that it is not necessarily true that there is a number c in the interval $a < t < b$ such that

$$\int_a^b w(t)\,dt = w(c)(b - a), \tag{5}$$

we write $a = 0$, $b = 2\pi$ and use the same function $w(t) = e^{it}\,(0 \le t \le 2\pi)$ as in Example 3, Sec. 41. It is easy to see that

$$\int_a^b w(t)\,dt = \int_0^{2\pi} e^{it}\,dt = \left.\frac{e^{it}}{i}\right]_0^{2\pi} = 0.$$

But, for any number c such that $0 < c < 2\pi$,

$$|w(c)(b-a)| = |e^{ic}|\,2\pi = 2\pi;$$

and we find that the left-hand side of equation (5) is zero but that the right-hand side is not.

EXERCISES

1. Use rules in calculus to establish the following rules when

$$w(t) = u(t) + iv(t)$$

is a complex-valued function of a real variable t and $w'(t)$ exists:

(*a*) $\dfrac{d}{dt}[z_0 w(t)] = z_0 w'(t)$, where $z_0 = x_0 + iy_0$ is a complex constant;

(*b*) $\dfrac{d}{dt}w(-t) = -w'(-t)$ where $w'(-t)$ denotes the derivative of $w(t)$ with respect to t, evaluated at $-t$;

Suggestion: In part (*a*). show that each side of the identity to be verified can be written

$$(x_0u' - y_0v') + i(y_0u' + x_0v').$$

2. Evaluate the following integrals:

(*a*) $\displaystyle\int_0^1 (1+it)^2 dt$; (*b*) $\displaystyle\int_1^2 \left(\frac{1}{t} - i\right)^2 dt$;

(*c*) $\displaystyle\int_0^{\pi/6} e^{i2t}\,dt$; (*d*) $\displaystyle\int_0^{\infty} e^{-zt}\,dt \quad (\operatorname{Re} z > 0)$.

Ans. (*a*) $\dfrac{2}{3} + i$; (*b*) $-\dfrac{1}{2} - i\ln 4$; (*c*) $\dfrac{\sqrt{3}}{4} + \dfrac{i}{4}$; (*d*) $\dfrac{1}{z}$.

3. Show that if m and n are integers,

$$\int_0^{2\pi} e^{im\theta} e^{-in\theta}\,d\theta = \begin{cases} 0 & \text{when } m \ne n, \\ 2\pi & \text{when } m = n. \end{cases}$$

4. According to definition (2), Sec. 42, of definite integrals of complex-valued functions of a real variable,

$$\int_0^{\pi} e^{(1+i)x}\,dx = \int_0^{\pi} e^x \cos x\,dx + i\int_0^{\pi} e^x \sin x\,dx.$$

Evaluate the two integrals on the right here by evaluating the single integral on the left and then using the real and imaginary parts of the value found.

Ans. $-(1+e^{\pi})/2, \quad (1+e^{\pi})/2$.

5. Let $w(t) = u(t) + iv(t)$ denote a continuous complex-valued function defined on an interval $-a \le t \le a$.

   (*a*) Suppose that $w(t)$ is *even*; that is, $w(-t) = w(t)$ for each point t in the given interval. Show that

$$\int_{-a}^{a} w(t)\,dt = 2\int_{0}^{a} w(t)\,dt.$$

   (*b*) Show that if $w(t)$ is an *odd* function, one where $w(-t) = -w(t)$ for each point t in the given interval, then

$$\int_{-a}^{a} w(t)\,dt = 0.$$

Suggestion: In each part of this exercise, use the corresponding property of integrals of *real-valued* functions of t, which is graphically evident.

43. CONTOURS

Integrals of complex-valued functions of a *complex* variable are defined on curves in the complex plane, rather than on just intervals of the real line. Classes of curves that are adequate for the study of such integrals are introduced in this section.

A set of points $z = (x, y)$ in the complex plane is said to be an ***arc*** if

$$x = x(t), \quad y = y(t) \qquad (a \le t \le b), \tag{1}$$

where $x(t)$ and $y(t)$ are continuous functions of the real parameter t. This definition establishes a continuous mapping of the interval $a \le t \le b$ into the xy, or z, plane; and the image points are ordered according to increasing values of t. It is convenient to describe the points of C by means of the equation

$$z = z(t) \qquad (a \le t \le b), \tag{2}$$

where

$$z(t) = x(t) + iy(t). \tag{3}$$

The arc C is a ***simple arc***, or a Jordan arc,* if it does not cross itself; that is, C is simple if $z(t_1) \ne z(t_2)$ when $t_1 \ne t_2$. When the arc C is simple except for the fact that $z(b) = z(a)$, we say that C is a ***simple closed curve***, or a Jordan curve. Such a curve is ***positively oriented*** when it is in the counterclockwise direction.

The geometric nature of a particular arc often suggests different notation for the parameter t in equation (2). This is, in fact, the case in the following examples.

*Named for C. Jordan (1838–1922), pronounced *jor-don′*.

EXAMPLE 1. The polygonal line (Sec. 12) defined by means of the equations

$$z = \begin{cases} x + ix & \text{when } 0 \le x \le 1, \\ x + i & \text{when } 1 \le x \le 2 \end{cases} \tag{4}$$

and consisting of a line segment from 0 to $1 + i$ followed by one from $1 + i$ to $2 + i$ (Fig. 36) is a simple arc.

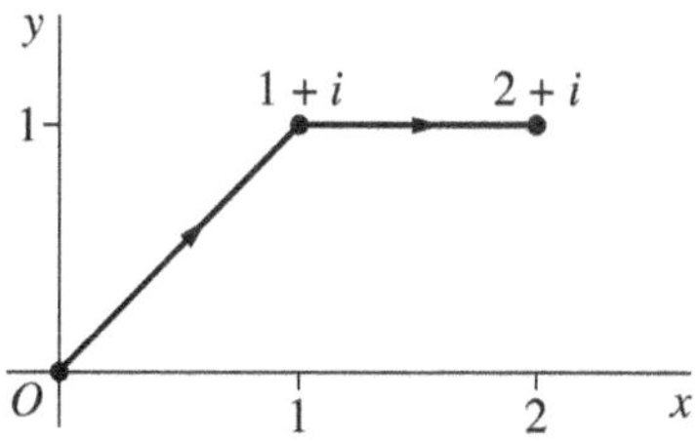

FIGURE 36

EXAMPLE 2. The unit circle

$$z = e^{i\theta} \qquad (0 \le \theta \le 2\pi) \tag{5}$$

about the origin is a simple closed curve, oriented in the counterclockwise direction. So is the circle

$$z = z_0 + Re^{i\theta} \qquad (0 \le \theta \le 2\pi), \tag{6}$$

centered at the point z_0 and with radius R (see Sec. 7).

The same set of points can make up different arcs.

EXAMPLE 3. The arc

$$z = e^{-i\theta} \qquad (0 \le \theta \le 2\pi) \tag{7}$$

is not the same as the arc described by equation (5). The set of points is the same, but now the circle is traversed in the *clockwise* direction.

EXAMPLE 4. The points on the arc

$$z = e^{i2\theta} \qquad (0 \le \theta \le 2\pi) \tag{8}$$

are the same as those making up the arcs (5) and (7). The arc here differs, however, from each of those arcs since the circle is traversed *twice* in the counterclockwise direction.

The parametric representation used for any given arc C is, of course, not unique. It is, in fact, possible to change the interval over which the parameter ranges to any other interval. To be specific, suppose that

$$t = \phi(\tau) \qquad (\alpha \le \tau \le \beta), \tag{9}$$

where ϕ is a real-valued function mapping an interval $\alpha \le \tau \le \beta$ onto the interval $a \le t \le b$ in representation (2). (See Fig. 37.) We assume that ϕ is continuous with a continuous derivative. We also assume that $\phi'(\tau) > 0$ for each τ; this ensures that t increases with τ. Representation (2) is then transformed by equation (9) into

$$z = Z(\tau) \qquad (\alpha \le \tau \le \beta), \tag{10}$$

where

$$Z(\tau) = z[\phi(\tau)]. \tag{11}$$

This is illustrated in Exercise 3.

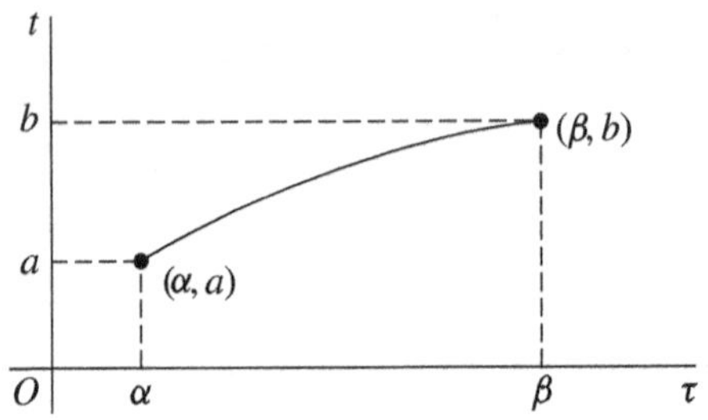

FIGURE 37
$t = \phi(\tau)$

Suppose now that the components $x'(t)$ and $y'(t)$ of the derivative (Sec. 41)

$$z'(t) = x'(t) + iy'(t) \tag{12}$$

of the function (3), used to represent C, are continuous on the entire interval $a \le t \le b$. The arc is then called a ***differentiable arc***, and the real-valued function

$$|z'(t)| = \sqrt{[x'(t)]^2 + [y'(t)]^2}$$

is integrable over the interval $a \le t \le b$. In fact, according to the definition of arc length in calculus, the length of C is the number

$$L = \int_a^b |z'(t)|\, dt. \tag{13}$$

The value of L is invariant under certain changes in the representation for C that is used, as one would expect. More precisely, with the change of variable indicated in equation (9), expression (13) takes the form [see Exercise 1(*b*)]

$$L = \int_\alpha^\beta |z'[\phi(\tau)]|\phi'(\tau)\, d\tau.$$

So, if representation (10) is used for C, the derivative (Exercise 4)

$$Z'(\tau) = z'[\phi(\tau)]\phi'(\tau) \tag{14}$$

enables us to write expression (13) as

$$L = \int_{\alpha}^{\beta} |Z'(\tau)|\, d\tau.$$

Thus the same length of C would be obtained if representation (10) were to be used.

If equation (2) represents a differentiable arc and if $z'(t) \neq 0$ anywhere in the interval $a < t < b$, then the unit tangent vector

$$\mathbf{T} = \frac{z'(t)}{|z'(t)|}$$

is well defined for all t in that open interval, with angle of inclination $\arg z'(t)$. Also, when $\mathbf{T}$ turns, it does so continuously as the parameter t varies over the entire interval $a < t < b$. This expression for $\mathbf{T}$ is the one learned in calculus when $z(t)$ is interpreted as a radius vector. Such an arc is said to be ***smooth***. In referring to a smooth arc $z = z(t)$ $(a \leq t \leq b)$, then, we agree that the derivative $z'(t)$ is continuous on the closed interval $a \leq t \leq b$ and nonzero throughout the open interval $a < t < b$.

A ***contour***, or piecewise smooth arc, is an arc consisting of a finite number of smooth arcs joined end to end. Hence if equation (2) represents a contour, $z(t)$ is continuous, whereas its derivative $z'(t)$ is piecewise continuous. The polygonal line (4) is, for example, a contour. When only the initial and final values of $z(t)$ are the same, a contour C is called a ***simple closed contour***. Examples are the circles (5) and (6), as well as the boundary of a triangle or a rectangle taken in a specific direction. The length of a contour or a simple closed contour is the sum of the lengths of the smooth arcs that make up the contour.

The points on any simple closed curve or simple closed contour C are boundary points of two distinct domains, one of which is the interior of C and is bounded. The other, which is the exterior of C, is unbounded. It will be convenient to accept this statement, known as the ***Jordan curve theorem***, as geometrically evident; the proof is not easy.*

EXERCISES

1. Show that if $w(t) = u(t) + iv(t)$ is continuous on an interval $a \leq t \leq b$, then

(*a*) $\displaystyle\int_{-b}^{-a} w(-t)\, dt = \int_{a}^{b} w(\tau)\, d\tau;$

(*b*) $\displaystyle\int_{a}^{b} w(t)\, dt = \int_{\alpha}^{\beta} w[\phi(\tau)]\phi'(\tau)\, d\tau,$ where $\phi(\tau)$ is the function in equation (9), Sec. 43.

Suggestion: These identities can be obtained by noting that they are valid for *real-valued* functions of t.

*See pp. 115–116 of the book by Newman or Sec. 13 of the one by Thron, both of which are cited in Appendix 1. The special case in which C is a simple closed polygon is proved on pp. 281–285 of Vol. 1 of the work by Hille, also cited in Appendix 1.

2. Let C denote the right-hand half of the circle $|z| = 2$, in the counterclockwise direction, and note that two parametric representations for C are

$$z = z(\theta) = 2\,e^{i\theta} \qquad \left(-\frac{\pi}{2} \le \theta \le \frac{\pi}{2}\right)$$

and

$$z = Z(y) = \sqrt{4 - y^2} + iy \qquad (-2 \le y \le 2).$$

Verify that $Z(y) = z[\phi(y)]$, where

$$\phi(y) = \arctan \frac{y}{\sqrt{4 - y^2}} \qquad \left(-\frac{\pi}{2} < \arctan t < \frac{\pi}{2}\right).$$

Also, show that this function ϕ has a positive derivative, as required in the conditions following equation (9), Sec. 43.

3. Derive the equation of the line through the points (α, a) and (β, b) in the τt plane that are shown in Fig. 37. Then use it to find the linear function $\phi(\tau)$ which can be used in equation (9), Sec. 43, to transform representation (2) in that section into representation (10) there.

Ans. $\displaystyle \phi(\tau) = \frac{b - a}{\beta - \alpha}\tau + \frac{a\beta - b\alpha}{\beta - \alpha}.$

4. Verify expression (14), Sec. 43, for the derivative of $Z(\tau) = z[\phi(\tau)]$.

Suggestion: Write $Z(\tau) = x[\phi(\tau)] + iy[\phi(\tau)]$ and apply the chain rule for real-valued functions of a real variable.

5. Suppose that a function $f(z)$ is analytic at a point $z_0 = z(t_0)$ lying on a smooth arc $z = z(t)$ $(a \le t \le b)$. Show that if $w(t) = f[z(t)]$, then

$$w'(t) = f'[z(t)]z'(t)$$

when $t = t_0$.

Suggestion: Write $f(z) = u(x, y) + iv(x, y)$ and $z(t) = x(t) + iy(t)$, so that

$$w(t) = u[x(t), y(t)] + iv[x(t), y(t)].$$

Then apply the chain rule in calculus for functions of two real variables to write

$$w' = (u_x x' + u_y y') + i(v_x x' + v_y y'),$$

and use the Cauchy–Riemann equations.

6. Let $y(x)$ be a real-valued function defined on the interval $0 \le x \le 1$ by means of the equations

$$y(x) = \begin{cases} x^3 \sin(\pi/x) & \text{when } 0 < x \le 1, \\ 0 & \text{when } x = 0. \end{cases}$$

(*a*) Show that the equation

$$z = x + iy(x) \qquad (0 \le x \le 1)$$

represents an arc C that intersects the real axis at the points $z = 1/n$ $(n = 1, 2, \ldots)$ and $z = 0$, as shown in Fig. 38.

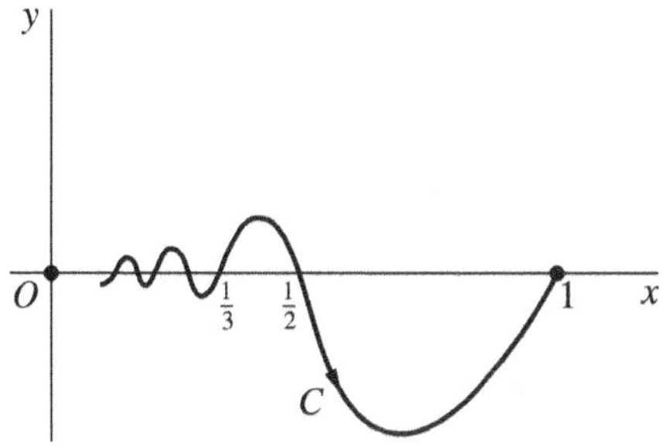

FIGURE 38

(*b*) Verify that the arc C in part (*a*) is, in fact, a *smooth* arc.

Suggestion: To establish the continuity of $y(x)$ at $x = 0$, observe that

$$0 \le \left| x^3 \sin\left(\frac{\pi}{x}\right) \right| \le x^3$$

when $x > 0$. A similar remark applies in finding $y'(0)$ and showing that $y'(x)$ is continuous at $x = 0$.

44. CONTOUR INTEGRALS

We turn now to integrals of complex-valued functions f of the complex variable z. Such an integral is defined in terms of the values $f(z)$ along a given contour C, extending from a point $z = z_1$ to a point $z = z_2$ in the complex plane. It is, therefore, a line integral; and its value depends, in general, on the contour C as well as on the function f. It is written

$$\int_C f(z)\,dz \quad \text{or} \quad \int_{z_1}^{z_2} f(z)\,dz,$$

the latter notation often being used when the value of the integral is independent of the choice of the contour taken between two fixed end points. While the integral can be defined directly as the limit of a sum,* we choose to define it in terms of a definite integral of the type introduced in Sec. 42.

Definite integrals in calculus can be interpreted as areas, and they have other interpretations as well. Except in special cases, no corresponding helpful interpretation, geometric or physical, is available for integrals in the complex plane.

Suppose that the equation

$$z = z(t) \quad (a \le t \le b) \tag{1}$$

represents a contour C, extending from a point $z_1 = z(a)$ to a point $z_2 = z(b)$. We assume that $f[z(t)]$ is *piecewise continuous* (Sec. 42) on the interval $a \le t \le b$ and

*See, for instance, pp. 245ff in Vol. I of the book by Markushevich that is listed in Appendix 1.

refer to the function $f(z)$ as being piecewise continuous on C. We then define the line integral, or ***contour integral***, of f along C in terms of the parameter t:

$$\int_C f(z)\,dz = \int_a^b f[z(t)]z'(t)\,dt. \tag{2}$$

Note that since C is a contour, $z'(t)$ is also piecewise continuous on $a \le t \le b$; and so the existence of integral (2) is ensured.

The value of a contour integral is invariant under a change in the representation of its contour when the change is of the type (11), Sec. 43. This can be seen by following the same general procedure that was used in Sec. 43 to show the invariance of arc length.

We mention here some important and expected properties of contour integrals; and we begin with the agreement that when a contour C is given, $-C$ denotes the same set of points on C but with the order of those points reversed (Fig. 39). Observe that if C has the representation (1), a representation for $-C$ is

$$z = z(-t) \qquad (-b \le t \le -a). \tag{3}$$

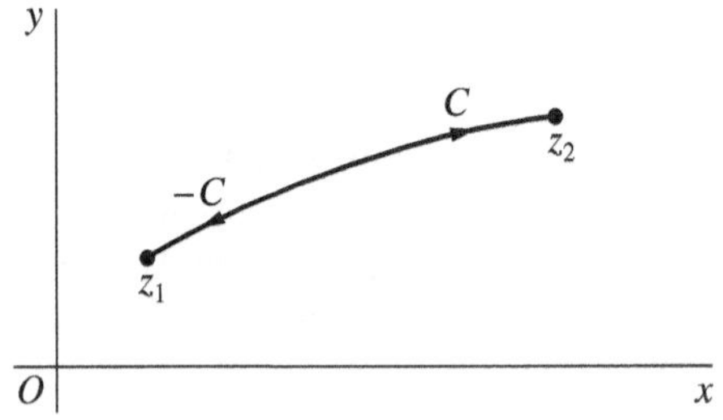

FIGURE 39

Also, if C_1 is a contour from z_1 to z_2 and C_2 is a contour from z_2 to z_3, the resulting contour is called a ***sum*** and we write $C = C_1 + C_2$ (see Fig. 40). Note, too, that the sum of contours C_1 and $-C_2$ is well defined when C_1 and C_2 have the same final points. It is denoted by $C = C_1 - C_2$.

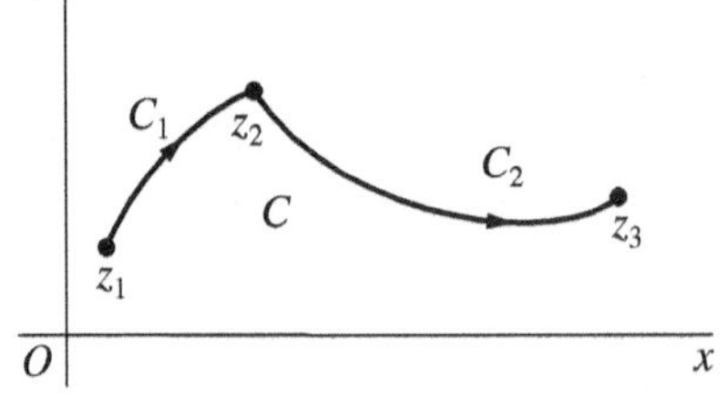

FIGURE 40
$C = C_1 + C_2$

In stating properties of contour integrals, we assume that all functions $f(z)$ and $g(z)$ are piecewise continuous on any contour used.

The first property is

$$\int_C z_0 f(z)dz = z_0 \int_C f(z)dz, \tag{4}$$

where z_0 is any complex constant. This follows from definition (2) and properties of integrals of complex-valued functions $w(t)$ mentioned in Sec. 42, and the same is true of the property

$$\int_C [f(z) + g(z)]dz = \int_C f(z)dz + \int_C g(z)dz. \tag{5}$$

By using representation (3) and referring to Exercise 1(*b*), Sec. 42, one can see that

$$\int_{-C} f(z)\,dz = \int_{-b}^{-a} f\,[z(-t)]\,\frac{d}{dt}z(-t)\,dt = -\int_{-b}^{-a} f\,[z(-t)]\,z'(-t)\,dt$$

where $z'(-t)$ denotes the derivative of $z(t)$ with respect to t, evaluated at $-t$. Then, by making the substitution $\tau = -t$ in this last integral and referring to Exercise 1(*a*), Sec. 43, we obtain the expression

$$\int_{-C} f(z)\,dz = -\int_a^b f[z(\tau)]z'(\tau)\,d\tau,$$

which is the same as

$$\int_{-C} f(z)\,dz = -\int_C f(z)\,dz. \tag{6}$$

Finally, consider a path C, with representation (1), that consists of a contour C_1 from z_1 to z_2 followed by a contour C_2 from z_2 to z_3, the initial point of C_2 being the final point of C_1 (Fig. 40). There is a value c of t, where $a < c < b$, such that $z(c) = z_2$. Consequently, C_1 is represented by

$$z = z(t) \qquad (a \le t \le c)$$

and C_2 is represented by

$$z = z(t) \qquad (c \le t \le b).$$

Also, by a rule for integrals of functions $w(t)$ that was noted in Sec. 42,

$$\int_a^b f[z(t)]z'(t)\,dt = \int_a^c f[z(t)]z'(t)\,dt + \int_c^b f[z(t)]z'(t)\,dt.$$

Evidently, then,

$$\int_C f(z)\,dz = \int_{C_1} f(z)\,dz + \int_{C_2} f(z)\,dz. \tag{7}$$

45. SOME EXAMPLES

The purpose of this and the next section is to illustrate how contour integrals are to be evaluated when definition (2), Sec. 44, of such integrals is used and to illustrate some of the properties of contour integrals that were mentioned in Sec. 44. We defer development of antiderivatives until Sec. 48.

EXAMPLE 1. Let us evaluate the contour integral

$$\int_{C_1} \frac{dz}{z}$$

where C_1 is the top half

$$z = e^{i\theta} \qquad (0 \le \theta \le \pi)$$

of the circle $|z| = 1$ from $z = 1$ to $z = -1$ (see Fig. 41). According to definition (2), Sec. 44,

$$(1) \qquad \int_{C_1} \frac{dz}{z} = \int_0^{\pi} \frac{1}{e^{i\theta}} ie^{i\theta}\, d\theta = i \int_0^{\pi} d\theta = \pi i.$$

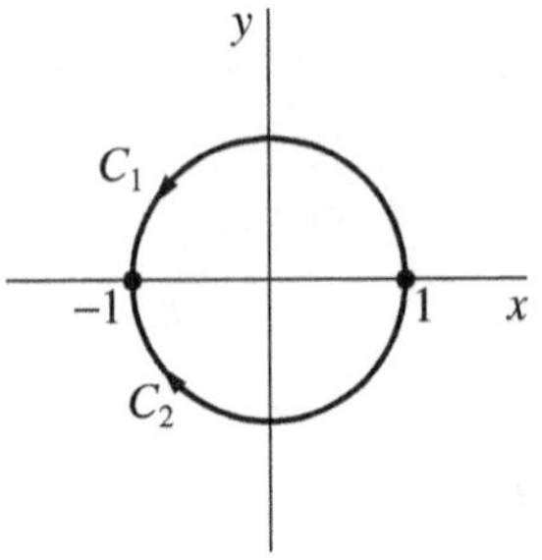

FIGURE 41
$C = C_1 - C_2$

Now let us evaluate the integral

$$\int_{C_2} \frac{dz}{z}$$

over the *bottom* half of the same circle $|z| = 1$ from $z = 1$ to $z = -1$, also shown in Fig. 41. To evaluate this integral, we use the parametric representation

$$z = e^{i\theta} \qquad (\pi \le \theta \le 2\pi)$$

of the contour $-C_2$. Then

$$(2) \qquad \int_{C_2} \frac{dz}{z} = -\int_{-C_2} \frac{dz}{z} = -\int_{\pi}^{2\pi} \frac{1}{e^{i\theta}}\, ie^{i\theta}\, d\theta = -i \int_{\pi}^{2\pi} d\theta = -\pi i.$$

Note that the values of integrals (1) and (2) are not the same. Note, too, that if C is the closed curve $C = C_1 - C_2$, then

$$(3) \qquad \int_C \frac{dz}{z} = \int_{C_1} \frac{dz}{z} - \int_{C_2} \frac{dz}{z} = \pi i - (-\pi i) = 2\pi i.$$

EXAMPLE 2. We begin here by letting C denote an arbitrary smooth arc (Sec. 43)

$$z = z(t) \qquad (a \le t \le b)$$

from a fixed point z_1 to a fixed point z_2 (Fig. 42). In order to evaluate the integral

$$\int_C z\, dz = \int_a^b z(t)z'(t)\, dt,$$

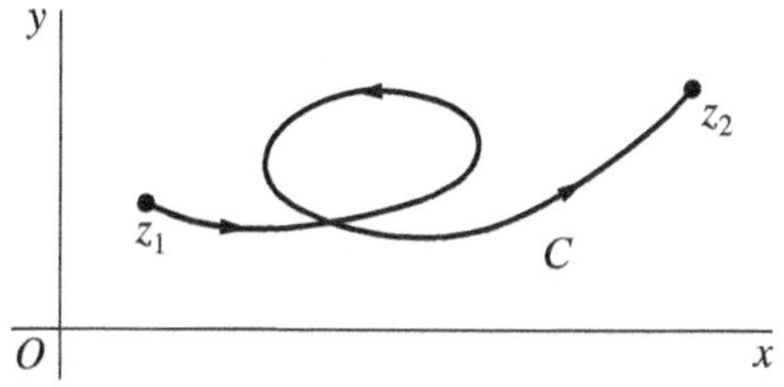

FIGURE 42

we note that according to Example 1, Sec. 41,

$$\frac{d}{dt}\frac{[z(t)]^2}{2} = z(t)z'(t).$$

Then, because $z(a) = z_1$ and $z(b) = z_2$, we have

$$\int_C z\,dz = \frac{[z(t)]^2}{2}\bigg]_a^b = \frac{[z(b)]^2 - [z(a)]^2}{2} = \frac{z_2^2 - z_1^2}{2}.$$

Inasmuch as the value of this integral depends only on the end points of C and is otherwise independent of the arc that is taken, we may write

$$\int_{z_1}^{z_2} z\,dz = \frac{z_2^2 - z_1^2}{2}. \tag{4}$$

Expression (4) is also valid when C is a contour that is not necessarily smooth since a contour consists of a finite number of smooth arcs C_k $(k = 1, 2, \ldots, n)$, joined end to end. More precisely, suppose that each C_k extends from z_k to z_{k+1}. Then

$$\int_C z\,dz = \sum_{k=1}^{n} \int_{C_k} z\,dz = \sum_{k=1}^{n} \int_{z_k}^{z_{k+1}} z\,dz = \sum_{k=1}^{n} \frac{z_{k+1}^2 - z_k^2}{2} = \frac{z_{n+1}^2 - z_1^2}{2}, \tag{5}$$

where this last summation has telescoped and z_1 is the initial point of C and z_{n+1} is its final point.

If $f(z)$ is given in the form $f(z) = u(x, y) + iv(x, y)$, where $z = x + iy$, one can sometimes apply definition (2), Sec. 44, using one of the variables x and y as the parameter.

EXAMPLE 3. Here we first let C_1 denote the polygonal line OAB shown in Fig. 43 and evaluate the integral

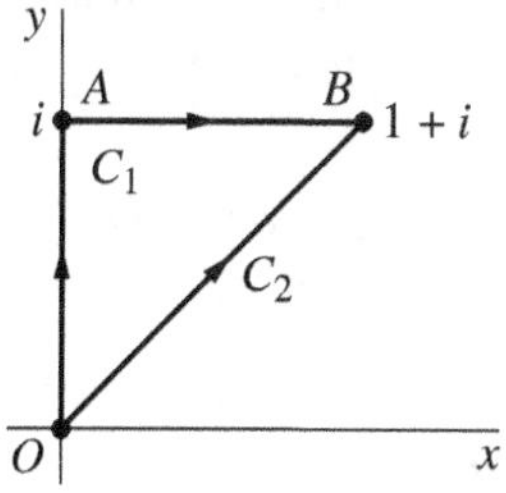

FIGURE 43
$C = C_1 - C_2$

$$(6) \qquad I_1 = \int_{C_1} f(z)\,dz = \int_{OA} f(z)\,dz + \int_{AB} f(z)\,dz,$$

where

$$f(z) = y - x - i3x^2 \quad (z = x + iy).$$

The leg OA may be represented parametrically as $z = 0 + iy$ $(0 \le y \le 1)$; and, since $x = 0$ at points on that line segment, the values of f there vary with the parameter y according to the equation $f(z) = y$ $(0 \le y \le 1)$. Consequently,

$$\int_{OA} f(z)\,dz = \int_0^1 yi\,dy = i\int_0^1 y\,dy = \frac{i}{2}.$$

On the leg AB, the points are $z = x + i$ $(0 \le x \le 1)$; and, since $y = 1$ on this segment,

$$\int_{AB} f(z)\,dz = \int_0^1 (1 - x - i3x^2)\cdot 1\,dx = \int_0^1 (1-x)\,dx - 3i\int_0^1 x^2\,dx = \frac{1}{2} - i.$$

In view of equation (6), we now see that

$$(7) \qquad I_1 = \frac{1-i}{2}.$$

If C_2 denotes the segment OB of the line $y = x$ in Fig. 43, with parametric representation $z = x + ix$ $(0 \le x \le 1)$, the fact that $y = x$ on OB enables us to write

$$I_2 = \int_{C_2} f(z)\,dz = \int_0^1 -i3x^2(1+i)\,dx = 3(1-i)\int_0^1 x^2\,dx = 1 - i.$$

Evidently, then, the integrals of $f(z)$ along the two paths C_1 and C_2 have *different values* even though those paths have the same initial and the same final points.

Observe how it follows that the integral of $f(z)$ over the simple closed contour $OABO$, or $C_1 - C_2$, has the *nonzero value*

$$I_1 - I_2 = \frac{-1+i}{2}.$$

These three examples serve to illustrate the following important facts about contour integrals:

(*a*) the value of a contour integral of a given function from one fixed point to another might be independent of the path taken (Example 2), but that is not always the case (Examples 1 and 3);

(*b*) contour integrals of a given function around every closed contour might all have value zero (Example 2), but that is not always the case (Examples 1 and 3).

The question of predicting when contour integrals are independent of path or always have value zero when the path is closed will be taken up in Secs. 48, 50, and 52.

46. EXAMPLES INVOLVING BRANCH CUTS

The path used in a contour integral can contain a point on a branch cut of the integrand involved. The next two examples illustrate this.

EXAMPLE 1. Let C denote the semicircular path

$$z = 3\,e^{i\theta} \qquad (0 \le \theta \le \pi)$$

from the point $z = 3$ to the point $z = -3$ (Fig. 44). Although the branch

$$f(z) = z^{1/2} = \exp\left(\frac{1}{2}\log z\right) \qquad (|z| > 0, 0 < \arg z < 2\pi)$$

of the multiple-valued function $z^{1/2}$ is not defined at the initial point $z = 3$ of the contour C, the integral

(1) $$I = \int_C z^{1/2}\,dz$$

nevertheless exists, since its integrand is piecewise continuous on C. To see that this is so, we first observe that when $z(\theta) = 3\,e^{i\theta}$,

$$f[z(\theta)] = \exp\left[\frac{1}{2}(\ln 3 + i\theta)\right] = \sqrt{3}\,e^{i\theta/2}.$$

Hence the right-hand limits of the real and imaginary components of the function

$$f[z(\theta)]z'(\theta) = \sqrt{3}\,e^{i\theta/2}3ie^{i\theta} = 3\sqrt{3}ie^{i3\theta/2} = -3\sqrt{3}\sin\frac{3\theta}{2} + i3\sqrt{3}\cos\frac{3\theta}{2}$$
$$(0 < \theta \le \pi)$$

at $\theta = 0$ exist, those limits being 0 and $i3\sqrt{3}$, respectively. This means that $f[z(\theta)]z'(\theta)$ is continuous on the closed interval $0 \le \theta \le \pi$ when its value at $\theta = 0$ is defined as $i3\sqrt{3}$. Consequently,

$$I = 3\sqrt{3}i\int_0^\pi e^{i3\theta/2}\,d\theta.$$

Since

$$\int_0^\pi e^{i3\theta/2}\,d\theta = \frac{2}{3i}e^{i3\theta/2}\Big]_0^\pi = -\frac{2}{3i}(1 + i),$$

we now have the value

(2) $$I = -2\sqrt{3}(1 + i)$$

of integral (1).

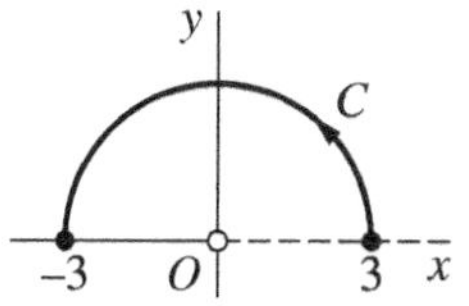

FIGURE 44

EXAMPLE 2. Using the principal branch

$$f(z) = z^{-1+i} = \exp[(-1+i)\text{Log}z] \qquad (|z| > 0, -\pi < \text{Arg}\, z < \pi)$$

of the power function z^{-1+i}, let us evaluate the integral

$$I = \int_C z^{-1+i}\, dz \tag{3}$$

where C is the positively oriented unit circle (Fig. 45)

$$z = e^{i\theta} \qquad (-\pi \le \theta \le \pi)$$

about the origin.

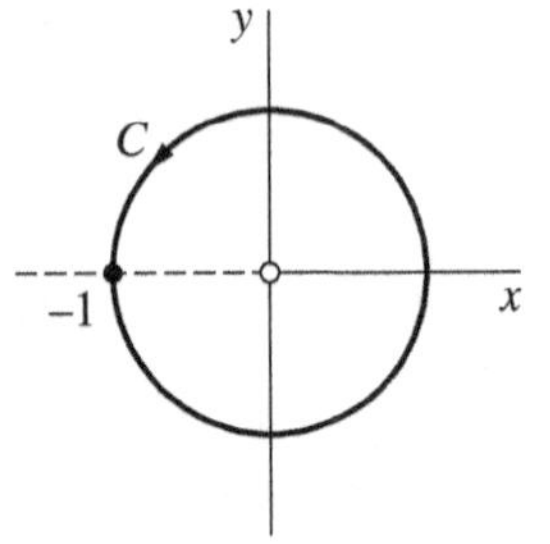

FIGURE 45

When $z(\theta) = e^{i\theta}$, it is easy to see that

$$f[z(\theta)]z'(\theta) = e^{(-1+i)(\ln 1 + i\theta)} i e^{i\theta} = i e^{-\theta}. \tag{4}$$

Inasmuch as the function (4) is piecewise continuous on $-\pi < \theta < \pi$, integral (3) exists. In fact,

$$I = i\int_{-\pi}^{\pi} e^{-\theta} d\theta = i\,[-e^{-\theta}]_{-\pi}^{\pi} = i(-e^{-\pi} + e^{\pi}),$$

or

$$I = i\,2\frac{e^{\pi} - e^{-\pi}}{2} = i\,2\sinh\pi.$$

EXERCISES

For the functions f and contours C in Exercises 1 through 8, use parametric representations for C, or legs of C, to evaluate

$$\int_C f(z)\, dz.$$

1. $f(z) = (z+2)/z$ and C is

(*a*) the semicircle $z = 2e^{i\theta}$ $(0 \le \theta \le \pi)$;

(*b*) the semicircle $z = 2e^{i\theta}$ $(\pi \le \theta \le 2\pi)$;

(*c*) the circle $z = 2e^{i\theta}$ $(0 \le \theta \le 2\pi)$.

Ans. (*a*) $-4 + 2\pi i$; (*b*) $4 + 2\pi i$; (*c*) $4\pi i$.

2. $f(z) = z - 1$ and C is the arc from $z = 0$ to $z = 2$ consisting of

(*a*) the semicircle $z = 1 + e^{i\theta}$ $(\pi \le \theta \le 2\pi)$;

(*b*) the segment $z = x$ $(0 \le x \le 2)$ of the real axis.

Ans. (*a*) 0; (*b*) 0.

3. $f(z) = \pi \exp(\pi \bar{z})$ and C is the boundary of the square with vertices at the points 0, 1, $1 + i$, and i, the orientation of C being in the counterclockwise direction.

Ans. $4(e^{\pi} - 1)$.

4. $f(z)$ is defined by means of the equations

$$f(z) = \begin{cases} 1 & \text{when } y < 0, \\ 4y & \text{when } y > 0, \end{cases}$$

and C is the arc from $z = -1 - i$ to $z = 1 + i$ along the curve $y = x^3$.

Ans. $2 + 3i$.

5. $f(z) = 1$ and C is an arbitrary contour from any fixed point z_1 to any fixed point z_2 in the z plane.

Ans. $z_2 - z_1$.

6. $f(z)$ is the principal branch

$$z^i = \exp(i\text{Log}\, z) \quad (|z| > 0, -\pi < \text{Arg}\, z < \pi)$$

of the power function z^i, and C is the semicircle $z = e^{i\theta}$ $(0 \le \theta \le \pi)$.

Ans. $-\dfrac{1 + e^{-\pi}}{2}(1 - i)$.

7. $f(z)$ is the principal branch

$$z^{-1-2i} = \exp[(-1 - 2i)\text{Log}z] \qquad (|z| > 0, -\pi < \text{Arg}z < \pi)$$

of the indicated power function, and C is the contour

$$z = e^{i\theta} \qquad \left(0 \le \theta \le \frac{\pi}{2}\right).$$

Ans. $i\dfrac{e^{\pi} - 1}{2}$.

8. $f(z)$ is the principal branch

$$z^{a-1} = \exp[(a - 1)\text{Log}z] \quad (|z| > 0, -\pi < \text{Arg}z < \pi)$$

of the power function z^{a-1}, where a is a nonzero real number, and C is the positively oriented circle of radius R about the origin.

Ans. $i\dfrac{2R^a}{a}\sin a\pi$, where the positive value of R^a is to be taken.

9. Let C denote the positively oriented unit circle $|z| = 1$ about the origin.

(*a*) Show that if $f(z)$ is the principal branch

$$z^{-3/4} = \exp\left[-\frac{3}{4}\text{Log}z\right] \quad (|z| > 0, -\pi < \text{Arg}z < \pi)$$

of $z^{-3/4}$, then

$$\int_C f(z)dz = 4\sqrt{2}\,i.$$

(*b*) Show that if $g(z)$ is the branch

$$z^{-3/4} = \exp\left[-\frac{3}{4}\log z\right] \quad (|z| > 0, 0 < \arg z < 2\pi)$$

of the same power function as in part (*a*), then

$$\int_C g(z)dz = -4 + 4i.$$

This exercise demonstrates how the value of an integral of a power function depends in general on the branch that is used.

10. With the aid of the result in Exercise 3, Sec. 42, evaluate the integral

$$\int_C z^m \bar{z}^n dz,$$

where m and n are integers and C is the unit circle $|z| = 1$, taken counterclockwise.

11. Let C denote the semicircular path shown in Fig. 46. Evaluate the integral of the function $f(z) = \bar{z}$ along C using the parametric representation (see Exercise 2, Sec. 43)

(*a*) $z = 2e^{i\theta}\left(-\frac{\pi}{2} \le \theta \le \frac{\pi}{2}\right)$; (*b*) $z = \sqrt{4 - y^2} + iy \quad (-2 \le y \le 2)$.

Ans. $4\pi i$.

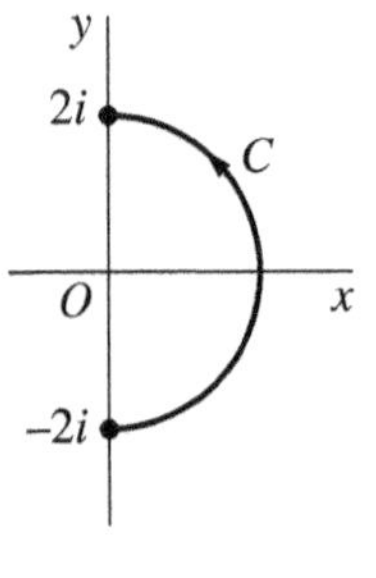

FIGURE 46

12. (*a*) Suppose that a function $f(z)$ is continuous on a smooth arc C, which has a parametric representation $z = z(t)$ $(a \le t \le b)$; that is, $f[z(t)]$ is continuous on the interval $a \le t \le b$. Show that if $\phi(\tau)$ $(\alpha \le \tau \le \beta)$ is the function described in Sec. 43, then

$$\int_a^b f[z(t)]z'(t)\,dt = \int_\alpha^\beta f[Z(\tau)]Z'(\tau)\,d\tau$$

where $Z(\tau) = z[\phi(\tau)]$.

(*b*) Point out how it follows that the identity obtained in part (*a*) remains valid when C is any contour, not necessarily a smooth one, and $f(z)$ is piecewise continuous on C. Thus show that the value of the integral of $f(z)$ along C is the same when the representation $z = Z(\tau)$ $(\alpha \le \tau \le \beta)$ is used, instead of the original one.

Suggestion: In part (*a*), use the result in Exercise 1(*b*), Sec. 43, and then refer to expression (14) in that section.

13. Let C_0 denote the circle centered at z_0 with radius R, and use the parametrization

$$z = z_0 + R\,e^{i\theta} \qquad (-\pi \le \theta \le \pi)$$

to show that

$$\int_{C_0} (z - z_0)^{n-1} dz = \begin{cases} 0 & \text{when } n = \pm 1, \pm 2, \ldots, \\ 2\pi i & \text{when } n = 0. \end{cases}$$

(Put $z_0 = 0$ and then compare the result with the one in Exercise 8 when the constant a there is a nonzero integer.)

47. UPPER BOUNDS FOR MODULI OF CONTOUR INTEGRALS

We turn now to an inequality involving contour integrals that is extremely important in various applications. We present the result as a theorem but preface it with a needed lemma involving functions $w(t)$ of the type encountered in Secs. 41 and 42.

Lemma. *If $w(t)$ is a piecewise continuous complex-valued function defined on an interval $a \le t \le b$, then*

$$\left| \int_a^b w(t)\, dt \right| \le \int_a^b |w(t)|\, dt. \tag{1}$$

This inequality clearly holds when the value of the integral on the left is zero. Thus, in the verification, we may assume that its value is a *nonzero* complex number and write

$$\int_a^b w(t)\, dt = r_0\, e^{i\theta_0}. \tag{2}$$

Solving for r_0, we have

$$r_0 = \int_a^b e^{-i\theta_0} w(t)\, dt. \tag{3}$$

Now the left-hand side of this equation is a real number, and so the right-hand side is too. Thus, using the fact that the real part of a real number is the number itself, we find that

$$r_0 = \text{Re} \int_a^b e^{-i\theta_0} w(t)\, dt.$$

Hence, in view of the first of properties (3) in Sec. 42,

$$r_0 = \int_a^b \text{Re}[e^{-i\theta_0} w(t)]\, dt. \tag{4}$$

But

$$\text{Re}[e^{-i\theta_0} w(t)] \le |e^{-i\theta_0} w(t)| = |e^{-i\theta_0}|\,|w(t)| = |w(t)|,$$

and it follows from equation (4) that

$$r_0 \le \int_a^b |w(t)|\, dt.$$

Finally, equation (2) tells us that r_0 is the same as the left-hand side of inequality (1), and the verification of the lemma is complete.

Theorem. *Let C denote a contour of length L, and suppose that a function $f(z)$ is piecewise continuous on C. If M is a nonnegative constant such that*

$$|f(z)| \le M \tag{5}$$

for all points z on C at which $f(z)$ is defined, then

$$\left| \int_C f(z)\, dz \right| \le ML. \tag{6}$$

To obtain inequality (6), we assume that inequality (5) holds and let

$$z = z(t) \qquad (a \le t \le b)$$

be a parametric representation of C. According to the lemma,

$$\left| \int_C f(z)\, dz \right| = \left| \int_a^b f[z(t)]z'(t)\, dt \right| \le \int_a^b |f[z(t)]z'(t)|\, dt.$$

Inasmuch as

$$|f[z(t)]z'(t)| = |f[z(t)]|\,|z'(t)| \le M\,|z'(t)|$$

when $a \le t \le b$, except possibly for a finite number of points, it follows that

$$\left| \int_C f(z)\, dz \right| \le M \int_a^b |z'(t)|\, dt.$$

Since the integral on the right here represents the length L of C (see Sec. 43), inequality (6) is established. It is, of course, a strict inequality if inequality (5) is strict.

Note that since C is a contour and f is piecewise continuous on C, a number M such as the one appearing in inequality (5) will always exist. This is because the real-valued function $|f[z(t)]|$ is continuous on the closed bounded interval $a \le t \le b$ when f is continuous on C; and such a function always reaches a maximum value M on that interval.* Hence $|f(z)|$ has a maximum value on C when f is continuous on it. The same is, then, true when f is *piecewise* continuous on C.

*See, for instance A. E. Taylor and W. R. Mann, "*Advanced Calculus*," 3d ed., pp. 86–90, 1983.

EXAMPLE 1. Let C be the arc of the circle $|z| = 2$ from $z = 2$ to $z = 2i$ that lies in the first quadrant (Fig. 47). Inequality (6) can be used to show that

$$\left| \int_C \frac{z-2}{z^4+1}\, dz \right| \le \frac{4\pi}{15}. \tag{7}$$

This is done by noting first that if z is a point on C, then

$$|z-2| = |z+(-2)| \le |z| + |-2| = 2+2 = 4$$

and

$$|z^4+1| \ge ||z|^4 - 1| = 15.$$

Thus, when z lies on C,

$$\left| \frac{z-2}{z^4+1} \right| = \frac{|z-2|}{|z^4+1|} \le \frac{4}{15}.$$

By writing $M = 4/15$ and observing that $L = \pi$ is the length of C, we may now use inequality (6) to obtain inequality (7).

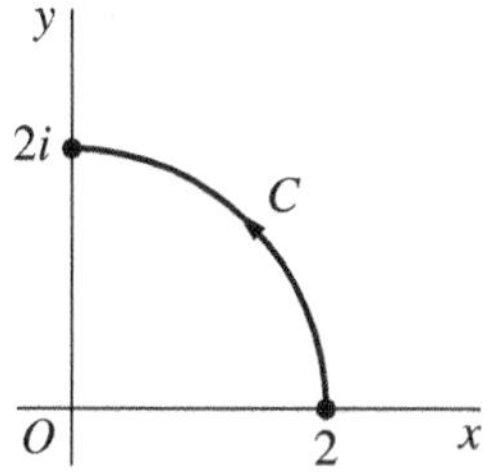

FIGURE 47

EXAMPLE 2. Let C_R denote the semicircle

$$z = Re^{i\theta} \qquad (0 \le \theta \le \pi)$$

from $z = R$ to $z = -R$, where $R > 3$ (Fig. 48). It is easy to show that

$$\lim_{R\to\infty} \int_{C_R} \frac{(z+1)\, dz}{(z^2+4)(z^2+9)} = 0 \tag{8}$$

without actually evaluating the integral. To do this, we observe that if z is a point on C_R,

$$|z+1| \le |z| + 1 = R+1,$$
$$|z^2+4| \ge ||z|^2 - 4| = R^2 - 4,$$

and

$$|z^2+9| \ge ||z|^2 - 9| = R^2 - 9.$$

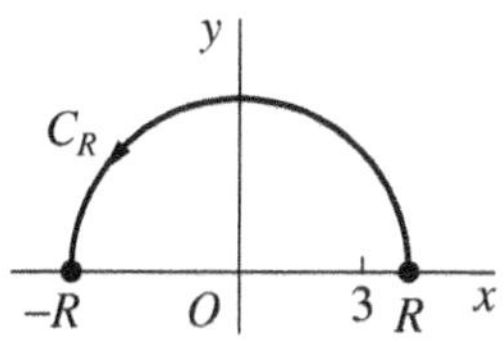

FIGURE 48

This means that if z is on C_R and $f(z)$ is the integrand in integral (8), then

$$|f(z)| = \left|\frac{z+1}{(z^2+4)\,(z^2+9)}\right| = \frac{|z+1|}{|z^2+4|\,|z^2+9|} \le \frac{R+1}{(R^2-4)\,(R^2-9)} = M_R,$$

where M_R serves as an upper bound for $|f(z)|$ on C_R. Since the length of the semicircle is πR, we may refer to the theorem in this section, using

$$M_R = \frac{R+1}{(R^2-4)\,(R^2-9)} \quad \text{and} \quad L = \pi R,$$

to write

(9) $$\left|\int_{C_R} \frac{(z+1)\,dz}{(z^2+4)(z^2+9)}\right| \le M_R L$$

where

$$M_R L = \frac{\pi(R^2+R)}{(R^2-4)\,(R^2-9)} \cdot \frac{\dfrac{1}{R^4}}{\dfrac{1}{R^4}} = \frac{\pi\left(\dfrac{1}{R^2}+\dfrac{1}{R^3}\right)}{\left(1-\dfrac{4}{R^2}\right)\left(1-\dfrac{9}{R^2}\right)}.$$

This shows that $M_R L \to 0$ as $R \to \infty$, and limit (8) follows from inequality (9).

EXERCISES

1. Without evaluating the integral, show that

(a) $\displaystyle\left|\int_C \frac{z+4}{z^3-1}\,dz\right| \le \frac{6\pi}{7}$; (b) $\displaystyle\left|\int_C \frac{dz}{z^2-1}\right| \le \frac{\pi}{3}$

when C is the arc that was used in Example 1, Sec. 47.

2. Let C denote the line segment from $z = i$ to $z = 1$ (Fig. 49), and show that

$$\left|\int_C \frac{dz}{z^4}\right| \le 4\sqrt{2}$$

without evaluating the integral.

Suggestion: Observe that of all the points on the line segment, the midpoint is closest to the origin, that distance being $d = \sqrt{2}/2$.

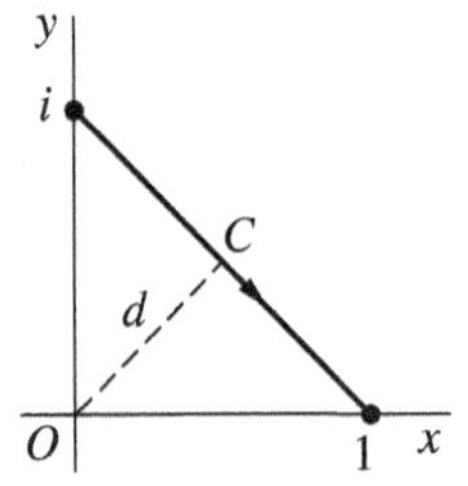

FIGURE 49

3. Show that if C is the boundary of the triangle with vertices at the points $0, 3i$, and -4, oriented in the counterclockwise direction (see Fig. 50), then

$$\left|\int_C (e^z - \bar{z})\,dz\right| \le 60.$$

Suggestion: Note that $|e^z - \bar{z}| \le e^x + \sqrt{x^2 + y^2}$ when $z = x + iy$.

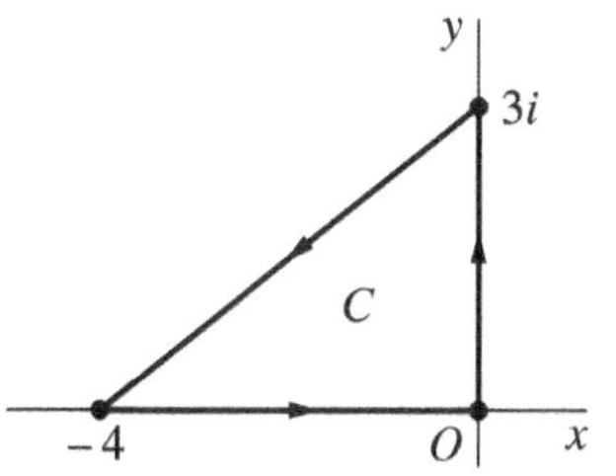

FIGURE 50

4. Let C_R denote the upper half of the circle $|z| = R\ (R > 2)$, taken in the counterclockwise direction. Show that

$$\left|\int_{C_R} \frac{2z^2 - 1}{z^4 + 5z^2 + 4}\,dz\right| \le \frac{\pi R(2R^2 + 1)}{(R^2 - 1)(R^2 - 4)}.$$

Then, by dividing the numerator and denominator on the right here by R^4, show that the value of the integral tends to zero as R tends to infinity. (Compare with Example 2 in Sec. 47.)

5. Let C_R be the circle $|z| = R\ (R > 1)$, described in the counterclockwise direction. Show that

$$\left|\int_{C_R} \frac{\operatorname{Log} z}{z^2}\,dz\right| < 2\pi\left(\frac{\pi + \ln R}{R}\right),$$

and then use l'Hospital's rule to show that the value of this integral tends to zero as R tends to infinity.

6. Let C_ρ denote a circle $|z| = \rho\ (0 < \rho < 1)$, oriented in the counterclockwise direction, and suppose that $f(z)$ is analytic in the disk $|z| \le 1$. Show that if $z^{-1/2}$ represents any particular branch of that power of z, then there is a nonnegative constant M, *independent of* ρ, such that

$$\left|\int_{C_\rho} z^{-1/2} f(z)\,dz\right| \le 2\pi M\sqrt{\rho}.$$

Thus show that the value of the integral here approaches 0 as ρ tends to 0.

Suggestion: Note that since $f(z)$ is analytic, and therefore continuous, throughout the disk $|z| \le 1$, it is bounded there (Sec. 18).

7. Apply inequality (1), Sec. 47, to show that for all values of x in the interval $-1 \le x \le 1$, the functions*

$$P_n(x) = \frac{1}{\pi}\int_0^{\pi} (x + i\sqrt{1-x^2}\cos\theta)^n \, d\theta \qquad (n = 0, 1, 2, \ldots)$$

satisfy the inequality $|P_n(x)| \le 1$.

8. Let C_N denote the boundary of the square formed by the lines

$$x = \pm\left(N + \frac{1}{2}\right)\pi \quad \text{and} \quad y = \pm\left(N + \frac{1}{2}\right)\pi,$$

where N is a positive integer and the orientation of C_N is counterclockwise.

(a) With the aid of the inequalities

$$|\sin z| \ge |\sin x| \quad \text{and} \quad |\sin z| \ge |\sinh y|,$$

obtained in Exercises 8(a) and 9(a) of Sec. 38, show that $|\sin z| \ge 1$ on the vertical sides of the square and that $|\sin z| > \sinh(\pi/2)$ on the horizontal sides. Thus show that there is a positive constant A, *independent of* N, such that $|\sin z| \ge A$ for all points z lying on the contour C_N.

(b) Using the final result in part (a), show that

$$\left|\int_{C_N} \frac{dz}{z^2 \sin z}\right| \le \frac{16}{(2N+1)\pi A}$$

and hence that the value of this integral tends to zero as N tends to infinity.

48. ANTIDERIVATIVES

Although the value of a contour integral of a function $f(z)$ from a fixed point z_1 to another fixed point z_2 depends, in general, on the path that is taken, there are certain functions whose integrals from z_1 to z_2 have values that are ***independent of path***.

Recall statements (a) and (b) at the end of Sec. 45. Those statements also remind us of the fact that the values of integrals around closed paths are sometimes, but not always, zero. Our next theorem is useful in determining when integration is independent of path and, moreover, when an integral around a closed path has value zero.

The theorem contains an extension of the fundamental theorem of calculus that simplifies the evaluation of many contour integrals. The extension involves the concept of an ***antiderivative*** of a continuous function $f(z)$ on a domain D, or a function $F(z)$ such that $F'(z) = f(z)$ for all z in D. Note that an antiderivative is, of necessity, an analytic function. Note, too, that *an antiderivative of a given function $f(z)$ is unique except for an additive constant*. This is because the derivative of the difference $F(z) - G(z)$ of any two such antiderivatives is zero; and, according to the theorem

*These functions are actually polynomials in x. The are known as ***Legendre polynomials*** and are important in applied mathematics. See, for example, the authors' book (2012) that is listed in Appendix 1. The expression for $P_n(x)$ used in Exercise 7 is sometimes called ***Laplace's first integral form***.

in Sec. 25, an analytic function is constant in a domain D when its derivative is zero throughout D.

Theorem. *Suppose that a function $f(z)$ is continuous in a domain D. If any one of the following statements is true, then so are the others:*

(*a*) *$f(z)$ has an antiderivative $F(z)$ throughout D;*

(*b*) *the integrals of $f(z)$ along contours lying entirely in D and extending from any fixed point z_1 to any fixed point z_2 all have the same value, namely*

$$\int_{z_1}^{z_2} f(z)\,dz = F(z)\Big]_{z_1}^{z_2} = F(z_2) - F(z_1)$$

where $F(z)$ is the antiderivative in statement (*a*);

(*c*) *the integrals of $f(z)$ around closed contours lying entirely in D all have value zero.*

It should be emphasized that the theorem does *not* claim that any of these statements is true for a given function $f(z)$. It says only that all of them are true or that none of them is true. The next section is devoted to the proof of the theorem and can be easily skipped by a reader who wishes to get on with other important aspects of integration theory. But we include here a number of examples illustrating how the theorem can be used.

EXAMPLE 1. The continuous function $f(z) = e^{\pi z}$ evidently has an antiderivative $F(z) = e^{\pi z}/\pi$ throughout the finite plane. Hence

$$\int_{i}^{i/2} e^{\pi z} dz = \frac{e^{\pi z}}{\pi}\Big]_{i}^{i/2} = \frac{1}{\pi}\left(e^{i\pi/2} - e^{i\pi}\right) = \frac{1}{\pi}(i+1) = \frac{1}{\pi}(1+i).$$

EXAMPLE 2. The function $f(z) = 1/z^2$, which is continuous everywhere except at the origin, has an antiderivative $F(z) = -1/z$ in the domain $|z| > 0$, consisting of the entire plane with the origin deleted. Consequently,

$$\int_C \frac{dz}{z^2} = 0$$

when C is the positively oriented unit circle $z = e^{i\theta}\,(-\pi \le \theta \le \pi)$ about the origin.

Note that the integral of the function $f(z) = 1/z$ around the same circle *cannot* be evaluated in a similar way. For, although the derivative of any branch $F(z)$ of $\log z$ is $1/z$ (Sec. 33), $F(z)$ is not differentiable, or even defined, along its branch cut. In particular, if a ray $\theta = \alpha$ from the origin is used to form the branch cut, $F'(z)$ fails to exist at the point where that ray intersects the circle C (see Fig. 51). So C does not lie in any domain throughout which $F'(z) = 1/z$, and one cannot make direct use of an

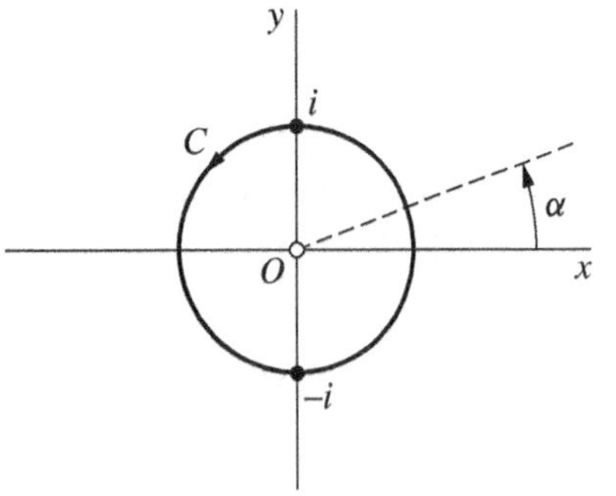

FIGURE 51

antiderivative. But Example 3, just below, illustrates how a combination of *two* different antiderivatives can be used to evaluate $f(z) = 1/z$ around C.

EXAMPLE 3. Let C_1 denote the *right* half

$$z = e^{i\theta} \qquad \left(-\frac{\pi}{2} \le \theta \le \frac{\pi}{2}\right)$$

of the circle C in Fig. 51. The principal branch

$$\text{Log}\, z = \ln r + i\Theta \qquad (r > 0, -\pi < \Theta < \pi)$$

of the logarithmic function serves as an antiderivative of the function $1/z$ in the evaluation of the integral of $1/z$ along C_1 (Fig. 52):

$$\int_{C_1} \frac{dz}{z} = \int_{-i}^{i} \frac{dz}{z} = \text{Log}\, z\Big]_{-i}^{i} = \text{Log}\, i - \text{Log}\,(-i)$$
$$= \left(\ln 1 + i\frac{\pi}{2}\right) - \left(\ln 1 - i\frac{\pi}{2}\right) = \pi i.$$

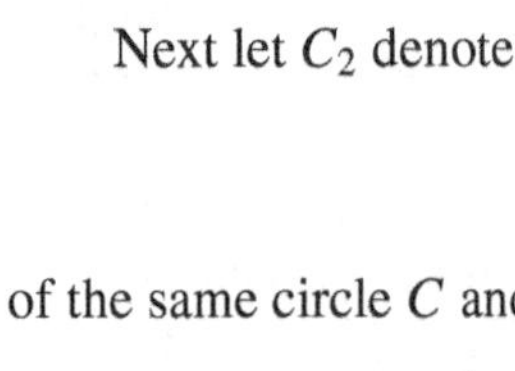

FIGURE 52

Next let C_2 denote the *left* half

$$z = e^{i\theta} \qquad \left(\frac{\pi}{2} \le \theta \le \frac{3\pi}{2}\right)$$

of the same circle C and consider the branch

$$\log z = \ln r + i\theta \qquad (r > 0, 0 < \theta < 2\pi)$$

of the logarithmic function (Fig. 53). One can write

$$\int_{C_2} \frac{dz}{z} = \int_{i}^{-i} \frac{dz}{z} = \log z \Big]_{i}^{-i} = \log(-i) - \log i$$
$$= \left(\ln 1 + i\frac{3\pi}{2} \right) - \left(\ln 1 + i\frac{\pi}{2} \right) = \pi i.$$

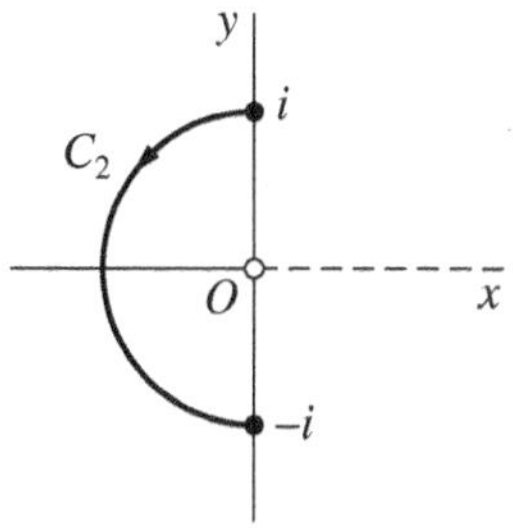

FIGURE 53

The value of the integral of $1/z$ around the entire circle $C = C_1 + C_2$ is thus obtained:

$$\int_C \frac{dz}{z} = \int_{C_1} \frac{dz}{z} + \int_{C_2} \frac{dz}{z} = \pi i + \pi i = 2\pi i.$$

EXAMPLE 4. Let us use an antiderivative to evaluate the integral

$$\int_{C_1} z^{1/2}\, dz, \tag{1}$$

where the integrand is the branch

$$f(z) = z^{1/2} = \exp\left(\frac{1}{2}\log z\right) = \sqrt{r}e^{i\theta/2} \qquad (r > 0, 0 < \theta < 2\pi) \tag{2}$$

of the square root function and where C_1 is any contour from $z = -3$ to $z = 3$ that, except for its end points, lies above the x axis (Fig. 54). Although the integrand is piecewise continuous on C_1, and the integral therefore exists, the branch (2) of $z^{1/2}$ is

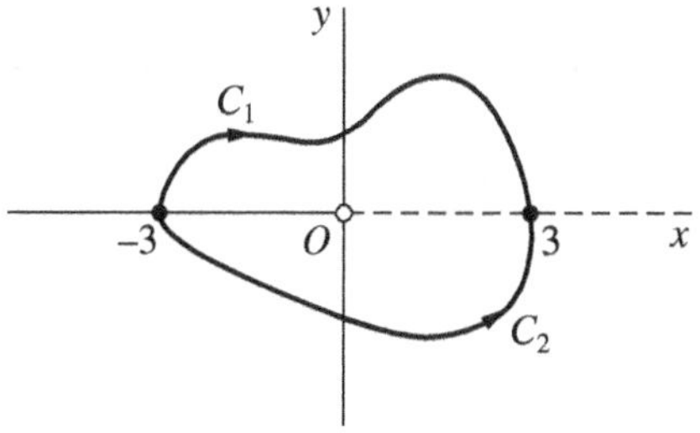

FIGURE 54

not defined on the ray $\theta = 0$, in particular at the point $z = 3$. But another branch,

$$f_1(z) = \sqrt{r}e^{i\theta/2} \qquad \left(r > 0, -\frac{\pi}{2} < \theta < \frac{3\pi}{2}\right),$$

is defined and continuous everywhere on C_1. The values of $f_1(z)$ at all points on C_1 except $z = 3$ coincide with those of our integrand (2); so the integrand can be replaced by $f_1(z)$. Since an antiderivative of $f_1(z)$ is the function

$$F_1(z) = \frac{2}{3}z^{3/2} = \frac{2}{3}r\sqrt{r}e^{i3\theta/2} \qquad \left(r > 0, -\frac{\pi}{2} < \theta < \frac{3\pi}{2}\right),$$

we can now write

$$\int_{C_1} z^{1/2}\,dz = \int_{-3}^{3} f_1(z)\,dz = F_1(z)\Big]_{-3}^{3} = 2\sqrt{3}(e^{i0} - e^{i3\pi/2}) = 2\sqrt{3}(1+i).$$

(Compare with Example 1 in Sec. 46.)

The integral

$$\int_{C_2} z^{1/2}\,dz \tag{3}$$

of the function (2) over any contour C_2 that extends from $z = -3$ to $z = 3$ *below* the real axis can be evaluated in a similar way. In this case, we can replace the integrand by the branch

$$f_2(z) = \sqrt{r}e^{i\theta/2} \left(r > 0, \frac{\pi}{2} < \theta < \frac{5\pi}{2}\right),$$

whose values coincide with those of the integrand at $z = -3$ and at all points on C_2 below the real axis. This enables us to use an antiderivative of $f_2(z)$ to evaluate integral (3). Details are left to the exercises.

49. PROOF OF THE THEOREM

In order to prove the theorem in Sec. 48, it is sufficient to show that statement (a) implies statement (b), that statement (b) implies statement (c), and that statement (c) implies statement (a). Thus, as pointed out in Sec. 48, either the statements are all true or none of them is true.

(a) implies (b)

We begin with the assumption that statement (a) is true, or that $f(z)$ has an antiderivative $F(z)$ on the domain D. To show how statement (b) follows, we need to show that integration is independent of path in D and that the fundamental theorem of calculus can be extended using $F(z)$. If a contour C from z_1 to z_2 is a *smooth* arc lying in D, with parametric representation $z = z(t)$ $(a \le t \le b)$, we know from Exercise 5, Sec. 43, that

$$\frac{d}{dt}F[z(t)] = F'[z(t)]z'(t) = f[z(t)]z'(t) \quad (a \le t \le b).$$

Because the fundamental theorem of calculus can be extended so as to apply to complex-valued functions of a real variable (Sec. 42), it follows that

$$\int_C f(z)\,dz = \int_a^b f[z(t)]z'(t)\,dt = F[z(t)]\Big]_a^b = F[z(b)] - F[z(a)].$$

Since $z(b) = z_2$ and $z(a) = z_1$, the value of this contour integral is then

$$F(z_2) - F(z_1);$$

and that value is evidently independent of the contour C as long as C extends from z_1 to z_2 and lies entirely in D. That is,

$$\int_{z_1}^{z_2} f(z)\,dz = F(z_2) - F(z_1) = F(z)\Big]_{z_1}^{z_2} \tag{1}$$

when C is smooth. Expression (1) is also valid when C is *any* contour, not necessarily a smooth one, that lies in D. For, if C consists of a finite number of smooth arcs C_k $(k = 1, 2, \ldots, n)$, each C_k extending from a point z_k to a point z_{k+1}, then

$$\int_C f(z)\,dz = \sum_{k=1}^{n} \int_{C_k} f(z)\,dz = \sum_{k=1}^{n} \int_{z_k}^{z_{k+1}} f(z)\,dz = \sum_{k=1}^{n} [F(z_{k+1}) - F(z_k)].$$

Because the last sum here telescopes to $F(z_{n+1}) - F(z_1)$, we arrive at the expression

$$\int_C f(z)\,dz = F(z_{n+1}) - F(z_1).$$

(Compare with Example 2, Sec. 45.) The fact that statement (*b*) follows from statement (*a*) is now established.

(*b*) implies (*c*)

To see that statement (*b*) implies statement (*c*), we now assume that integration of $f(z)$ is independent of path in D and show how it follows that the values of integrals of $f(z)$ around closed paths in D are zero. To do this, we let z_1 and z_2 denote two points on any closed contour C lying in D and form two paths C_1 and C_2, each with initial point z_1 and final point z_2, such that $C = C_1 - C_2$ (Fig. 55). Assuming that integration is independent of path in D, one can write

$$\int_{C_1} f(z)\,dz = \int_{C_2} f(z)\,dz, \tag{2}$$

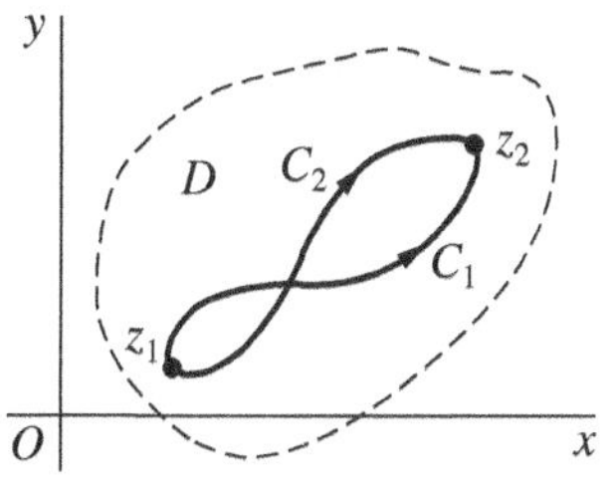

FIGURE 55

or

$$(3) \qquad \int_{C_1} f(z)\,dz + \int_{-C_2} f(z)\,dz = 0.$$

That is, the integral of $f(z)$ around the closed contour $C = C_1 - C_2$ has value zero.

(*c*) implies (*a*)

It remains to show that if integrals of a given function $f(z)$ around closed contours in D always have value zero, then $f(z)$ has an antiderivative on D. Assuming that the values of such integrals are in fact zero, we start by showing that integration is independent of path in D. We let C_1 and C_2 denote any two contours, lying in D, from a point z_1 to a point z_2 and observe that since integrals around closed paths lying in D have value zero, equation (3) holds (see Fig. 55). Thus equation (2) holds. Integration is, therefore, independent of path in D; and we can define the function

$$F(z) = \int_{z_0}^{z} f(s)\,ds$$

on D. The proof of the theorem is complete once we show that $F'(z) = f(z)$ everywhere in D. We do this by letting $z + \Delta z$ be any point distinct from z and lying in some neighborhood of z that is small enough to be contained in D. Then

$$F(z+\Delta z) - F(z) = \int_{z_0}^{z+\Delta z} f(s)\,ds - \int_{z_0}^{z} f(s)\,ds = \int_{z}^{z+\Delta z} f(s)\,ds,$$

where the path of integration may be selected as a line segment (Fig. 56). Since

$$\int_{z}^{z+\Delta z} ds = \Delta z$$

(see Exercise 5, Sec. 46), one can write

$$f(z) = \frac{1}{\Delta z}\int_{z}^{z+\Delta z} f(z)\,ds;$$

and it follows that

$$\frac{F(z+\Delta z) - F(z)}{\Delta z} - f(z) = \frac{1}{\Delta z}\int_{z}^{z+\Delta z} [f(s) - f(z)]\,ds.$$

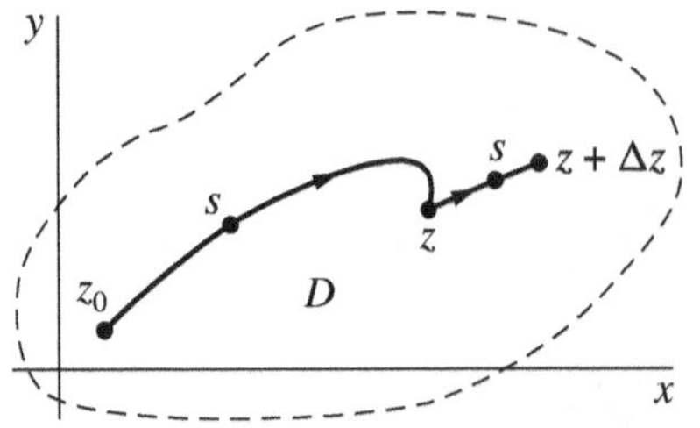

FIGURE 56

But f is continuous at the point z. Hence, for each positive number ε, a positive number δ exists such that

$$|f(s) - f(z)| < \varepsilon \quad \text{whenever} \quad |s - z| < \delta.$$

Consequently, if the point $z + \Delta z$ is close enough to z so that $|\Delta z| < \delta$, then

$$\left| \frac{F(z + \Delta z) - F(z)}{\Delta z} - f(z) \right| < \frac{1}{|\Delta z|} \varepsilon |\Delta z| = \varepsilon;$$

that is,

$$\lim_{\Delta z \to 0} \frac{F(z + \Delta z) - F(z)}{\Delta z} = f(z),$$

or $F'(z) = f(z)$.

EXERCISES

1. Use an antiderivative to show that for every contour C extending from a point z_1 to a point z_2,

$$\int_C z^n \, dz = \frac{1}{n+1}(z_2^{n+1} - z_1^{n+1}) \qquad (n = 0, 1, 2, \ldots).$$

2. By finding an antiderivative, evaluate each of these integrals, where the path is any contour between the indicated limits of integration:

$$(a) \int_0^{1+i} z^2 dz; \qquad (b) \int_0^{\pi+2i} \cos\left(\frac{z}{2}\right) dz; \qquad (c) \int_1^3 (z-2)^3 \, dz.$$

Ans. $(a)\ \frac{2}{3}(-1+i)$; $(b)\ e + \frac{1}{e}$; $(c)\ 0$.

3. Use the theorem in Sec. 48 to show that

$$\int_{C_0} (z - z_0)^{n-1} \, dz = 0 \qquad (n = \pm 1, \pm 2, \ldots)$$

when C_0 is any closed contour which does not pass through the point z_0. (Compare with Exercise 13, Sec. 46.)

4. Find an antiderivative $F_2(z)$ of the branch $f_2(z)$ of $z^{1/2}$ in Example 4, Sec. 48, to show that integral (3) there has value $2\sqrt{3}(-1+i)$. Note that the value of the integral of the function (2) around the closed contour $C_2 - C_1$ in that example is, therefore, $-4\sqrt{3}$.

5. Show that

$$\int_{-1}^{1} z^i \, dz = \frac{1 + e^{-\pi}}{2}(1 - i),$$

where the integrand denotes the principal branch

$$z^i = \exp(i \operatorname{Log} z) \qquad (|z| > 0, -\pi < \operatorname{Arg} z < \pi)$$

of z^i and where the path of integration is any contour from $z = -1$ to $z = 1$ that, except for its end points, lies above the real axis. (Compare with Exercise 6, Sec. 46.)

Suggestion: Use an antiderivative of the branch

$$z^i = \exp(i \log z) \qquad \left(|z| > 0, -\frac{\pi}{2} < \arg z < \frac{3\pi}{2}\right)$$

of the same power function.

50. CAUCHY–GOURSAT THEOREM

In Sec. 48, we saw that when a continuous function f has an antiderivative on a domain D, the integral of $f(z)$ around any given closed contour C lying entirely in D has value zero. In this section, we present a theorem giving other conditions on a function f which ensure that the value of the integral of $f(z)$ around a ***simple closed contour*** (Sec. 43) is zero. The theorem is central to the theory of functions of a complex variable; and some modifications of it, involving certain special types of domains, will be given in Secs. 52 and 53.

We let C denote a simple closed contour $z = z(t)$ $(a \leq t \leq b)$, described in the ***positive sense*** (counterclockwise), and we assume that f is analytic at each point interior to and on C. According to Sec. 44,

$$\int_C f(z)\,dz = \int_a^b f[z(t)]z'(t)\,dt; \tag{1}$$

and if

$$f(z) = u(x, y) + iv(x, y) \quad \text{and} \quad z(t) = x(t) + iy(t),$$

the integrand $f[z(t)]z'(t)$ in expression (1) is the product of the functions

$$u[x(t), y(t)] + iv[x(t), y(t)], \quad x'(t) + iy'(t)$$

of the real variable t. Thus

$$\int_C f(z)\,dz = \int_a^b (ux' - vy')\,dt + i\int_a^b (vx' + uy')\,dt. \tag{2}$$

In terms of line integrals of real-valued functions of two real variables, then,

$$\int_C f(z)\,dz = \int_C u\,dx - v\,dy + i\int_C v\,dx + u\,dy. \tag{3}$$

Observe that expression (3) can be obtained formally by replacing $f(z)$ and dz on the left with the binomials

$$u + iv \quad \text{and} \quad dx + i\,dy,$$

respectively, and expanding their product. Expression (3) is, of course, also valid when C is any contour, not necessarily a simple closed one, and when $f[z(t)]$ is only piecewise continuous on it.

We next recall a result from calculus that enables us to express the line integrals on the right in equation (3) as double integrals. Suppose that two real-valued functions $P(x, y)$ and $Q(x, y)$, together with their first-order partial derivatives, are continuous throughout the closed region R consisting of all points interior to and on the simple closed contour C. Green's theorem states that

$$\int_C P dx + Q\,dy = \iint_R (Q_x - P_y)\,dA.$$

Now f is continuous on R, since it is analytic there. Hence the functions u and v are also continuous on R. Likewise, if the derivative f' of f is continuous on R, so are the first-order partial derivatives of u and v. Green's theorem then enables us to rewrite equation (3) as

$$\int_C f(z)\,dz = \iint_R (-v_x - u_y)\,dA + i \iint_R (u_x - v_y)\,dA. \tag{4}$$

But, in view of the Cauchy–Riemann equations

$$u_x = v_y, \quad u_y = -v_x,$$

the integrands of these two double integrals are zero throughout R. So *when f is analytic in R and f' is continuous there,*

$$\int_C f(z)\,dz = 0. \tag{5}$$

This result was obtained by Cauchy in the early part of the nineteenth century.

Note that once it has been established that the value of this integral is zero, the orientation of C is immaterial. That is, statement (5) is also true if C is taken in the clockwise direction, since then

$$\int_C f(z)\,dz = -\int_{-C} f(z)\,dz = 0.$$

EXAMPLE. If C is any simple closed contour, in either direction, then

$$\int_C \sin(z^2)\,dz = 0.$$

This is because the composite function $f(z) = \sin(z^2)$ is analytic everywhere and its derivative $f'(z) = 2z\cos(z^2)$ is continuous everywhere.

Goursat* was the first to prove that *the condition of continuity on f' can be omitted.* Its removal is important and will allow us to show, for example, that the derivative f' of an analytic function f is analytic without having to assume the continuity of f', which follows as a consequence. We now state the revised form of Cauchy's result, which is known as the ***Cauchy-Goursat theorem***.

Theorem. *If a function f is analytic at all points interior to and on a simple closed contour C, then*

$$\int_C f(z)\,dz = 0.$$

The proof is presented in the next section, where, to be specific, we assume that C is positively oriented. The reader who wishes to accept this theorem without proof may pass directly to Sec. 52.

---

*E. Goursat (1858–1936), pronounced *gour-sah'*.

51. PROOF OF THE THEOREM

Since the proof of the Cauchy-Goursat theorem is necessarily rather lengthy, we present that proof in three parts. The reader is encouraged to digest each part before continuing to another.

A Preliminary Lemma

We begin with a lemma to be used in proving the theorem. In this lemma, we form subsets of the region R which consists of the points on a positively oriented simple closed contour C together with the points interior to C. To do this, we draw equally spaced lines parallel to the real and imaginary axes such that the distance between adjacent vertical lines is the same as that between adjacent horizontal lines. We thus form a finite number of closed square subregions, where each point of R lies in at least one such subregion and each subregion contains points of R. We refer to these square subregions simply as *squares*, always keeping in mind that by a square we mean a boundary together with the points interior to it. If a particular square contains points that are not in R, we remove those points and call what remains a *partial square*. We thus *cover* the region R with a finite number of squares and partial squares (Fig. 57), and our proof of the following lemma starts with this covering.

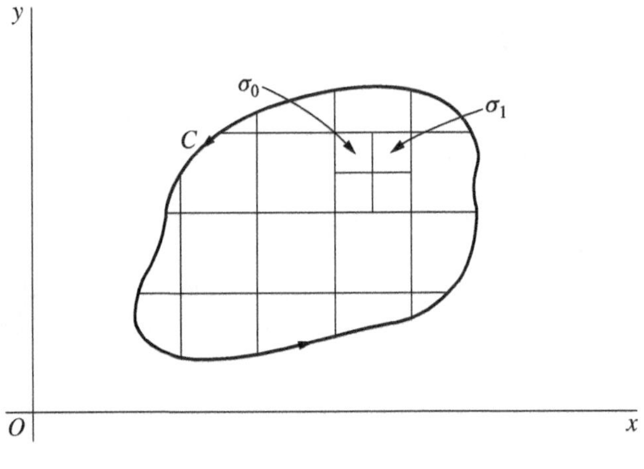

FIGURE 57

Lemma. *Let f be analytic throughout a closed region R consisting of the points interior to a positively oriented simple closed contour C together with the points on C itself. For any positive number ε, the region R can be covered with a finite number of squares and partial squares, indexed by $j = 1, 2, \ldots, n$, such that in each one there is a fixed point z_j for which the inequality*

$$\left| \frac{f(z) - f(z_j)}{z - z_j} - f'(z_j) \right| < \varepsilon \tag{1}$$

is satisfied by all points other than z_j in that square or partial square.

To start the proof, we consider the possibility that in the covering constructed just prior to the statement of the lemma, there is some square or partial square in which no point z_j exists such that inequality (1) holds for all other points z in it. If that subregion is a square, we construct four smaller squares by drawing line segments joining the midpoints of its opposite sides (Fig. 57). If the subregion is a partial square, we treat the whole square in the same manner and then let the portions that lie outside of R be discarded. If in any one of these smaller subregions, no point z_j exists such that inequality (1) holds for all other points z in it, we construct still smaller squares and partial squares, etc. When this is done to each of the original subregions that requires it, we find that *after a finite number of steps*, the region R can be covered with a finite number of squares and partial squares such that the lemma is true.

To verify this, we suppose that the needed points z_j do *not* exist after subdividing one of the original subregions a finite number of times and reach a contradiction. We let σ_0 denote that subregion if it is a square; if it is a partial square, we let σ_0 denote the entire square of which it is a part. After we subdivide σ_0, at least one of the four smaller squares, denoted by σ_1, must contain points of R but no appropriate point z_j. We then subdivide σ_1 and continue in this manner. It may be that after a square σ_{k-1} $(k = 1, 2, \ldots)$ has been subdivided, more than one of the four smaller squares constructed from it can be chosen. To make a specific choice, we take σ_k to be the one lowest and then furthest to the left.

In view of the manner in which the nested infinite sequence

$$\sigma_0, \sigma_1, \sigma_2, \ldots, \sigma_{k-1}, \sigma_k, \ldots \tag{2}$$

of squares is constructed, it is easily shown (Exercise 9, Sec. 53) that there is a point z_0 common to each σ_k; also, each of these squares contains points of R other than possibly z_0. Recall how the sizes of the squares in the sequence are decreasing, and note that any δ neighborhood $|z - z_0| < \delta$ of z_0 contains such squares when their diagonals have lengths less than δ. Every δ neighborhood $|z - z_0| < \delta$ therefore contains points of R distinct from z_0, and this means that z_0 is an accumulation point of R. Since the region R is a closed set, it follows that z_0 is a point in R. (See Sec. 12.)

Now the function f is analytic throughout R and, in particular, at z_0. Consequently, $f'(z_0)$ exists. According to the definition of derivative (Sec. 19), there is, for each positive number ε, a δ neighborhood $|z - z_0| < \delta$ such that the inequality

$$\left| \frac{f(z) - f(z_0)}{z - z_0} - f'(z_0) \right| < \varepsilon$$

is satisfied by all points distinct from z_0 in that neighborhood. But the neighborhood $|z - z_0| < \delta$ contains a square σ_K when the integer K is large enough that the length of a diagonal of that square is less than δ (Fig. 58). Consequently, z_0 serves as the point z_j in inequality (1) for the subregion consisting of the square σ_K or a part of σ_K. Contrary to the way in which the sequence (2) was formed, then, it is not necessary to subdivide σ_K. We thus arrive at a contradiction, and the proof of the lemma is complete.

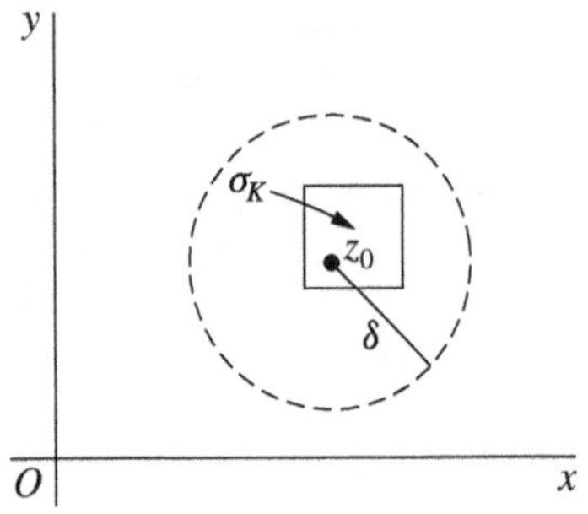

FIGURE 58

An Upper Bound for the Modulus of an Integral

Continuing with a function f which is analytic throughout a region R consisting of a positively oriented simple closed contour C and points interior to it, we are now ready to prove the Cauchy–Goursat theorem, namely that

$$\int_C f(z)\,dz = 0. \tag{3}$$

Given an arbitrary positive number ε, we consider the covering of R in the statement of the lemma. We then define on the jth square or partial square a function $\delta_j(z)$ whose values are $\delta_j(z_j) = 0$, where z_j is the fixed point in inequality (1), and

$$\delta_j(z) = \frac{f(z) - f(z_j)}{z - z_j} - f'(z_j) \quad \text{when } z \neq z_j. \tag{4}$$

According to inequality (1),

$$|\delta_j(z)| < \varepsilon \tag{5}$$

at all points z in the subregion on which $\delta_j(z)$ is defined. Also, the function $\delta_j(z)$ is continuous throughout the subregion since $f(z)$ is continuous there and

$$\lim_{z \to z_j} \delta_j(z) = f'(z_j) - f'(z_j) = 0.$$

Next, we let C_j $(j = 1, 2, \ldots, n)$ denote the positively oriented boundaries of the above squares or partial squares covering R. In view of our definition of $\delta_j(z)$, the value of f at a point z on any particular C_j can be written

$$f(z) = f(z_j) - z_j f'(z_j) + f'(z_j)z + (z - z_j)\delta_j(z);$$

and this means that

$$\int_{C_j} f(z)\,dz = [f(z_j) - z_j f'(z_j)] \int_{C_j} dz + f'(z_j) \int_{C_j} z\,dz + \int_{C_j} (z - z_j)\delta_j(z)\,dz. \tag{6}$$

But

$$\int_{C_j} dz = 0 \quad \text{and} \quad \int_{C_j} z\,dz = 0$$

since the functions 1 and z possess antiderivatives everywhere in the finite plane. So equation (6) reduces to

$$(7) \qquad \int_{C_j} f(z)\,dz = \int_{C_j} (z - z_j)\delta_j(z)\,dz \qquad (j = 1, 2, \ldots, n).$$

The sum of all n integrals on the left in equations (7) can be written

$$\sum_{j=1}^{n} \int_{C_j} f(z)\,dz = \int_C f(z)\,dz$$

since the two integrals along the common boundary of every pair of adjacent subregions cancel each other, the integral being taken in one sense along that line segment in one subregion and in the opposite sense in the other (Fig. 59). Only the integrals along the arcs that are parts of C remain. Thus, in view of equations (7),

$$\int_C f(z)\,dz = \sum_{j=1}^{n} \int_{C_j} (z - z_j)\delta_j(z)\,dz;$$

and so

$$(8) \qquad \left| \int_C f(z)\,dz \right| \le \sum_{j=1}^{n} \left| \int_{C_j} (z - z_j)\delta_j(z)\,dz \right|.$$

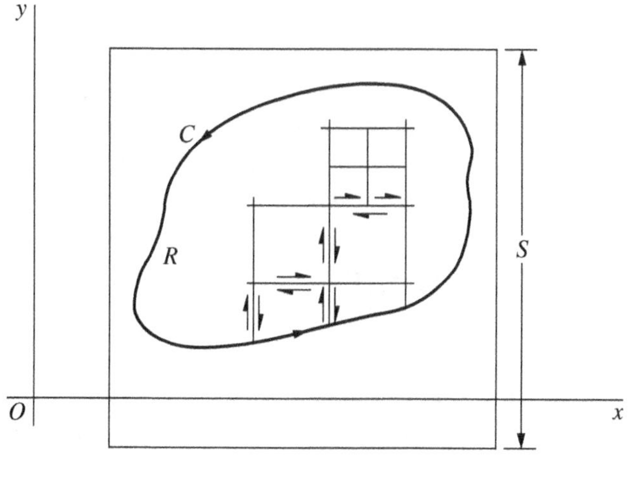

FIGURE 59

Conclusion

We now use the theorem in Sec. 47 to find an upper bound for each modulus on the right in inequality (8). To do this, we first recall that each C_j coincides either entirely or partially with the boundary of a square. In either case, we let s_j denote the length of a side of the square. Since, in the jth integral, both the variable z and the point z_j lie in that square,

$$|z - z_j| \leq \sqrt{2}s_j.$$

In view of inequality (5), then, we know that each integrand on the right in inequality (8) satisfies the condition

$$|(z - z_j)\delta_j(z)| = |z - z_j|\,|\delta_j(z)| < \sqrt{2}s_j\varepsilon. \tag{9}$$

As for the length of the path C_j, it is $4s_j$ if C_j is the boundary of a square. In that case, we let A_j denote the area of the square and observe that

$$\left|\int_{C_j} (z - z_j)\delta_j(z)\,dz\right| < \sqrt{2}s_j\varepsilon 4s_j = 4\sqrt{2}A_j\varepsilon. \tag{10}$$

If C_j is the boundary of a partial square, its length does not exceed $4s_j + L_j$, where L_j is the length of that part of C_j which is also a part of C. Again letting A_j denote the area of the full square, we find that

$$\left|\int_{C_j} (z - z_j)\delta_j(z)\,dz\right| < \sqrt{2}s_j\varepsilon(4s_j + L_j) < 4\sqrt{2}A_j\varepsilon + \sqrt{2}SL_j\varepsilon, \tag{11}$$

where S is the length of a side of some square that encloses the entire contour C as well as all of the squares originally used in covering R (Fig. 59). Note that the sum of all the A_j's does not exceed S^2.

If L denotes the length of C, it now follows from inequalities (8), (10), and (11) that

$$\left|\int_C f(z)\,dz\right| < (4\sqrt{2}S^2 + \sqrt{2}SL)\varepsilon.$$

Since the value of the positive number ε is arbitrary, we can choose it so that the right-hand side of this last inequality is as small as we please. The left-hand side, which is independent of ε, must therefore be equal to zero; and statement (3) follows. This completes the proof of the Cauchy–Goursat theorem.

52. SIMPLY CONNECTED DOMAINS

A ***simply connected*** domain D is a domain such that every simple closed contour within it encloses only points of D. The set of points interior to a simple closed contour is an example. The annular domain between two concentric circles is, however, *not* simply connected. Domains that are not simply connected are discussed in the next section.

The closed contour in the Cauchy–Goursat theorem (Sec. 50) need not be simple when the theorem is adapted to simply connected domains. More precisely, the contour can actually cross itself. The following theorem allows for this possibility.

Theorem. *If a function f is analytic throughout a simply connected domain D, then*

$$\int_C f(z)\,dz = 0 \tag{1}$$

for every closed contour C lying in D.

The proof is easy if C is a *simple* closed contour or if it is a closed contour that intersects itself a *finite* number of times. For if C is simple and lies in D, the function f is analytic at each point interior to and on C; and the Cauchy–Goursat theorem ensures that equation (1) holds. Furthermore, if C is closed but intersects itself a finite number of times, it consists of a finite number of simple closed contours, and the Cauchy-Goursat theorem can again be applied. This is illustrated in Fig. 60, where two simple closed contours C_1 and C_2 make up C. Since the values of the integrals around C_1 and C_2 are zero, *regardless of their orientations*,

$$\int_C f(z)\,dz = \int_{C_1} f(z)\,dz + \int_{C_2} f(z)\,dz = 0.$$

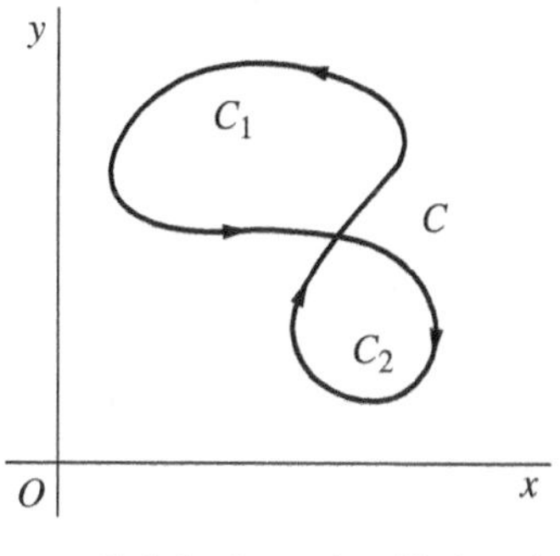

FIGURE 60

Subtleties arise if the closed contour has an *infinite* number of self-intersection points. One method that can sometimes be used to show that the theorem still applies is illustrated in Exercise 5, Sec. 53.*

EXAMPLE. If C denotes any closed contour lying in the open disk $|z| < 2$ (Fig. 61), then

$$\int_C \frac{\sin z}{(z^2+9)^5}\,dz = 0.$$

*For a proof of the theorem involving more general paths of finite length, see, for example, Secs. 63–65 in Vol. I of the book by Markushevich that is cited in Appendix 1.

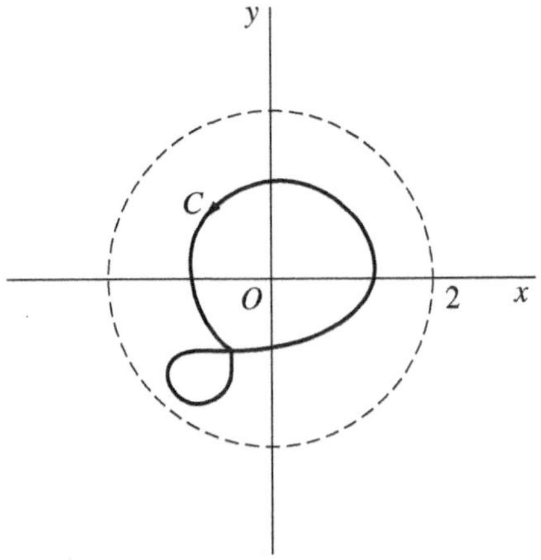

FIGURE 61

This is because the disk is a simply connected domain and the two singularities $z = \pm 3i$ of the integrand are exterior to the disk.

Corollary 1. *A function f that is analytic throughout a simply connected domain D must have an antiderivative everywhere in D.*

We begin the proof of this corollary with the observation that a function f is continuous on a domain D when it is analytic there. Consequently, since equation (1) holds for the function in the hypothesis of this corollary and for each closed contour C in D, f has an antiderivative throughout D, according to the theorem in Sec. 48.

Corollary 2. *Entire functions always possess antiderivatives.*

This corollary is an immediate consequence of Corollary 1 and the fact that the finite plane is simply connected.

53. MULTIPLY CONNECTED DOMAINS

A domain that is not simply connected (Sec. 52) is said to be ***multiply connected***. The following theorem is an adaptation of the Cauchy–Goursat theorem to multiply connected domains. While the statement of the theorem involves n contours labeled $C_k (k = 1, 2, \ldots, n)$, we shall be guided in the proof by Fig. 62, where $n = 2$.

Theorem. *Suppose that*

(*a*) *C is a simple closed contour, described in the counterclockwise direction;*

(*b*) *C_k $(k = 1, 2, \ldots, n)$ are simple closed contours interior to C, all described in the clockwise direction, that are disjoint and whose interiors have no points in common* (Fig. 62).

If a function f is analytic on all of these contours and throughout the multiply connected domain consisting of the points inside C and exterior to each C_k, then

$$\int_C f(z)\,dz + \sum_{k=1}^{n} \int_{C_k} f(z)\,dz = 0. \tag{1}$$

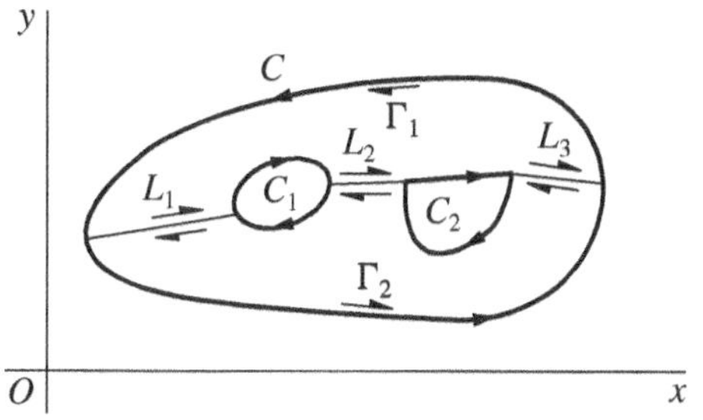

FIGURE 62

Note that in equation (1), the direction of each path of integration is such that the multiply connected domain lies to the *left* of that path.

To prove the theorem, we introduce a polygonal path L_1, consisting of a finite number of line segments joined end to end, to connect the outer contour C to the inner contour C_1. We introduce another polygonal path L_2 which connects C_1 to C_2; and we continue in this manner, with L_{n+1} connecting C_n to C. As indicated by the single-barbed arrows in Fig. 62, two simple closed contours Γ_1 and Γ_2 can be formed, each consisting of polygonal paths L_k or $-L_k$ and pieces of C and C_k and each described in such a direction that the points enclosed by them lie to the left. The Cauchy–Goursat theorem can now be applied to f on Γ_1 and Γ_2, and the sum of the values of the integrals over those contours is found to be zero. Since the integrals in opposite directions along each path L_k cancel, only the integrals along C and the C_k remain; and we arrive at statement (1).

Corollary. *Let C_1 and C_2 denote positively oriented simple closed contours, where C_1 is interior to C_2* (Fig. 63). *If a function f is analytic in the closed region consisting of those contours and all points between them, then*

$$\int_{C_1} f(z)\,dz = \int_{C_2} f(z)\,dz. \tag{2}$$

This corollary is known as the ***principle of deformation of paths*** since it tells us that if C_1 is continuously deformed into C_2, always passing through points at which f is analytic, then the value of f over C_1 never changes. To verify this corollary. we need only observe how it follows from the theorem that

$$\int_{C_2} f(z)\,dz + \int_{-C_1} f(z)\,dz = 0.$$

But this the same as equation (2).

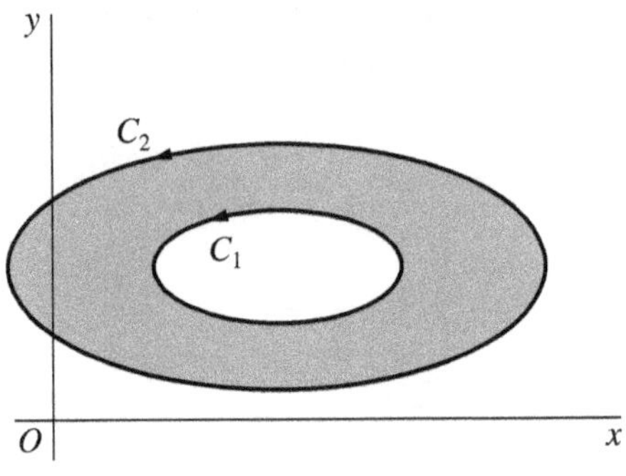

FIGURE 63

EXAMPLE. When C is any positively oriented simple closed contour surrounding the origin, the corollary can be used to show that

$$\int_C \frac{dz}{z} = 2\pi i.$$

This is done by constructing a positively oriented circle C_0 with center at the origin and radius so small that C_0 lies entirely inside C (Fig. 64). Since (see Exercise 13, Sec. 46)

$$\int_{C_0} \frac{dz}{z} = 2\pi i$$

and since $1/z$ is analytic everywhere except at $z = 0$, the desired result follows.

Note that the radius of C_0 could equally well have been so large that C lies entirely inside C_0.

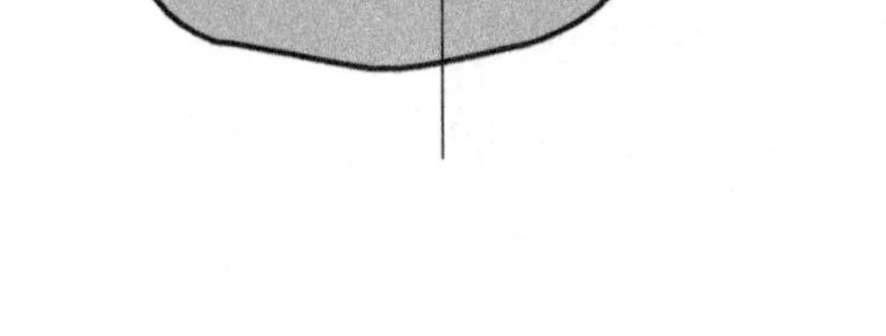

FIGURE 64

EXERCISES

1. Apply the Cauchy–Goursat theorem to show that

$$\int_C f(z)\,dz = 0$$

when the contour C is the unit circle $|z| = 1$, in either direction, and when

(*a*) $f(z) = \dfrac{z^2}{z+3}$; (*b*) $f(z) = z\,e^{-z}$; (*c*) $f(z) = \dfrac{1}{z^2+2z+2}$;

(*d*) $f(z) = \text{sech}\, z$; (*e*) $f(z) = \tan z$; (*f*) $f(z) = \text{Log}(z+2)$.

2. Let C_1 denote the positively oriented boundary of the square whose sides lie along the lines $x = \pm 1$, $y = \pm 1$ and let C_2 be the positively oriented circle $|z| = 4$ (Fig. 65). With the aid of the corollary in Sec. 53, point out why

$$\int_{C_1} f(z)\,dz = \int_{C_2} f(z)\,dz$$

when

(*a*) $f(z) = \dfrac{1}{3z^2+1}$; (*b*) $f(z) = \dfrac{z+2}{\sin(z/2)}$; (*c*) $f(z) = \dfrac{z}{1-e^z}$.

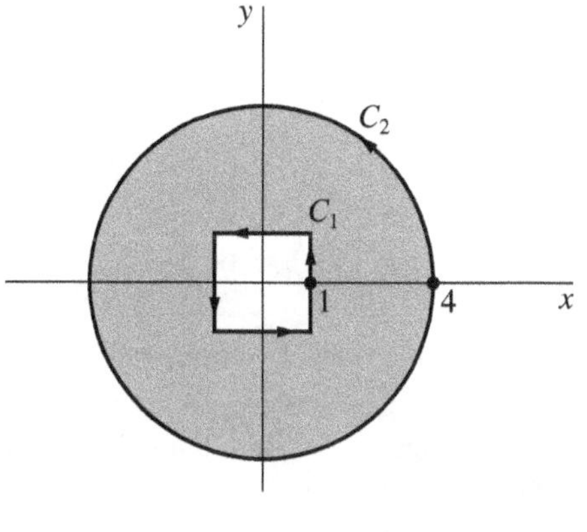

FIGURE 65

3. If C_0 denotes a positively oriented circle $|z - z_0| = R$, then

$$\int_{C_0} (z - z_0)^{n-1}\,dz = \begin{cases} 0 & \text{when } n = \pm 1, \pm 2, \ldots, \\ 2\pi i & \text{when } n = 0, \end{cases}$$

according to Exercise 13, Sec. 46. Use that result and the corollary in Sec. 53 to show that if C is the boundary of the rectangle $0 \le x \le 3$, $0 \le y \le 2$, described in the positive sense, then

$$\int_C (z - 2 - i)^{n-1}\,dz = \begin{cases} 0 & \text{when } n = \pm 1, \pm 2, \ldots, \\ 2\pi i & \text{when } n = 0. \end{cases}$$

4. Use the following method to derive the integration formula

$$\int_0^\infty e^{-x^2} \cos 2bx\,dx = \frac{\sqrt{\pi}}{2} e^{-b^2} \qquad (b > 0).$$

(*a*) Show that the sum of the integrals of e^{-z^2} along the lower and upper horizontal legs of the rectangular path in Fig. 66 can be written

$$2\int_0^a e^{-x^2}\,dx - 2e^{b^2}\int_0^a e^{-x^2}\cos 2bx\,dx$$

and that the sum of the integrals along the vertical legs on the right and left can be written

$$ie^{-a^2}\int_0^b e^{y^2}e^{-i2ay}\,dy - ie^{-a^2}\int_0^b e^{y^2}e^{i2ay}\,dy.$$

Thus, with the aid of the Cauchy–Goursat theorem, show that

$$\int_0^a e^{-x^2}\cos 2bx\,dx = e^{-b^2}\int_0^a e^{-x^2}\,dx + e^{-(a^2+b^2)}\int_0^b e^{y^2}\sin 2ay\,dy.$$

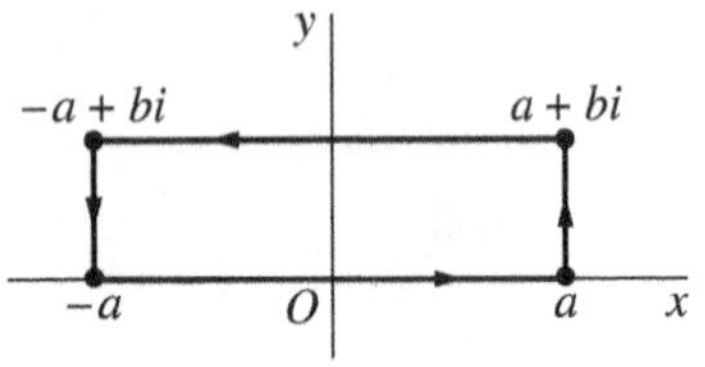

FIGURE 66

(*b*) By accepting the fact that*

$$\int_0^\infty e^{-x^2}\,dx = \frac{\sqrt{\pi}}{2}$$

and observing that

$$\left|\int_0^b e^{y^2}\sin 2ay\,dy\right| \le \int_0^b e^{y^2}\,dy,$$

obtain the desired integration formula by letting a tend to infinity in the equation at the end of part (*a*).

5. According to Exercise 6, Sec. 43, the path C_1 from the origin to the point $z = 1$ along the graph of the function defined by means of the equations

$$y(x) = \begin{cases} x^3\sin(\pi/x) & \text{when } 0 < x \le 1, \\ 0 & \text{when } x = 0 \end{cases}$$

is a smooth arc that intersects the real axis an infinite number of times. Let C_2 denote the line segment along the real axis from $z = 1$ back to the origin, and let C_3 denote any smooth arc from the origin to $z = 1$ that does not intersect itself and has only its end points in common with the arcs C_1 and C_2 (Fig. 67). Apply the Cauchy–Goursat

*The usual way to evaluate this integral is by writing its square as

$$\int_0^\infty e^{-x^2}dx\int_0^\infty e^{-y^2}dy = \int_0^\infty\int_0^\infty e^{-(x^2+y^2)}dxdy$$

and then evaluating this iterated integral by changing to polar coordinates. Details are given in, for example, A. E. Taylor and W. R. Mann, "Advanced Calculus," 3d ed., pp. 680–681, 1983.

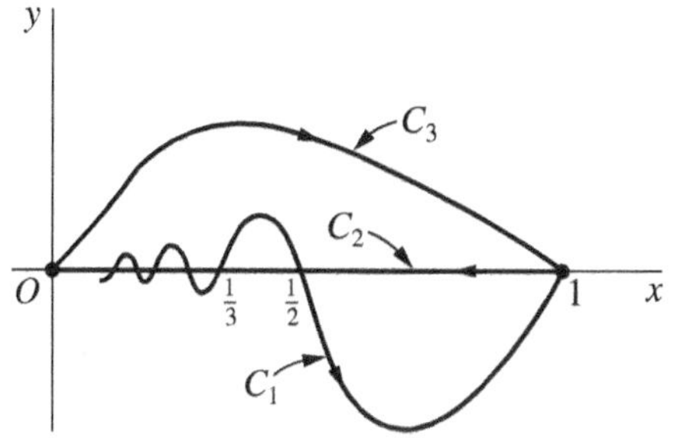

FIGURE 67

theorem to show that if a function f is entire, then

$$\int_{C_1} f(z)\,dz = \int_{C_3} f(z)\,dz \quad \text{and} \quad \int_{C_2} f(z)\,dz = -\int_{C_3} f(z)\,dz.$$

Conclude that even though the closed contour $C = C_1 + C_2$ intersects itself an infinite number of times,

$$\int_C f(z)\,dz = 0.$$

6. Let C denote the positively oriented boundary of the half disk $0 \le r \le 1, 0 \le \theta \le \pi$, and let $f(z)$ be a continuous function defined on that half disk by writing $f(0) = 0$ and using the branch

$$f(z) = \sqrt{r}e^{i\theta/2} \qquad \left(r > 0, -\frac{\pi}{2} < \theta < \frac{3\pi}{2}\right)$$

of the multiple-valued function $z^{1/2}$. Show that

$$\int_C f(z)\,dz = 0$$

by evaluating separately the integrals of $f(z)$ over the semicircle and the two radii which make up C. Why does the Cauchy–Goursat theorem not apply here?

7. Show that if C is a positively oriented simple closed contour, then the area of the region enclosed by C can be written

$$\frac{1}{2i}\int_C \bar{z}\,dz.$$

Suggestion: Note that expression (4), Sec. 50, can be used here even though the function $f(z) = \bar{z}$ is not analytic anywhere [see Example 2, Sec. 19].

8. *Nested Intervals.* An infinite sequence of closed intervals $a_n \le x \le b_n$ $(n = 0, 1, 2, \ldots)$ is formed in the following way. The interval $a_1 \le x \le b_1$ is either the left-hand or right-hand half of the first interval $a_0 \le x \le b_0$, and the interval $a_2 \le x \le b_2$ is then one of the two halves of $a_1 \le x \le b_1$, etc. Prove that there is a point x_0 which belongs to every one of the closed intervals $a_n \le x \le b_n$.

Suggestion: Note that the left-hand end points a_n represent a bounded nondecreasing sequence of numbers, since $a_0 \le a_n \le a_{n+1} < b_0$; hence they have a limit A as n tends to infinity. Show that the end points b_n also have a limit B. Then show that $A = B$, and write $x_0 = A = B$.

9. *Nested Squares.* A square $\sigma_0 : a_0 \le x \le b_0, c_0 \le y \le d_0$ is divided into four equal squares by line segments parallel to the coordinate axes. One of those four smaller squares $\sigma_1 : a_1 \le x \le b_1, c_1 \le y \le d_1$ is selected according to some rule. It, in turn, is divided into four equal squares one of which, called σ_2, is selected, etc. (see Sec. 49). Prove that there is a point (x_0, y_0) which belongs to each of the closed regions of the infinite sequence $\sigma_0, \sigma_1, \sigma_2, \ldots$.

Suggestion: Apply the result in Exercise 8 to each of the sequences of closed intervals $a_n \le x \le b_n$ and $c_n \le y \le d_n$ $(n = 0, 1, 2, \ldots)$.

54. CAUCHY INTEGRAL FORMULA

Another fundamental result will now be established.

Theorem. *Let f be analytic everywhere inside and on a simple closed contour C, taken in the positive sense. If z_0 is any point interior to C, then*

$$f(z_0) = \frac{1}{2\pi i}\int_C \frac{f(z)\,dz}{z - z_0}. \tag{1}$$

Expression (1) is called the ***Cauchy integral formula.*** It tells us that if a function f is to be analytic within and on a simple closed contour C, then the values of f interior to C are completely determined by the values of f *on* C.

We begin the proof of the theorem by letting C_ρ denote a positively oriented circle $|z - z_0| = \rho$, where ρ is small enough that C_ρ is interior to C (see Fig. 68). Since the quotient $f(z)/(z - z_0)$ is analytic between and on the contours C_ρ and C, it follows from the principle of deformation of paths (Sec. 53) that

$$\int_C \frac{f(z)\,dz}{z - z_0} = \int_{C_\rho} \frac{f(z)\,dz}{z - z_0}.$$

This enables us to write

$$\int_C \frac{f(z)\,dz}{z - z_0} - f(z_0)\int_{C_\rho} \frac{dz}{z - z_0} = \int_{C_\rho} \frac{f(z) - f(z_0)}{z - z_0}\,dz. \tag{2}$$

But [see Exercise 13, Sec. 46]

$$\int_{C_\rho} \frac{dz}{z - z_0} = 2\pi i,$$

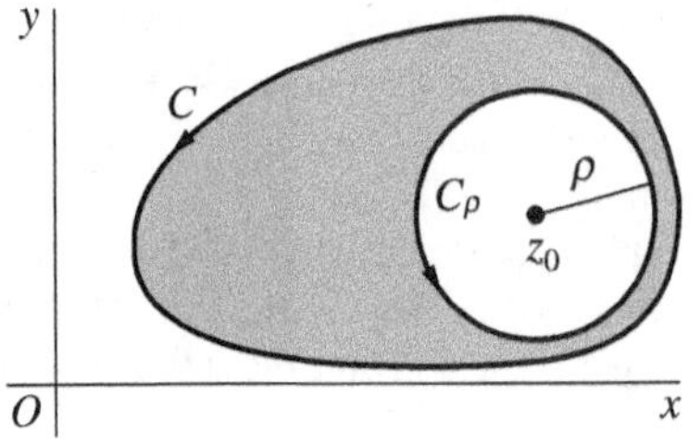

FIGURE 68

and so equation (2) becomes

$$\int_C \frac{f(z)\,dz}{z-z_0} - 2\pi i f(z_0) = \int_{C_\rho} \frac{f(z)-f(z_0)}{z-z_0}\,dz. \tag{3}$$

Now the fact that f is analytic, and therefore continuous, at z_0 ensures that corresponding to each positive number ε, however small, there is a positive number δ such that

$$|f(z)-f(z_0)| < \varepsilon \quad \text{whenever} \quad |z-z_0| < \delta. \tag{4}$$

Let the radius ρ of the circle C_ρ be smaller than the number δ in the second of these inequalities. Since $|z-z_0| = \rho < \delta$ when z is on C_ρ, it follows that the *first* of inequalities (4) holds when z is such a point; and the theorem in Sec. 47, giving upper bounds for the moduli of contour integrals, tells us that

$$\left|\int_{C_\rho} \frac{f(z)-f(z_0)}{z-z_0}\,dz\right| < \frac{\varepsilon}{\rho}\,2\pi\rho = 2\pi\varepsilon.$$

In view of equation (3), then,

$$\left|\int_C \frac{f(z)\,dz}{z-z_0} - 2\pi i f(z_0)\right| < 2\pi\varepsilon.$$

Since the left-hand side of this inequality is a nonnegative constant that is less than an arbitrarily small positive number, it follows that

$$\int_C \frac{f(z)\,dz}{z-z_0} - 2\pi i f(z_0) = 0.$$

Hence equation (1) is valid, and the theorem is proved.

When the Cauchy integral formula is written as

$$\int_C \frac{f(z)\,dz}{z-z_0} = 2\pi i f(z_0), \tag{5}$$

it can be used to evaluate certain integrals along simple closed contours.

EXAMPLE. Let C be the positively oriented circle $|z| = 1$ about the origin. Since the function

$$f(z) = \frac{\cos z}{z^2+9}$$

is analytic inside and on C and since the origin $z_0 = 0$ is interior to C, equation (5) tells us that

$$\int_C \frac{\cos z}{z(z^2+9)}\,dz = \int_C \frac{(\cos z)/(z^2+9)}{z-0}\,dz = 2\pi i f(0) = \frac{2\pi i}{9}.$$

55. AN EXTENSION OF THE CAUCHY INTEGRAL FORMULA

The Cauchy integral formula in the theorem in Sec. 50 can be extended so as to provide an integral representation for derivatives $f^{(n)}(z_0)$ of f at z_0.

Theorem. *Let f be analytic inside and on a simple closed contour C, taken in the positive sense. If z_0 is any point interior to C, then*

$$f^{(n)}(z_0) = \frac{n!}{2\pi i} \int_C \frac{f(z)\,dz}{(z - z_0)^{n+1}} \qquad (n = 0, 1, 2, \ldots), \tag{1}$$

With the agreement that

$$f^{(0)}(z_0) = f(z_0) \quad \text{and} \quad 0! = 1,$$

this theorem includes the Cauchy integral formula

$$f(z_0) = \frac{1}{2\pi i} \int_C \frac{f(z)\,dz}{z - z_0}. \tag{2}$$

Verification of expression (1) will be taken up in Sec. 56.

When written in the form

$$\int_C \frac{f(z)\,dz}{(z - z_0)^{n+1}} = \frac{2\pi i}{n!} f^{(n)}(z_0) \qquad (n = 0, 1, 2, \ldots), \tag{3}$$

expression (1) can be useful in evaluating certain integrals when f is analytic inside and on a simple closed contour C, taken in the positive sense, and z_0 is any point interior to C. It has already been illustrated in Sec. 50 when $n = 0$.

EXAMPLE 1. If C is the positively oriented unit circle $|z| = 1$ and

$$f(z) = \exp(2z),$$

then

$$\int_C \frac{\exp(2z)\,dz}{z^4} = \int_C \frac{f(z)\,dz}{(z - 0)^{3+1}} = \frac{2\pi i}{3!} f'''(0) = \frac{8\pi i}{3}.$$

EXAMPLE 2. Let z_0 be any point interior to a positively oriented simple closed contour C. When $f(z) = 1$, expression (3) shows that

$$\int_C \frac{dz}{z - z_0} = 2\pi i$$

and

$$\int_C \frac{dz}{(z - z_0)^{n+1}} = 0 \qquad (n = 1, 2, \ldots).$$

(Compare with Exercise 13, Sec. 46.)

Expression (1) can also be useful in slightly different notation. Namely, if s denotes points on C and if z is a point interior to C, then

$$f^{(n)}(z) = \frac{n!}{2\pi i}\int_C \frac{f(s)\,ds}{(s-z)^{n+1}} \qquad (n = 0, 1, 2, \ldots), \tag{4}$$

where $f^{(0)}(z) = f(z)$ and, of course, $0! = 1$. Our next example illustrates the use of expression (4) in the form

$$\int_C \frac{f(s)\,ds}{(s-z)^{n+1}} = \frac{2\pi i}{n!} f^{(n)}(z) \qquad (n = 0, 1, 2, \ldots), \tag{5}$$

which includes the special case

$$\int_C \frac{f(s)\,ds}{s-z} = 2\pi i\, f(z). \tag{6}$$

EXAMPLE 3. If n is a nonnegative integer and $f(z) = (z^2 - 1)^n$, expression (4), becomes

$$\frac{d^n}{dz^n}(z^2-1)^n = \frac{n!}{2\pi i}\int_C \frac{(s^2-1)^n ds}{(s-z)^{n+1}} \qquad (n = 0, 1, 2, \ldots), \tag{7}$$

where C is any simple closed contour surrounding z. In view of equation (7), one can write the Legendre polynomial*

$$P_n(z) = \frac{1}{n!2^n}\frac{d^n}{dz^n}(z^2-1)^n \qquad (n = 0, 1, 2, \ldots) \tag{8}$$

as

$$P_n(z) = \frac{1}{2^{n+1}\pi i}\int_C \frac{(s^2-1)^n ds}{(s-z)^{n+1}} \qquad (n = 0, 1, 2, \ldots). \tag{9}$$

Because

$$\frac{(s^2-1)^n}{(s-1)^{n+1}} = \frac{(s-1)^n(s+1)^n}{(s-1)^{n+1}} = \frac{(s+1)^n}{s-1},$$

expression (9) reveals that

$$P_n(1) = \frac{1}{2^{n+1}\pi i}\int_C \frac{(s+1)^n ds}{s-1} \qquad (n = 0, 1, 2, \ \ldots);$$

and by writing $f(s) = (s+1)^n$ and $z = 1$ in equation (6), we arrive at the values

$$P_n(1) = \frac{1}{2^{n+1}\pi i}\, 2\pi i\ (1+1)^n = 1 \qquad (n = 0, 1, 2, \ldots).$$

The values $P_n(-1) = (-1)^n (n = 0, 1, 2, \ldots)$ can be found (Exercise 8, Sec. 57) in a similar way.

*See Exercise 10, Sec. 20, and the footnote with it.

Finally, we note how expression (4) is suggested. If s denotes points on C and z is a point interior to C, the Cauchy integral formula is

$$f(z) = \frac{1}{2\pi i}\int_C \frac{f(s)\,ds}{s-z}. \tag{10}$$

By differentiating formally under this integral sign, without rigorous justification, we find that

$$f'(z) = \frac{1}{2\pi i}\int_C f(s)\frac{\partial}{\partial z}(s-z)^{-1}ds,$$

or

$$f'(z) = \frac{1}{2\pi i}\int_C \frac{f(s)\,ds}{(s-z)^2}.$$

Likewise,

$$f''(z) = \frac{(2)(1)}{2\pi i}\int_C \frac{f(s)\,ds}{(s-z)^{2+1}}$$

and

$$f'''(z) = \frac{(3)(2)(1)}{2\pi i}\int_C \frac{f(s)\,ds}{(s-z)^{3+1}}.$$

These three special cases suggest that expression (4), which is to be verified in Sec. 56, *may* be valid. A reader who wishes to accept expression (4) without verification can easily pass to Sec. 57.

56. VERIFICATION OF THE EXTENSION

We turn now to the verification of the extended Cauchy integral formula that was introduced in Sec. 55. Specifically, we consider a function f that is analytic inside and on a simple closed contour C, taken in the positive sense, and we let z be any point interior to C. We begin with statement (10), Sec. 55, of the Cauchy integral formula:

$$f(z) = \frac{1}{2\pi i}\int_C \frac{f(s)\,ds}{s-z}. \tag{1}$$

In order to verify that $f'(z)$ exists and that the expression

$$f'(z) = \frac{1}{2\pi i}\int_C \frac{f(s)\,ds}{(s-z)^2} \tag{2}$$

in Sec. 55 is valid, we let d denote the smallest distance from z to points s on C and assume that $0 < |\Delta z| < d$ (see Fig. 69). It then follows from expression (1) that

$$\frac{f(z+\Delta z)-f(z)}{\Delta z} = \frac{1}{2\pi i}\int_C \left(\frac{1}{s-z-\Delta z} - \frac{1}{s-z}\right)\frac{f(s)}{\Delta z}ds.$$

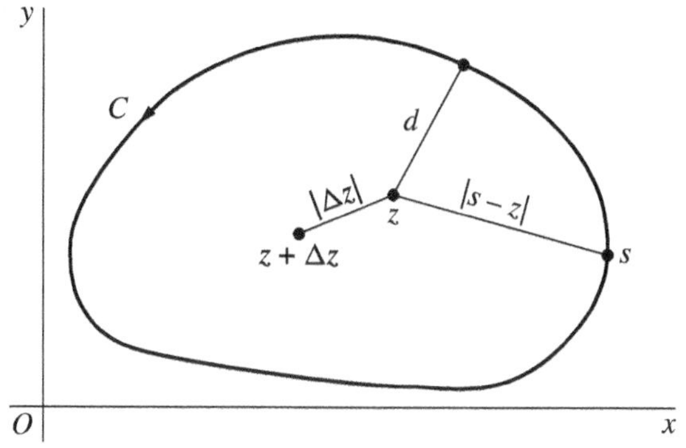

FIGURE 69

Evidently, then,

$$\frac{f(z+\Delta z)-f(z)}{\Delta z}=\frac{1}{2\pi i}\int_C \frac{f(s)\,ds}{(s-z-\Delta z)\,(s-z)}.$$

But

$$\frac{1}{(s-z-\Delta z)\,(s-z)}=\frac{1}{(s-z)^2}+\frac{\Delta z}{(s-z-\Delta z)\,(s-z)^2},$$

and this means that

$$(3)\qquad \frac{f(z+\Delta z)-f(z)}{\Delta z}-\frac{1}{2\pi i}\int_C \frac{f(s)\,ds}{(s-z)^2}=\frac{1}{2\pi i}\int_C \frac{\Delta z f(s)\,ds}{(s-z-\Delta z)(s-z)^2}.$$

Next, we let M denote the maximum value of $|f(s)|$ on C and observe that since $|s-z|\ge d$ and $|\Delta z|<d$,

$$|s-z-\Delta z|=|(s-z)-\Delta z|\ge ||s-z|-|\Delta z||\ge d-|\Delta z|>0.$$

Thus

$$\left|\int_C \frac{\Delta z\, f(s)\,ds}{(s-z-\Delta z)(s-z)^2}\right|\le \frac{|\Delta z|M}{(d-|\Delta z|)d^2}L,$$

where L is the length of C. Upon letting Δz tend to zero, we find from this inequality that the right-hand side of equation (3) also tends to zero. Consequently,

$$\lim_{\Delta z\to 0}\frac{f(z+\Delta z)-f(z)}{\Delta z}-\frac{1}{2\pi i}\int_C \frac{f(s)\,ds}{(s-z)^2}=0;$$

and the desired expression for $f'(z)$ is established.

The same technique can be used to verify the expression

$$(4)\qquad f''(z)=\frac{1}{\pi i}\int_C \frac{f(s)\,ds}{(s-z)^3}.$$

The details, which are outlined in Exercise 9, Sec. 57, are left to the reader. Mathematical induction can, moreover, be used to obtain the formula

$$f^{(n)}(z) = \frac{n!}{2\pi i} \int_C \frac{f(s)\,ds}{(s-z)^{n+1}} \qquad (n = 1, 2, \ldots). \tag{5}$$

The verification is considerably more involved than for just $n = 1$ and $n = 2$, and we refer the interested reader to other texts for it.* As already pointed out in Sec. 55, expression (5) is also valid when $n = 0$, in which case it is simply the Cauchy integral formula.

57. SOME CONSEQUENCES OF THE EXTENSION

We turn now to some important consequences of the extension of the Cauchy integral formula in Sec. 55.

Theorem 1. *If a function f is analytic at a given point, then its derivatives of all orders are analytic there too.*

To prove this remarkable theorem, we assume that a function f is analytic at a point z_0. There must, then, be a neighborhood $|z - z_0| < \varepsilon$ of z_0 throughout which f is analytic (see Sec. 25). Consequently, there is a positively oriented circle C_0, centered at z_0 and with radius $\varepsilon/2$, such that f is analytic inside and on C_0 (Fig. 70). From expression (4), Sec. 55, we know that

$$f''(z) = \frac{1}{\pi i} \int_{C_0} \frac{f(s)\,ds}{(s-z)^3}$$

at each point z interior to C_0, and the existence of $f''(z)$ throughout the neighborhood $|z - z_0| < \varepsilon/2$ means that f' is analytic at z_0. One can apply the same argument to the analytic function f' to conclude that its derivative f'' is analytic, etc. Theorem 1 is now established.

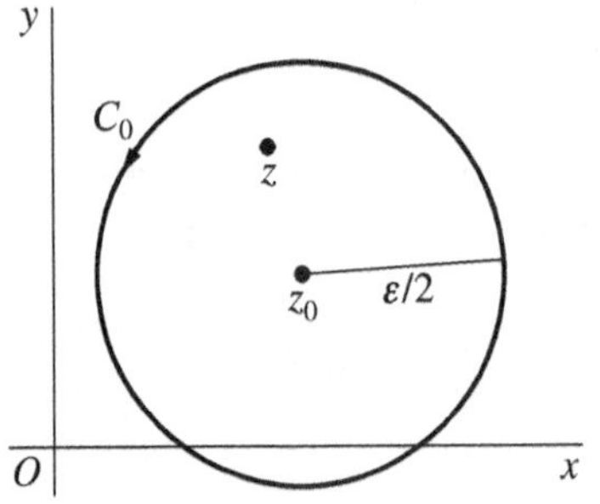

FIGURE 70

*See, for example, pp. 299–301 in Vol. I of the book by Markushevich, cited in Appendix 1.

As a consequence, when a function

$$f(z) = u(x, y) + iv(x, y)$$

is analytic at a point $z = (x, y)$, the differentiability of f' ensures the continuity of f' there (Sec. 19). Then, since (Sec. 21)

$$f'(z) = u_x + iv_x = v_y - iu_y,$$

we may conclude that the first-order partial derivatives of u and v are continuous at that point. Furthermore, since f'' is analytic and continuous at z and since

$$f''(z) = u_{xx} + iv_{xx} = v_{yx} - iu_{yx},$$

etc., we arrive at a corollary that was anticipated in Sec. 27, where harmonic functions were introduced.

Corollary. *If a function* $f(z) = u(x, y) + iv(x, y)$ *is analytic at a point* $z = (x, y)$, *then the component functions* u *and* v *have continuous partial derivatives of all orders at that point.*

The proof of the next theorem, due to E. Morera (1856–1909), depends on the fact that the derivative of an analytic function is itself analytic, as stated in Theorem 1.

Theorem 2. *Let* f *be continuous on a domain* D. *If*

$$\int_C f(z)\,dz = 0 \tag{1}$$

for every closed contour C *in* D, *then* f *is analytic throughout* D.

In particular, when D is *simply connected*, we have for the class of continuous functions defined on D the converse of the theorem in Sec. 52, which is the adaptation of the Cauchy–Goursat theorem to such domains.

To prove Theorem 2, we observe that when its hypothesis is satisfied, the theorem in Sec. 48 ensures that f has an antiderivative in D; that is, there exists an analytic function F such that $F'(z) = f(z)$ at each point in D. Since f is the derivative of F, it then follows from Theorem 1 that f is analytic in D.

Our final theorem here will be essential in the next section.

Theorem 3. *Suppose that a function* f *is analytic inside and on a positively oriented circle* C_R, *centered at* z_0 *and with radius* R (Fig. 71). *If* M_R *denotes the*

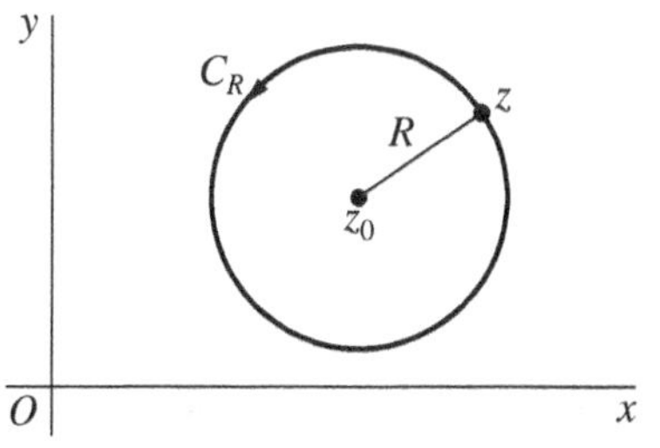

FIGURE 71

maximum value of $|f(z)|$ *on* C_R*, then*

$$(2) \qquad |f^{(n)}(z_0)| \le \frac{n!M_R}{R^n} \quad (n = 1, 2, \ldots).$$

Inequality (2) is called ***Cauchy's inequality*** and is an immediate consequence of the expression

$$f^{(n)}(z_0) = \frac{n!}{2\pi i}\int_{C_R} \frac{f(z)\,dz}{(z - z_0)^{n+1}} \quad (n = 1, 2, \ldots),$$

in the theorem in Sec. 55 when n is a positive integer. We need only apply the theorem in Sec. 47, which gives upper bounds for the moduli of the values of contour integrals, to see that

$$|f^{(n)}(z_0)| \le \frac{n!}{2\pi}\cdot\frac{M_R}{R^{n+1}}2\pi R \quad (n = 1, 2, \ldots),$$

where M_R is as in the statement of Theorem 3. This inequality is, of course, the same as inequality (2).

EXERCISES

1. Let C denote the positively oriented boundary of the square whose sides lie along the lines $x = \pm 2$ and $y = \pm 2$. Evaluate each of these integrals:

$(a)\ \displaystyle\int_C \frac{e^{-z}\,dz}{z - (\pi i/2)}$; $\quad (b)\ \displaystyle\int_C \frac{\cos z}{z(z^2 + 8)}\,dz$; $\quad (c)\ \displaystyle\int_C \frac{z\,dz}{2z + 1}$;

$(d)\ \displaystyle\int_C \frac{\cosh z}{z^4}\,dz$; $\quad (e)\ \displaystyle\int_C \frac{\tan(z/2)}{(z - x_0)^2}\,dz \quad (-2 < x_0 < 2)$.

Ans. $(a)\ 2\pi$; $(b)\ \pi i/4$; $(c)\ -\pi i/2$; $(d)\ 0$; $(e)\ i\pi \sec^2(x_0/2)$.

2. Find the value of the integral of $g(z)$ around the circle $|z - i| = 2$ in the positive sense when

$(a)\ g(z) = \dfrac{1}{z^2 + 4}$; $\quad (b)\ g(z) = \dfrac{1}{(z^2 + 4)^2}$.

Ans. $(a)\ \pi/2$; $(b)\ \pi/16$.

3. Let C be the circle $|z| = 3$, described in the positive sense. Show that if

$$g(z) = \int_C \frac{2s^2 - s - 2}{s - z}\,ds \qquad (|z| \ne 3),$$

then $g(2) = 8\pi i$. What is the value of $g(z)$ when $|z| > 3$?

4. Let C be any simple closed contour, described in the positive sense in the z plane, and write

$$g(z) = \int_C \frac{s^3 + 2s}{(s - z)^3}\,ds.$$

Show that $g(z) = 6\pi i z$ when z is inside C and that $g(z) = 0$ when z is outside.

5. Show that if f is analytic within and on a simple closed contour C and z_0 is not on C, then

$$\int_C \frac{f'(z)\,dz}{z - z_0} = \int_C \frac{f(z)\,dz}{(z - z_0)^2}.$$

6. Let f denote a function that is *continuous* on a simple closed contour C. Following the procedure used in Sec. 56, prove that the function

$$g(z) = \frac{1}{2\pi i}\int_C \frac{f(s)\,ds}{s - z}$$

is *analytic* at each point z interior to C and that

$$g'(z) = \frac{1}{2\pi i}\int_C \frac{f(s)\,ds}{(s - z)^2}$$

at such a point.

7. Let C be the unit circle $z = e^{i\theta}\,(-\pi \le \theta \le \pi)$. First show that for any real constant a,

$$\int_C \frac{e^{az}}{z}\,dz = 2\pi i.$$

Then write this integral in terms of θ to derive the integration formula

$$\int_0^{\pi} e^{a\cos\theta}\cos(a\sin\theta)\,d\theta = \pi.$$

8. Show that $P_n(-1) = (-1)^n\,(n = 0, 1, 2, \ldots)$, where $P_n(z)$ are the Legendre polynomials in Example 3, Sec. 55.

Suggestion: Note that

$$\frac{(s^2 - 1)^n}{(s + 1)^{n+1}} = \frac{(s - 1)^n}{s + 1}.$$

9. Follow the steps below to verify the expression

$$f''(z) = \frac{1}{\pi i}\int_C \frac{f(s)\,ds}{(s - z)^3}$$

in Sec. 56.

(*a*) Use expression (2) in Sec. 56 for $f'(z)$ to show that

$$\frac{f'(z + \Delta z) - f'(z)}{\Delta z} - \frac{1}{\pi i}\int_C \frac{f(s)\,ds}{(s - z)^3} = \frac{1}{2\pi i}\int_C \frac{3(s - z)\Delta z - 2(\Delta z)^2}{(s - z - \Delta z)^2(s - z)^3}\,f(s)\,ds.$$

(*b*) Let D and d denote the largest and smallest distances, respectively, from z to points on C. Also, let M be the maximum value of $|f(s)|$ on C and L the length of C. With the aid of the triangle inequality and by referring to the derivation of expression (2) in Sec. 56 for $f'(z)$, show that when $0 < |\Delta z| < d$, the value of the integral on the right-hand side in part *(a)* is bounded from above by

$$\frac{(3D|\Delta z| + 2|\Delta z|^2)M}{(d - |\Delta z|)^2 d^3}L.$$

(*c*) Use the results in parts (*a*) and (*b*) to obtain the desired expression for $f''(z)$.

10. Let f be an entire function such that $|f(z)| \le A|z|$ for all z, where A is a fixed positive number. Show that $f(z) = a_1 z$, where a_1 is a complex constant.

Suggestion: Use Cauchy's inequality (Sec. 57) to show that the second derivative $f''(z)$ is zero everywhere in the plane. Note that the constant M_R in Cauchy's inequality is less than or equal to $A(|z_0| + R)$.

58. LIOUVILLE'S THEOREM AND THE FUNDAMENTAL THEOREM OF ALGEBRA

Cauchy's inequality in Theorem 3 of Sec. 57 can be used to show that no entire function except a constant is bounded in the complex plane. Our first theorem here, which is known as ***Liouville's theorem***, states this result in a slightly different way.

Theorem 1. *If a function f is entire and bounded in the complex plane, then $f(z)$ is constant throughout the plane.*

To start the proof, we assume that f is as stated and note that since f is entire, Theorem 3 in Sec. 57 can be applied with any choice of z_0 and R. In particular, Cauchy's inequality (2) in that theorem tells us that when $n = 1$,

$$|f'(z_0)| \le \frac{M_R}{R}. \tag{1}$$

Moreover, the boundedness condition on f tells us that a nonnegative constant M exists such that $|f(z)| \le M$ for all z; and, because the constant M_R in inequality (1) is always less than or equal to M, it follows that

$$|f'(z_0)| \le \frac{M}{R}, \tag{2}$$

where R can be arbitrarily large. Now the number M in inequality (2) is independent of the value of R that is taken. Hence that inequality holds for arbitrarily large values of R only if $f'(z_0) = 0$. Since the choice of z_0 was arbitrary, this means that $f'(z) = 0$ everywhere in the complex plane. Consequently, f is a constant function, according to the theorem in Sec. 25.

The following theorem is called the ***fundamental theorem of algebra*** and follows readily from Liouville's theorem.

Theorem 2. *Any polynomial*

$$P(z) = a_0 + a_1 z + a_2 z^2 + \cdots + a_n z^n \qquad (a_n \ne 0)$$

of degree n $(n \ge 1)$ has at least one zero. That is, there exists at least one point z_0 such that $P(z_0) = 0$.

The proof here is by contradiction. Suppose that $P(z)$ is *not* zero for any value of z. Then the quotient $1/P(z)$ is clearly entire. It is also bounded in the complex plane.

To see that it is bounded, we first recall statement (6) in Sec. 5. Namely, there is a positive number R such that

$$\left|\frac{1}{P(z)}\right| < \frac{2}{|a_n|R^n} \quad \text{whenever } |z| > R.$$

So $1/P(z)$ is bounded in the region *exterior to* the disk $|z| \le R$. But $1/P(z)$ is continuous on that closed disk, and this means that $1/P(z)$ is bounded there too (Sec. 18). Hence $1/P(z)$ is bounded in the entire plane.

It now follows from Liouville's theorem that $1/P(z)$, and consequently $P(z)$, is constant. But $P(z)$ is not constant, and we have reached a contradiction.*

The fundamental theorem tells us that any polynomial $P(z)$ of degree n ($n \ge 1$) can be expressed as a product of linear factors:

$$P(z) = c(z - z_1)(z - z_2)\cdots(z - z_n), \tag{3}$$

where c and z_k ($k = 1, 2, \ldots, n$) are complex constants. More precisely, the theorem ensures that $P(z)$ has a zero z_1. Then, according to Exercise 8, Sec. 59,

$$P(z) = (z - z_1)Q_1(z),$$

where $Q_1(z)$ is a polynomial of degree $n - 1$. The same argument, applied to $Q_1(z)$, reveals that there is a number z_2 such that

$$P(z) = (z - z_1)(z - z_2)Q_2(z),$$

where $Q_2(z)$ is a polynomial of degree $n - 2$. Continuing in this way, we arrive at expression (3). Some of the constants z_k in expression (3) may, of course, appear more than once, but it is clear that $P(z)$ can have no more than n *distinct* zeros.

59. MAXIMUM MODULUS PRINCIPLE

In this section, we derive an important result involving maximum values of the moduli of analytic functions. We begin with a needed lemma.

Lemma. *Suppose that $|f(z)| \le |f(z_0)|$ at each point z in some neighborhood $|z - z_0| < \varepsilon$ in which f is analytic. Then $f(z)$ has the constant value $f(z_0)$ throughout that neighborhood.*

To prove this, we assume that f satisfies the stated conditions and let z_1 be any point other than z_0 in the given neighborhood. We then let ρ be the distance between z_1 and z_0. If C_ρ denotes the positively oriented circle $|z - z_0| = \rho$, centered at z_0 and

*For an interesting proof of the fundamental theorem of algebra using the Cauchy–Goursat theorem, see R. P. Boas, Jr., *Amer. Math. Monthly*, Vol. 71, No. 2, p. 180, 1964.

passing through z_1 (Fig. 72), the Cauchy integral formula tells us that

$$f(z_0) = \frac{1}{2\pi i} \int_{C_\rho} \frac{f(z)\,dz}{z - z_0}; \tag{1}$$

and the parametric representation

$$z = z_0 + \rho e^{i\theta} \qquad (0 \le \theta \le 2\pi)$$

for C_ρ enables us to write equation (1) as

$$f(z_0) = \frac{1}{2\pi} \int_0^{2\pi} f(z_0 + \rho e^{i\theta})\,d\theta. \tag{2}$$

We note from expression (2) that when a function is analytic within and on a given circle, its value at the center is the arithmetic mean of its values on the circle. This result is called ***Gauss's mean value theorem***.

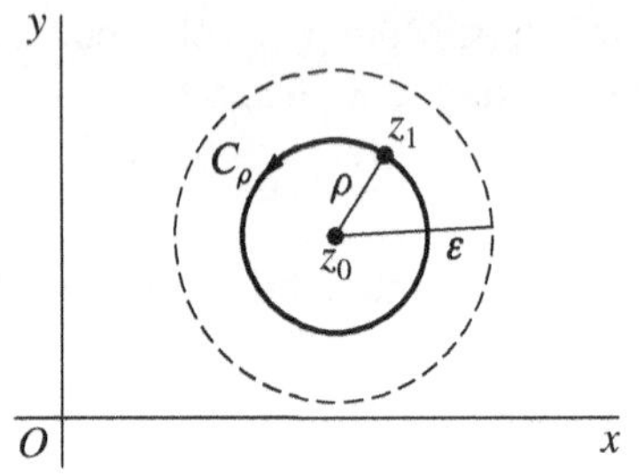

FIGURE 72

From equation (2), we obtain the inequality

$$|f(z_0)| \le \frac{1}{2\pi} \int_0^{2\pi} |f(z_0 + \rho e^{i\theta})|\,d\theta. \tag{3}$$

On the other hand, since

$$|f(z_0 + \rho e^{i\theta})| \le |f(z_0)| \qquad (0 \le \theta \le 2\pi), \tag{4}$$

we find that

$$\int_0^{2\pi} |f(z_0 + \rho e^{i\theta})|\,d\theta \le \int_0^{2\pi} |f(z_0)|\,d\theta = 2\pi |f(z_0)|.$$

Thus

$$|f(z_0)| \ge \frac{1}{2\pi} \int_0^{2\pi} |f(z_0 + \rho e^{i\theta})|\,d\theta. \tag{5}$$

It is now evident from inequalities (3) and (5) that

$$|f(z_0)| = \frac{1}{2\pi} \int_0^{2\pi} |f(z_0 + \rho e^{i\theta})|\,d\theta,$$

or

$$\int_0^{2\pi} [|f(z_0)| - |f(z_0 + \rho e^{i\theta})|]\,d\theta = 0.$$

The integrand in this last integral is continuous in the variable θ; and, in view of condition (4), it is greater than or equal to zero on the entire interval $0 \le \theta \le 2\pi$. Because the value of the integral is zero, then, the integrand must be identically equal to zero. That is,

$$(6) \qquad |f(z_0 + \rho e^{i\theta})| = |f(z_0)| \qquad (0 \le \theta \le 2\pi).$$

This shows that $|f(z)| = |f(z_0)|$ *for all points* z *on the circle* $|z - z_0| = \rho$.

Finally, since z_1 is any point in the deleted neighborhood $0 < |z - z_0| < \varepsilon$, we see that the equation $|f(z)| = |f(z_0)|$ is, in fact, satisfied by all points z lying on any circle $|z - z_0| = \rho$, where $0 < \rho < \varepsilon$. Consequently, $|f(z)| = |f(z_0)|$ everywhere in the neighborhood $|z - z_0| < \varepsilon$. But we know from Example 4. Sec. 26, that when the modulus of an analytic function is constant in a domain, the function itself is constant there. Thus $f(z) = f(z_0)$ for each point z in the neighborhood, and the proof of the lemma is complete.

This lemma can be used to prove the following theorem, which is known as the ***maximum modulus principle.***

Theorem. *If a function f is analytic and not constant in a given domain D, then $|f(z)|$ has no maximum value in D. That is, there is no point z_0 in the domain such that $|f(z)| \le |f(z_0)|$ for all points z in it.*

Given that f is analytic in D, we shall prove the theorem by assuming that $|f(z)|$ *does* have a maximum value at some point z_0 in D and then showing that $f(z)$ must be constant throughout D.

The general approach here is similar to that taken in the proof of the lemma in Sec. 28. We draw a polygonal line L lying in D and extending from z_0 to any other point P in D. Also, d represents the shortest distance from points on L to the boundary of D. When D is the entire plane, d may have any positive value. Next, we observe that there is a finite sequence of points

$$z_0, z_1, z_2, \ldots, z_{n-1}, z_n$$

along L such that z_n coincides with the point P and

$$|z_k - z_{k-1}| < d \qquad (k = 1, 2, \ldots, n).$$

In forming a finite sequence of neighborhoods (Fig. 73)

$$N_0, N_1, N_2, \ldots, N_{n-1}, N_n$$

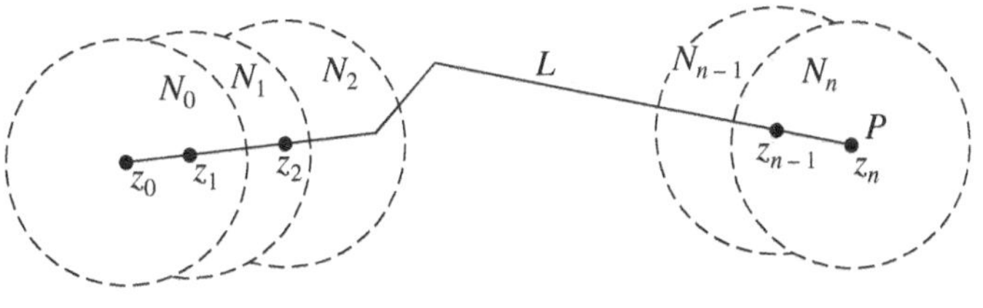

FIGURE 73

where each N_k has center z_k and radius d, we see that f is analytic in each of these neighborhoods, which are all contained in D, and that the center of each neighborhood N_k $(k = 1, 2, \ldots, n)$ lies in the neighborhood N_{k-1}.

Since $|f(z)|$ was assumed to have a maximum value in D at z_0, it also has a maximum value in N_0 at that point. Hence, according to the preceding lemma, $f(z)$ has the constant value $f(z_0)$ throughout N_0. In particular, $f(z_1) = f(z_0)$. This means that $|f(z)| \leq |f(z_1)|$ for each point z in N_1; and the lemma can be applied again, this time telling us that

$$f(z) = f(z_1) = f(z_0)$$

when z is in N_1. Since z_2 is in N_1, then, $f(z_2) = f(z_0)$. Hence $|f(z)| \leq |f(z_2)|$ when z is in N_2; and the lemma is once again applicable, showing that

$$f(z) = f(z_2) = f(z_0)$$

when z is in N_2. Continuing in this manner, we eventually reach the neighborhood N_n and arrive at the fact that $f(z_n) = f(z_0)$.

Recalling that z_n coincides with the point P, which is any point other than z_0 in D, we may conclude that $f(z) = f(z_0)$ for *every* point z in D. Inasmuch as $f(z)$ has now been shown to be constant throughout D, the theorem is proved.

If a function f that is analytic at each point in the interior of a closed bounded region R is also continuous throughout R, then the modulus $|f(z)|$ has a maximum value somewhere in R (Sec. 18). That is, there exists a nonnegative constant M such that $|f(z)| \leq M$ for all points z in R, and equality holds for at least one such point. If f is a constant function, then $|f(z)| = M$ for all z in R. If, however, $f(z)$ is not constant, then, according to the theorem just proved, $|f(z)| \neq M$ for any point z in the interior of R. We thus arrive at an important corollary.

Corollary. *Suppose that a function f is continuous on a closed bounded region R and that it is analytic and not constant in the interior of R. Then the maximum value of $|f(z)|$ in R, which is always reached, occurs somewhere on the boundary of R and never in the interior.*

When the function f in the corollary is written $f(z) = u(x, y) + iv(x, y)$, *the component function $u(x, y)$ also has a maximum value in R which is assumed on the boundary of R and never in the interior*, where it is harmonic (Sec. 27). This is because the composite function $g(z) = \exp[f(z)]$ is continuous in R and analytic and not constant in the interior. Hence its modulus $|g(z)| = \exp[u(x, y)]$, which is continuous in R, must assume its maximum value in R on the boundary. In view of the increasing nature of the exponential function, it follows that the maximum value of $u(x, y)$ also occurs on the boundary.

Properties of *minimum* values of $|f(z)|$ and $u(x, y)$ are similar and treated in the exercises.

EXAMPLE. Consider the function $f(z) = (z+1)^2$ defined on the closed triangular region R with vertices at the points

$$z = 0, \quad z = 2, \quad \text{and} \quad z = i.$$

A simple geometric argument can be used to locate points in R at which the modulus $|f(z)|$ has its maximum and minimum values. The argument is based on the interpretation of $|f(z)|$ as the square of the distance d between -1 and any point z in R:

$$d^2 = |f(z)| = |z - (-1)|^2.$$

As one can see in Fig. 74, the maximum and minimum values of d, and therefore $|f(z)|$, occur at boundary points, namely $z = 2$ and $z = 0$, respectively.

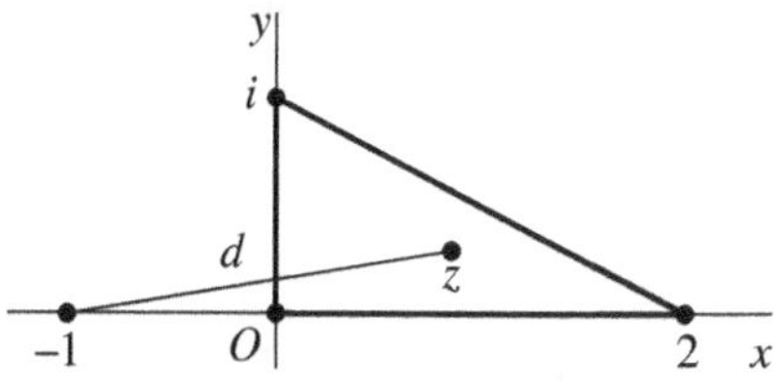

FIGURE 74

EXERCISES

1. Suppose that $f(z)$ is entire and that the harmonic function $u(x, y) = \text{Re}[f(z)]$ has an upper bound u_0; that is, $u(x, y) \le u_0$ for all points (x, y) in the xy plane. Show that $u(x, y)$ must be constant throughout the plane.

   Suggestion: Apply Liouville's theorem (Sec. 58) to the function $g(z) = \exp[f(z)]$.

2. Let a function f be continuous on a closed bounded region R, and let it be analytic and not constant throughout the interior of R. Assuming that $f(z) \ne 0$ anywhere in R, prove that $|f(z)|$ has a *minimum value m* in R which occurs on the boundary of R and never in the interior. Do this by applying the corresponding result for maximum values (Sec. 59) to the function $g(z) = 1/f(z)$.

3. Use the function $f(z) = z$ to show that in Exercise 2 the condition $f(z) \ne 0$ anywhere in R is necessary in order to obtain the result of that exercise. That is, show that $|f(z)|$ *can* reach its minimum value at an interior point when the minimum value is zero.

4. Let R region $0 \le x \le \pi, 0 \le y \le 1$ (Fig. 75). Show that the modulus of the entire function $f(z) = \sin z$ has a maximum value in R at the boundary point $z = (\pi/2) + i$.

   Suggestion: Write $|f(z)|^2 = \sin^2 x + \sinh^2 y$ (see Sec. 37) and locate points in R at which $\sin^2 x$ and $\sinh^2 y$ are the largest.

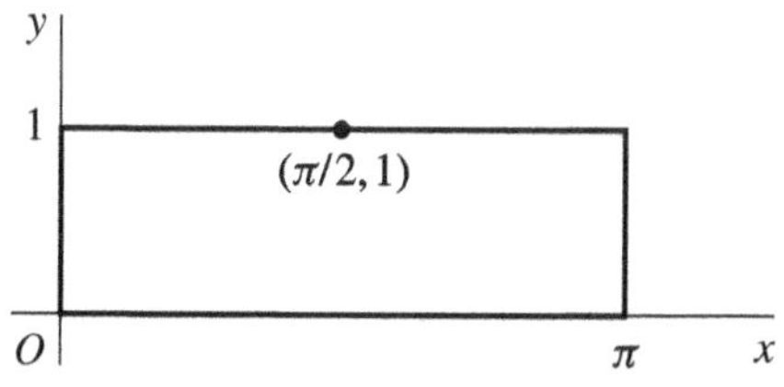

FIGURE 75

5. Let $f(z) = u(x, y) + iv(x, y)$ be a function that is continuous on a closed bounded region R and analytic and not constant throughout the interior of R. Prove that the component function $u(x, y)$ has a minimum value in R which occurs on the boundary of R and never in the interior. (See Exercise 2.)

6. Let f be the function $f(z) = e^z$ and R the rectangular region $0 \leq x \leq 1, 0 \leq y \leq \pi$. Illustrate results in Sec. 59 and Exercise 5 by finding points in R where the component function $u(x, y) = \text{Re}[f(z)]$ reaches its maximum and minimum values.

Ans. $z = 1, z = 1 + \pi i$.

7. Let the function $f(z) = u(x, y) + iv(x, y)$ be continuous on a closed bounded region R, and suppose that it is analytic and not constant in the interior of R. Show that the component function $v(x, y)$ has maximum and minimum values in R which are reached on the boundary of R and never in the interior, where it is harmonic.

Suggestion: Apply results in Sec. 59 and Exercise 5 to the function $g(z) = -if(z)$.

8. Let z_0 be a zero of the polynomial

$$P(z) = a_0 + a_1 z + a_2 z^2 + \cdots + a_n z^n \qquad (a_n \neq 0)$$

of degree n $(n \geq 1)$. Show in the following way that

$$P(z) = (z - z_0)Q(z)$$

where $Q(z)$ is a polynomial of degree $n - 1$.

(*a*) Verify that

$$z^k - z_0^k = (z - z_0)(z^{k-1} + z^{k-2}z_0 + \cdots + z\, z_0^{k-2} + z_0^{k-1}) \qquad (k = 2, 3, \ldots).$$

(*b*) Use the factorization in part (*a*) to show that

$$P(z) - P(z_0) = (z - z_0)Q(z)$$

where $Q(z)$ is a polynomial of degree $n - 1$, and deduce the desired result from this.

CHAPTER 5

SERIES

This chapter is devoted mainly to series representations of analytic functions. We present theorems that guarantee the existence of such representations, and we develop some facility in manipulating series.

60. CONVERGENCE OF SEQUENCES

An infinite ***sequence*** $z_1, z_2, \ldots, z_n, \ldots$ of complex numbers has a ***limit*** z if, for each positive number ε, there exists a positive integer n_0 such that

(1) $$|z_n - z| < \varepsilon \quad \text{whenever} \quad n > n_0.$$

Geometrically, this means that for sufficiently large values of n, the points z_n lie in any given ε neighborhood of z (Fig. 76). Since we can choose ε as small as we please, it follows that the points z_n become arbitrarily close to z as their subscripts increase. Note that the value of n_0 that is needed will, in general, depend on the value of ε.

A sequence can have at most one limit. That is, a limit z is unique if it exists (Exercise 5, Sec. 61). When the limit z exists, the sequence is said to ***converge*** to z, and we write

(2) $$\lim_{n\to\infty} z_n = z.$$

If a sequence has no limit, it ***diverges***.

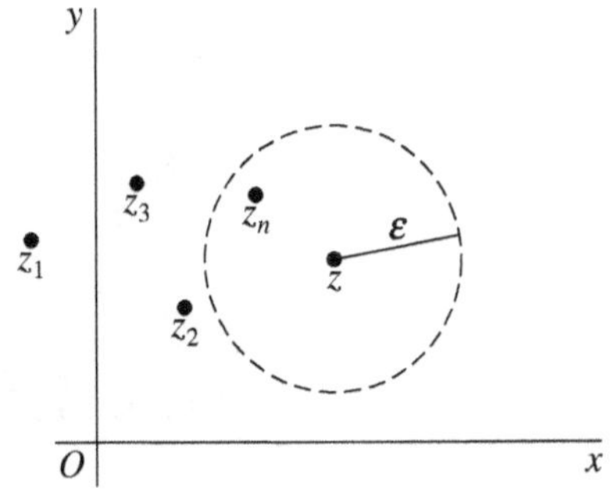

FIGURE 76

Theorem. *Suppose that* $z_n = x_n + iy_n$ $(n = 1, 2, \ldots)$ *and* $z = x + iy$. *Then*

$$\lim_{n\to\infty} z_n = z \tag{3}$$

if and only if

$$\lim_{n\to\infty} x_n = x \quad \textit{and} \quad \lim_{n\to\infty} y_n = y. \tag{4}$$

To prove this theorem, we first assume that conditions (4) hold and obtain condition (3) from it. According to conditions (4), there exist, for each positive number ε, positive integers n_1 and n_2 such that

$$|x_n - x| < \frac{\varepsilon}{2} \quad \text{whenever} \quad n > n_1$$

and

$$|y_n - y| < \frac{\varepsilon}{2} \quad \text{whenever} \quad n > n_2.$$

Hence if n_0 is the larger of the two integers n_1 and n_2,

$$|x_n - x| < \frac{\varepsilon}{2} \quad \text{and} \quad |y_n - y| < \frac{\varepsilon}{2} \quad \text{whenever} \quad n > n_0.$$

Since

$$|(x_n + iy_n) - (x + iy)| = |(x_n - x) + i(y_n - y)| \le |x_n - x| + |y_n - y|,$$

then,

$$|z_n - z| < \frac{\varepsilon}{2} + \frac{\varepsilon}{2} = \varepsilon \quad \text{whenever} \quad n > n_0.$$

Condition (3) thus holds.

Conversely, if we start with condition (3), we know that for each positive number ε, there exists a positive integer n_0 such that

$$|(x_n + iy_n) - (x + iy)| < \varepsilon \quad \text{whenever} \quad n > n_0.$$

But

$$|x_n - x| \le |(x_n - x) + i(y_n - y)| = |(x_n + iy_n) - (x + iy)|$$

and

$$|y_n - y| \le |(x_n - x) + i(y_n - y)| = |(x_n + iy_n) - (x + iy)|;$$

and this means that

$$|x_n - x| < \varepsilon \quad \text{and} \quad |y_n - y| < \varepsilon \quad \text{whenever} \quad n > n_0.$$

That is, conditions (4) are satisfied.

Note how the theorem enables us to write

$$\lim_{n\to\infty}(x_n + iy_n) = \lim_{n\to\infty} x_n + i \lim_{n\to\infty} y_n$$

whenever we know that both limits on the right exist or that the one on the left exists.

EXAMPLE 1. The sequence

$$z_n = -1 + i\frac{(-1)^n}{n^2} \qquad (n = 1, 2, \ldots)$$

converges to -1 since

$$\lim_{n\to\infty}\left[-1 + i\frac{(-1)^n}{n^2}\right] = \lim_{n\to\infty}(-1) + i\lim_{n\to\infty}\frac{(-1)^n}{n^2} = -1 + i\cdot 0 = -1.$$

Definition (1) can also be used to obtain this result. More precisely,

$$|z_n - (-1)| = \left|i\frac{(-1)^n}{n^2}\right| = \frac{1}{n^2} < \varepsilon \quad \text{whenever} \quad n > \frac{1}{\sqrt{\varepsilon}}.$$

One must be careful when adapting our theorem to polar coordinates, as the following example shows.

EXAMPLE 2. Consider now the same sequence

$$z_n = -1 + i\frac{(-1)^n}{n^2} \qquad (n = 1, 2, \ldots)$$

as in Example 1. If we use the polar coordinates

$$r_n = |z_n| \quad \text{and} \quad \Theta_n = \text{Arg}\, z_n \qquad (n = 1, 2, \ldots)$$

where Arg z_n denotes *principal* arguments $(-\pi < \Theta_n \le \pi)$, we find that

$$\lim_{n\to\infty} r_n = \lim_{n\to\infty}\sqrt{1 + \frac{1}{n^4}} = 1$$

but that

$$\lim_{n\to\infty}\Theta_{2n} = \pi \quad \text{and} \quad \lim_{n\to\infty}\Theta_{2n-1} = -\pi \qquad (n = 1, 2, \ldots).$$

Evidently, then, the limit of Θ_n does not exist as n tends to infinity. (See also Exercise 2, Sec. 61.)

61. CONVERGENCE OF SERIES

An infinite ***series***

(1) $$\sum_{n=1}^{\infty} z_n = z_1 + z_2 + \cdots + z_n + \cdots$$

of complex numbers ***converges*** to the ***sum*** S if the sequence

(2) $$S_N = \sum_{n=1}^{N} z_n = z_1 + z_2 + \cdots + z_N \qquad (N = 1, 2, \ldots)$$

of ***partial sums*** converges to S; we then write

$$\sum_{n=1}^{\infty} z_n = S.$$

Note that since a sequence can have at most one limit, a series can have at most one sum. When a series does not converge, we say that it ***diverges.***

Theorem. *Suppose that $z_n = x_n + iy_n$ $(n = 1, 2, \ldots)$ and $S = X + iY$. Then*

(3) $$\sum_{n=1}^{\infty} z_n = S$$

if and only if

(4) $$\sum_{n=1}^{\infty} x_n = X \quad \text{and} \quad \sum_{n=1}^{\infty} y_n = Y.$$

This theorem tells us, of course, that one can write

$$\sum_{n=1}^{\infty} (x_n + iy_n) = \sum_{n=1}^{\infty} x_n + i \sum_{n=1}^{\infty} y_n$$

whenever it is known that the two series on the right converge or that the one on the left does.

To prove the theorem, we first write the partial sums (2) as

(5) $$S_N = X_N + iY_N,$$

where

$$X_N = \sum_{n=1}^{N} x_n \quad \text{and} \quad Y_N = \sum_{n=1}^{N} y_n.$$

Now statement (3) is true if and only if

(6) $$\lim_{N\to\infty} S_N = S;$$

and, in view of relation (5) and the theorem on sequences in Sec. 60, limit (6) holds if and only if

$$\lim_{N\to\infty} X_N = X \quad \text{and} \quad \lim_{N\to\infty} Y_N = Y. \tag{7}$$

Limits (7) therefore imply statement (3), and conversely. Since X_N and Y_N are the partial sums of the series (4), the theorem here is proved.

This theorem can be useful in showing that a number of familiar properties of series in calculus carry over to series whose terms are complex numbers. To illustrate how this is done, we include here two such properties and present them as corollaries.

Corollary 1. *If a series of complex numbers converges, the nth term converges to zero as n tends to infinity.*

Assuming that series (1) converges, we know from the theorem that if

$$z_n = x_n + iy_n \quad (n = 1, 2, \ldots),$$

then each of the series

$$\sum_{n=1}^{\infty} x_n \quad \text{and} \quad \sum_{n=1}^{\infty} y_n \tag{8}$$

converges. We know, moreover, from calculus that the nth term of a convergent series of real numbers approaches zero as n tends to infinity. Thus, by the theorem in Sec. 60,

$$\lim_{n\to\infty} z_n = \lim_{n\to\infty} x_n + i \lim_{n\to\infty} y_n = 0 + 0 \cdot i = 0;$$

and the proof of Corollary 1 is complete.

It follows from this corollary that the terms of convergent series are ***bounded.*** That is, when series (1) converges, there exists a positive constant M such that $|z_n| \le M$ for each positive integer n. (See Exercise 9.)

For another important property of series of complex numbers that follows from a corresponding property in calculus, series (1) is said to be ***absolutely convergent*** if the series

$$\sum_{n=1}^{\infty} |z_n| = \sum_{n=1}^{\infty} \sqrt{x_n^2 + y_n^2} \qquad (z_n = x_n + iy_n)$$

of real numbers $\sqrt{x_n^2 + y_n^2}$ converges.

Corollary 2. *The absolute convergence of a series of complex numbers implies the convergence of that series.*

To prove Corollary 2, we assume that series (1) converges absolutely. Since

$$|x_n| \le \sqrt{x_n^2 + y_n^2} \quad \text{and} \quad |y_n| \le \sqrt{x_n^2 + y_n^2},$$

we know from the comparison test in calculus that the two series

$$\sum_{n=1}^{\infty} |x_n| \quad \text{and} \quad \sum_{n=1}^{\infty} |y_n|$$

must converge. Moreover, since the absolute convergence of a series of real numbers implies the convergence of the series itself, it follows that the series (8) both converge. In view of the theorem in this section, then, series (1) converges. This finishes the proof of Corollary 2.

In establishing the fact that the sum of a series is a given number S, it is often convenient to define the ***remainder*** ρ_N after N terms, using the partial sums (2):

$$\rho_N = S - S_N. \tag{9}$$

Thus $S = S_N + \rho_N$; and, since $|S_N - S| = |\rho_N - 0|$, we see that *a series converges to a number S if and only if the sequence of remainders tends to zero.* We shall make considerable use of this observation in our treatment of ***power series.*** They are series of the form

$$\sum_{n=0}^{\infty} a_n(z - z_0)^n = a_0 + a_1(z - z_0) + a_2(z - z_0)^2 + \cdots + a_n(z - z_0)^n + \cdots,$$

where z_0 and the coefficients a_n are complex constants and z may be any point in a stated region containing z_0. In such series, involving a variable z, we shall denote sums, partial sums, and remainders by $S(z)$, $S_N(z)$, and $\rho_N(z)$, respectively.

EXAMPLE. With the aid of remainders, it is easy to verify that

$$\sum_{n=0}^{\infty} z^n = \frac{1}{1 - z} \quad \text{whenever} \quad |z| < 1. \tag{10}$$

We need only recall the identity (Exercise 9, Sec. 9)

$$1 + z + z^2 + \cdots + z^n = \frac{1 - z^{n+1}}{1 - z} \qquad (z \neq 1)$$

to write the partial sums

$$S_N(z) = \sum_{n=0}^{N-1} z^n = 1 + z + z^2 + \cdots + z^{N-1} \qquad (z \neq 1)$$

as

$$S_N(z) = \frac{1 - z^N}{1 - z}.$$

If

$$S(z) = \frac{1}{1 - z},$$

then,

$$\rho_N(z) = S(z) - S_N(z) = \frac{z^N}{1-z} \qquad (z \neq 1).$$

Thus

$$|\rho_N(z)| = \frac{|z|^N}{|1-z|},$$

and it is clear from this that the remainders $\rho_N(z)$ tend to zero when $|z| < 1$ but not when $|z| \geq 1$. Summation formula (10) is, therefore, established.

EXERCISES

1. Use definition (1), Sec. 60, of limits of sequences to show that

$$\lim_{n\to\infty}\left(\frac{1}{n^2} + i\right) = i.$$

2. Let Θ_n $(n = 1, 2, \ldots)$ denote the principal arguments of the numbers

$$z_n = 1 + i\frac{(-1)^n}{n^2} \qquad (n = 1, 2, \ldots),$$

and point out why

$$\lim_{n\to\infty} \Theta_n = 0.$$

(Compare with Example 2, Sec. 60.)

3. Use the inequality (see Sec. 5) $||z_n| - |z|| \leq |z_n - z|$ to show that

$$\text{if} \quad \lim_{n\to\infty} z_n = z, \quad \text{then} \quad \lim_{n\to\infty} |z_n| = |z|.$$

4. Write $z = re^{i\theta}$, where $0 < r < 1$, in the summation formula (10), Sec. 61. Then, with the aid of the theorem in Sec. 61, show that

$$\sum_{n=1}^{\infty} r^n \cos n\theta = \frac{r\cos\theta - r^2}{1 - 2r\cos\theta + r^2} \quad \text{and} \quad \sum_{n=1}^{\infty} r^n \sin n\theta = \frac{r\sin\theta}{1 - 2r\cos\theta + r^2}$$

when $0 < r < 1$. (Note that these formulas are also valid when $r = 0$.)

5. Show that a limit of a convergent sequence of complex numbers is unique by appealing to the corresponding result for a sequence of real numbers.

6. Show that

$$\text{if} \quad \sum_{n=1}^{\infty} z_n = S, \quad \text{then} \quad \sum_{n=1}^{\infty} \overline{z_n} = \overline{S}.$$

7. Let c denote any complex number and show that

$$\text{if} \quad \sum_{n=1}^{\infty} z_n = S, \quad \text{then} \quad \sum_{n=1}^{\infty} cz_n = cS.$$

8. By recalling the corresponding result for series of real numbers and referring to the theorem in Sec. 61, show that

$$\text{if} \quad \sum_{n=1}^{\infty} z_n = S \quad \text{and} \quad \sum_{n=1}^{\infty} w_n = T, \qquad \text{then} \quad \sum_{n=1}^{\infty} (z_n + w_n) = S + T.$$

9. Let a sequence z_n $(n = 1, 2, \ldots)$ converge to a number z. Show that there exists a positive number M such that the inequality $|z_n| \le M$ holds for all n. Do this in each of the following ways.

(*a*) Note that there is a positive integer n_0 such that

$$|z_n| = |z + (z_n - z)| < |z| + 1$$

whenever $n > n_0$.

(*b*) Write $z_n = x_n + iy_n$ and recall from the theory of sequences of real numbers that the convergence of x_n and y_n $(n = 1, 2, \ldots)$ implies that $|x_n| \le M_1$ and $|y_n| \le M_2$ $(n = 1, 2, \ldots)$ for some positive numbers M_1 and M_2.

62. TAYLOR SERIES

We turn now to ***Taylor's theorem,*** which is one of the most important results of the chapter.

Theorem. *Suppose that a function f is analytic throughout a disk $|z - z_0| < R_0$, centered at z_0 and with radius R_0* (Fig. 77). *Then $f(z)$ has the power series representation*

$$f(z) = \sum_{n=0}^{\infty} a_n (z - z_0)^n \qquad (|z - z_0| < R_0), \tag{1}$$

where

$$a_n = \frac{f^{(n)}(z_0)}{n!} \qquad (n = 0, 1, 2, \ldots). \tag{2}$$

That is, series (1) *converges to $f(z)$ when z lies in the stated open disk.*

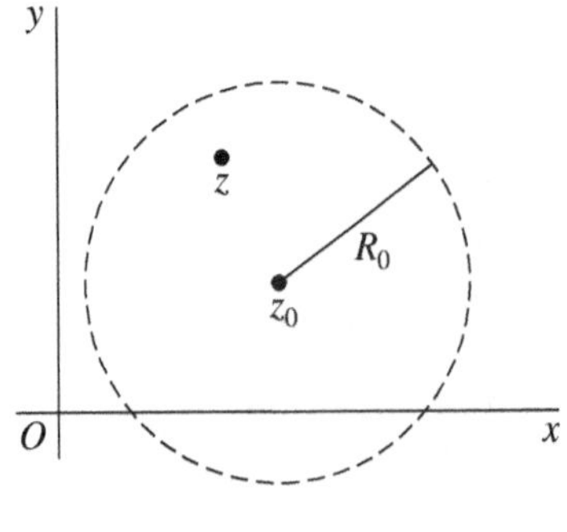

FIGURE 77

This is the expansion of $f(z)$ into a ***Taylor series*** about the point z_0. It is the familiar Taylor series from calculus, adapted to functions of a complex variable. With the agreement that

$$f^{(0)}(z_0) = f(z_0) \quad \text{and} \quad 0! = 1,$$

series (1) can, of course, be written

(3) $$f(z) = f(z_0) + \frac{f'(z_0)}{1!}(z - z_0) + \frac{f''(z_0)}{2!}(z - z_0)^2 + \cdots \quad (|z - z_0| < R_0).$$

Any function which is analytic at a point z_0 must have a Taylor series about z_0. For, if f is analytic at z_0, it is analytic throughout some neighborhood $|z - z_0| < \varepsilon$ of that point (Sec. 25); and ε may serve as the value of R_0 in the statement of Taylor's theorem. Also, if f is entire, R_0 can be chosen arbitrarily large; and the condition of validity becomes $|z - z_0| < \infty$. The series then converges to $f(z)$ at each point z in the finite plane.

When it is known that f is analytic everywhere inside a circle centered at z_0, convergence of its Taylor series about z_0 to $f(z)$ for each point z within that circle is ensured; no test for the convergence of the series is even required. In fact, according to Taylor's theorem, the series converges to $f(z)$ within the circle about z_0 whose radius is the distance from z_0 to the nearest point z_1 at which f *fails* to be analytic. In Sec. 71, we shall find that this is actually the largest circle centered at z_0 such that the series converges to $f(z)$ for all z interior to it.

In the following section, we shall first prove Taylor's theorem when $z_0 = 0$, in which case f is assumed to be analytic throughout a disk $|z| < R_0$. Series (1) then becomes a ***Maclaurin series***:

(4) $$f(z) = \sum_{n=0}^{\infty} \frac{f^{(n)}(0)}{n!} z^n \quad (|z| < R_0).$$

The proof when z_0 is nonzero will follow as an immediate consequence. A reader who wishes to accept the proof of Taylor's theorem can easily skip to the examples in Sec. 64.

63. PROOF OF TAYLOR'S THEOREM

As indicated at the end of Sec. 62, the proof falls naturally into two parts.

The case $z_0 = 0$

To begin the derivation of representation (4) in Sec. 62, we write $|z| = r$ and let C_0 denote the positively oriented circle $|z| = r_0$ where $r < r_0 < R_0$ (see Fig. 78). Since f is analytic inside and on the circle C_0 and since the point z is interior to C_0, the Cauchy integral formula

(1) $$f(z) = \frac{1}{2\pi i} \int_{C_0} \frac{f(s)\,ds}{s - z}$$

applies.

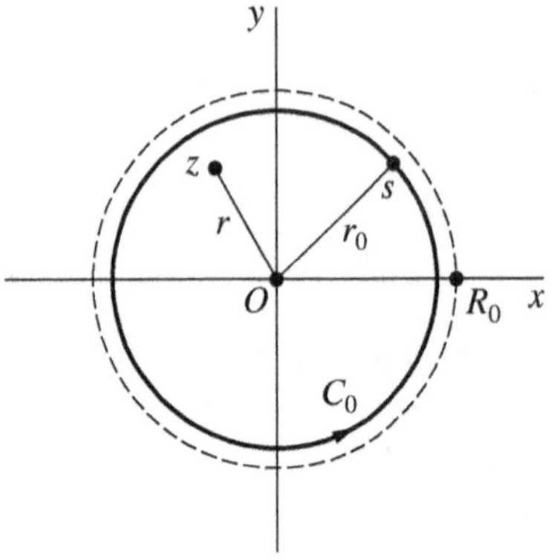

FIGURE 78

Now the factor $1/(s-z)$ in the integrand here can be put in the form

$$\frac{1}{s-z} = \frac{1}{s} \cdot \frac{1}{1-(z/s)}; \tag{2}$$

and we know from the example in Sec. 56 that

$$\frac{1}{1-z} = \sum_{n=0}^{N-1} z^n + \frac{z^N}{1-z} \tag{3}$$

when z is any complex number other than unity. Replacing z by z/s in expression (3), then, we can rewrite equation (2) as

$$\frac{1}{s-z} = \sum_{n=0}^{N-1} \frac{1}{s^{n+1}} z^n + z^N \frac{1}{(s-z)s^N}. \tag{4}$$

Multiplying through this equation by $f(s)$ and then integrating each side with respect to s around C_0, we find that

$$\int_{C_0} \frac{f(s)\,ds}{s-z} = \sum_{n=0}^{N-1} \int_{C_0} \frac{f(s)\,ds}{s^{n+1}} z^n + z^N \int_{C_0} \frac{f(s)\,ds}{(s-z)s^N}.$$

In view of expression (1) and the fact that (Sec. 55)

$$\frac{1}{2\pi i} \int_{C_0} \frac{f(s)\,ds}{s^{n+1}} = \frac{f^{(n)}(0)}{n!} \qquad (n = 0, 1, 2, \ldots),$$

this reduces, after we multiply through by $1/(2\pi i)$, to

$$f(z) = \sum_{n=0}^{N-1} \frac{f^{(n)}(0)}{n!} z^n + \rho_N(z), \tag{5}$$

where

$$\rho_N(z) = \frac{z^N}{2\pi i} \int_{C_0} \frac{f(s)\,ds}{(s-z)s^N}. \tag{6}$$

Representation (4) in Sec. 62 now follows once it is shown that

$$\lim_{N\to\infty} \rho_N(z) = 0. \tag{7}$$

To accomplish this, we recall that $|z| = r$ and that C_0 has radius r_0, where $r_0 > r$. Then, if s is a point on C_0, we can see that

$$|s - z| \geq ||s| - |z|| = r_0 - r.$$

Consequently, if M denotes the maximum value of $|f(s)|$ on C_0,

$$|\rho_N(z)| \leq \frac{r^N}{2\pi} \cdot \frac{M}{(r_0 - r)r_0^N} 2\pi r_0 = \frac{Mr_0}{r_0 - r}\left(\frac{r}{r_0}\right)^N.$$

Inasmuch as $(r/r_0) < 1$, limit (7) clearly holds.

The case $z_0 \neq 0$

In order to verify the theorem when the disk of radius R_0 is centered at an arbitrary point z_0, we suppose that f is analytic when $|z - z_0| < R_0$ and note that the composite function $f(z + z_0)$ must be analytic when $|(z + z_0) - z_0| < R_0$. This last inequality is, of course, just $|z| < R_0$; and, if we write $g(z) = f(z + z_0)$, the analyticity of g in the disk $|z| < R_0$ ensures the existence of a Maclaurin series representation:

$$g(z) = \sum_{n=0}^{\infty} \frac{g^{(n)}(0)}{n!} z^n \qquad (|z| < R_0).$$

That is,

$$f(z + z_0) = \sum_{n=0}^{\infty} \frac{f^{(n)}(z_0)}{n!} z^n \qquad (|z| < R_0).$$

After replacing z by $z - z_0$ in this equation and its condition of validity, we have the desired Taylor series expansion (1) in Sec. 62.

64. EXAMPLES

In Sec. 72, we shall see that any Taylor series representing a function $f(z)$ about a given point z_0 is unique. More precisely, we will show that if

$$f(z) = \sum_{n=0}^{\infty} a_n (z - z_0)^n$$

for all points z interior to some circle centered at z_0, then the power series here must be *the* Taylor series for f about z_0, regardless of how those constants arise. This observation often allows us to find the coefficients a_n in Taylor series in more efficient ways than by appealing directly to the formula $a_n = f^{(n)}(z_0)/n!$ in Taylor's theorem.

This section is devoted to finding the following six Maclaurin series expansions, where $z_0 = 0$, and to illustrate how they can be used to find related expansions:

$$\frac{1}{1-z} = \sum_{n=0}^{\infty} z^n = 1 + z + z^2 + \cdots \qquad (|z| < 1), \tag{1}$$

$$e^z = \sum_{n=0}^{\infty} \frac{z^n}{n!} = 1 + \frac{z}{1!} + \frac{z^2}{2!} + \cdots \qquad (|z| < \infty), \tag{2}$$

$$\sin z = \sum_{n=0}^{\infty} (-1)^n \frac{z^{2n+1}}{(2n+1)!} = z - \frac{z^3}{3!} + \frac{z^5}{5!} - \cdots \qquad (|z| < \infty), \tag{3}$$

$$\cos z = \sum_{n=0}^{\infty} (-1)^n \frac{z^{2n}}{(2n)!} = 1 - \frac{z^2}{2!} + \frac{z^4}{4!} - \cdots \qquad (|z| < \infty), \tag{4}$$

$$\sinh z = \sum_{n=0}^{\infty} \frac{z^{2n+1}}{(2n+1)!} = z + \frac{z^3}{3!} + \frac{z^5}{5!} + \cdots \qquad (|z| < \infty), \tag{5}$$

$$\cosh z = \sum_{n=0}^{\infty} \frac{z^{2n}}{(2n)!} = 1 + \frac{z^2}{2!} + \frac{z^4}{4!} + \cdots \qquad (|z| < \infty). \tag{6}$$

We list these results together in order to have them for ready reference later on. Since the expansions are familiar ones from calculus with z instead of x, the reader should, however, find them easy to remember.

In addition to collecting expansions (1) through (6) together, we now present their derivations as Examples 1 through 6, along with some other series that are immediate consequences. The reader should always keep in mind that

(*a*) the regions of convergence can be determined before the actual series are found;
(*b*) there may be several reasonable ways to find the desired series.

EXAMPLE 1. Representation (1) was, of course, obtained earlier in Sec. 61, where Taylor's theorem was not used. In order to see how Taylor's theorem can be used, we first note that the point $z = 1$ is the only singularity of the function

$$f(z) = \frac{1}{1-z}$$

in the finite plane. So the desired Maclaurin series converges to $f(z)$ when $|z| < 1$.

The derivatives of $f(z)$ are

$$f^{(n)}(z) = \frac{n!}{(1-z)^{n+1}} \qquad (n = 1, 2, \ldots).$$

Hence if we agree that $f^{(0)}(z) = f(z)$ and $0! = 1$, we find that $f^{(n)}(0) = n!$ when $n = 0, 1, 2, \ldots$; and upon writing

$$f(z) = \sum_{n=0}^{\infty} \frac{f^{(n)}(0)}{n!} z^n = \sum_{n=0}^{\infty} z^n,$$

we arrive at the series representation (1).

If we substitute $-z$ for z in equation (1) and its condition of validity, and note that $|z| < 1$ when $|-z| < 1$, we see that

$$\frac{1}{1+z} = \sum_{n=0}^{\infty}(-1)^n z^n \qquad (|z| < 1).$$

If, on the other hand, we replace the variable z in equation (1) by $1 - z$, we have the Taylor series representation

$$\frac{1}{z} = \sum_{n=0}^{\infty}(-1)^n (z-1)^n \qquad (|z-1| < 1).$$

This condition of validity follows from the one associated with expansion (1) since $|1 - z| < 1$ is the same as $|z - 1| < 1$.

For another application of expansion (1), we now seek a Taylor series representation of the function

$$f(z) = \frac{1}{1-z}$$

about the point $z_0 = i$. Since the distance between z_0 and the singularity $z = 1$ is $|1 - i| = \sqrt{2}$, the condition of validity is $|z - i| < \sqrt{2}$. (See Fig. 79.) To find the series, which involves powers of $z - i$, we first write

$$\frac{1}{1-z} = \frac{1}{(1-i)-(z-i)} = \frac{1}{1-i} \cdot \frac{1}{1 - \left(\dfrac{z-i}{1-i}\right)}.$$

Because

$$\left|\frac{z-i}{1-i}\right| = \frac{|z-i|}{|1-i|} = \frac{|z-i|}{\sqrt{2}} < 1$$

when $|z - i| < \sqrt{2}$, expansion (1) now tells us that

$$\frac{1}{1 - \left(\dfrac{z-i}{1-i}\right)} = \sum_{n=0}^{\infty}\left(\frac{z-i}{1-i}\right)^n \qquad (|z-i| < \sqrt{2});$$

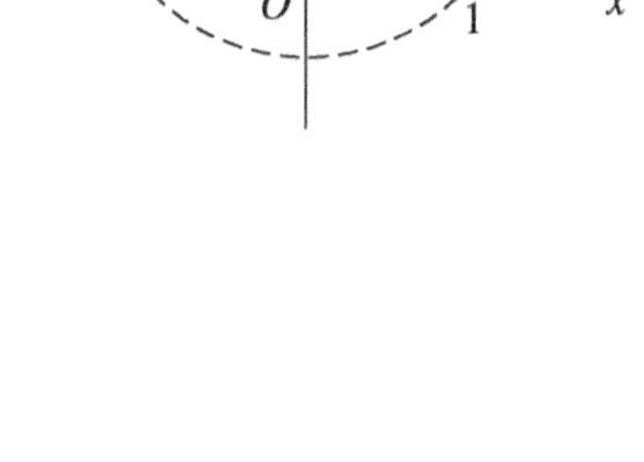

FIGURE 79
$|z - i| < \sqrt{2}$

and we arrive at the Taylor series expansion

$$\frac{1}{1-z} = \frac{1}{1-i}\sum_{n=0}^{\infty}\left(\frac{z-i}{1-i}\right)^n = \sum_{n=0}^{\infty}\frac{(z-i)^n}{(1-i)^{n+1}} \qquad (|z-i| < \sqrt{2}).$$

EXAMPLE 2. Since the function $f(z) = e^z$ is entire, it has a Maclaurin series representation that is valid for all z. Here $f^{(n)}(z) = e^z$ $(n = 0, 1, 2, \ldots)$; and because $f^{(n)}(0) = 1 (n = 0, 1, 2, \ldots)$, expansion (2) follows. Note that if $z = x + i0$, the expansion becomes

$$e^x = \sum_{n=0}^{\infty}\frac{x^n}{n!} \qquad (-\infty < x < \infty).$$

The entire function z^3e^{2z} is also represented by a Maclaurin series. The simplest way to show this is to replace z by $2z$ in expression (2) and then multiply through the result by z^3:

$$z^3e^{2z} = \sum_{n=0}^{\infty}\frac{2^n}{n!}z^{n+3} \qquad (|z| < \infty).$$

Finally, if we replace n by $n-3$ here, we have

$$z^3e^{2z} = \sum_{n=3}^{\infty}\frac{2^{n-3}}{(n-3)!}z^n \qquad (|z| < \infty).$$

EXAMPLE 3. One can use expansion (2) and the definition (Sec. 37)

$$\sin z = \frac{e^{iz} - e^{-iz}}{2i}$$

to find the Maclaurin series for the entire function $f(z) = \sin z$. To give the details, we refer to expansion (1) and write

$$\sin z = \frac{1}{2i}\left[\sum_{n=0}^{\infty}\frac{(iz)^n}{n!} - \sum_{n=0}^{\infty}\frac{(-iz)^n}{n!}\right] = \frac{1}{2i}\sum_{n=0}^{\infty}\left[1-(-1)^n\right]\frac{i^nz^n}{n!} \qquad (|z| < \infty).$$

But $1 - (-1)^n = 0$ when n is even, and so we can replace n by $2n+1$ in this last series:

$$\sin z = \frac{1}{2i}\sum_{n=0}^{\infty}\left[1-(-1)^{2n+1}\right]\frac{i^{2n+1}z^{2n+1}}{(2n+1)!} \qquad (|z| < \infty).$$

Inasmuch as

$$1 - (-1)^{2n+1} = 2 \quad \text{and} \quad i^{2n+1} = (i^2)^n i = (-1)^n i,$$

this reduces to expansion (3).

EXAMPLE 4. Using term by term differentiation, which will be justified in Sec. 71, we differentiate each side of equation (3) and write

$$\cos z = \sum_{n=0}^{\infty} \frac{(-1)^n}{(2n+1)!} \frac{d}{dz} z^{2n+1} = \sum_{n=0}^{\infty} (-1)^n \frac{2n+1}{(2n+1)!} z^{2n} = \sum_{n=0}^{\infty} (-1)^n \frac{z^{2n}}{(2n)!}$$
$$(|z| < \infty).$$

Expansion (4) is now verified.

EXAMPLE 5. Because $\sinh z = -i \sin(iz)$, as pointed out in Sec. 39, we need only recall expansion (3) for $\sin z$ and write

$$\sinh z = -i \sum_{n=0}^{\infty} (-1)^n \frac{(iz)^{2n+1}}{(2n+1)!} \qquad (|z| < \infty),$$

which becomes

$$\sinh z = \sum_{n=0}^{\infty} \frac{z^{2n+1}}{(2n+1)!} \qquad (|z| < \infty).$$

EXAMPLE 6. Since $\cosh z = \cos(iz)$, according to Sec. 39, the Maclaurin series (4) for $\cos z$ reveals that

$$\cosh z = \sum_{n=0}^{\infty} (-1)^n \frac{(iz)^{2n}}{(2n)!} \qquad (|z| < \infty),$$

and we arrive at the Maclaurin series representation

$$\cosh z = \sum_{n=0}^{\infty} \frac{z^{2n}}{(2n)!} \qquad (|z| < \infty).$$

Observe that the Taylor series for $\cosh z$ about the point $z_0 = -2\pi i$, for example, is obtained by replacing the variable z on each side of this last equation by $z + 2\pi i$ and then recalling (Sec. 39) that $\cosh(z + 2\pi i) = \cosh z$ for all z:

$$\cosh z = \sum_{n=0}^{\infty} \frac{(z + 2\pi i)^{2n}}{(2n)!} \qquad (|z| < \infty).$$

65. NEGATIVE POWERS OF $(z - z_0)$

If a function f fails to be analytic at a point z_0, one cannot apply Taylor's theorem there. It is often possible, however, to find a series representation for $f(z)$ involving both positive and negative powers of $(z - z_0)$. Such series are extremely important and are taken up in the next section. They are often obtained by using one or more of the six Maclaurin series listed at the beginning of Sec. 64. In order that the reader be accustomed to series involving negative powers of $(z - z_0)$, we pause here with several examples before exploring their general theory.

EXAMPLE 1. Using the familiar Maclaurin series

$$e^z = 1 + \frac{z}{1!} + \frac{z^2}{2!} + \frac{z^3}{3!} + \frac{z^4}{4!} + \cdots \qquad (|z| < \infty),$$

we can see that

$$\frac{e^{-z}}{z^2} = \frac{1}{z^2}\left(1 - \frac{z}{1!} + \frac{z^2}{2!} - \frac{z^3}{3!} + \frac{z^4}{4!} - \cdots\right) = \frac{1}{z^2} - \frac{1}{z} + \frac{1}{2!} - \frac{z}{3!} + \frac{z^2}{4!} - \cdots$$

when $0 < |z| < \infty$.

EXAMPLE 2. From the Maclaurin series

$$\cosh z = \sum_{n=0}^{\infty} \frac{z^{2n}}{(2n)!} \qquad (|z| < \infty)$$

it follows that when $0 < |z| < \infty$,

$$z^3 \cosh\left(\frac{1}{z}\right) = z^3 \sum_{n=0}^{\infty} \frac{1}{(2n)!z^{2n}} = \sum_{n=0}^{\infty} \frac{1}{(2n)!z^{2n-3}}.$$

We note that $2n - 3 < 0$ when n is 0 or 1 but that $2n - 3 > 0$ when $n \geq 2$. Hence this last series can be rewritten so that

$$z^3 \cosh\left(\frac{1}{z}\right) = z^3 + \frac{z}{2} + \sum_{n=2}^{\infty} \frac{1}{(2n)!z^{2n-3}} \qquad (0 < |z| < \infty).$$

Anticipating a standard form for such an expansion in the next section, we can replace n by $n + 1$ in this series to arrive at

$$z^3 \cos\left(\frac{1}{z}\right) = \frac{z}{2} + z^3 + \sum_{n=1}^{\infty} \frac{1}{(2n+2)!} \cdot \frac{1}{z^{2n-1}} \qquad (0 < |z| < \infty).$$

EXAMPLE 3. For our next example, let us expand the function

$$f(z) = \frac{1 + 2z^2}{z^3 + z^5} = \frac{1}{z^3} \cdot \frac{2(1 + z^2) - 1}{1 + z^2} = \frac{1}{z^3}\left(2 - \frac{1}{1 + z^2}\right)$$

into a series involving powers of z. We cannot find a Maclaurin series since $f(z)$ is not analytic at $z = 0$. But we do know that

$$\frac{1}{1 - z} = 1 + z + z^2 + z^3 + z^4 + \cdots \qquad (|z| < 1);$$

and, after replacing z by $-z^2$ on each side here, we have

$$\frac{1}{1 + z^2} = 1 - z^2 + z^4 - z^6 + z^8 - \cdots \qquad (|z| < 1).$$

So when $0 < |z| < 1$,

$$f(z) = \frac{1}{z^3}(2 - 1 + z^2 - z^4 + z^6 - z^8 + \cdots) = \frac{1}{z^3} + \frac{1}{z} - z + z^3 - z^5 + \cdots.$$

We call such terms as $1/z^3$ and $1/z$ *negative* powers of z since they can be written z^{-3} and z^{-1}, respectively. As already noted at the beginning of this section, the theory of expansions involving negative powers of $(z - z_0)$ will be discussed in the next section.

The reader will notice that in the series obtained in Examples 1 and 3 the negative powers appear first but that the positive powers appear first in Example 2. Whether the positive or negative powers come first is usually immaterial in the applications later on. Also, these three examples involve powers of $(z - z_0)$ when $z_0 = 0$. Our final example here does, however, involve a nonzero z_0.

EXAMPLE 4. We propose here to expand the function

$$\frac{e^z}{(z+1)^2}$$

in powers of $(z + 1)$. We start with the Maclaurin series

$$e^z = \sum_{n=0}^{\infty} \frac{z^n}{n!} \qquad (|z| < \infty)$$

and replace z by $(z + 1)$:

$$e^{z+1} = \sum_{n=0}^{\infty} \frac{(z+1)^n}{n!} \qquad (|z+1| < \infty).$$

Dividing through this equation by $e(z + 1)^2$ reveals that

$$\frac{e^z}{(z+1)^2} = \sum_{n=0}^{\infty} \frac{(z+1)^{n-2}}{n!e}.$$

So we have

$$\frac{e^z}{(z+1)^2} = \frac{1}{e}\left[\frac{1}{(z+1)^2} + \frac{1}{z+1} + \sum_{n=2}^{\infty} \frac{(z+1)^{n-2}}{n!}\right] \qquad (0 < |z+1| < \infty),$$

which is the same as

$$\frac{e^z}{(z+1)^2} = \frac{1}{e}\left[\sum_{n=0}^{\infty} \frac{(z+1)^n}{(n+2)!} + \frac{1}{z+1} + \frac{1}{(z+1)^2}\right] \qquad (0 < |z+1| < \infty).$$

EXERCISES*

1. Obtain the Maclaurin series representation

$$z\cosh(z^2) = \sum_{n=0}^{\infty} \frac{z^{4n+1}}{(2n)!} \qquad (|z| < \infty).$$

*In these and subsequent exercises on series expansions, it is recommended that the reader use, when possible, representations (1) through (6) in Sec. 64.

2. Obtain the Taylor series

$$e^z = e\sum_{n=0}^{\infty}\frac{(z-1)^n}{n!} \qquad (|z-1| < \infty)$$

for the function $f(z) = e^z$ by

(*a*) using $f^{(n)}(1)$ $(n = 0, 1, 2, \ldots)$; (*b*) writing $e^z = e^{z-1}e$.

3. Find the Maclaurin series expansion of the function

$$f(z) = \frac{z}{z^4+4} = \frac{z}{4}\cdot\frac{1}{1+(z^4/4)}.$$

Ans. $f(z) = \sum_{n=0}^{\infty}\frac{(-1)^n}{2^{2n+2}}z^{4n+1} \quad (|z| < \sqrt{2})$.

4. With the aid of the identity (see Sec. 37)

$$\cos z = -\sin\left(z - \frac{\pi}{2}\right),$$

expand $\cos z$ into a Taylor series about the point $z_0 = \pi/2$.

5. Use the identity $\sinh(z + \pi i) = -\sinh z$, verified in Exercise 7(*a*), Sec. 39, and the fact that $\sinh z$ is periodic with period $2\pi i$ to find the Taylor series for $\sinh z$ about the point $z_0 = \pi i$.

Ans. $-\sum_{n=0}^{\infty}\frac{(z-\pi i)^{2n+1}}{(2n+1)!} \quad (|z-\pi i| < \infty)$.

6. What is the largest circle within which the Maclaurin series for the function $\tanh z$ converges to $\tanh z$? Write the first two nonzero terms of that series.

7. Show that if $f(z) = \sin z$, then

$$f^{(2n)}(0) = 0 \quad\text{and}\quad f^{(2n+1)}(0) = (-1)^n \qquad (n = 0, 1, 2, \ldots).$$

Thus give an alternative derivation of the Maclaurin series (3) for $\sin z$ in Sec. 64.

8. Rederive the Maclaurin series (4) in Sec. 64 for the function $f(z) = \cos z$ by

(*a*) using the definition

$$\cos z = \frac{e^{iz} + e^{-iz}}{2}$$

in Sec. 37 and appealing to the Maclaurin series (2) for e^z in Sec. 64;

(*b*) showing that

$$f^{(2n)}(0) = (-1)^n \quad\text{and}\quad f^{(2n+1)}(0) = 0 \qquad (n = 0, 1, 2, \ldots).$$

9. Use representation (3), Sec. 64, for $\sin z$ to write the Maclaurin series for the function

$$f(z) = \sin(z^2),$$

and point out how it follows that

$$f^{(4n)}(0) = 0 \quad\text{and}\quad f^{(2n+1)}(0) = 0 \qquad (n = 0, 1, 2, \ldots).$$

10. Derive the expansions

(*a*) $$\frac{\sinh z}{z^2} = \frac{1}{z} + \sum_{n=0}^{\infty} \frac{z^{2n+1}}{(2n+3)!} \qquad (0 < |z| < \infty);$$

(*b*) $$\frac{\sin(z^2)}{z^4} = \frac{1}{z^2} - \frac{z^2}{3!} + \frac{z^6}{5!} - \frac{z^{10}}{7!} + \cdots \qquad (0 < |z| < \infty).$$

11. Show that when $0 < |z| < 4$,

$$\frac{1}{4z - z^2} = \frac{1}{4z} + \sum_{n=0}^{\infty} \frac{z^n}{4^{n+2}}.$$

66. LAURENT SERIES

We turn now to a statement of ***Laurent's theorem***, which enables us to expand a function $f(z)$ into a series involving positive and negative powers of $(z - z_0)$ when the function fails to be analytic at z_0.

Theorem. *Suppose that a function f is analytic throughout an annular domain $R_1 < |z - z_0| < R_2$, centered at z_0, and let C denote any positively oriented simple closed contour around z_0 and lying in that domain* (Fig. 80). *Then, at each point in the domain, $f(z)$ has the series representation*

$$f(z) = \sum_{n=0}^{\infty} a_n (z - z_0)^n + \sum_{n=1}^{\infty} \frac{b_n}{(z - z_0)^n} \qquad (R_1 < |z - z_0| < R_2), \tag{1}$$

where

$$a_n = \frac{1}{2\pi i} \int_C \frac{f(z)\,dz}{(z - z_0)^{n+1}} \qquad (n = 0, 1, 2, \ldots) \tag{2}$$

and

$$b_n = \frac{1}{2\pi i} \int_C \frac{f(z)\,dz}{(z - z_0)^{-n+1}} \qquad (n = 1, 2, \ldots). \tag{3}$$

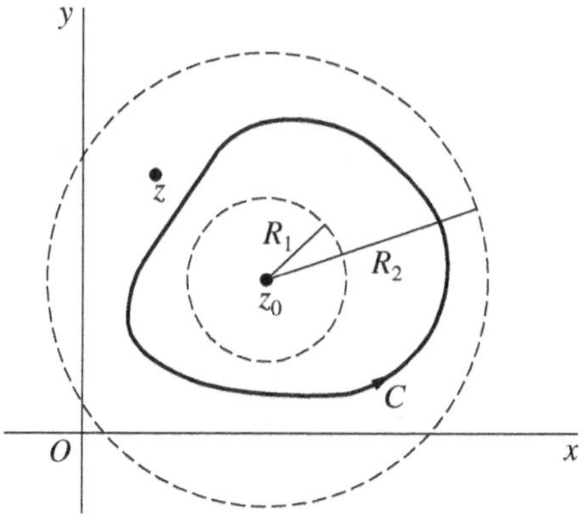

FIGURE 80

Note how replacing n by $-n$ in the second series in representation (1) enables us to write that series as

$$\sum_{n=-\infty}^{-1} \frac{b_{-n}}{(z - z_0)^{-n}},$$

where

$$b_{-n} = \frac{1}{2\pi i} \int_C \frac{f(z)\,dz}{(z - z_0)^{n+1}} \qquad (n = -1, -2, \ldots).$$

Thus

$$f(z) = \sum_{n=-\infty}^{-1} b_{-n}(z - z_0)^n + \sum_{n=0}^{\infty} a_n(z - z_0)^n \qquad (R_1 < |z - z_0| < R_2).$$

If

$$c_n = \begin{cases} b_{-n} & \text{when } n \le -1, \\ a_n & \text{when } n \ge 0, \end{cases}$$

this becomes

(4) $$f(z) = \sum_{n=-\infty}^{\infty} c_n(z - z_0)^n \qquad (R_1 < |z - z_0| < R_2)$$

where

(5) $$c_n = \frac{1}{2\pi i} \int_C \frac{f(z)\,dz}{(z - z_0)^{n+1}} \qquad (n = 0, \pm 1, \pm 2, \ldots).$$

In either one of the forms (1) and (4), the representation of $f(z)$ is called a ***Laurent series***.

Observe that the integrand in expression (3) can be written $f(z)(z - z_0)^{n-1}$. Thus it is clear that when f is actually analytic throughout the disk $|z - z_0| < R_2$, this integrand is too. Hence all of the coefficients b_n are zero; and, because (Sec. 55)

$$\frac{1}{2\pi i} \int_C \frac{f(z)\,dz}{(z - z_0)^{n+1}} = \frac{f^{(n)}(z_0)}{n!} \qquad (n = 0, 1, 2, \ldots),$$

expansion (1) reduces to a Taylor series about z_0.

If, however, f fails to be analytic at z_0 but is otherwise analytic in the disk $|z - z_0| < R_2$, the radius R_1 can be chosen arbitrarily small. Representation (1) is then valid in the punctured disk $0 < |z - z_0| < R_2$. Similarly, if f is analytic at each point in the finite plane exterior to the circle $|z - z_0| = R_1$, the condition of validity is $R_1 < |z - z_0| < \infty$. Note that if f is analytic *everywhere* in the finite plane except at z_0, series (1) is valid at each point of analyticity, or when $0 < |z - z_0| < \infty$.

We shall prove Laurent's theorem first when $z_0 = 0$, which means that the annulus is centered at the origin. The verification of the theorem when z_0 is arbitrary will follow readily; and, as was the case with Taylor's theorem, a reader can skip the entire proof without difficulty.

67. PROOF OF LAURENT'S THEOREM

As was the case with the proof of Taylor's theorem, we divide the proof here into two parts, the first when $z_0 = 0$ and the second when z_0 is any nonzero point in the finite plane.

The case $z_0 = 0$

We start the proof by forming a closed annular region $r_1 \leq |z| \leq r_2$ that is contained in the domain $R_1 < |z| < R_2$ and whose interior contains both the point z and the contour C (Fig. 81). We let C_1 and C_2 denote the circles $|z| = r_1$ and $|z| = r_2$, respectively, and we assign each of them a positive orientation. Observe that f is analytic on C_1 and C_2, as well as in the annular domain between them.

Next, we construct a positively oriented circle γ with center at z and small enough to be contained in the interior of the annular region $r_1 \leq |z| \leq r_2$, as shown in Fig. 81. It then follows from the adaptation of the Cauchy–Goursat theorem to integrals of analytic functions around oriented boundaries of multiply connected domains (Sec. 53) that

$$\int_{C_2} \frac{f(s)\,ds}{s-z} - \int_{C_1} \frac{f(s)\,ds}{s-z} - \int_{\gamma} \frac{f(s)\,ds}{s-z} = 0.$$

But, according to the Cauchy integral formula (Sec. 54), the value of the third integral here is $2\pi i f(z)$. Hence

$$f(z) = \frac{1}{2\pi i}\int_{C_2} \frac{f(s)\,ds}{s-z} + \frac{1}{2\pi i}\int_{C_1} \frac{f(s)\,ds}{z-s}. \tag{1}$$

Now the factor $1/(s-z)$ in the first of these integrals is the same as in expression (1), Sec. 63, where Taylor's theorem was proved; and we shall need here the

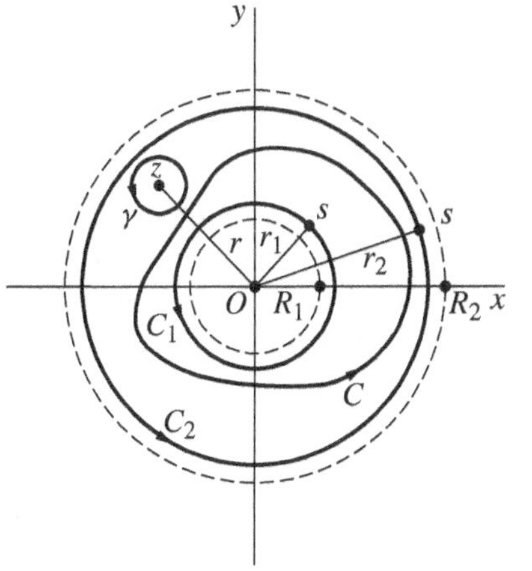

FIGURE 81

expansion

$$\frac{1}{s-z} = \sum_{n=0}^{N-1} \frac{1}{s^{n+1}} z^n + z^N \frac{1}{(s-z)s^N}, \tag{2}$$

which was used in that earlier section. As for the factor $1/(z-s)$ in the second integral, an interchange of s and z in equation (2) reveals that

$$\frac{1}{z-s} = \sum_{n=0}^{N-1} \frac{1}{s^{-n}} \cdot \frac{1}{z^{n+1}} + \frac{1}{z^N} \cdot \frac{s^N}{z-s}.$$

If we replace the index of summation n here by $n-1$, this expansion takes the form

$$\frac{1}{z-s} = \sum_{n=1}^{N} \frac{1}{s^{-n+1}} \cdot \frac{1}{z^n} + \frac{1}{z^N} \cdot \frac{s^N}{z-s}, \tag{3}$$

which is to be used in what follows.

Multiplying through equations (2) and (3) by $f(s)/(2\pi i)$ and then integrating each side of the resulting equations with respect to s around C_2 and C_1, respectively, we find from expression (1) that

$$f(z) = \sum_{n=0}^{N-1} a_n z^n + \rho_N(z) + \sum_{n=1}^{N} \frac{b_n}{z^n} + \sigma_N(z), \tag{4}$$

where the numbers a_n $(n = 0, 1, 2, \ldots, N-1)$ and b_n $(n = 1, 2, \ldots, N)$ are given by the equations

$$a_n = \frac{1}{2\pi i} \int_{C_2} \frac{f(s)\,ds}{s^{n+1}}, \qquad b_n = \frac{1}{2\pi i} \int_{C_1} \frac{f(s)\,ds}{s^{-n+1}} \tag{5}$$

and where

$$\rho_N(z) = \frac{z^N}{2\pi i} \int_{C_2} \frac{f(s)\,ds}{(s-z)s^N}, \qquad \sigma_N(z) = \frac{1}{2\pi i\, z^N} \int_{C_1} \frac{s^N f(s)\,ds}{z-s}.$$

As N tends to ∞, expression (4) evidently takes the proper form of a Laurent series in the domain $R_1 < |z| < R_2$, provided that

$$\lim_{N\to\infty} \rho_N(z) = 0 \quad \text{and} \quad \lim_{N\to\infty} \sigma_N(z) = 0. \tag{6}$$

These limits are readily established by a method already used in the proof of Taylor's theorem in Sec. 63. We write $|z| = r$, so that $r_1 < r < r_2$, and let M denote the maximum value of $|f(s)|$ on C_1 and C_2. We also note that if s is a point on C_2, then $|s - z| \geq r_2 - r$; and if s is on C_1, we have $|z - s| \geq r - r_1$. This enables us to write

$$|\rho_N(z)| \leq \frac{Mr_2}{r_2 - r}\left(\frac{r}{r_2}\right)^N \quad \text{and} \quad |\sigma_N(z)| \leq \frac{Mr_1}{r - r_1}\left(\frac{r_1}{r}\right)^N.$$

Since $(r/r_2) < 1$ and $(r_1/r) < 1$, it is now clear that both $\rho_N(z)$ and $\sigma_N(z)$ tend to zero as N tends to infinity.

Finally, we need only recall the corollary in Sec. 53 to see that the contours used in integrals (5) here may be replaced by the contour C. This completes the proof of Laurent's theorem when $z_0 = 0$ since, if z is used instead of s as the variable of integration, expressions (5) for the coefficients a_n and b_n are the same as expressions (2) and (3) in Sec. 66 when $z_0 = 0$ there.

The case $z_0 \neq 0$

To extend the proof to the general case in which z_0 is an arbitrary point in the finite plane, we let f be a function satisfying the conditions in the theorem; and, just as we did in the proof of Taylor's theorem, we write $g(z) = f(z + z_0)$. Since $f(z)$ is analytic in the annulus $R_1 < |z - z_0| < R_2$, the function $f(z + z_0)$ is analytic when $R_1 < |(z + z_0) - z_0| < R_2$. That is, g is analytic in the annulus $R_1 < |z| < R_2$, which is centered at the origin. Now the simple closed contour C in the statement of the theorem has some parametric representation $z = z(t)$ $(a \leq t \leq b)$, where

$$R_1 < |z(t) - z_0| < R_2 \tag{7}$$

for all t in the interval $a \leq t \leq b$. Hence if Γ denotes the path

$$z = z(t) - z_0 \qquad (a \leq t \leq b), \tag{8}$$

Γ is not only a simple closed contour but, in view of inequalities (7), it lies in the domain $R_1 < |z| < R_2$. Consequently, $g(z)$ has a Laurent series representation

$$g(z) = \sum_{n=0}^{\infty} a_n z^n + \sum_{n=1}^{\infty} \frac{b_n}{z^n} \qquad (R_1 < |z| < R_2), \tag{9}$$

where

$$a_n = \frac{1}{2\pi i} \int_\Gamma \frac{g(z)\,dz}{z^{n+1}} \qquad (n = 0, 1, 2, \ldots), \tag{10}$$

$$b_n = \frac{1}{2\pi i} \int_\Gamma \frac{g(z)\,dz}{z^{-n+1}} \qquad (n = 1, 2, \ldots). \tag{11}$$

Representation (1) in Sec. 66 is obtained if we write $f(z + z_0)$ instead of $g(z)$ in equation (9) and then replace z by $z - z_0$ in the resulting equation, as well as in the condition of validity $R_1 < |z| < R_2$. Expression (10) for the coefficients a_n is, moreover, the same as expression (2), Sec. 66, since

$$\int_\Gamma \frac{g(z)\,dz}{z^{n+1}} = \int_a^b \frac{f[z(t)]z'(t)}{[z(t) - z_0]^{n+1}}\,dt = \int_C \frac{f(z)\,dz}{(z - z_0)^{n+1}}.$$

Similarly, the coefficients b_n in expression (11) are the same as those in expression (3), Sec. 66.

68. EXAMPLES

The coefficients in a Laurent series are generally found by means other than appealing directly to the integral representations in Laurent's theorem (Sec. 66). This has already been illustrated in Sec. 65, where the series found were actually Laurent series. The reader is encouraged to go back to Sec. 65, as well as to Exercises 10 and 11 of that section, in order to see how in each case the punctured plane or disk in which the series is valid can now be predicted by Laurent's theorem. Also, we shall always assume that the Maclaurin series expansions (1) through (6) in Sec. 64 are well known, since we shall need them so often in finding Laurent series. As was the case with Taylor series, we defer the proof of uniqueness of Laurent series till Sec. 72.

EXAMPLE 1. The function

$$f(z) = \frac{1}{z(1+z^2)} = \frac{1}{z} \cdot \frac{1}{1+z^2}$$

has singularities at the points $z = 0$ and $z = \pm i$. Let us find the Laurent series representation of $f(z)$ that is valid in the punctured disk $0 < |z| < 1$ (see Fig. 82).

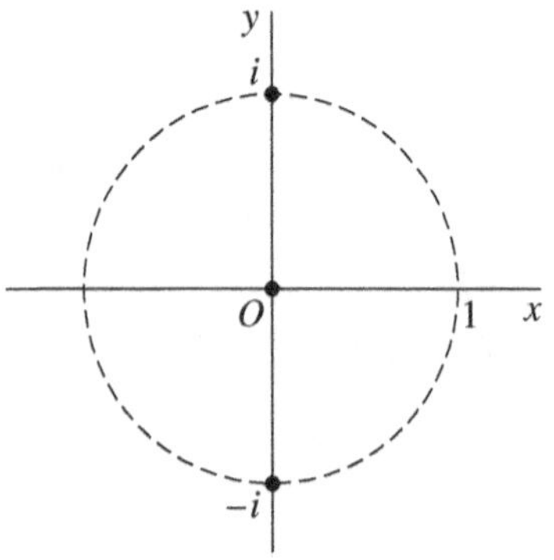

FIGURE 82

Since $|-z^2| < 1$ when $|z| < 1$, we may substitute $-z^2$ for z in the Maclaurin series expansion

$$(1) \qquad \frac{1}{1-z} = \sum_{n=0}^{\infty} z^n \qquad (|z| < 1).$$

The result is

$$\frac{1}{1+z^2} = \sum_{n=0}^{\infty} (-1)^n z^{2n} \qquad (|z| < 1),$$

and so

$$f(z) = \frac{1}{z} \sum_{n=0}^{\infty} (-1)^n z^{2n} = \sum_{n=0}^{\infty} (-1)^n z^{2n-1} \qquad (0 < |z| < 1).$$

That is,

$$f(z) = \frac{1}{z} + \sum_{n=1}^{\infty} (-1)^n z^{2n-1} \qquad (0 < |z| < 1).$$

Replacing n by $n+1$, we arrive at

$$f(z) = \frac{1}{z} + \sum_{n=0}^{\infty} (-1)^{n+1} z^{2n+1} \qquad (0 < |z| < 1).$$

In standard form, then,

$$(2) \qquad f(z) = \sum_{n=0}^{\infty} (-1)^{n+1} z^{2n+1} + \frac{1}{z} \qquad (0 < |z| < 1).$$

(See also Exercise 3.)

EXAMPLE 2. The function

$$f(z) = \frac{z+1}{z-1},$$

which has the singular point $z = 1$, is analytic in the domains (Fig. 83)

$$D_1 : |z| < 1 \quad \text{and} \quad D_2 : 1 < |z| < \infty.$$

In these domains $f(z)$ has series representations in powers of z. Both series can be found by making appropriate replacements for z in the same expansion (1) that was used in Example 1.

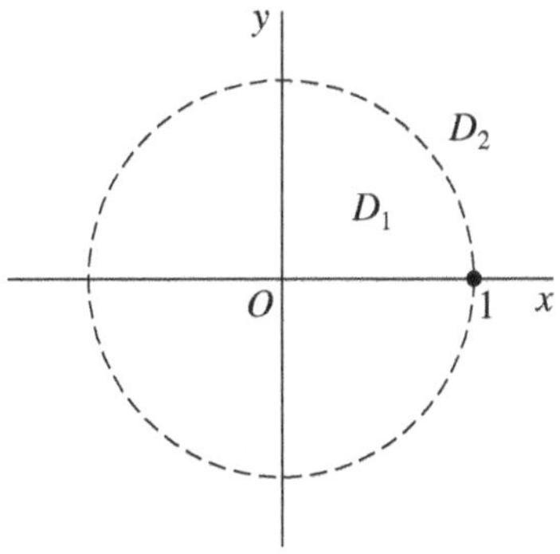

FIGURE 83

We consider first the domain D_1 and note that the series asked for is a Maclaurin series. In order to use series (1), we write

$$f(z) = -(z+1)\frac{1}{1-z} = -z\frac{1}{1-z} - \frac{1}{1-z}.$$

Then

$$f(z) = -z\sum_{n=0}^{\infty} z^n - \sum_{n=0}^{\infty} z^n = -\sum_{n=0}^{\infty} z^{n+1} - \sum_{n=0}^{\infty} z^n \qquad (|z| < 1).$$

Replacing n by $n-1$ in the first of the two series on the far right here yields the desired Maclaurin series:

(3) $$f(z) = -\sum_{n=1}^{\infty} z^n - \sum_{n=0}^{\infty} z^n = -1 - 2\sum_{n=1}^{\infty} z^n \qquad (|z| < 1).$$

The representation of $f(z)$ in the unbounded domain D_2 is a Laurent series, and the fact that $|1/z| < 1$ when z is a point in D_2 suggests that we use series (1) to write

$$f(z) = \frac{1+\dfrac{1}{z}}{1-\dfrac{1}{z}} = \left(1+\frac{1}{z}\right)\frac{1}{1-\dfrac{1}{z}} = \left(1+\frac{1}{z}\right)\sum_{n=0}^{\infty}\frac{1}{z^n} = \sum_{n=0}^{\infty}\frac{1}{z^n} + \sum_{n=0}^{\infty}\frac{1}{z^{n+1}}$$
$$(1 < |z| < \infty).$$

Substituting $n-1$ for n in the last of these series reveals that

$$f(z) = \sum_{n=0}^{\infty}\frac{1}{z^n} + \sum_{n=1}^{\infty}\frac{1}{z^n} \qquad (1 < |z| < \infty),$$

and we arrive at the Laurent series

(4) $$f(z) = 1 + 2\sum_{n=1}^{\infty}\frac{1}{z^n} \qquad (1 < |z| < \infty).$$

EXAMPLE 3. Replacing z by $1/z$ in the Maclaurin series expansion

$$e^z = \sum_{n=0}^{\infty}\frac{z^n}{n!} = 1 + \frac{z}{1!} + \frac{z^2}{2!} + \frac{z^3}{3!} + \cdots \qquad (|z| < \infty),$$

we have the Laurent series representation

$$e^{1/z} = \sum_{n=0}^{\infty}\frac{1}{n!\,z^n} = 1 + \frac{1}{1!z} + \frac{1}{2!z^2} + \frac{1}{3!z^3} + \cdots \qquad (0 < |z| < \infty).$$

Note that no positive powers of z appear here, since the coefficients of the positive powers are zero. Note, too, that the coefficient of $1/z$ is unity; and, according to Laurent's theorem in Sec. 66, that coefficient is the number

$$b_1 = \frac{1}{2\pi i}\int_C e^{1/z}\,dz$$

where C is any positively oriented simple closed contour around the origin. Since $b_1 = 1$, then,

$$\int_C e^{1/z}\,dz = 2\pi i.$$

This method of evaluating certain integrals around simple closed contours will be developed in considerable detail in Chap. 6 and then used extensively in Chap. 7.

EXAMPLE 4. The function $f(z) = 1/(z-i)^2$ is already in the form of a Laurent series, where $z_0 = i$. That is,

$$\frac{1}{(z-i)^2} = \sum_{n=-\infty}^{\infty} c_n (z-i)^n \qquad (0 < |z-i| < \infty)$$

where $c_{-2} = 1$ and all of the other coefficients are zero. From expression (5), Sec. 66, for the coefficients in a Laurent series, we know that

$$c_n = \frac{1}{2\pi i}\int_C \frac{dz}{(z-i)^{n+3}} \qquad (n = 0, \pm 1, \pm 2, \ldots)$$

where C is, for instance, any positively oriented circle $|z-i| = R$ about the point $z_0 = i$. Thus [compare with Exercise 13, Sec. 46]

$$\int_C \frac{dz}{(z-i)^{n+3}} = \begin{cases} 0 & \text{when } n \neq -2, \\ 2\pi i & \text{when } n = -2. \end{cases}$$

EXERCISES

1. Find the Laurent series that represents the function

$$f(z) = z^2 \sin\left(\frac{1}{z^2}\right)$$

in the domain $0 < |z| < \infty$.

Ans. $1 + \sum_{n=1}^{\infty} \frac{(-1)^n}{(2n+1)!} \cdot \frac{1}{z^{4n}}$.

2. Find a representation for the function

$$f(z) = \frac{1}{1+z} = \frac{1}{z} \cdot \frac{1}{1+(1/z)}$$

in negative powers of z that is valid when $1 < |z| < \infty$.

Ans. $\sum_{n=1}^{\infty} \frac{(-1)^{n+1}}{z^n}$.

3. Find the Laurent series that represents the function $f(z)$ in Example 1, Sec. 68, when $1 < |z| < \infty$.

Ans. $\sum_{n=1}^{\infty} \frac{(-1)^{n+1}}{z^{2n+1}}$.

4. Give two Laurent series expansions in powers of z for the function

$$f(z) = \frac{1}{z^2(1-z)},$$

and specify the regions in which those expansions are valid.

Ans. $\displaystyle\sum_{n=0}^{\infty} z^n + \frac{1}{z} + \frac{1}{z^2} \quad (0 < |z| < 1); \qquad -\sum_{n=3}^{\infty} \frac{1}{z^n} \quad (1 < |z| < \infty).$

5. The function

$$f(z) = \frac{-1}{(z-1)(z-2)} = \frac{1}{z-1} - \frac{1}{z-2},$$

which has the two singular points $z = 1$ and $z = 2$, is analytic in the domains (Fig. 84)

$$D_1 : |z| < 1, \quad D_2 : 1 < |z| < 2, \quad D_3 : 2 < |z| < \infty.$$

Find the series representation in powers of z for $f(z)$ in each of those domains.

Ans. $\displaystyle\sum_{n=0}^{\infty} (2^{-n-1} - 1) z^n$ in D_1; $\displaystyle\sum_{n=0}^{\infty} \frac{z^n}{2^{n+1}} + \sum_{n=1}^{\infty} \frac{1}{z^n}$ in D_2; $\displaystyle\sum_{n=1}^{\infty} \frac{1 - 2^{n-1}}{z^n}$ in D_3.

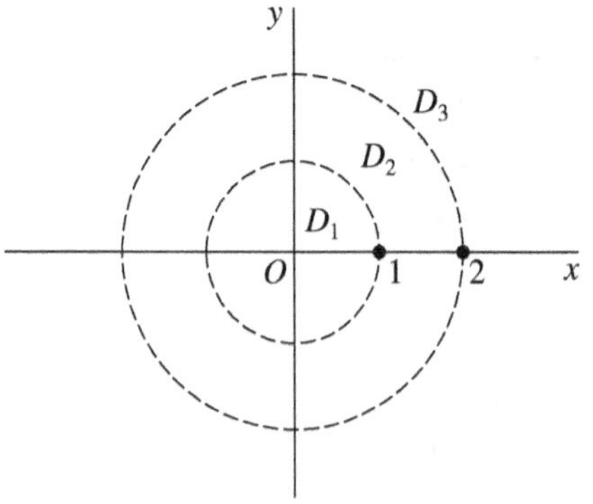

FIGURE 84

6. Show that when $0 < |z-1| < 2$,

$$\frac{z}{(z-1)(z-3)} = -3\sum_{n=0}^{\infty} \frac{(z-1)^n}{2^{n+2}} - \frac{1}{2(z-1)}.$$

7. (*a*) Let a denote a real number, where $-1 < a < 1$, and derive the Laurent series representation

$$\frac{a}{z-a} = \sum_{n=1}^{\infty} \frac{a^n}{z^n} \qquad (|a| < |z| < \infty).$$

(*b*) After writing $z = e^{i\theta}$ in the equation obtained in part (*a*), equate real parts and then imaginary parts on each side of the result to derive the summation formulas

$$\sum_{n=1}^{\infty} a^n \cos n\theta = \frac{a\cos\theta - a^2}{1 - 2a\cos\theta + a^2} \quad \text{and} \quad \sum_{n=1}^{\infty} a^n \sin n\theta = \frac{a\sin\theta}{1 - 2a\cos\theta + a^2},$$

where $-1 < a < 1$. (Compare with Exercise 4, Sec. 61.)

8. Suppose that a series

$$\sum_{n=-\infty}^{\infty} x[n]z^{-n}$$

converges to an analytic function $X(z)$ in some annulus $R_1 < |z| < R_2$. That sum $X(z)$ is called the ***z-transform*** of $x[n]$ $(n = 0, \pm 1, \pm 2, \ldots)$.* Use expression (5), Sec. 66, for the coefficients in a Laurent series to show that if the annulus contains the unit circle $|z| = 1$, then the *inverse* z-transform of $X(z)$ can be written

$$x[n] = \frac{1}{2\pi}\int_{-\pi}^{\pi} X(e^{i\theta})e^{in\theta}\,d\theta \qquad (n = 0, \pm 1, \pm 2, \ldots).$$

9. (*a*) Let z be any complex number, and let C denote the unit circle

$$w = e^{i\phi} \qquad (-\pi \le \phi \le \pi)$$

in the w plane. Then use that contour in expression (5), Sec. 66, for the coefficients in a Laurent series, adapted to such series about the origin in the w plane, to show that

$$\exp\left[\frac{z}{2}\left(w - \frac{1}{w}\right)\right] = \sum_{n=-\infty}^{\infty} J_n(z)w^n \qquad (0 < |w| < \infty)$$

where

$$J_n(z) = \frac{1}{2\pi}\int_{-\pi}^{\pi} \exp[-i(n\phi - z\sin\phi)]\,d\phi \qquad (n = 0, \pm 1, \pm 2, \ldots).$$

(*b*) With the aid of Exercise 5, Sec. 42, regarding certain definite integrals of even and odd complex-valued functions of a real variable, show that the coefficients in part (*a*) here can be written†

$$J_n(z) = \frac{1}{\pi}\int_{0}^{\pi} \cos(n\phi - z\sin\phi)\,d\phi \qquad (n = 0, \pm 1, \pm 2, \ldots).$$

10. (*a*) Let $f(z)$ denote a function which is analytic in some annular domain about the origin that includes the unit circle $z = e^{i\phi}$ $(-\pi \le \phi \le \pi)$. By taking that circle as the path of integration in expressions (2) and (3), Sec. 66, for the coefficients a_n and b_n in a Laurent series in powers of z, show that

$$f(z) = \frac{1}{2\pi}\int_{-\pi}^{\pi} f(e^{i\phi})\,d\phi + \frac{1}{2\pi}\sum_{n=1}^{\infty}\int_{-\pi}^{\pi} f(e^{i\phi})\left[\left(\frac{z}{e^{i\phi}}\right)^n + \left(\frac{e^{i\phi}}{z}\right)^n\right] d\phi$$

when z is any point in the annular domain.

---

*The z-transform arises in studies of discrete-time linear systems. See, for instance, the book by Oppenheim, Schafer, and Buck that is listed in Appendix 1.

†These coefficients $J_n(z)$ are called ***Bessel functions*** of the first kind. They play a prominent role in certain areas of applied mathematics. See, for example, the authors' "*Fourier Series and Boundary Value Problems*," 8th ed., Chap. 9, 2012.

(*b*) Write $u(\theta) = \text{Re}[f(e^{i\theta})]$ and show how it follows from the expansion in part (*a*) that

$$u(\theta) = \frac{1}{2\pi}\int_{-\pi}^{\pi} u(\phi)\,d\phi + \frac{1}{\pi}\sum_{n=1}^{\infty}\int_{-\pi}^{\pi} u(\phi)\cos[n(\theta-\phi)]\,d\phi.$$

This is one form of the ***Fourier series*** expansion of the real-valued function $u(\theta)$ on the interval $-\pi \le \theta \le \pi$. The restriction on $u(\theta)$ is more severe than is necessary in order for it to be represented by a Fourier series.*

69. ABSOLUTE AND UNIFORM CONVERGENCE OF POWER SERIES

This section and the three following it are devoted mainly to various properties of power series. A reader who wishes to simply accept the theorems and the corollary in these sections can easily skip the proofs in order to reach Sec. 73 more quickly.

We recall from Sec. 61 that a series of complex numbers converges *absolutely* if the series of absolute values of those numbers converges. The following theorem concerns the absolute convergence of power series.

Theorem 1. *If a power series*

$$\sum_{n=0}^{\infty} a_n(z-z_0)^n \tag{1}$$

converges when $z = z_1$ $(z_1 \ne z_0)$, *then it is absolutely convergent at each point* z *in the open disk* $|z-z_0| < R_1$ *where* $R_1 = |z_1 - z_0|$ (Fig. 85).

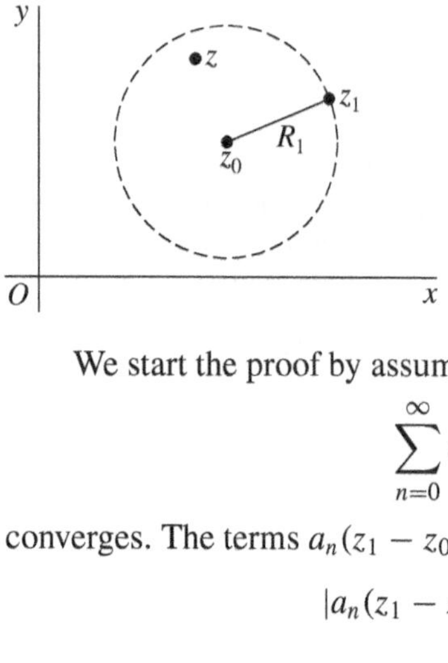

FIGURE 85

We start the proof by assuming that the series

$$\sum_{n=0}^{\infty} a_n(z_1-z_0)^n \quad (z_1 \ne z_0)$$

converges. The terms $a_n(z_1-z_0)^n$ are thus bounded; that is,

$$|a_n(z_1-z_0)^n| \le M \quad (n = 0, 1, 2, \ldots)$$

*For other sufficient conditions, see Secs. 12 and 13 of the book cited in the footnote to Exercise 9.

for some positive constant M (see Sec. 61). If $|z - z_0| < R_1$ and if we write

$$\rho = \frac{|z - z_0|}{|z_1 - z_0|},$$

we can see that

$$|a_n(z - z_0)^n| = |a_n(z_1 - z_0)^n| \left(\frac{|z - z_0|}{|z_1 - z_0|}\right)^n \leq M\rho^n \quad (n = 0, 1, 2, \ldots).$$

Now the series

$$\sum_{n=0}^{\infty} M\rho^n$$

is a geometric series, which converges since $\rho < 1$. Hence, by the comparison test for series of real numbers,

$$\sum_{n=0}^{\infty} |a_n(z - z_0)^n|$$

converges in the open disk $|z - z_0| < R_1$. This completes the proof.

The theorem tells us that the set of all points inside some circle centered at z_0 is a region of convergence for the power series (1), provided it converges at some point other than z_0. The greatest circle centered at z_0 such that series (1) converges at each point inside is called the ***circle of convergence*** of series (1). The series cannot converge at any point z_2 outside that circle, according to the theorem; for if it did, it would converge everywhere inside the circle centered at z_0 and passing through z_2. The first circle could not, then, be the circle of convergence.

Our next theorem involves terminology that we must first define. Suppose that the power series (1) has circle of convergence $|z - z_0| = R$, and let $S(z)$ and $S_N(z)$ represent the sum and partial sums, respectively, of that series:

$$S(z) = \sum_{n=0}^{\infty} a_n(z - z_0)^n, \quad S_N(z) = \sum_{n=0}^{N-1} a_n(z - z_0)^n \qquad (|z - z_0| < R).$$

Then write the remainder function (see Sec. 61)

$$\rho_N(z) = S(z) - S_N(z) \qquad (|z - z_0| < R). \tag{2}$$

Since the power series converges for any fixed value of z when $|z - z_0| < R$, we know that the remainder $\rho_N(z)$ approaches zero for any such z as N tends to infinity. According to definition (1), Sec. 60, of the limit of a sequence, this means that corresponding to each positive number ε, there is a positive integer N_ε such that

$$|\rho_N(z)| < \varepsilon \quad \text{whenever} \quad N > N_\varepsilon. \tag{3}$$

When the choice of N_ε depends only on the value of ε and is independent of the point z taken in a specified region within the circle of convergence, the convergence is said to be ***uniform*** in that region.

Theorem 2. *If z_1 is a point inside the circle of convergence $|z - z_0| = R$ of a power series*

$$\sum_{n=0}^{\infty} a_n(z - z_0)^n, \tag{4}$$

then that series must be uniformly convergent in the closed disk $|z - z_0| \leq R_1$, where $R_1 = |z_1 - z_0|$ (Fig. 86).

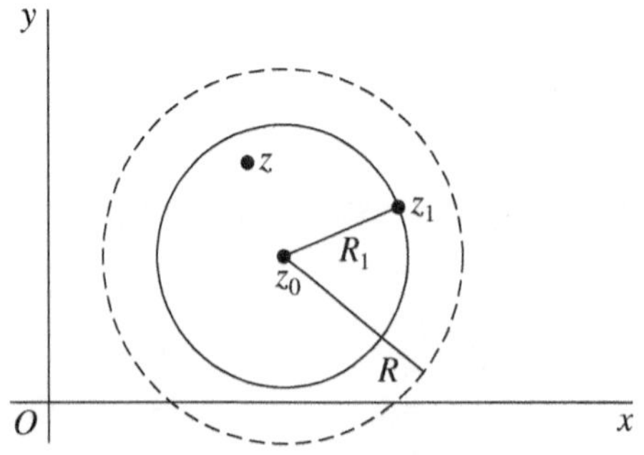

FIGURE 86

Our proof of this theorem depends on Theorem 1. Given that z_1 is a point lying inside the circle of convergence of series (4), we note that there are points inside that circle and farther from z_0 than z_1 for which the series converges. So, according to Theorem 1,

$$\sum_{n=0}^{\infty} |a_n(z_1 - z_0)^n| \tag{5}$$

converges. Letting m and N denote positive integers, where $m > N$, one can write the remainders of series (4) and (5) as

$$\rho_N(z) = \lim_{m\to\infty} \sum_{n=N}^{m} a_n(z - z_0)^n \tag{6}$$

and

$$\sigma_N = \lim_{m\to\infty} \sum_{n=N}^{m} |a_n(z_1 - z_0)^n|, \tag{7}$$

respectively.

Now, in view of Exercise 3, Sec. 61,

$$|\rho_N(z)| = \lim_{m\to\infty} \left| \sum_{n=N}^{m} a_n(z - z_0)^n \right|;$$

and, when $|z - z_0| \leq |z_1 - z_0|$,

$$\left| \sum_{n=N}^{m} a_n(z - z_0)^n \right| \leq \sum_{n=N}^{m} |a_n||z - z_0|^n \leq \sum_{n=N}^{m} |a_n||z_1 - z_0|^n = \sum_{n=N}^{m} |a_n(z_1 - z_0)^n|.$$

Consequently,

$$(8) \qquad |\rho_N(z)| \le \sigma_N \quad \text{when} \quad |z - z_0| \le R_1.$$

Since σ_N are the remainders of a convergent series, they tend to zero as N tends to infinity. That is, for each positive number ε, an integer N_ε exists such that

$$(9) \qquad \sigma_N < \varepsilon \quad \text{whenever} \quad N > N_\varepsilon.$$

Because of conditions (8) and (9), then, condition (3) holds for all points z in the disk $|z - z_0| \le R_1$; and the value of N_ε is independent of the choice of z. Hence the convergence of series (4) is uniform in that disk.

70. CONTINUITY OF SUMS OF POWER SERIES

Our next theorem is an important consequence of uniform convergence, discussed in the Sec. 69.

Theorem. *A power series*

$$(1) \qquad \sum_{n=0}^{\infty} a_n (z - z_0)^n$$

represents a continuous function $S(z)$ at each point inside its circle of convergence $|z - z_0| = R$.

Another way to state this theorem is to say that if $S(z)$ denotes the sum of series (1) within its circle of convergence $|z - z_0| = R$ and if z_1 is a point inside that circle, then for each positive number ε there is a positive number δ such that

$$(2) \qquad |S(z) - S(z_1)| < \varepsilon \quad \text{whenever} \quad |z - z_1| < \delta.$$

[See definition (4), Sec. 18, of continuity.] The number δ here is small enough so that z lies in the domain of definition $|z - z_0| < R$ of $S(z)$ (Fig. 87).

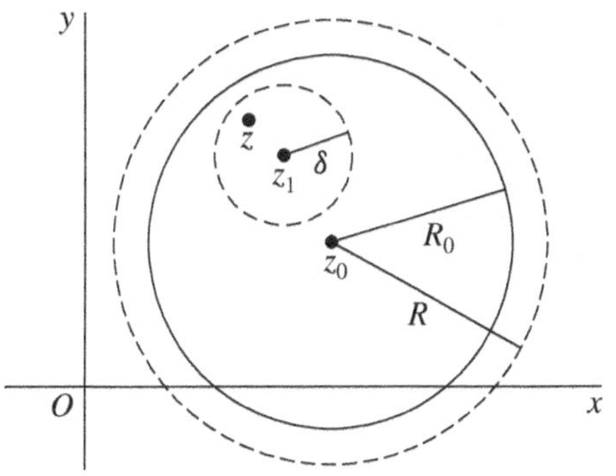

FIGURE 87

To prove the theorem, we let $S_n(z)$ denote the sum of the first N terms of series (1) and write the remainder function

$$\rho_N(z) = S(z) - S_N(z) \qquad (|z - z_0| < R).$$

Then, because

$$S(z) = S_N(z) + \rho_N(z) \qquad (|z - z_0| < R),$$

one can see that

$$|S(z) - S(z_1)| = |S_N(z) - S_N(z_1) + \rho_N(z) - \rho_N(z_1)|,$$

or

$$(3) \qquad |S(z) - S(z_1)| \le |S_N(z) - S_N(z_1)| + |\rho_N(z)| + |\rho_N(z_1)|.$$

If z is any point lying in some closed disk $|z - z_0| \le R_0$ whose radius R_0 is greater than $|z_1 - z_0|$ but less than the radius R of the circle of convergence of series (1) (see Fig. 87), the uniform convergence stated in Theorem 2, Sec. 69, ensures that there is a positive integer N_ε such that

$$(4) \qquad |\rho_N(z)| < \frac{\varepsilon}{3} \quad \text{whenever} \quad N > N_\varepsilon.$$

In particular, condition (4) holds for each point z in some neighborhood $|z - z_1| < \delta$ of z_1 that is small enough to be contained in the disk $|z - z_0| \le R_0$.

Now the partial sum $S_N(z)$ is a polynomial and is, therefore, continuous at z_1 for each value of N. In particular, when $N = N_\varepsilon + 1$, we can choose our δ so small that

$$(5) \qquad |S_N(z) - S_N(z_1)| < \frac{\varepsilon}{3} \quad \text{whenever} \quad |z - z_1| < \delta.$$

By writing $N = N_\varepsilon + 1$ in inequality (3) and using the fact that statements (4) and (5) are true when $N = N_\varepsilon + 1$, we now find that

$$|S(z) - S(z_1)| < \frac{\varepsilon}{3} + \frac{\varepsilon}{3} + \frac{\varepsilon}{3} \quad \text{whenever} \quad |z - z_1| < \delta.$$

This is statement (2), and the theorem is now established.

By writing $w = 1/(z - z_0)$, one can modify the two theorems in the previous section and the theorem here so as to apply to series of the type

$$(6) \qquad \sum_{n=1}^{\infty} \frac{b_n}{(z - z_0)^n}.$$

If, for instance, series (6) converges at a point z_1 $(z_1 \ne z_0)$, the series

$$\sum_{n=1}^{\infty} b_n w^n$$

must converge absolutely to a continuous function when

$$|w| < \frac{1}{|z_1 - z_0|}. \tag{7}$$

Thus, since inequality (7) is the same as $|z - z_0| > |z_1 - z_0|$, series (6) must converge absolutely to a continuous function in the domain *exterior to* the circle $|z - z_0| = R_1$, where $R_1 = |z_1 - z_0|$. Also, we know that if a Laurent series representation

$$f(z) = \sum_{n=0}^{\infty} a_n (z - z_0)^n + \sum_{n=1}^{\infty} \frac{b_n}{(z - z_0)^n}$$

is valid in an annulus $R_1 < |z - z_0| < R_2$, then *both* of the series on the right converge uniformly in any closed annulus which is concentric to and interior to that region of validity.

71. INTEGRATION AND DIFFERENTIATION OF POWER SERIES

We have just seen that a power series

$$S(z) = \sum_{n=0}^{\infty} a_n (z - z_0)^n \tag{1}$$

represents a continuous function at each point interior to its circle of convergence. In this section, we prove that the sum $S(z)$ is actually analytic within that circle. Our proof depends on the following theorem, which is of interest in itself.

Theorem 1. *Let C denote any contour interior to the circle of convergence of the power series* (1), *and let $g(z)$ be any function that is continuous on C. The series formed by multiplying each term of the power series by $g(z)$ can be integrated term by term over C; that is,*

$$\int_C g(z)S(z)\,dz = \sum_{n=0}^{\infty} a_n \int_C g(z)(z - z_0)^n\,dz. \tag{2}$$

To prove this theorem, we note that since both $g(z)$ and the sum $S(z)$ of the power series are continuous on C, the integral over C of the product

$$g(z)S(z) = \sum_{n=0}^{N-1} a_n\, g(z)(z - z_0)^n + g(z)\rho_N(z),$$

where $\rho_N(z)$ is the remainder of the given series after N terms, exists. The terms of the finite sum here are also continuous on the contour C, and so their integrals over

C exist. Consequently, the integral of the quantity $g(z)\rho_N(z)$ must exist; and we may write

$$\int_C g(z)S(z)\,dz = \sum_{n=0}^{N-1} a_n \int_C g(z)(z-z_0)^n\,dz + \int_C g(z)\rho_N(z)\,dz. \tag{3}$$

Now let M be the maximum value of $|g(z)|$ on C, and let L denote the length of C. In view of the uniform convergence of the given power series (Sec. 69), we know that for each positive number ε there exists a positive integer N_ε such that, for all points z on C,

$$|\rho_N(z)| < \varepsilon \quad \text{whenever} \quad N > N_\varepsilon.$$

Since N_ε is independent of z, we find that

$$\left|\int_C g(z)\rho_N(z)\,dz\right| < M\varepsilon L \quad \text{whenever} \quad N > N_\varepsilon;$$

that is,

$$\lim_{N\to\infty} \int_C g(z)\rho_N(z)\,dz = 0.$$

It follows, therefore, from equation (3) that

$$\int_C g(z)S(z)\,dz = \lim_{N\to\infty} \sum_{n=0}^{N-1} a_n \int_C g(z)(z-z_0)^n\,dz.$$

This is the same as equation (2), and Theorem 1 is proved.

If $|g(z)| = 1$ for each value of z in the open disk bounded by the circle of convergence of power series (1), the fact that $(z-z_0)^n$ is entire when $n = 0, 1, 2, \ldots$ ensures that

$$\int_C g(z)(z-z_0)^n\,dz = \int_C (z-z_0)^n\,dz = 0 \qquad (n = 0, 1, 2, \ldots)$$

for every *closed* contour C lying in that domain. According to equation (2), then,

$$\int_C S(z)\,dz = 0$$

for every such contour; and, by Morera's theorem (Sec. 57), the function $S(z)$ is analytic throughout the domain. We state this result as a corollary.

Corollary. *The sum $S(z)$ of power series* (1) *is analytic at each point z interior to the circle of convergence of that series.*

This corollary is often helpful in establishing the analyticity of functions and in evaluating limits.

EXAMPLE 1. To illustrate, let us show that the function defined by means of the equations

$$f(z) = \begin{cases} (\sin z)/z & \text{when } z \neq 0, \\ 1 & \text{when } z = 0 \end{cases}$$

is entire. Since the Maclaurin series representation

$$\sin z = \sum_{n=0}^{\infty} (-1)^n \frac{z^{2n+1}}{(2n+1)!} \tag{4}$$

is valid for every value of z, the series

$$\sum_{n=0}^{\infty} (-1)^n \frac{z^{2n}}{(2n+1)!} = 1 - \frac{z^2}{3!} + \frac{z^4}{5!} - \cdots, \tag{5}$$

obtained by dividing each side of equation (4) by z, converges to $f(z)$ when $z \neq 0$. Also, series (5) clearly converges to $f(z)$ when $z = 0$. Hence $f(z)$ is represented by the convergent series (5) for all z; and f is, therefore, an entire function.

Note that since $(\sin z)/z = f(z)$ when $z \neq 0$ and f is continuous at $z = 0$,

$$\lim_{z \to 0} \frac{\sin z}{z} = \lim_{z \to 0} f(z) = f(0) = 1.$$

This is a result known beforehand because the limit here is the definition of the derivative of $\sin z$ at $z = 0$. That is,

$$\lim_{z \to 0} \frac{\sin z}{z} = \lim_{z \to 0} \frac{\sin z - \sin 0}{z - 0} = \cos 0 = 1.$$

We observed in Sec. 62 that the Taylor series for a function f about a point z_0 converges to $f(z)$ at each point z interior to the circle centered at z_0 and passing through the nearest point z_1 where f fails to be analytic. In view of our corollary to Theorem 1, we now know that *there is no larger circle* about z_0 such that at each point z interior to it the Taylor series converges to $f(z)$. For if there were such a circle, f would be analytic at z_1; but f is not analytic at z_1.

We now present a companion to Theorem 1.

Theorem 2. *The power series* (1) *can be differentiated term by term. That is, at each point z interior to the circle of convergence of that series,*

$$S'(z) = \sum_{n=1}^{\infty} n a_n (z - z_0)^{n-1}. \tag{6}$$

To prove this, let z denote any point interior to the circle of convergence of series (1). Then let C be some positively oriented simple closed contour surrounding z and interior to that circle. Also, define the function

$$g(s) = \frac{1}{2\pi i} \cdot \frac{1}{(s - z)^2} \tag{7}$$

at each point s on C. Since $g(s)$ is continuous on C, Theorem 1 tells us that

$$\int_C g(s)S(s)\,ds = \sum_{n=0}^{\infty} a_n \int_C g(s)(s-z_0)^n\,ds. \tag{8}$$

Now $S(z)$ is analytic inside and on C, and this enables us to write

$$\int_C g(s)S(s)\,ds = \frac{1}{2\pi i}\int_C \frac{S(s)\,ds}{(s-z)^2} = S'(z)$$

with the aid of the integral representation for derivatives in Sec. 55. Furthermore,

$$\int_C g(s)(s-z_0)^n\,ds = \frac{1}{2\pi i}\int_C \frac{(s-z_0)^n}{(s-z)^2}\,ds = \frac{d}{dz}(z-z_0)^n \qquad (n = 0, 1, 2, \ldots).$$

Thus equation (8) reduces to

$$S'(z) = \sum_{n=0}^{\infty} a_n \frac{d}{dz}(z-z_0)^n,$$

which is the same as equation (6). This completes the proof.

EXAMPLE 2. In Example 1, Sec. 64, we saw that

$$\frac{1}{z} = \sum_{n=0}^{\infty}(-1)^n(z-1)^n \qquad (|z-1| < 1).$$

Differentiation of each side of this equation reveals that

$$-\frac{1}{z^2} = \sum_{n=1}^{\infty}(-1)^n n(z-1)^{n-1} \qquad (|z-1| < 1),$$

or

$$\frac{1}{z^2} = \sum_{n=0}^{\infty}(-1)^n(n+1)(z-1)^n \qquad (|z-1| < 1).$$

72. UNIQUENESS OF SERIES REPRESENTATIONS

The uniqueness of Taylor and Laurent series representations, anticipated in Secs. 64 and 68, respectively, follows readily from Theorem 1 in Sec. 71. We consider first the uniqueness of Taylor series representations.

Theorem 1. *If a series*

$$\sum_{n=0}^{\infty} a_n(z-z_0)^n \tag{1}$$

converges to $f(z)$ at all points interior to some circle $|z-z_0| = R$, then it is the Taylor series expansion for f in powers of $z-z_0$.

To start the proof, we write the series representation

$$f(z) = \sum_{n=0}^{\infty} a_n (z - z_0)^n \qquad (|z - z_0| < R) \tag{2}$$

in the hypothesis of the theorem using the index of summation m:

$$f(z) = \sum_{m=0}^{\infty} a_m (z - z_0)^m \qquad (|z - z_0| < R).$$

Then, by appealing to Theorem 1 in Sec. 71, we may write

$$\int_C g(z) f(z)\, dz = \sum_{m=0}^{\infty} a_m \int_C g(z)(z - z_0)^m\, dz, \tag{3}$$

where $g(z)$ is any one of the functions

$$g(z) = \frac{1}{2\pi i} \cdot \frac{1}{(z - z_0)^{n+1}} \qquad (n = 0, 1, 2, \ldots) \tag{4}$$

and C is some circle centered at z_0 and with radius less than R.

In view of the extension (3), Sec. 55, of the Cauchy integral formula (see also the corollary in Sec. 71), we find that

$$\int_C g(z) f(z)\, dz = \frac{1}{2\pi i} \int_C \frac{f(z)\, dz}{(z - z_0)^{n+1}} = \frac{f^{(n)}(z_0)}{n!}; \tag{5}$$

and, since (see Exercise 13, Sec. 46)

$$\int_C g(z)(z - z_0)^m\, dz = \frac{1}{2\pi i} \int_C \frac{dz}{(z - z_0)^{n-m+1}} = \begin{cases} 0 & \text{when } m \neq n, \\ 1 & \text{when } m = n, \end{cases} \tag{6}$$

it is clear that

$$\sum_{m=0}^{\infty} a_m \int_C g(z)(z - z_0)^m\, dz = a_n. \tag{7}$$

Because of equations (5) and (7), equation (3) now reduces to

$$\frac{f^{(n)}(z_0)}{n!} = a_n.$$

This shows that series (2) is, in fact, the Taylor series for f about the point z_0.

Note how it follows from Theorem 1 that if series (1) converges to zero throughout some neighborhood of z_0, then the coefficients a_n must all be zero.

Our second theorem here concerns the uniqueness of Laurent series representations.

Theorem 2. *If a series*

$$\sum_{n=-\infty}^{\infty} c_n (z - z_0)^n = \sum_{n=0}^{\infty} a_n (z - z_0)^n + \sum_{n=1}^{\infty} \frac{b_n}{(z - z_0)^n} \tag{8}$$

converges to $f(z)$ at all points in some annular domain about z_0, then it is the Laurent series expansion for f in powers of $z - z_0$ for that domain.

The method of proof here is similar to the one used in proving Theorem 1. The hypothesis of this theorem tells us that there is an annular domain about z_0 such that

$$f(z) = \sum_{n=-\infty}^{\infty} c_n (z - z_0)^n$$

for each point z in it. Let $g(z)$ be as defined by equation (4), but now allow n to be a negative integer too. Also, let C be any circle around the annulus, centered at z_0 and taken in the positive sense. Then, using the index of summation m and adapting Theorem 1 in Sec. 71 to series involving both nonnegative *and* negative powers of $z - z_0$ (Exercise 10), write

$$\int_C g(z) f(z)\, dz = \sum_{m=-\infty}^{\infty} c_m \int_C g(z)(z - z_0)^m\, dz,$$

or

$$\frac{1}{2\pi i}\int_C \frac{f(z)\, dz}{(z - z_0)^{n+1}} = \sum_{m=-\infty}^{\infty} c_m \int_C g(z)(z - z_0)^m\, dz. \tag{9}$$

Since equations (6) are also valid when the integers m and n are allowed to be negative, equation (9) reduces to

$$\frac{1}{2\pi i}\int_C \frac{f(z)\, dz}{(z - z_0)^{n+1}} = c_n \qquad (n = 0, \pm 1, \pm 2, \ldots),$$

which is expression (5), Sec. 66, for the coefficients c_n in the Laurent series for f in the annulus.

EXERCISES

1. By differentiating the Maclaurin series representation

$$\frac{1}{1 - z} = \sum_{n=0}^{\infty} z^n \qquad (|z| < 1),$$

obtain the expansions

$$\frac{1}{(1 - z)^2} = \sum_{n=0}^{\infty} (n + 1)\, z^n \qquad (|z| < 1)$$

and

$$\frac{2}{(1 - z)^3} = \sum_{n=0}^{\infty} (n + 1)(n + 2)\, z^n \qquad (|z| < 1).$$

2. By substituting $1/(1-z)$ for z in the expansion

$$\frac{1}{(1-z)^2} = \sum_{n=0}^{\infty}(n+1)\,z^n \qquad (|z| < 1),$$

found in Exercise 1, derive the Laurent series representation

$$\frac{1}{z^2} = \sum_{n=2}^{\infty}\frac{(-1)^n(n-1)}{(z-1)^n} \qquad (1 < |z-1| < \infty).$$

(Compare with Example 2, Sec. 71.)

3. Find the Taylor series for the function

$$\frac{1}{z} = \frac{1}{2+(z-2)} = \frac{1}{2}\cdot\frac{1}{1+(z-2)/2}$$

about the point $z_0 = 2$. Then, by differentiating that series term by term, show that

$$\frac{1}{z^2} = \frac{1}{4}\sum_{n=0}^{\infty}(-1)^n(n+1)\left(\frac{z-2}{2}\right)^n \qquad (|z-2| < 2).$$

4. Show that the function defined by means of the equations

$$f(z) = \begin{cases}(1-\cos z)/z^2 & \text{when } z \neq 0,\\ 1/2 & \text{when } z = 0\end{cases}$$

is entire. (See Example 1, Sec. 71.)

5. Prove that if

$$f(z) = \begin{cases}\dfrac{\cos z}{z^2-(\pi/2)^2} & \text{when } z \neq \pm\pi/2,\\[2ex] -\dfrac{1}{\pi} & \text{when } z = \pm\pi/2,\end{cases}$$

then f is an entire function.

6. In the w plane, integrate the Taylor series expansion (see Example 1, Sec. 64)

$$\frac{1}{w} = \sum_{n=0}^{\infty}(-1)^n(w-1)^n \qquad (|w-1| < 1)$$

along a contour interior to its circle of convergence from $w = 1$ to $w = z$ to obtain the representation

$$\text{Log}\, z = \sum_{n=1}^{\infty}\frac{(-1)^{n+1}}{n}(z-1)^n \qquad (|z-1| < 1).$$

7. Use the result in Exercise 6 to show that if

$$f(z) = \frac{\text{Log}\, z}{z-1} \qquad \text{when } z \neq 1$$

and $f(1) = 1$, then f is analytic throughout the domain

$$0 < |z| < \infty,\ -\pi < \text{Arg}\, z < \pi.$$

8. Prove that if f is analytic at z_0 and $f(z_0) = f'(z_0) = \cdots = f^{(m)}(z_0) = 0$, then the function g defined by means of the equations

$$g(z) = \begin{cases} \dfrac{f(z)}{(z-z_0)^{m+1}} & \text{when } z \neq z_0, \\ \dfrac{f^{(m+1)}(z_0)}{(m+1)!} & \text{when } z = z_0 \end{cases}$$

is analytic at z_0.

9. Suppose that a function $f(z)$ has a power series representation

$$f(z) = \sum_{n=0}^{\infty} a_n (z - z_0)^n$$

inside some circle $|z - z_0| = R$. Use Theorem 2 in Sec. 71, regarding term by term differentiation of such a series, and mathematical induction to show that

$$f^{(n)}(z) = \sum_{k=0}^{\infty} \frac{(n+k)!}{k!} a_{n+k} (z - z_0)^k \qquad (n = 0, 1, 2, \ldots)$$

when $|z - z_0| < R$. Then, by setting $z = z_0$, show that the coefficients a_n $(n = 0, 1, 2, \ldots)$ are the coefficients in the Taylor series for f about z_0. Thus give an alternative proof of Theorem 1 in Sec. 72.

10. Consider two series

$$S_1(z) = \sum_{n=0}^{\infty} a_n (z - z_0)^n \quad \text{and} \quad S_2(z) = \sum_{n=1}^{\infty} \frac{b_n}{(z - z_0)^n},$$

which converge in some annular domain centered at z_0. Let C denote any contour lying in that annulus, and let $g(z)$ be a function which is continuous on C. Modify the proof of Theorem 1, Sec. 71, which tells us that

$$\int_C g(z) S_1(z)\, dz = \sum_{n=0}^{\infty} a_n \int_C g(z)(z - z_0)^n\, dz,$$

to prove that

$$\int_C g(z) S_2(z)\, dz = \sum_{n=1}^{\infty} b_n \int_C \frac{g(z)}{(z - z_0)^n}\, dz.$$

Conclude from these results that if

$$S(z) = \sum_{n=-\infty}^{\infty} c_n (z - z_0)^n = \sum_{n=0}^{\infty} a_n (z - z_0)^n + \sum_{n=1}^{\infty} \frac{b_n}{(z - z_0)^n},$$

then

$$\int_C g(z)S(z)\,dz = \sum_{n=-\infty}^{\infty} c_n \int_C g(z)(z-z_0)^n\,dz.$$

11. Show that the function

$$f_2(z) = \frac{1}{z^2+1} \qquad (z \neq \pm i)$$

is the analytic continuation (Sec. 28) of the function

$$f_1(z) = \sum_{n=0}^{\infty} (-1)^n z^{2n} \qquad (|z| < 1)$$

into the domain consisting of all points in the z plane except $z = \pm i$.

12. Show that the function $f_2(z) = 1/z^2$ $(z \neq 0)$ is the analytic continuation (Sec. 28) of the function

$$f_1(z) = \sum_{n=0}^{\infty} (n+1)(z+1)^n \qquad (|z+1| < 1)$$

into the domain consisting of all points in the z plane except $z = 0$.

73. MULTIPLICATION AND DIVISION OF POWER SERIES

Suppose that each of the power series

$$\sum_{n=0}^{\infty} a_n(z-z_0)^n \quad \text{and} \quad \sum_{n=0}^{\infty} b_n(z-z_0)^n \tag{1}$$

converges within some circle $|z-z_0| = R$. Their sums $f(z)$ and $g(z)$, respectively, are then analytic functions in the disk $|z-z_0| < R$ (Sec. 71), and the product of those sums has a Taylor series expansion which is valid there:

$$f(z)g(z) = \sum_{n=0}^{\infty} c_n(z-z_0)^n \qquad (|z-z_0| < R). \tag{2}$$

According to Theorem 1 in Sec. 72, the series (1) are themselves Taylor series. Hence the first three coefficients in series (2) are given by the equations

$$c_0 = f(z_0)g(z_0) = a_0b_0,$$

$$c_1 = \frac{f(z_0)g'(z_0) + f'(z_0)g(z_0)}{1!} = a_0b_1 + a_1b_0,$$

and

$$c_2 = \frac{f(z_0)g''(z_0) + 2f'(z_0)g'(z_0) + f''(z_0)g(z_0)}{2!} = a_0b_2 + a_1b_1 + a_2b_0.$$

The general expression for any coefficient c_n is easily obtained by referring to ***Leibniz's rule*** (Exercise 7)

$$(3)\qquad [f(z)g(z)]^{(n)} = \sum_{k=0}^{n} \binom{n}{k} f^{(k)}(z) g^{(n-k)}(z) \qquad (n = 1, 2, \ldots),$$

where

$$\binom{n}{k} = \frac{n!}{k!(n-k)!} \qquad (k = 0, 1, 2, \ldots, n),$$

for the nth derivative of the product of two differentiable functions. As usual, $f^{(0)}(z) = f(z)$ and $0! = 1$. Evidently,

$$c_n = \sum_{k=0}^{n} \frac{f^{(k)}(z_0)}{k!} \cdot \frac{g^{(n-k)}(z_0)}{(n-k)!} = \sum_{k=0}^{n} a_k b_{n-k};$$

and so expansion (2) can be written

$$(4)\qquad f(z)g(z) = a_0 b_0 + (a_0 b_1 + a_1 b_0)(z - z_0) + (a_0 b_2 + a_1 b_1 + a_2 b_0)(z - z_0)^2 + \cdots + \left(\sum_{k=0}^{n} a_k b_{n-k}\right)(z - z_0)^n + \cdots \qquad (|z - z_0| < R).$$

Series (4) is the same as the series obtained by formally multiplying the two series (1) term by term and collecting the resulting terms in like powers of $z - z_0$; it is called the ***Cauchy product*** of the two given series.

EXAMPLE 1. The function

$$f(z) = \frac{\sinh z}{1 + z}$$

has a singular point at $z = -1$, and so its Maclaurin series representation is valid in the open disk $|z| < 1$. The first four nonzero terms are easily found by writing

$$(\sinh z)\left(\frac{1}{1+z}\right) = \left(z + \frac{1}{6}z^3 + \frac{1}{120}z^5 + \cdots\right)(1 - z + z^2 - z^3 + \cdots)$$

and multiplying these two series term by term. To be precise, we may multiply each term in the first series by 1, then each term in the first series by $-z$, etc. The following systematic approach is suggested, where like powers of z are assembled vertically so that their coefficients can be readily added:

$$\begin{array}{ccccccc}
z & & +\frac{1}{6}z^3 & & +\frac{1}{120}z^5 & & +\cdots \\
 & -z^2 & & -\frac{1}{6}z^4 & & -\frac{1}{120}z^6 & -\cdots \\
 & & z^3 & & +\frac{1}{6}z^5 & & +\cdots \\
 & & & -z^4 & & +\frac{1}{6}z^6 & -\cdots \\
 & & & & \vdots & &
\end{array}$$

The desired result, involving four nonzero terms, is found to be

$$\frac{\sinh z}{1+z} = z - z^2 + \frac{7}{6}z^3 - \frac{7}{6}z^4 + \cdots \qquad (|z| < 1). \tag{5}$$

Continuing to let $f(z)$ and $g(z)$ denote the sums of series (1), suppose that $g(z) \neq 0$ when $|z - z_0| < R$. Since the quotient $f(z)/g(z)$ is analytic throughout the disk $|z - z_0| < R$, it has a Taylor series representation

$$\frac{f(z)}{g(z)} = \sum_{n=0}^{\infty} d_n (z - z_0)^n \qquad (|z - z_0| < R), \tag{6}$$

where the coefficients d_n can be found by differentiating $f(z)/g(z)$ successively and evaluating the derivatives at $z = z_0$. The results are the same as those found by formally carrying out the division of the first of series (1) by the second. Since it is usually only the first few terms that are needed in practice, this method is not difficult.

EXAMPLE 2. As pointed out in Sec. 39, the zeros of the entire function $\sinh z$ are $z = n\pi i$ $(n = 0, \pm 1, \pm 2, \ldots)$. So the reciprocal

$$\frac{1}{\sinh z} = \frac{1}{z + \dfrac{z^3}{3!} + \dfrac{z^5}{5!} + \cdots},$$

which can be written

$$\frac{1}{\sinh z} = \frac{1}{z}\left(\frac{1}{1 + \dfrac{z^2}{3!} + \dfrac{z^4}{5!} + \cdots}\right), \tag{7}$$

has a Laurent series representation in the punctured disk $0 < |z| < \pi$. A power series representation of the function in parentheses here can be found by dividing the series in the denominator into unity as follows:

$$\begin{array}{r|l} & 1 - \frac{1}{3!}z^2 + \left[\frac{1}{(3!)^2} - \frac{1}{5!}\right]z^4 + \cdots \\ \hline 1 + \frac{1}{3!}z^2 + \frac{1}{5!}z^4 + \cdots & 1 \\ & 1 + \frac{1}{3!}z^2 \qquad + \frac{1}{5!}z^4 + \cdots \\ \hline & -\frac{1}{3!}z^2 \qquad - \frac{1}{5!}z^4 + \cdots \\ & -\frac{1}{3!}z^2 \qquad - \frac{1}{(3!)^2}z^4 - \cdots \\ \hline & \left[\frac{1}{(3!)^2} - \frac{1}{5!}\right]z^4 + \cdots \\ & \left[\frac{1}{(3!)^2} - \frac{1}{5!}\right]z^4 + \cdots \\ \hline & \vdots \end{array}$$

This shows that

$$\frac{1}{1 + \dfrac{z^2}{3!} + \dfrac{z^4}{5!} + \cdots} = 1 - \frac{1}{3!}z^2 + \left[\frac{1}{(3!)^2} - \frac{1}{5!}\right]z^4 + \cdots \qquad (|z| < \pi),$$

or

$$\frac{1}{1 + \dfrac{z^2}{3!} + \dfrac{z^4}{5!} + \cdots} = 1 - \frac{1}{6}z^2 + \frac{7}{360}z^4 + \cdots \qquad (|z| < \pi). \tag{8}$$

In view of equation (7), then,

$$\frac{1}{\sinh z} = \frac{1}{z} - \frac{1}{6}z + \frac{7}{360}z^3 + \cdots \qquad (0 < |z| < \pi). \tag{9}$$

Although we have given only the first three nonzero terms of this Laurent series, any number of terms can, of course, be found by continuing the division.

EXERCISES

1. Use multiplication of series to show that

$$\frac{e^z}{z(z^2+1)} = \frac{1}{z} + 1 - \frac{1}{2}z - \frac{5}{6}z^2 + \cdots \qquad (0 < |z| < 1).$$

2. By multiplying two Maclaurin series term by term, show that

(*a*) $e^z \sin z = z + z^2 + \frac{1}{3}z^3 + \cdots \qquad (|z| < \infty);$

(*b*) $\dfrac{e^2}{1+z} = 1 + \dfrac{1}{2}z^2 - \dfrac{1}{3}z^3 + \cdots \qquad (|z| < 1).$

3. By writing $\csc z = 1/\sin z$ and then using division, show that

$$\csc z = \frac{1}{z} + \frac{1}{3!}z + \left[\frac{1}{(3!)^2} - \frac{1}{5!}\right] z^3 + \cdots \qquad (0 < |z| < \pi).$$

4. Use division to obtain the Laurent series representation

$$\frac{1}{e^z - 1} = \frac{1}{z} - \frac{1}{2} + \frac{1}{12}z - \frac{1}{720}z^3 + \cdots \qquad (0 < |z| < 2\pi).$$

5. Note how the expansion

$$\frac{1}{z^2 \sinh z} = \frac{1}{z^3} - \frac{1}{6} \cdot \frac{1}{z} + \frac{7}{360}z + \cdots \qquad (0 < |z| < \pi)$$

is an immediate consequence of the Laurent series (8) in Sec. 73. Then use the method illustrated in Example 4, Sec. 68, to show that

$$\int_C \frac{dz}{z^2 \sinh z} = -\frac{\pi i}{3}$$

when C is the positively oriented unit circle $|z| = 1$.

6. Follow these steps, which illustrate an alternative to straightforward division, to obtain equation (8) in Example 2, Sec. 73.

(*a*) Write

$$\frac{1}{1 + z^2/3! + z^4/5! + \cdots} = d_0 + d_1 z + d_2 z^2 + d_3 z^3 + d_4 z^4 + \cdots,$$

where the coefficients in the power series on the right are to be determined by multiplying the two series in the equation

$$1 = \left(1 + \frac{1}{3!}z^2 + \frac{1}{5!}z^4 + \cdots\right)(d_0 + d_1 z + d_2 z^2 + d_3 z^3 + d_4 z^4 + \cdots).$$

Perform this multiplication to show that

$$(d_0 - 1) + d_1 z + \left(d_2 + \frac{1}{3!}d_0\right)z^2 + \left(d_3 + \frac{1}{3!}d_1\right)z^3$$
$$+ \left(d_4 + \frac{1}{3!}d_2 + \frac{1}{5!}d_0\right)z^4 + \cdots = 0$$

when $|z| < \pi$.

(*b*) By setting the coefficients in the last series in part (*a*) equal to zero, find the values of d_0, d_1, d_2, d_3, and d_4. With these values, the first equation in part (*a*) becomes equation (8), Sec. 73.

7. Use mathematical induction to establish Leibniz's rule (Sec. 73)

$$(fg)^{(n)} = \sum_{k=0}^{n} \binom{n}{k} f^{(k)} g^{(n-k)} \qquad (n = 1, 2, \ldots)$$

for the nth derivative of the product of two differentiable functions $f(z)$ and $g(z)$.

Suggestion: Note that the rule is valid when $n = 1$. Then, assuming that it is valid when $n = m$ where m is any positive integer, show that

$$\begin{aligned}(fg)^{(m+1)} &= (fg')^{(m)} + (f'g)^{(m)} \\ &= fg^{(m+1)} + \sum_{k=1}^{m}\left[\binom{m}{k} + \binom{m}{k-1}\right] f^{(k)}g^{(m+1-k)} + f^{(m+1)}g.\end{aligned}$$

Finally, with the aid of the identify

$$\binom{m}{k} + \binom{m}{k-1} = \binom{m+1}{k}$$

that was used in Exercise 8, Sec. 3, show that

$$\begin{aligned}(fg)^{(m+1)} &= fg^{(m+1)} + \sum_{k=1}^{m}\binom{m+1}{k} f^{(k)}g^{(m+1-k)} + f^{(m+1)}g \\ &= \sum_{k=0}^{m+1}\binom{m+1}{k} f^{(k)}g^{(m+1-k)}.\end{aligned}$$

8. Let $f(z)$ be an entire function that is represented by a series of the form

$$f(z) = z + a_2z^2 + a_3z^3 + \cdots \qquad (|z| < \infty).$$

(*a*) By differentiating the composite function $g(z) = f[f(z)]$ successively, find the first three nonzero terms in the Maclaurin series for $g(z)$ and thus show that

$$f[f(z)] = z + 2\,a_2z^2 + 2\,(a_2^2 + a_3)z^3 + \cdots \qquad (|z| < \infty).$$

(*b*) Obtain the result in part (*a*) in a *formal* manner by writing

$$f[f(z)] = f(z) + a_2[f(z)]^2 + a_3[f(z)]^3 + \cdots,$$

replacing $f(z)$ on the right-hand side here by its series representation, and then collecting terms in like powers of z.

(*c*) By applying the result in part (*a*) to the function $f(z) = \sin z$, show that

$$\sin(\sin z) = z - \frac{1}{3}z^3 + \cdots \qquad (|z| < \infty).$$

9. The ***Euler numbers*** are the numbers E_n $(n = 0, 1, 2, \ldots)$ in the Maclaurin series representation

$$\frac{1}{\cosh z} = \sum_{n=0}^{\infty}\frac{E_n}{n!}z^n \qquad (|z| < \pi/2).$$

Point out why this representation is valid in the indicated disk and why

$$E_{2n+1} = 0 \qquad (n = 0, 1, 2, \ldots).$$

Then show that

$$E_0 = 1, \quad E_2 = -1, \quad E_4 = 5, \quad \text{and} \quad E_6 = -61.$$

CHAPTER 6

RESIDUES AND POLES

The Cauchy–Goursat theorem (Sec. 50) states that if a function is analytic at all points interior to and on a simple closed contour C, then the value of an integral of the function around that contour is zero. If, however, the function fails to be analytic at a finite number of points interior to C, there is, as we shall see in this chapter, a specific number, called a residue, which each of those points contributes to the value of the integral. We develop here the theory of residues; and, in Chap. 7, we shall illustrate their use in certain areas of applied mathematics.

74. ISOLATED SINGULAR POINTS

We saw in Sec. 25 that a function f is analytic at a point z_0 if it has a derivative at each point in some neighborhood of z_0. If, on the other hand, f fails to be analytic at z_0 but is analytic at some point in every neighborhood of it, we also saw in Sec. 25 that z_0 is a singular point of f.

The theory of residues in this chapter centers around a special type of singular point. Namely, a singular point z_0 is said to be ***isolated*** if there is a deleted ε neighborhood $0 < |z - z_0| < \varepsilon$ of z_0 throughout which f is analytic.

EXAMPLE 1. The function

$$f(z) = \frac{z-1}{z^5(z^2+9)}$$

has the three isolated singular points $z = 0$ and $z = \pm 3i$. In fact, the singular points of a rational function, or quotient of two polynomials, are always isolated. This because the zeros of the polynomial in the denominator are finite in number (Sec. 58).

EXAMPLE 2. The origin $z = 0$ is a singular point of the principal branch (Sec. 33)

$$F(z) = \operatorname{Log} z = \ln r + i\Theta \qquad (r > 0, -\pi < \Theta < \pi)$$

of the logarithmic function. It is *not*, however, an isolated singular point since every deleted ε neighborhood of it contains points on the negative real axis (see Fig. 88) and the branch is not even defined there. Similar remarks can be made regarding *any* branch

$$f(z) = \log z = \ln z + i\theta \qquad (r > 0, \alpha < \theta < \alpha + 2\pi)$$

of the logarithmic function.

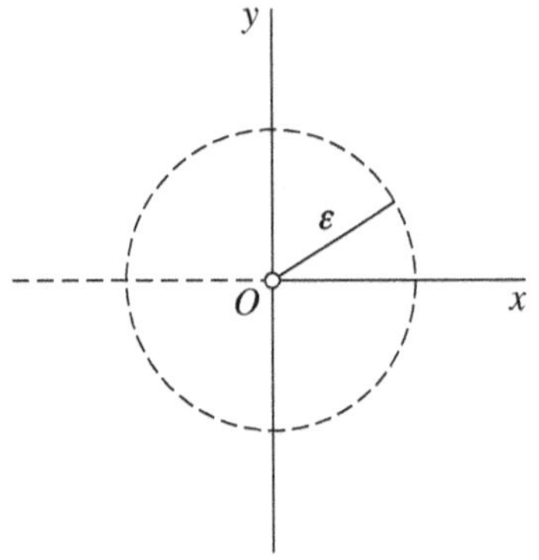

FIGURE 88

EXAMPLE 3. The function

$$f(z) = \frac{1}{\sin(\pi/z)}$$

clearly does not have a derivative at the origin $z = 0$; and because $\sin(\pi/z) = 0$ when $\pi/z = n\pi$ $(n = \pm 1, \pm 2, \ldots)$, the derivative of f also fails to exist at each of the points $z = 1/n$ $(n = \pm 1, \pm 2, \ldots)$. Inasmuch as the derivative of f does exist at every point that is not on the real axis, it follows that f is analytic at some point in every neighborhood of each of the points

$$(1) \qquad z = 0 \quad \text{and} \quad z = 1/n \;\; (n = \pm 1, \pm 2, \ldots).$$

Hence each of the points (1) is a singularity of f.

The singularity $z = 0$ is *not* isolated because every deleted ε neighborhood of it contains other singular points. More precisely, when a positive number ε is specified and m is any positive integer such that $m > 1/\varepsilon$, the fact that $0 < 1/m < \varepsilon$ means that the singularity $z = 1/m$ lies in the deleted ε neighborhood $0 < |z| < \varepsilon$.

The remaining points $z = 1/n$ $(n = \pm 1, \pm 2, \ldots)$ *are* in fact, isolated. In order to see this, let m denote any fixed positive integer and observe that f is analytic in the deleted neighborhood of $z = 1/m$ whose radius is

$$\varepsilon = \frac{1}{m} - \frac{1}{m+1} = \frac{1}{m(m+1)}.$$

(See Fig. 89.) A similar observation can be made when m is a negative integer.

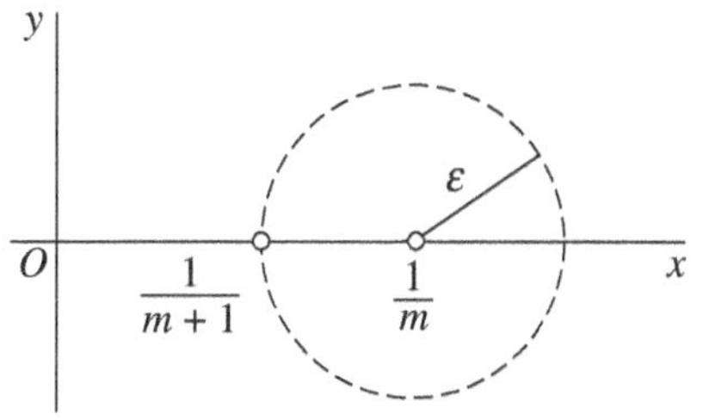

FIGURE 89

In this chapter, it will be important to keep in mind that if a function is analytic everywhere inside a simple closed contour C except for a *finite* number of singular points $z_1, z_2, \ldots, z_n$, those points must all be isolated and the deleted neighborhoods about them can be made small enough to lie entirely inside C. To see that this is so, consider any one of the points z_k. The radius ε of the needed deleted neighborhood can be any positive number that is smaller than the distances to the other singular points and also smaller than the distance from z_k to the closest point on C.

Finally, we mention that it is sometimes convenient to consider the point at infinity (Sec. 17) as an isolated singular point. To be specific, if there is a positive number R_1 such that f is analytic for $R_1 < |z| < \infty$, then f is said to have an ***isolated singular point at*** $z_0 = \infty$. Such a singular point will be used in Sec. 77.

75. RESIDUES

When z_0 is an isolated singular point of a function f, there is a positive number R_2 such that f is analytic at each point z for which $0 < |z - z_0| < R_2$. Consequently, $f(z)$ has a Laurent series representation

$$(1) \quad f(z) = \sum_{n=0}^{\infty} a_n (z - z_0)^n + \frac{b_1}{z - z_0} + \frac{b_2}{(z - z_0)^2} + \cdots + \frac{b_n}{(z - z_0)^n} + \cdots$$
$$(0 < |z - z_0| < R_2),$$

where the coefficients a_n and b_n have certain integral representations (Sec. 66). In particular,

$$b_n = \frac{1}{2\pi i} \int_C \frac{f(z)\,dz}{(z - z_0)^{-n+1}} \qquad (n = 1, 2, \ldots)$$

where C is any positively oriented simple closed contour around z_0 that lies in the punctured disk $0 < |z - z_0| < R_2$ (Fig. 90). When $n = 1$, this expression for b_n becomes

$$b_1 = \frac{1}{2\pi i}\int_C f(z)\,dz$$

or

$$\int_C f(z)\,dz = 2\pi i b_1. \tag{2}$$

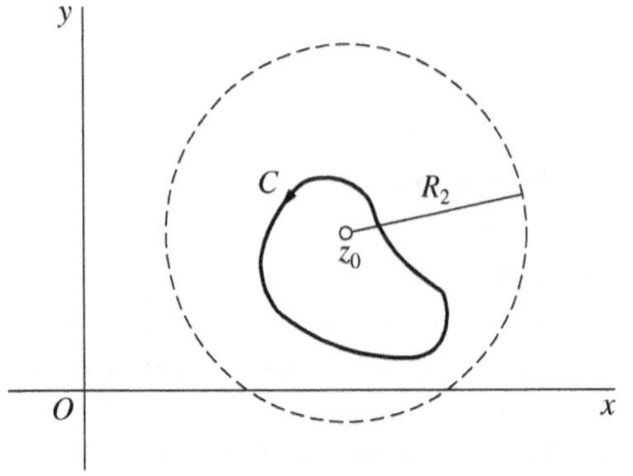

FIGURE 90

The complex number b_1, which is the coefficient of $1/(z - z_0)$ in expansion (1), is called the ***residue*** of f at the isolated singular point z_0, and we shall often write

$$b_1 = \operatorname*{Res}_{z=z_0} f(z).$$

Equation (2) then becomes

$$\int_C f(z)\,dz = 2\pi i \operatorname*{Res}_{z=z_0} f(z). \tag{3}$$

Sometimes we simply use B to denote the residue when the function f and the point z_0 are clearly indicated.

Equation (3) provides a powerful method for evaluating certain integrals around simple closed contours.

EXAMPLE 1. Consider the integral

$$\int_C \frac{e^z - 1}{z^4}\,dz \tag{4}$$

where C is the positively oriented unit circle $|z| = 1$ (Fig. 91). Since the integrand is analytic everywhere in the finite plane except at $z = 0$, it has a Laurent series representation that is valid when $0 < |z| < \infty$. Thus, according to equation (3), the value of integral (4) is $2\pi i$ times the residue of its integrand at $z = 0$.

To determine that residue, we recall (Sec. 64) the Maclaurin series representation

$$e^z = \sum_{n=0}^{\infty} \frac{z^n}{n!} \qquad (|z| < \infty)$$

and use it to write

$$\frac{e^z - 1}{z^5} = \frac{1}{z^5} \sum_{n=1}^{\infty} \frac{z^n}{n!} = \sum_{n=1}^{\infty} \frac{z^{n-5}}{n!} \qquad (0 < |z| < \infty).$$

The coefficient of $1/z$ in this last series occurs when $n - 5 = -1$, or when $n = 4$. Hence

$$\operatorname*{Res}_{z=0} \frac{e^z - 1}{z^5} = \frac{1}{4!} = \frac{1}{24};$$

and so

$$\int_C \frac{e^z - 1}{z^4}\, dz = 2\pi i \left(\frac{1}{24}\right) = \frac{\pi i}{12}.$$

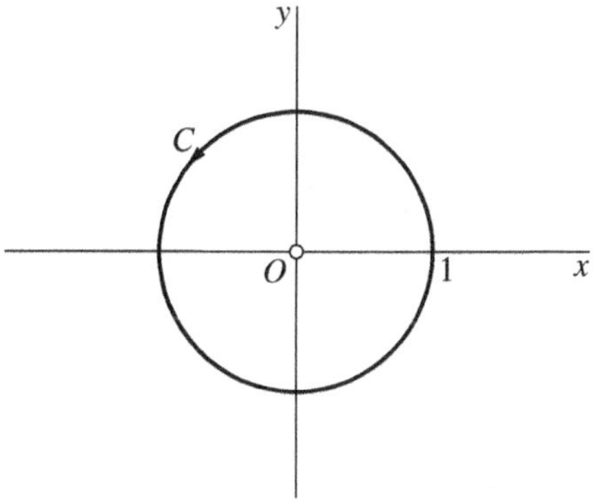

FIGURE 91

EXAMPLE 2. Let us show that

$$\int_C \cosh\left(\frac{1}{z^2}\right) dz = 0 \tag{5}$$

where C is the same positively oriented unit circle $|z| = 1$ as in Example 1. The composite function $\cosh(1/z^2)$ is analytic everywhere except at the origin since the same is true of $1/z^2$ and since $\cosh z$ is entire. The isolated singular point $z = 0$ is interior to C, and Fig. 91 in Example 1 can be used here as well. With the help of the Maclaurin series expansion (Sec. 64)

$$\cosh z = 1 + \frac{z^2}{2!} + \frac{z^4}{4!} + \frac{z^6}{6!} + \cdots \qquad (|z| < \infty),$$

one can write the Laurent series expansion

$$\cosh\left(\frac{1}{z}\right) = 1 + \frac{1}{2!} \cdot \frac{1}{z^2} + \frac{1}{4!} \cdot \frac{1}{z^4} + \frac{1}{6!} \cdot \frac{1}{z^6} \cdots \qquad (0 < |z| < \infty).$$

The residue of the integrand at its isolated singular point $z = 0$ is, therefore, zero ($b_1 = 0$), and the value of integral (5) is established.

We are reminded in this example that although the analyticity of a function within and on a simple closed contour C is a sufficient condition for the value of the integral around C to be zero, it is not a *necessary* condition.

EXAMPLE 3. A residue can be used to evaluate the integral

$$\int_C \frac{dz}{z(z-2)^5} \tag{6}$$

where C is the positively oriented circle $|z-2| = 1$ (Fig. 92). Since the integrand is analytic everywhere in the finite plane except at the points $z = 0$ and $z = 2$, it has a Laurent series representation that is valid in the punctured disk $0 < |z-2| < 2$, which is shown in Fig. 92. Thus, according to equation (3), the value of integral (6) is $2\pi i$ times the residue of its integrand at $z = 2$. The nature of that integrand suggests that we might use the geometric series (Sec. 64)

$$\frac{1}{1-z} = \sum_{n=0}^{\infty} z^n \qquad (|z| < 1)$$

to determine the residue. We write

$$\frac{1}{z(z-2)^5} = \frac{1}{(z-2)^5} \cdot \frac{1}{2+(z-2)} = \frac{1}{2(z-2)^5} \cdot \frac{1}{1-\left(-\dfrac{z-2}{2}\right)},$$

and then use the geometric series:

$$\frac{1}{z(z-2)^5} = \frac{1}{2(z-2)^5} \sum_{n=0}^{\infty} \left(-\frac{z-2}{2}\right)^n = \sum_{n=0}^{\infty} \frac{(-1)^n}{2^{n+1}} (z-2)^{n-5} \qquad (0 < |z-2| < 2).$$

In this Laurent series, which could be written in the form (1), the coefficient of $1/(z-2)$ is the desired residue, namely $1/32$. Consequently,

$$\int_C \frac{dz}{z(z-2)^5} = 2\pi i \left(\frac{1}{32}\right) = \frac{\pi i}{16}.$$

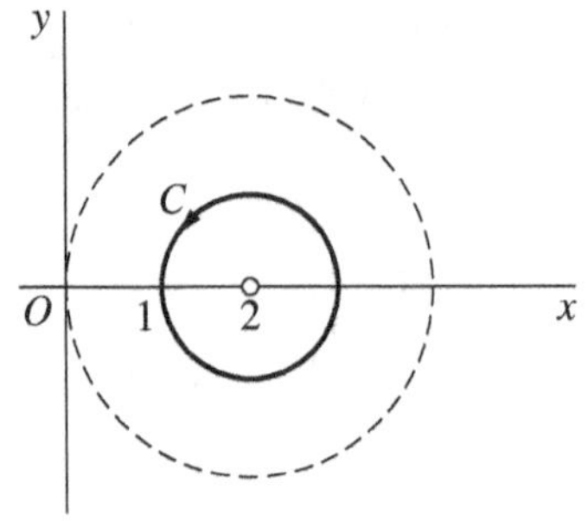

FIGURE 92

76. CAUCHY'S RESIDUE THEOREM

If, except for a *finite* number of singular points, a function f is analytic inside a simple closed contour C, those singular points must all be isolated (Sec. 74). The following theorem, which is known as ***Cauchy's residue theorem,*** is a precise statement of the fact that if f is also analytic on C and if C is positively oriented, then the value of the integral of f around C is $2\pi i$ times the sum of the residues of f at the singular points inside C.

Theorem. *Let C be a simple closed contour, described in the positive sense. If a function f is analytic inside and on C except for a finite number of singular points z_k $(k = 1, 2, \ldots, n)$ inside C* (Fig. 93), *then*

$$\int_C f(z)\,dz = 2\pi i \sum_{k=1}^{n} \operatorname*{Res}_{z=z_k} f(z). \tag{1}$$

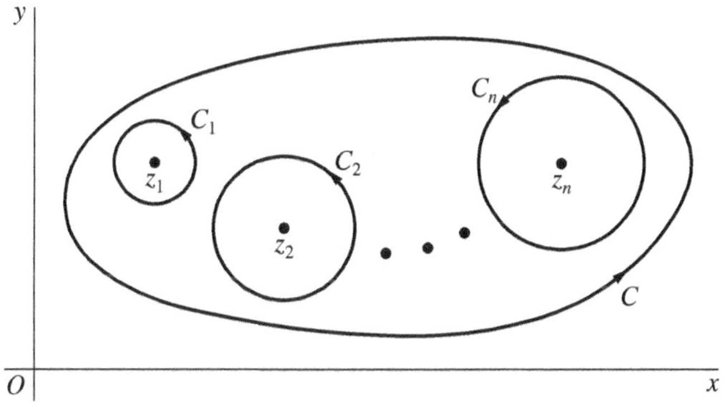

FIGURE 93

To prove the theorem, let the points z_k $(k = 1, 2, \ldots, n)$ be centers of positively oriented circles C_k which are interior to C and are so small that no two of them have points in common. The circles C_k, together with the simple closed contour C, form the boundary of a closed region throughout which f is analytic and whose interior is a multiply connected domain consisting of the points inside C and exterior to each C_k. Hence, according to the adaptation of the Cauchy–Goursat theorem to such domains (Sec. 53),

$$\int_C f(z)\,dz - \sum_{k=1}^{n} \int_{C_k} f(z)\,dz = 0.$$

This reduces to equation (1) because (Sec. 75)

$$\int_{C_k} f(z)\,dz = 2\pi i \operatorname*{Res}_{z=z_k} f(z) \quad (k = 1, 2, \ldots, n),$$

and the proof is complete.

EXAMPLE. Let us use the theorem to evaluate the integral

$$\int_C \frac{4z-5}{z(z-1)}\,dz \tag{2}$$

where C is the circle $|z| = 2$, described in the counterclockwise direction (Fig. 94). The integrand has the two isolated singularities $z = 0$ and $z = 1$, both of which are interior to C. The corresponding residues B_1 at $z = 0$ and B_2 at $z = 1$ are readily found with the aid of the Maclaurin series representation (Sec. 64)

$$\frac{1}{1-z} = 1 + z + z^2 + \cdots \qquad (|z| < 1).$$

We observe first that when $0 < |z| < 1$,

$$\frac{4z-5}{z(z-1)} = \frac{4z-5}{z} \cdot \frac{-1}{1-z} = \left(4 - \frac{5}{z}\right)(-1 - z - z^2 - \cdots);$$

and by identifying the coefficient of $1/z$ in the product on the right here, we find that

$$B_1 = 5. \tag{3}$$

Also, since

$$\frac{4z-5}{z(z-1)} = \frac{4(z-1)-1}{z-1} \cdot \frac{1}{1+(z-1)}$$
$$= \left(4 - \frac{1}{z-1}\right)[1 - (z-1) + (z-1)^2 - \cdots]$$

when $0 < |z-1| < 1$, it follows that

$$B_2 = -1. \tag{4}$$

Thus

$$\int_C \frac{4z-5}{z(z-1)}\,dz = 2\pi i(B_1 + B_2) = 8\pi i. \tag{5}$$

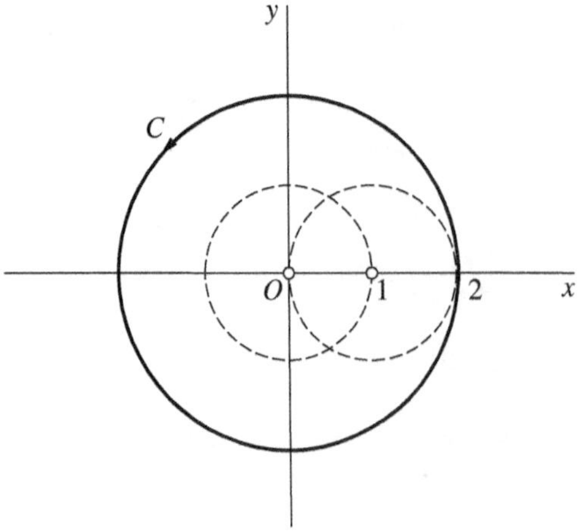

FIGURE 94

In this example, it is actually easier to start by writing the integrand in integral (2) as the sum of its partial fractions:

$$\frac{4z-5}{z(z-1)} = \frac{5}{z} + \frac{-1}{z-1}.$$

Then, since $5/z$ is already a Laurent series when $0 < |z| < 1$ and since $-1/(z-1)$ is a Laurent series when $0 < |z-1| < 1$, it follows that statement (5) is true.

77. RESIDUE AT INFINITY

Suppose that a function f is analytic throughout the finite plane except for a finite number of singular points interior to a positively oriented simple closed contour C. Next, let R_1 denote a positive number which is large enough that C lies inside the circle $|z| = R_1$ (see Fig. 95). The function f is evidently analytic throughout the domain $R_1 < |z| < \infty$ and, as already mentioned at the end of Sec. 74, the point at infinity is then said to be an isolated singular point of f.

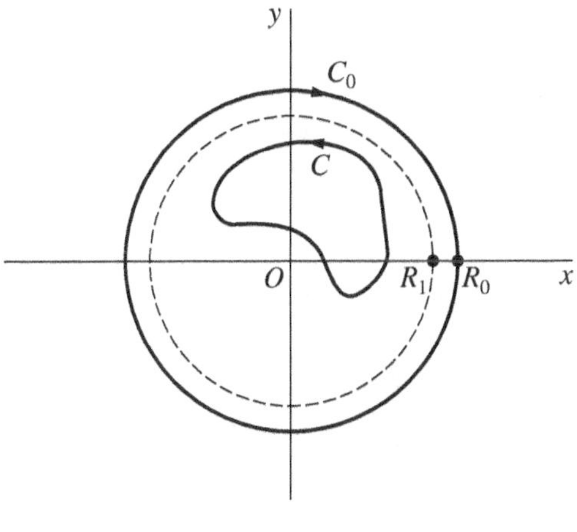

FIGURE 95

Now let C_0 denote a circle $|z| = R_0$, oriented in the *clockwise* direction, where $R_0 > R_1$. The ***residue of f at infinity*** is defined by means of the equation

$$\int_{C_0} f(z)\,dz = 2\pi i \operatorname*{Res}_{z=\infty} f(z). \tag{1}$$

Note that the circle C_0 keeps the point at infinity on the left, just as the singular point in the finite plane is on the left in equation (3), Sec. 75. Since f is analytic throughout the closed region bounded by C and C_0, the principle of deformation of paths (Sec. 53) tells us that

$$\int_C f(z)\,dz = \int_{-C_0} f(z)\,dz = -\int_{C_0} f(z)\,dz.$$

So, in view of definition (1),

$$\int_C f(z)\,dz = -2\pi i \operatorname*{Res}_{z=\infty} f(z). \tag{2}$$

To find this residue, write the Laurent series (see Sec. 66)

$$f(z) = \sum_{n=-\infty}^{\infty} c_n z^n \quad (R_1 < |z| < \infty), \tag{3}$$

where

$$c_n = \frac{1}{2\pi i}\int_{-C_0} \frac{f(z)\,dz}{z^{n+1}} \quad (n = 0, \pm 1, \pm 2, \ldots). \tag{4}$$

Replacing z by $1/z$ in equation (3) and then multiplying through the result by $1/z^2$, we see that

$$\frac{1}{z^2} f\left(\frac{1}{z}\right) = \sum_{n=-\infty}^{\infty} \frac{c_n}{z^{n+2}} = \sum_{n=-\infty}^{\infty} \frac{c_{n-2}}{z^n} \quad \left(0 < |z| < \frac{1}{R_1}\right)$$

and

$$c_{-1} = \operatorname*{Res}_{z=0}\left[\frac{1}{z^2} f\left(\frac{1}{z}\right)\right].$$

Putting $n = -1$ in expression (4), we now have

$$c_{-1} = \frac{1}{2\pi i}\int_{-C_0} f(z)\,dz,$$

or

$$\int_{C_0} f(z)\,dz = -2\pi i \operatorname*{Res}_{z=0}\left[\frac{1}{z^2} f\left(\frac{1}{z}\right)\right]. \tag{5}$$

Note how it follows from this and definition (1) that

$$\operatorname*{Res}_{z=\infty} f(z) = -\operatorname*{Res}_{z=0}\left[\frac{1}{z^2} f\left(\frac{1}{z}\right)\right]. \tag{6}$$

With equations (2) and (6), the following theorem is now established. This theorem is sometimes more efficient to use than Cauchy's residue theorem in Sec. 76 since it involves only one residue.

Theorem. *If a function f is analytic everywhere in the finite plane except for a finite number of singular points interior to a positively oriented simple closed contour C, then*

$$\int_C f(z)\,dz = 2\pi i \operatorname*{Res}_{z=0}\left[\frac{1}{z^2} f\left(\frac{1}{z}\right)\right]. \tag{7}$$

EXAMPLE. It is easy to see that the singularities of the function

$$f(z) = \frac{z^3(1-3z)}{(1+z)(1+2z^4)}$$

all lie inside the positively oriented circle C centered at the origin with radius 3. In order to use the theorem in this section, we write

$$\frac{1}{z^2} f\left(\frac{1}{z}\right) = \frac{1}{z} \cdot \frac{z-3}{(z+1)(z^4+2)}. \tag{8}$$

Inasmuch as the quotient

$$\frac{z-3}{(z+1)(z^4+2)}$$

is analytic at the origin, it has a Maclaurin series representation whose first term is the nonzero number $-3/2$. Hence, in view of expression (8),

$$\frac{1}{z^2} f\left(\frac{1}{z}\right) = \frac{1}{z}\left(-\frac{3}{2} + a_1 z + a_2 z^2 + a_3 z^3 + \cdots\right) = -\frac{3}{2} \cdot \frac{1}{z} + a_1 + a_2 z + a_3 z^2 + \cdots$$

for all z in some punctured disk $0 < |z| < R_0$. It is now clear that

$$\operatorname*{Res}_{z=0}\left[\frac{1}{z^2} f\left(\frac{1}{z}\right)\right] = -\frac{3}{2},$$

and so

$$\int_C \frac{z^3(1-3z)}{(1+z)(1+2z^4)}\,dz = 2\pi i\left(-\frac{3}{2}\right) = -3\pi i. \tag{9}$$

EXERCISES

1. Find the residue at $z = 0$ of the function

(*a*) $\dfrac{1}{z+z^2}$; (*b*) $z\cos\left(\dfrac{1}{z}\right)$; (*c*) $\dfrac{z-\sin z}{z}$; (*d*) $\dfrac{\cot z}{z^4}$; (*e*) $\dfrac{\sinh z}{z^4(1-z^2)}$.

Ans. (*a*) 1; (*b*) $-1/2$; (*c*) 0; (*d*) $-1/45$; (*e*) $7/6$.

2. Use Cauchy's residue theorem (Sec. 76) to evaluate the integral of each of these functions around the circle $|z| = 3$ in the positive sense:

(*a*) $\dfrac{\exp(-z)}{z^2}$; (*b*) $\dfrac{\exp(-z)}{(z-1)^2}$; (*c*) $z^2\exp\left(\dfrac{1}{z}\right)$; (*d*) $\dfrac{z+1}{z^2-2z}$.

Ans. (*a*) $-2\pi i$; (*b*) $-2\pi i/e$; (*c*) $\pi i/3$; (*d*) $2\pi i$.

3. In the example in Sec. 76, two residues were used to evaluate the integral

$$\int_C \frac{4z-5}{z(z-1)}\,dz$$

where C is the positively oriented circle $|z| = 2$. Evaluate this integral once again by using the theorem in Sec. 77 and finding only one residue.

4. Use the theorem in Sec. 77, involving a single residue, to evaluate the integral of each of these functions around the circle $|z| = 2$ in the positive sense:

$$(a)\ \frac{z^5}{1 - z^3}; \qquad (b)\ \frac{1}{1 + z^2}; \qquad (c)\ \frac{1}{z}.$$

Ans. $(a)\ -2\pi i$; $(b)\ 0$; $(c)\ 2\pi i$.

5. Let C denote the circle $|z| = 1$, taken counterclockwise, and use the following steps to show that

$$\int_C \exp\left(z + \frac{1}{z}\right) dz = 2\pi i \sum_{n=0}^{\infty} \frac{1}{n!\,(n+1)!}.$$

(*a*) By using the Maclaurin series for e^z and referring to Theorem 1 in Sec. 71, which justifies the term by term integration that is to be used, write the above integral as

$$\sum_{n=0}^{\infty} \frac{1}{n!} \int_C z^n \exp\left(\frac{1}{z}\right) dz.$$

(*b*) Apply the theorem in Sec. 76 to evaluate the integrals appearing in part (*a*) to arrive at the desired result.

6. Suppose that a function f is analytic throughout the finite plane except for a finite number of singular points $z_1, z_2, \ldots, z_n$. Show that

$$\operatorname*{Res}_{z=z_1} f(z) + \operatorname*{Res}_{z=z_2} f(z) + \cdots + \operatorname*{Res}_{z=z_n} f(z) + \operatorname*{Res}_{z=\infty} f(z) = 0.$$

7. Let the degrees of the polynomials

$$P(z) = a_0 + a_1 z + a_2 z^2 + \cdots + a_n z^n \qquad (a_n \neq 0)$$

and

$$Q(z) = b_0 + b_1 z + b_2 z^2 + \cdots + b_m z^m \qquad (b_m \neq 0)$$

be such that $m \geq n + 2$. Use the theorem in Sec. 77 to show that if all of the zeros of $Q(z)$ are interior to a simple closed contour C, then

$$\int_C \frac{P(z)}{Q(z)}\, dz = 0.$$

[Compare with Exercise 4(*b*).]

78. THE THREE TYPES OF ISOLATED SINGULAR POINTS

We saw in Sec. 75 that the theory of residues is based on the fact that if f has an isolated singular point at z_0, then $f(z)$ has a Laurent series representation

$$(1) \qquad f(z) = \sum_{n=0}^{\infty} a_n (z - z_0)^n + \frac{b_1}{z - z_0} + \frac{b_2}{(z - z_0)^2} + \cdots + \frac{b_n}{(z - z_0)^n} + \cdots$$

in a punctured disk $0 < |z - z_0| < R_2$. The portion

$$\frac{b_1}{z - z_0} + \frac{b_2}{(z - z_0)^2} + \cdots + \frac{b_n}{(z - z_0)^n} + \cdots \tag{2}$$

of the series, involving negative powers of $z - z_0$, is called the ***principal part*** of f at z_0. We now use the principal part to identify the isolated singular point z_0 as one of three special types. This classification will aid us in the development of residue theory that appears in following sections.

There are two extremes, the case in which every coefficient in the principal part (2) is zero and the case in which an infinite number of them are nonzero.

(*a*) *Removable Singular Points*

When every b_n is zero, so that

$$f(z) = \sum_{n=0}^{\infty} a_n (z - z_0)^n = a_0 + a_1(z - z_0) + a_2(z - z_0)^2 + \cdots \tag{3}$$

$$(0 < |z - z_0| < R_2),$$

z_0 is known as a ***removable singular point***. Note that the residue at a removable singular point is always zero. If we define, or possibly redefine, f at z_0 so that $f(z_0) = a_0$, expansion (3) becomes valid throughout the entire disk $|z - z_0| < R_2$. Since a power series always represents an analytic function interior to its circle of convergence (Sec. 71), it follows that f is analytic at z_0 when it is assigned the value a_0 there. The singularity z_0 is, therefore, *removed*.

(*b*) *Essential Singular Points*

If an infinite number of the coefficients b_n in the principal part (2) are nonzero, z_0 is said to be an ***essential singular point*** of f.

(*c*) *Poles of Order m*

If the principal part of f at z_0 contains at least one nonzero term but the number of such terms is only finite, then there exists a positive integer m $(m \geq 1)$ such that

$$b_m \neq 0 \quad \text{and} \quad b_{m+1} = b_{m+2} = \cdots = 0.$$

That is, expansion (1) takes the form

$$f(z) = \sum_{n=0}^{\infty} a_n (z - z_0)^n + \frac{b_1}{z - z_0} + \frac{b_2}{(z - z_0)^2} + \cdots + \frac{b_m}{(z - z_0)^m} \tag{4}$$

$$(0 < |z - z_0| < R_2),$$

where $b_m \neq 0$. In this case, the isolated singular point z_0 is called a ***pole of order m***.* A pole of order $m = 1$ is usually referred to as a ***simple pole***.

In the next section, we shall give examples of these three types of isolated singular points; and in the remaining sections of the chapter, we shall examine in greater depth the theory of the three types of isolated singular points just described. The emphasis will be on useful and efficient methods for identifying poles and finding the corresponding residues.

The final section (Sec. 84) of the chapter includes three theorems that point out fundamental differences in the behavior of functions at the three types of isolated singular points.

79. EXAMPLES

The examples in this section illustrate the three types of isolated singularities described in Sec. 78.

EXAMPLE 1. The point $z_0 = 0$ is a removable singular point of the function

$$f(z) = \frac{1 - \cosh z}{z^2} \tag{1}$$

because

$$f(z) = \frac{1}{z^2}\left[1 - \left(1 + \frac{z^2}{2!} + \frac{z^4}{4!} + \frac{z^6}{6!} + \cdots\right)\right] = -\frac{1}{2!} - \frac{z^2}{4!} - \frac{z^4}{6!} - \cdots$$
$$(0 < |z| < \infty).$$

When the value $f(0) = -1/2$ is assigned, f becomes entire.

EXAMPLE 2. We recall from Example 3 in Sec. 68 that

$$e^{1/z} = \sum_{n=0}^{\infty} \frac{1}{n!} \cdot \frac{1}{z^n} = 1 + \frac{1}{1!} \cdot \frac{1}{z} + \frac{1}{2!} \cdot \frac{1}{z^2} + \cdots \qquad (0 < |z| < \infty), \tag{2}$$

and it follows that $e^{1/z}$ has an essential singularity at $z_0 = 0$, where the residue b_1 is unity.

This example can be used to illustrate an important result known as ***Picard's theorem***. It concerns the behavior of a function near an essential singular point and states that *in each neighborhood of an essential singular point, a function assumes every finite value, with one possible exception, an infinite number of times.*†

*The reason for the terminology *pole* is pointed out on pp. 348–349 of the book (2005) by A. D. Wunsch as well as on p. 62 of the one (2010) by R. P. Boas, both of which are listed in Appendix 1. Also, the reason will be touched on in Sec. 84.

†For a proof of Picard's theorem, see Sec. 51 in Vol. III of the book by Markushevich, cited in Appendix 1.

It is easy to see, for instance, that $e^{1/z}$ assumes the value -1 an infinite number of times in each neighborhood of the origin. More precisely, since $e^z = -1$ when

$$z = (2n+1)\pi i \qquad (n = 0, \pm 1, \pm 2, \ldots),$$

(see Sec. 30), it follows that $e^{1/z} = -1$ when

$$z = \frac{1}{(2n+1)\pi i} \cdot \frac{i}{i} = -\frac{i}{(2n+1)\pi} \qquad (n = 0, \pm 1, \pm 2, \ldots),$$

So if n is large enough, an infinite number of such points lie in any given ε neighborhood of the origin. Zero is evidently the exceptional value when Picard's theorem is applied to $e^{1/z}$ at the origin.

EXAMPLE 3. From the representation

$$f(z) = \frac{1}{z^2(1-z)} = \frac{1}{z^2}(1 + z + z^2 + z^3 + z^4 + \cdots) \tag{3}$$

$$= \frac{1}{z^2} + \frac{1}{z} + 1 + z + z^2 + \cdots \qquad (0 < |z| < 1),$$

one can see that f has a pole of order $m = 2$ at the origin and that

$$\operatorname*{Res}_{z=0} f(z) = 1.$$

From the limit

$$\lim_{z\to 0} \frac{1}{f(z)} = \lim_{z\to 0}[z^2(1-z)] = 0,$$

it follows that (see Sec. 17)

$$\lim_{z\to 0} f(z) = \infty. \tag{4}$$

Such a limit always occurs at poles, as will be shown in Sec. 84.

EXAMPLE 4. Finally, we observe that the function

$$f(z) = \frac{z^2+z-2}{z+1} = \frac{z(z+1)-2}{z+1} = z - \frac{2}{z+1} = -1 + (z+1) - \frac{2}{z+1}$$

$$(0 < |z+1| < \infty)$$

has a simple pole at $z_0 = -1$. The residue there is -2. Moreover, since

$$\lim_{z\to -1} \frac{1}{f(z)} = \lim_{z\to -1} \frac{z+1}{z^2+z-2} = \frac{0}{-2} = 0,$$

we find that

$$\lim_{z\to -1} f(z) = \infty. \tag{5}$$

[Compare with limit (4) in Example 3.]

In the remaining sections of this chapter, we shall develop in greater depth the theory of the three types of isolated singular points just illustrated. The emphasis will be on useful and efficient methods for identifying poles and finding the corresponding residues.

EXERCISES

1. In each case, write the principal part of the function at its isolated singular point and determine whether that point is a removable singular point, an essential singular point, or a pole:

$$(a)\ z\exp\left(\frac{1}{z}\right);\quad (b)\ \frac{z^2}{1+z};\quad (c)\ \frac{\sin z}{z};\quad (d)\ \frac{\cos z}{z};\quad (e)\ \frac{1}{(2-z)^3}.$$

2. Show that the singular point of each of the following functions is a pole. Determine the order m of that pole and the corresponding residue B.

$$(a)\ \frac{1-\cosh z}{z^3};\quad (b)\ \frac{1-\exp(2z)}{z^4};\quad (c)\ \frac{\exp(2z)}{(z-1)^2}.$$

Ans. $(a)\ m=1,\ B=-1/2;\quad (b)\ m=3,\ B=-4/3;\quad (c)\ m=2,\ B=2e^2.$

3. Suppose that a function f is analytic at z_0, and write $g(z)=f(z)/(z-z_0)$. Show that

(*a*) if $f(z_0)\neq 0$, then z_0 is a simple pole of g, with residue $f(z_0)$;

(*b*) if $f(z_0)=0$, then z_0 is a removable singular point of g.

Suggestion: As pointed out in Sec. 62, there is a Taylor series for $f(z)$ about z_0 since f is analytic there. Start each part of this exercise by writing out a few terms of that series.

4. Write the function

$$f(z)=\frac{8a^3z^2}{(z^2+a^2)^3}\qquad (a>0)$$

as

$$f(z)=\frac{\phi(z)}{(z-ai)^3}\quad \text{where}\quad \phi(z)=\frac{8a^3z^2}{(z+ai)^3}.$$

Point out why $\phi(z)$ has a Taylor series representation about $z=ai$, and then use it to show that the principal part of f at that point is

$$\frac{\phi''(ai)/2}{z-ai}+\frac{\phi'(ai)}{(z-ai)^2}+\frac{\phi(ai)}{(z-ai)^3}=-\frac{i/2}{z-ai}-\frac{a/2}{(z-ai)^2}-\frac{a^2i}{(z-ai)^3}.$$

80. RESIDUES AT POLES

When a function f has an isolated singularity at a point z_0, the basic method for identifying z_0 as a pole and finding the residue there is to write the appropriate Laurent series and to note the coefficient of $1/(z-z_0)$. The following theorem provides an alternative characterization of poles and a way of finding residues at poles that is often more convenient.

Theorem. *Let z_0 be an isolated singular point of a function f. The following two statements are equivalent:*

(*a*) *z_0 is a pole of order m ($m = 1, 2, \ldots$) of f;*

(*b*) *$f(z)$ can be written in the form*

$$f(z) = \frac{\phi(z)}{(z - z_0)^m} \qquad (m = 1, 2, \ldots),$$

where $\phi(z)$ is analytic and nonzero at z_0.

Moreover, if statements (a) and (b) are true,

$$\operatorname*{Res}_{z=z_0} f(z) = \phi(z_0) \quad \textit{when } m = 1$$

and

$$\operatorname*{Res}_{z=z_0} f(z) = \frac{\phi^{(m-1)}(z_0)}{(m-1)!} \quad \textit{when } m = 2, 3, \ldots.$$

Observe that these two expressions for residues need not have been written separately since, with the conventions that $\phi^{(0)}(z_0) = \phi(z_0)$ and $0! = 1$, the second expression reduces to the first when $m = 1$.

To prove the theorem, we first assume that statement (*a*) is true. That is, $f(z)$ has a Laurent series representation

$$f(z) = \sum_{n=0}^{\infty} a_n (z - z_0)^n + \frac{b_1}{z - z_0} + \frac{b_2}{(z - z_0)^2} + \cdots + \frac{b_{m-1}}{(z - z_0)^{m-1}} + \frac{b_m}{(z - z_0)^m} \qquad (b_m \neq 0),$$

which is valid in a punctured disk $0 < |z - z_0| < R_2$. Now a function $\phi(z)$ defined by means of the equations

$$\phi(z) = \begin{cases} (z - z_0)^m f(z) & \text{when } z \neq z_0, \\ b_m & \text{when } z = z_0 \end{cases}$$

evidently has the power series representation

$$\phi(z) = b_m + b_{m-1}(z - z_0) + \cdots + b_2(z - z_0)^{m-2} + b_1(z - z_0)^{m-1} + \sum_{n=0}^{\infty} a_n (z - z_0)^{m+n}$$

throughout the entire disk $|z - z_0| < R_2$. Consequently, $\phi(z)$ is analytic in that disk (Sec. 71) and, in particular, at z_0. Inasmuch as $\phi(z_0) = b_m \neq 0$, the expression for $f(z)$ in statement (*b*) follows.

Suppose, on the other hand, that we know only that $f(z)$ has the form in statement (b) and recall (Sec. 62) that since $\phi(z)$ is analytic at z_0, it has a Taylor series representation

$$\phi(z) = \phi(z_0) + \frac{\phi'(z_0)}{1!}(z - z_0) + \frac{\phi''(z_0)}{2!}(z - z_0)^2 + \cdots + \frac{\phi^{(m-1)}(z_0)}{(m-1)!}(z - z_0)^{m-1} + \sum_{n=m}^{\infty} \frac{\phi^{(n)}(z_0)}{n!}(z - z_0)^n$$

in some neighborhood $|z - z_0| < \varepsilon$ of z_0. The quotient in statement (b) then tells us that

$$f(z) = \frac{\phi(z_0)}{(z - z_0)^m} + \frac{\phi'(z_0)/1!}{(z - z_0)^{m-1}} + \frac{\phi''(z_0)/2!}{(z - z_0)^{m-2}} + \cdots + \frac{\phi^{(m-1)}(z_0)/(m-1)!}{z - z_0} + \sum_{n=m}^{\infty} \frac{\phi^{(n)}(z_0)}{n!}(z - z_0)^{n-m}$$

when $0 < |z - z_0| < \varepsilon$. This Laurent series representation, together with the fact that $\phi(z_0) \neq 0$, reveals that z_0 is, indeed, a pole of order m of $f(z)$. The coefficient of $1/(z - z_0)$ tells us, of course, that the residue of $f(z)$ at z_0 is as stated in the theorem, whose proof is now complete.

81. EXAMPLES

The following examples serve to illustrate the use of the theorem in Sec. 80.

EXAMPLE 1. The function

$$f(z) = \frac{z + 4}{z^2 + 1}$$

has an isolated singular point at $z = i$ and can be written

$$f(z) = \frac{\phi(z)}{z - i} \quad \text{where} \quad \phi(z) = \frac{z + 4}{z + i}.$$

Since $\phi(z)$ is analytic at $z = i$ and $\phi(i) \neq 0$, that point is a simple pole of f; and the residue there is

$$B_1 = \phi(i) = \frac{i + 4}{2i} \cdot \frac{i}{i} = \frac{-1 + 4i}{-2} = \frac{1}{2} - 2i.$$

The point $z = -i$ is also a simple pole of f, with residue

$$B_2 = \frac{1}{2} + 2i.$$

EXAMPLE 2. If

$$f(z) = \frac{z^3 + 2z}{(z - i)^3},$$

then

$$f(z) = \frac{\phi(z)}{(z-i)^3} \quad \text{where} \quad \phi(z) = z^3 + 2z.$$

The function $\phi(z)$ is entire, and $\phi(i) = i \neq 0$. Hence f has a pole of order 3 at $z = i$, with residue

$$B = \frac{\phi''(i)}{2!} = \frac{6i}{2!} = 3i.$$

The theorem can, of course, be used when branches of multiple-valued functions are involved.

EXAMPLE 3. Suppose that

$$f(z) = \frac{(\log z)^3}{z^2 + 1},$$

where the branch

$$\log z = \ln r + i\theta \qquad (r > 0, 0 < \theta < 2\pi)$$

of the logarithmic function is to be used. To find the residue of f at the singularity $z = i$, we write

$$f(z) = \frac{\phi(z)}{z - i} \quad \text{where} \quad \phi(z) = \frac{(\log z)^3}{z + i}.$$

The function $\phi(z)$ is clearly analytic at $z = i$; and, since

$$\phi(i) = \frac{(\log i)^3}{2i} = \frac{(\ln 1 + i\pi/2)^3}{2i} = -\frac{\pi^3}{16} \neq 0,$$

f has a simple pole there. The residue is

$$B = \phi(i) = -\frac{\pi^3}{16}.$$

While the theorem in Sec. 80 can be extremely useful, the identification of an isolated singular point as a pole of a certain order is sometimes done most efficiently by appealing directly to a Laurent series.

EXAMPLE 4. If, for instance, the residue of the function

$$f(z) = \frac{1 - \cos z}{z^3}$$

is needed at the singularity $z = 0$, it would be incorrect to write

$$f(z) = \frac{\phi(z)}{z^3} \quad \text{where} \quad \phi(z) = 1 - \cos z$$

and to attempt an application of the theorem in Sec. 80 with $m = 3$. For it is necessary that $\phi(0) \neq 0$ if the theorem is to be used here. In this case, the simplest way to obtain the desired residue is to write out a few terms in the Laurent series

$$f(z) = \frac{1}{z^3}\left[1 - \left(1 - \frac{z^2}{2!} + \frac{z^4}{4!} - \frac{z^6}{6!} + \cdots\right)\right] = \frac{1}{z^3}\left(\frac{z^2}{2!} - \frac{z^4}{4!} + \frac{z^6}{6!} - \cdots\right)$$

$$= \frac{1}{2!}\cdot\frac{1}{z} - \frac{z}{4!} + \frac{z^3}{6!} - \cdots \qquad (0 < |z| < \infty).$$

This shows that $f(z)$ has a *simple pole* at $z = 0$, not a pole of order 3, the residue at $z = 0$ being $B = 1/2$.

EXAMPLE 5. Since $z^2 \sinh z$ is entire and its zeros are (Sec. 39)

$$z = n\pi i \qquad (n = 0, \pm 1, \pm 2, \ldots),$$

the point $z = 0$ is clearly an isolated singularity of the function

$$f(z) = \frac{1}{z^2 \sinh z}.$$

Here it would be a mistake to write

$$f(z) = \frac{\phi(z)}{z^2} \quad \text{where} \quad \phi(z) = \frac{1}{\sinh z}$$

and try to use the theorem in Sec. 80 with $m = 2$. This is because the function $\phi(z)$ is not even defined at $z = 0$. The needed residue, namely $B = -1/6$, follows at once from the Laurent series

$$\frac{1}{z^2 \sinh z} = \frac{1}{z^3} - \frac{1}{6}\cdot\frac{1}{z} + \frac{7}{360}z + \cdots \qquad (0 < |z| < \pi)$$

that was obtained in Exercise 5, Sec.73. The singularity at $z = 0$ is, of course, a pole of the *third* order, not the second order.

EXERCISES

1. In each case, show that any singular point of the function is a pole. Determine the order m of each pole, and find the corresponding residue B.

(*a*) $\dfrac{z+1}{z^2+9}$; (*b*) $\dfrac{z^2+2}{z-1}$; (*c*) $\left(\dfrac{z}{2z+1}\right)^3$; (*d*) $\dfrac{e^z}{z^2+\pi^2}$.

Ans. (*a*) $m = 1, B = \dfrac{3 \pm i}{6}$; (*b*) $m = 1, B = 3$; (*c*) $m = 3, B = -\dfrac{3}{16}$;

(*d*) $m = 1, B = \pm\dfrac{i}{2\pi}$.

2. Show that

(*a*) $\displaystyle \operatorname*{Res}_{z=-1} \frac{z^{1/4}}{z+1} = \frac{1+i}{\sqrt{2}} \quad (|z| > 0, 0 < \arg z < 2\pi)$;

(*b*) $\displaystyle \operatorname*{Res}_{z=i} \frac{\operatorname{Log} z}{(z^2+1)^2} = \frac{\pi + 2i}{8}$;

(*c*) $\displaystyle \operatorname*{Res}_{z=i} \frac{z^{1/2}}{(z^2+1)^2} = \frac{1-i}{8\sqrt{2}} \quad (|z| > 0, 0 < \arg z < 2\pi)$.

3. In each case, find the order m of the pole and the corresponding residue B at the singularity $z = 0$:

$$(a)\ \frac{\sinh z}{z^4}; \qquad (b)\ \frac{1}{z(e^z - 1)}.$$

Ans. $(a)\ m = 3,\ B = \dfrac{1}{6};\quad (b)\ m = 2,\ B = -\dfrac{1}{2}.$

4. Find the value of the integral

$$\int_C \frac{3z^3 + 2}{(z-1)(z^2+9)}\,dz,$$

taken counterclockwise around the circle $(a)\ |z - 2| = 2$; $(b)\ |z| = 4$.
Ans. $(a)\ \pi i;\quad (b)\ 6\pi i.$

5. Find the value of the integral

$$\int_C \frac{dz}{z^3(z+4)},$$

taken counterclockwise around the circle $(a)\ |z| = 2$; $(b)\ |z + 2| = 3$.
Ans. $(a)\ \pi i/32;\quad (b)\ 0.$

6. Evaluate the integral

$$\int_C \frac{\cosh \pi z}{z(z^2+1)}\,dz$$

when C is the circle $|z| = 2$, described in the positive sense.
Ans. $4\pi i.$

7. Use the theorem in Sec. 77, involving a single residue, to evaluate the integral of $f(z)$ around the positively oriented circle $|z| = 3$ when

$$(a)\ f(z) = \frac{(3z+2)^2}{z(z-1)(2z+5)}; \qquad (b)\ f(z) = \frac{z^3 e^{1/z}}{1+z^3}.$$

Ans. $(a)\ 9\pi i;\quad (b)\ 2\pi i.$

8. Let z_0 be an isolated singular point of a function f and suppose that

$$f(z) = \frac{\phi(z)}{(z-z_0)^m},$$

where m is a positive integer and $\phi(z)$ is analytic and nonzero at z_0. By applying the extended form (3), Sec. 55, of the Cauchy integral formula to the function $\phi(z)$, show that

$$\operatorname*{Res}_{z=z_0} f(z) = \frac{\phi^{(m-1)}(z_0)}{(m-1)!},$$

as stated in the theorem of Sec. 80.

Suggestion: Since there is a neighborhood $|z - z_0| < \varepsilon$ throughout which $\phi(z)$ is analytic (see Sec. 25), the contour used in the extended Cauchy integral formula can be the positively oriented circle $|z - z_0| = \varepsilon/2$.

82. ZEROS OF ANALYTIC FUNCTIONS

Zeros and poles of functions are closely related. In fact, we shall see in the next section how zeros can be a source of poles. We need, however, some preliminary results regarding zeros of analytic functions.

Suppose that a function f is analytic at a point z_0. We know from Sec. 57 that all of the derivatives $f^{(n)}(z)$ $(n = 1, 2, \ldots)$ exist at z_0. If $f(z_0) = 0$ and if there is a positive integer m such that

$$(1) \qquad f(z_0) = f'(z_0) = f''(z_0) = \cdots = f^{(m-1)}(z_0) = 0 \quad \text{and} \quad f^{(m)}(z_0) \neq 0,$$

where m is a positive integer, f is said to have a ***zero of order m*** at z_0. We agree, of course, that $f^{(0)}(z_0) = f(z_0)$ when $m = 1$. Our first theorem here provides a useful alternative definition of zeros of order m.

Theorem 1. *Let f denote a function that is analytic at a point z_0. The following two statements are equivalent:*

(a) *f has a zero of order m at z_0;*

(b) *there is a function g, which is analytic and nonzero at z_0, such that*

$$f(z) = (z - z_0)^m g(z).$$

Our proof of this theorem has two parts. First, we need to show that the truth of statement (a) implies the truth of statement (b). Once that is accomplished, we need to show that if statement (b) is true, then so is statement (a). Both parts use the fact (Sec. 62) that if a given function is analytic at a point z_0, then it must have a Taylor series representation in powers of $(z - z_0)$ that is valid throughout some neighborhood $|z - z_0| < \varepsilon$ of z_0.

(a) implies (b)

We start the first part of the proof by assuming that f has a zero of order m at z_0 and showing how statement (b) follows. The analyticity of f at z_0 and conditions (1) tell us that in some neighborhood $|z - z_0| < \varepsilon$ there is a Taylor series representation

$$\begin{aligned} f(z) &= \frac{f^{(m)}(z_0)}{m!}(z - z_0)^m + \frac{f^{(m+1)}(z_0)}{(m+1)!}(z - z_0)^{m+1} + \frac{f^{(m+2)}(z_0)}{(m+2)!}(z - z_0)^{m+2} + \cdots \\ &= (z - z_0)^m \left[\frac{f^{(m)}(z_0)}{m!} + \frac{f^{(m+1)}(z_0)}{(m+1)!}(z - z_0) + \frac{f^{(m+2)}(z_0)}{(m+2)!}(z - z_0)^2 + \cdots \right]. \end{aligned}$$

Consequently, $f(z)$ has the form shown in statement (b), where

$$g(z) = \frac{f^{(m)}(z_0)}{m!} + \frac{f^{(m+1)}(z_0)}{(m+1)!}(z - z_0) + \frac{f^{(m+2)}(z_0)}{(m+2)!}(z - z_0)^2 + \cdots \qquad (|z - z_0| < \varepsilon).$$

The convergence of this last series when $|z - z_0| < \varepsilon$ ensures that g is analytic in that neighborhood and, in particular, at z_0 (Sec. 71). Moreover,

$$g(z_0) = \frac{f^{(m)}(z_0)}{m!} \neq 0.$$

This completes the proof of the first part of the theorem.

(*b*) implies (*a*)

Here we assume that the expression for $f(z)$ in part (*b*) holds; and we note that since the function $g(z)$ is analytic at z_0, it has a Taylor series representation

$$g(z) = g(z_0) + \frac{g'(z_0)}{1!}(z - z_0) + \frac{g''(z_0)}{2!}(z - z_0)^2 + \cdots$$

in some neighborhood $|z - z_0| < \varepsilon$ of z_0. The expression for $f(z)$ in part (*b*) thus takes the form

$$f(z) = g(z_0)(z - z_0)^m + \frac{g'(z_0)}{1!}(z - z_0)^{m+1} + \frac{g''(z_0)}{2!}(z - z_0)^{m+2} + \cdots$$

when $|z - z_0| < \varepsilon$. Since this is actually a Taylor series expansion for $f(z)$, according to Theorem 1 in Sec. 72, conditions (1) hold; in particular,

$$f^{(m)}(z_0) = m!g(z_0) \neq 0.$$

Hence z_0 is a zero of order m of f. The proof is now complete.

EXAMPLE. The polynomial $f(z) = z^3 - 1$ has a zero of order $m = 1$ at $z_0 = 1$ since

$$f(z) = (z - 1)g(z),$$

where $g(z) = z^2 + z + 1$, and because f and g are entire and $g(1) = 3 \neq 0$. Note how the fact that $z_0 = 1$ is a zero of order $m = 1$ of f also follows from the observations that

$$f(1) = 0 \quad \text{and} \quad f'(1) = 3 \neq 0.$$

Our next theorem is a precise statement of the fact that an analytic function $f(z)$ has only ***isolated zeros*** when is not identically equal to zero. This means that if z_0 is a zero of such a function $f(z)$, there is a deleted neighborhood $0 < |z - z_0| < \varepsilon$ of z_0 in which $f(z)$ is nonzero. (Compare with the definition of an isolated singularity in Sec. 74.)

Theorem 2. *Given a function f and a point z_0, suppose that*

(*a*) *f is analytic at z_0;*

(*b*) *$f(z_0) = 0$ but $f(z)$ is not identically equal to zero in any neighborhood of z_0.*

Then $f(z) \neq 0$ throughout some deleted neighborhood $0 < |z - z_0| < \varepsilon$ of z_0.

To prove this, let f be as stated and observe that not all of the derivatives of f at z_0 are zero. If they were, all of the coefficients in the Taylor series for f about z_0 would be zero; and that would mean that $f(z)$ is identically equal to zero in some neighborhood of z_0. So it is clear from the definition of zeros of order m at the beginning of this section that f must have a zero of some finite order m at z_0. According to Theorem 1, then,

$$f(z) = (z - z_0)^m g(z) \tag{2}$$

where $g(z)$ is analytic and nonzero at z_0.

Now g is continuous, in addition to being nonzero, at z_0 because it is analytic there. Hence there is some neighborhood $|z - z_0| < \varepsilon$ in which equation (2) holds and in which $g(z) \neq 0$ (see Sec. 18). Consequently, $f(z) \neq 0$ in the *deleted* neighborhood $0 < |z - z_0| < \varepsilon$; and the proof is complete.

Our final theorem here concerns functions with zeros that are not all isolated. It was referred to earlier in Sec. 28 and makes an interesting contrast to Theorem 2 just above.

Theorem 3. *Given a function f and a point z_0, suppose that*

(*a*) *f is analytic throughout a neighborhood N_0 of z_0;*

(*b*) *$f(z) = 0$ at each point z of a domain D or line segment L containing z_0* (Fig. 96).

Then $f(z) \equiv 0$ in N_0; that is, $f(z)$ is identically equal to zero throughout N_0.

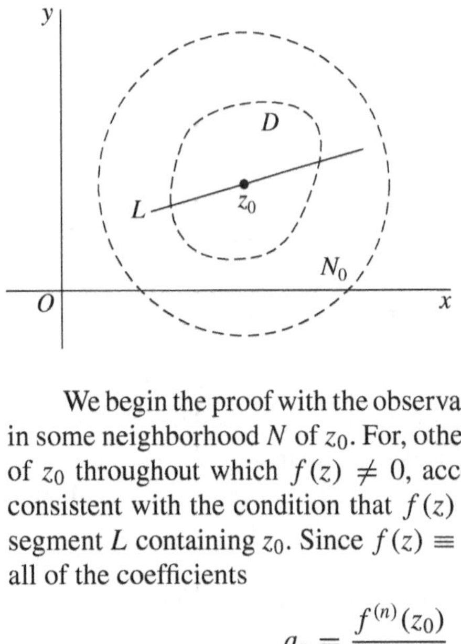

FIGURE 96

We begin the proof with the observation that under the stated conditions, $f(z) \equiv 0$ in some neighborhood N of z_0. For, otherwise, there would be a deleted neighborhood of z_0 throughout which $f(z) \neq 0$, according to Theorem 2; and that would be inconsistent with the condition that $f(z) = 0$ everywhere in a domain D or on a line segment L containing z_0. Since $f(z) \equiv 0$ in the neighborhood N, then, it follows that all of the coefficients

$$a_n = \frac{f^{(n)}(z_0)}{n!} \qquad (n = 0, 1, 2, \ldots)$$

in the Taylor series for $f(z)$ about z_0 must be zero. Thus $f(z) \equiv 0$ in the neighborhood N_0, since the Taylor series also represents $f(z)$ in N_0. This completes the proof.

83. ZEROS AND POLES

The following theorem establishes a connection between zeros of order m and poles of order m.

Theorem 1. *Suppose that*

(*a*) *two functions p and q are analytic at a point z_0;*

(*b*) *$p(z_0) \neq 0$ and q has a zero of order m at z_0.*

Then the quotient $p(z)/q(z)$ has a pole of order m at z_0.

The proof is easy. Let p and q be as in the statement of the theorem. Since q has a zero of order m at z_0, we know from Theorem 2 in Sec. 82 that there is a deleted neighborhood of z_0 throughout which $q(z) \neq 0$; and so z_0 is an isolated singular point of the quotient $p(z)/q(z)$. Theorem 1 in Sec. 82 tells us, moreover, that

$$q(z) = (z - z_0)^m g(z),$$

where $g(z)$ is analytic and nonzero at z_0. Consequently,

$$\frac{p(z)}{q(z)} = \frac{\phi(z)}{(z - z_0)^m} \quad \text{where} \quad \phi(z) = \frac{p(z)}{g(z)}. \tag{1}$$

Since $\phi(z)$ is analytic and nonzero at z_0, it now follows from the theorem in Sec. 80 that z_0 is a pole of order m of $p(z)/q(z)$.

EXAMPLE 1. The two functions

$$p(z) = 1 \quad \text{and} \quad q(z) = 1 - \cos z$$

are entire, and we know from Exercise 2 that $q(z)$ has a zero of order $m = 2$ at the point $z_0 = 0$. Hence it follows from Theorem 1 that the quotient

$$\frac{p(z)}{q(z)} = \frac{1}{1 - \cos z}$$

has a pole of order $m = 2$ at that point.

Theorem 1 leads us to another method for identifying *simple* poles and finding the corresponding residues. This method, stated just below as Theorem 2, is sometimes easier to use than the theorem in Sec. 80.

Theorem 2. *Let two functions p and q be analytic at a point z_0. If*

$$p(z_0) \neq 0, \quad q(z_0) = 0, \quad \textit{and} \quad q'(z_0) \neq 0,$$

then z_0 is a simple pole of the quotient $p(z)/q(z)$ and

$$\operatorname*{Res}_{z=z_0} \frac{p(z)}{q(z)} = \frac{p(z_0)}{q'(z_0)}. \tag{2}$$

To show this, we assume that p and q are as stated and observe that because of the conditions on q, the point z_0 is a zero of order $m = 1$ of that function. According to Theorem 1 in Sec. 82, then,

$$q(z) = (z - z_0)g(z) \tag{3}$$

where $g(z)$ is analytic and nonzero at z_0. Furthermore, Theorem 1 in this section tells us that z_0 is a simple pole of $p(z)/q(z)$; and expression (1) for $p(z)/q(z)$ in the proof of that theorem becomes

$$\frac{p(z)}{q(z)} = \frac{\phi(z)}{z - z_0} \quad \text{where} \quad \phi(z) = \frac{p(z)}{g(z)}.$$

Since this $\phi(z)$ is analytic and nonzero at z_0, we know from the theorem in Sec. 80 that

$$\operatorname*{Res}_{z=z_0} \frac{p(z)}{q(z)} = \frac{p(z_0)}{g(z_0)}. \tag{4}$$

But $g(z_0) = q'(z_0)$, as is seen by differentiating each side of equation (3) and then setting $z = z_0$. Expression (4) thus takes the form (2).

EXAMPLE 2. Consider the function

$$f(z) = \cot z = \frac{\cos z}{\sin z},$$

which is a quotient of the entire functions $p(z) = \cos z$ and $q(z) = \sin z$. Its singularities occur at the zeros of q, or at the points

$$z = n\pi \qquad (n = 0, \pm 1, \pm 2, \ldots).$$

Since

$$p(n\pi) = (-1)^n \neq 0, \quad q(n\pi) = 0, \quad \text{and} \quad q'(n\pi) = (-1)^n \neq 0,$$

Theorem 2 tells us that each singular point $z = n\pi$ of f is a simple pole, with residue

$$B_n = \frac{p(n\pi)}{q'(n\pi)} = \frac{(-1)^n}{(-1)^n} = 1.$$

EXAMPLE 3. The residue of the function

$$f(z) = \frac{z - \sinh z}{z^2 \sinh z}$$

at the zero $z = \pi i$ of $\sinh z$ (see Sec. 39) is readily found by writing

$$p(z) = z - \sinh z \quad \text{and} \quad q(z) = z^2 \sinh z.$$

Because

$$p(\pi i) = \pi i \neq 0, \quad q(\pi i) = 0, \quad \text{and} \quad q'(\pi i) = \pi^2 \neq 0,$$

Theorem 2 tells us that $z = \pi i$ is a simple pole of f and that the residue there is

$$B = \frac{p(\pi i)}{q'(\pi i)} = \frac{\pi i}{\pi^2} = \frac{i}{\pi}.$$

EXAMPLE 4. Since the point

$$z_0 = \sqrt{2}e^{i\pi/4} = 1 + i$$

is a zero of the polynomial $z^4 + 4$ (see Exercise 6, Sec. 11), it is also an isolated singularity of the function

$$f(z) = \frac{z}{z^4 + 4}.$$

Writing $p(z) = z$ and $q(z) = z^4 + 4$, we find that

$$p(z_0) = z_0 \neq 0, \quad q(z_0) = 0, \quad \text{and} \quad q'(z_0) = 4z_0^3 \neq 0.$$

Theorem 2 then reveals that z_0 is a simple pole of f. The residue there is, moreover,

$$B_0 = \frac{p(z_0)}{q'(z_0)} = \frac{z_0}{4z_0^3} = \frac{1}{4z_0^2} = \frac{1}{8i} = -\frac{i}{8}.$$

Although this residue can also be found by the method in Sec. 80, the computation is somewhat more involved.

There are expressions similar to expression (2) for residues at poles of higher order, but they are lengthier and, in general, not practical.

EXERCISES

1. Show that the point $z = 0$ is a simple pole of the function

$$f(z) = \csc z = \frac{1}{\sin z}$$

and that the residue there is unity by appealing to Theorem 2 in Sec. 83. (Compare with Exercise 3, Sec. 73, where this result is evident from a Laurent series.)

2. Use conditions (1) in Sec. 82 to show that the function

$$q(z) = 1 - \cos z$$

has a zero of order $m = 2$ at the point $z_0 = 0$.

3. Show that

(*a*) $\displaystyle \operatorname*{Res}_{z=\pi i/2} \frac{\sinh z}{z^2 \cosh z} = -\frac{4}{\pi^2};$

(*b*) $\displaystyle \operatorname*{Res}_{z=\pi i} \frac{\exp(zt)}{\sinh z} + \operatorname*{Res}_{z=-\pi i} \frac{\exp(zt)}{\sinh z} = -2\cos(\pi t).$

4. Show that

(*a*) $\displaystyle \operatorname*{Res}_{z=z_n}(z \sec z) = (-1)^{n+1} z_n \text{ where } z_n = \frac{\pi}{2} + n\pi \quad (n = 0, \pm 1, \pm 2, \ldots);$

(*b*) $\displaystyle \operatorname*{Res}_{z=z_n}(\tanh z) = 1 \text{ where } z_n = \left(\frac{\pi}{2} + n\pi\right)i \quad (n = 0, \pm 1, \pm 2, \ldots).$

5. Let C denote the positively oriented circle $|z| = 2$ and evaluate the integral

$$(a)\ \int_C \tan z\, dz; \qquad (b)\ \int_C \frac{dz}{\sinh 2z}.$$

Ans. $(a)\ -4\pi i$; $(b)\ -\pi i$.

6. Let C_N denote the positively oriented boundary of the square whose edges lie along the lines

$$x = \pm\left(N + \frac{1}{2}\right)\pi \quad \text{and} \quad y = \pm\left(N + \frac{1}{2}\right)\pi,$$

where N is a positive integer. Show that

$$\int_{C_N} \frac{dz}{z^2 \sin z} = 2\pi i \left[\frac{1}{6} + 2\sum_{n=1}^{N} \frac{(-1)^n}{n^2\pi^2}\right].$$

Then, using the fact that the value of this integral tends to zero as N tends to infinity (Exercise 8, Sec. 47), point out how it follows that

$$\sum_{n=1}^{\infty} \frac{(-1)^{n+1}}{n^2} = \frac{\pi^2}{12}.$$

7. Show that

$$\int_C \frac{dz}{(z^2-1)^2+3} = \frac{\pi}{2\sqrt{2}},$$

where C is the positively oriented boundary of the rectangle whose sides lie along the lines $x = \pm 2$, $y = 0$, and $y = 1$.

Suggestion: By observing that the four zeros of the polynomial $q(z) = (z^2-1)^2+3$ are the square roots of the numbers $1 \pm \sqrt{3}i$, show that the reciprocal $1/q(z)$ is analytic inside and on C except at the points

$$z_0 = \frac{\sqrt{3}+i}{\sqrt{2}} \quad \text{and} \quad -\overline{z_0} = \frac{-\sqrt{3}+i}{\sqrt{2}}.$$

Then apply Theorem 2 in Sec. 83.

8. Consider the function

$$f(z) = \frac{1}{[q(z)]^2}$$

where q is analytic at z_0, $q(z_0) = 0$, and $q'(z_0) \neq 0$. Show that z_0 is a pole of order $m = 2$ of the function f, with residue

$$B_0 = -\frac{q''(z_0)}{[q'(z_0)]^3}.$$

Suggestion: Note that z_0 is a zero of order $m = 1$ of the function q, so that

$$q(z) = (z - z_0)g(z)$$

where $g(z)$ is analytic and nonzero at z_0. Then write

$$f(z) = \frac{\phi(z)}{(z-z_0)^2} \quad \text{where} \quad \phi(z) = \frac{1}{[g(z)]^2}.$$

The desired form of the residue $B_0 = \phi'(z_0)$ can be obtained by showing that

$$q'(z_0) = g(z_0) \quad \text{and} \quad q''(z_0) = 2g'(z_0).$$

9. Use the result in Exercise 7 to find the residue at $z = 0$ of the function

$$(a)\ f(z) = \csc^2 z; \qquad (b)\ f(z) = \frac{1}{(z + z^2)^2}.$$

Ans. (*a*) 0; (*b*) −2.

10. Let p and q denote functions that are analytic at a point z_0, where $p(z_0) \neq 0$ and $q(z_0) = 0$. Show that if the quotient $p(z)/q(z)$ has a pole of order m at z_0, then z_0 is a zero of order m of q. (Compare with Theorem 1 in Sec. 83.)

Suggestion: Note that the theorem in Sec. 80 enables one to write

$$\frac{p(z)}{q(z)} = \frac{\phi(z)}{(z - z_0)^m},$$

where $\phi(z)$ is analytic and nonzero at z_0. Then solve for $q(z)$.

11. Recall (Sec. 12) that a point z_0 is an accumulation point of a set S if each deleted neighborhood of z_0 contains at least one point of S. One form of the *Bolzano–Weierstrass theorem* can be stated as follows: *an infinite set of points lying in a closed bounded region R has at least one accumulation point in R.** Use that theorem and Theorem 2 in Sec. 82 to show that if a function f is analytic in the region R consisting of all points inside and on a simple closed contour C, except possibly for poles inside C, and if all the zeros of f in R are interior to C and are of finite order, then those zeros must be finite in number.

12. Let R denote the region consisting of all points inside and on a simple closed contour C. Use the Bolzano–Weierstrass theorem (see Exercise 11) and the fact that poles are isolated singular points to show that if f is analytic in the region R except for poles interior to C, then those poles must be finite in number.

84. BEHAVIOR OF FUNCTIONS NEAR ISOLATED SINGULAR POINTS

The behavior of a function f near an isolated singular point z_0 varies, depending on whether z_0 is a removable singular point, an essential singular point, or a pole of some order m. In this section, we describe some of that behavior. Since the results presented here will not be used elsewhere in the book, the reader who wishes to reach applications of residue theory more quickly may pass directly to Chap. 7 without disruption.

(*a*) *Removable Singular Points*

We start with two theorems about removable singular points.

---

*See, for example, A. E. Taylor and W. R. Mann. "*Advanced Calculus*," 3d ed., pp. 517 and 521, 1983.

Theorem 1. *If z_0 is a removable singular point of a function f, then f is bounded and analytic in some deleted neighborhood $0 < |z - z| < \varepsilon$ of z_0.*

The proof is easy and is based on the fact that the function f here is analytic in a disk $|z - z_0| < R_2$ when $f(z_0)$ is properly defined; f is then continuous in any closed disk $|z - z_0| \leq \varepsilon$ where $\varepsilon < R_2$. Consequently, f is bounded in that disk, according to Theorem 4 in Sec. 18; and this means that, in addition to being analytic, f must be bounded in the deleted neighborhood $0 < |z - z_0| < \varepsilon$.

The next theorem is known as ***Riemann's theorem*** and is closely related to Theorem 1.

Theorem 2. *Suppose that a function f is bounded and analytic in some deleted neighborhood $0 < |z - z| < \varepsilon$ of z_0. If f is not analytic at z_0, then it has a removable singularity there.*

To prove this, we assume that f is not analytic at z_0. As a consequence, the point z_0 must be an isolated singularity of f; and $f(z)$ is represented by a Laurent series

$$f(z) = \sum_{n=0}^{\infty} a_n(z - z_0)^n + \sum_{n=1}^{\infty} \frac{b_n}{(z - z_0)^n} \tag{1}$$

throughout the deleted neighborhood $0 < |z - z_0| < \varepsilon$. If C denotes a positively oriented circle $|z - z_0| = \rho$, where $\rho < \varepsilon$ (Fig. 97), we know from Sec. 66 that the coefficients b_n in expansion (1) can be written

$$b_n = \frac{1}{2\pi i} \int_C \frac{f(z)\,dz}{(z - z_0)^{-n+1}} \qquad (n = 1, 2, \ldots). \tag{2}$$

Now the boundedness condition on f tells us that there is a positive constant M such that $|f(z)| \leq M$ whenever $0 < |z - z_0| < \varepsilon$. Hence it follows from expression (2) that

$$|b_n| \leq \frac{1}{2\pi} \cdot \frac{M}{\rho^{-n+1}} 2\pi\rho = M\rho^n \qquad (n = 1, 2, \ldots).$$

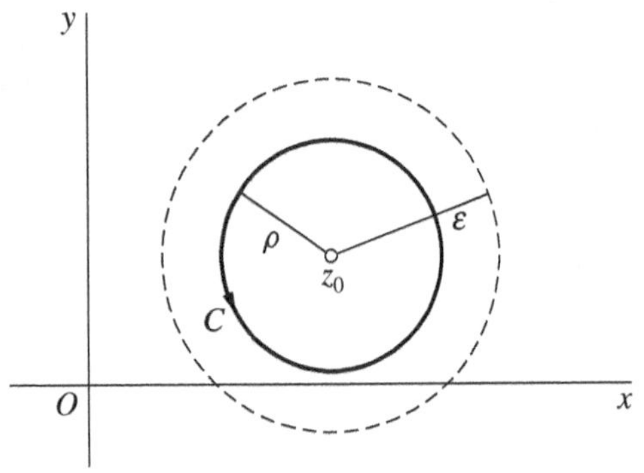

FIGURE 97

Since the coefficients b_n are constants and since ρ can be chosen arbitrarily small, we may conclude that $b_n = 0$ $(n = 1, 2, \ldots)$ in the Laurent series (1). This tells us that z_0 is a removable singularity of f, and the proof of Theorem 2 is complete.

(b) Essential Singular Points

We know from Example 2 in Sec. 79 that the behavior of a function near an essential singular point can be quite irregular. The next theorem, regarding such behavior, is related to Picard's theorem in that earlier example and is usually referred to as the ***Casorati–Weierstrass theorem***. It states that in each deleted neighborhood of an essential singular point, a function assumes values arbitrarily close to any given number.

Theorem 3. *Suppose that* z_0 *is an essential singularity of a function* f*, and let* w_0 *be any complex number. Then, for any positive number* ε*, the inequality*

$$|f(z) - w_0| < \varepsilon \tag{3}$$

is satisfied at some point z *in each deleted neighborhood* $0 < |z - z_0| < \delta$ *of* z_0 (Fig. 98).

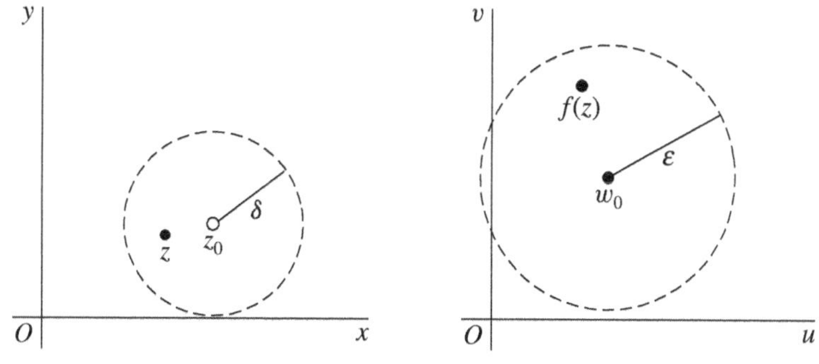

FIGURE 98

The proof is by contradiction. Since z_0 is an isolated singularity of f, there is a deleted neighborhood $0 < |z - z_0| < \delta$ throughout which f is analytic; and we assume that condition (3) is *not* satisfied for any point z there. Thus $|f(z) - w_0| \geq \varepsilon$ when $0 < |z - z_0| < \delta$; and so the function

$$g(z) = \frac{1}{f(z) - w_0} \qquad (0 < |z - z_0| < \delta) \tag{4}$$

is bounded and analytic in its domain of definition. Hence, according to Theorem 2, z_0 is a removable singularity of g; and we let g be defined at z_0 so that it is analytic there.

If $g(z_0) \neq 0$, the function $f(z)$, which can be written

$$f(z) = \frac{1}{g(z)} + w_0 \tag{5}$$

when $0 < |z - z_0| < \delta$, becomes analytic at z_0 when it is defined there as

$$f(z_0) = \frac{1}{g(z_0)} + w_0.$$

But this means that z_0 is a removable singularity of f, not an essential one, and we have a contradiction.

If $g(z_0) = 0$, the function g must have a zero of some finite order m (Sec. 82) at z_0 because $g(z)$ is not identically equal to zero in the neighborhood $|z - z_0| < \delta$. In view of equation (5), then, f has a pole of order m at z_0 (see Theorem 1 in Sec. 83). So, once again, we have a contradiction; and Theorem 3 here is proved.

(c) *Poles of Order m*

Our next theorem shows how the behavior of functions near poles is fundamentally different from their behavior near removable and essential singularities.*

Theorem 4. *If z_0 is a pole of a function f, then*

$$\lim_{z \to z_0} f(z) = \infty. \tag{6}$$

To verify limit (6), we assume that f has a pole of order m at z_0 and use the theorem in Sec. 80. It tells us that

$$f(z) = \frac{\phi(z)}{(z - z_0)^m},$$

where $\phi(z)$ is analytic and nonzero at z_0. Since

$$\lim_{z \to z_0} \frac{1}{f(z)} = \lim_{z \to z_0} \frac{(z - z_0)^m}{\phi(z)} = \frac{\lim\limits_{z \to z_0} (z - z_0)^m}{\lim\limits_{z \to z_0} \phi(z)} = \frac{0}{\phi(z_0)} = 0,$$

then, limit (6) holds, according to the theorem in Sec. 17 regarding limits involving the point at infinity.

*As pointed out in the two books referred to in the footnote in Sec. 78, the theorem here tells us that the modulus $|f(z)|$ increases without bound as z tends to z_0 and thus suggests the existence of a pole in the nonmathematical sense.

CHAPTER

7

APPLICATIONS OF RESIDUES

We turn now to some important applications of the theory of residues, which was developed in Chap. 6. The applications include evaluation of certain types of definite and improper integrals occurring in *real* analysis and applied mathematics. Considerable attention is also given to a method, based on residues, for locating zeros of functions and to finding inverse Laplace transforms by summing residues.

85. EVALUATION OF IMPROPER INTEGRALS

In calculus, the improper integral of a continuous function $f(x)$ over the semi-infinite interval $0 \le x < \infty$ is defined by means of the equation

$$(1) \qquad \int_0^\infty f(x)\,dx = \lim_{R\to\infty} \int_0^R f(x)\,dx.$$

When the limit on the right exists, the improper integral is said to ***converge*** to that limit. If $f(x)$ is continuous for *all* x, its improper integral over the infinite interval $-\infty < x < \infty$ is defined by writing

$$(2) \qquad \int_{-\infty}^\infty f(x)\,dx = \lim_{R_1\to\infty} \int_{-R_1}^0 f(x)\,dx + \lim_{R_2\to\infty} \int_0^{R_2} f(x)\,dx;$$

and when both of the limits here exist, we say that integral (2) converges to their sum. Another value that is assigned to integral (2) is often useful. Namely, the ***Cauchy***

principal value (P.V.) of integral (2) is the number

$$\text{(3)} \qquad \text{P.V.} \int_{-\infty}^{\infty} f(x)\,dx = \lim_{R\to\infty} \int_{-R}^{R} f(x)\,dx,$$

provided this single limit exists.

If integral (2) converges, its Cauchy principal value (3) exists; and that value is the number to which integral (2) converges. This is because

$$\lim_{R\to\infty} \int_{-R}^{R} f(x)\,dx = \lim_{R\to\infty} \left[\int_{-R}^{0} f(x)\,dx + \int_{0}^{R} f(x)\,dx\right]$$
$$= \lim_{R\to\infty} \int_{-R}^{0} f(x)\,dx + \lim_{R\to\infty} \int_{0}^{R} f(x)\,dx$$

and these last two limits are the same as the limits on the right in equation (2).

It is *not*, however, always true that integral (2) converges when its Cauchy principal value exists, as the following example shows.

EXAMPLE. Observe that

$$\text{(4)} \qquad \text{P.V.} \int_{-\infty}^{\infty} x\,dx = \lim_{R\to\infty} \int_{-R}^{R} x\,dx = \lim_{R\to\infty} \left[\frac{x^2}{2}\right]_{-R}^{R} = \lim_{R\to\infty} 0 = 0.$$

On the other hand,

$$\text{(5)} \qquad \int_{-\infty}^{\infty} x\,dx = \lim_{R_1\to\infty} \int_{-R_1}^{0} x\,dx + \lim_{R_2\to\infty} \int_{0}^{R_2} x\,dx$$
$$= \lim_{R_1\to\infty} \left[\frac{x^2}{2}\right]_{-R_1}^{0} + \lim_{R_2\to\infty} \left[\frac{x^2}{2}\right]_{0}^{R_2}$$
$$= -\lim_{R_1\to\infty} \frac{R_1^2}{2} + \lim_{R_2\to\infty} \frac{R_2^2}{2};$$

and since these last two limits do not exist, we find that the improper integral (5) fails to exist.

But suppose that $f(x)$ $(-\infty < x < \infty)$ is an *even* function, one where

$$f(-x) = f(x) \quad \text{for all } x,$$

and *assume that the Cauchy principal value* (3) *exists*. The symmetry of the graph of $y = f(x)$ with respect to the y axis tells us that

$$\int_{-R_1}^{0} f(x)\,dx = \frac{1}{2} \int_{-R_1}^{R_1} f(x)\,dx$$

and

$$\int_{0}^{R_2} f(x)\,dx = \frac{1}{2} \int_{-R_2}^{R_2} f(x)\,dx.$$

Thus

$$\int_{-R_1}^{0} f(x)\,dx + \int_{0}^{R_2} f(x)\,dx = \frac{1}{2}\int_{-R_1}^{R_1} f(x)\,dx + \frac{1}{2}\int_{-R_2}^{R_2} f(x)\,dx.$$

If we let R_1 and R_2 tend to ∞ on each side here, the fact that the limits on the right exist means that the limits on the left do too. In fact,

$$\int_{-\infty}^{\infty} f(x)\,dx = \text{P.V.}\int_{-\infty}^{\infty} f(x)\,dx. \tag{6}$$

Moreover, since

$$\int_{0}^{R} f(x)\,dx = \frac{1}{2}\int_{-R}^{R} f(x)\,dx,$$

it is also true that

$$\int_{0}^{\infty} f(x)\,dx = \frac{1}{2}\left[\text{P.V.}\int_{-\infty}^{\infty} f(x)\,dx\right]. \tag{7}$$

We now describe a method involving sums of residues, to be illustrated in the next section, that is often used to evaluate improper integrals of ***rational functions*** $f(x) = p(x)/q(x)$, where $p(x)$ and $q(x)$ are polynomials with real coefficients and no factors in common. We agree that $q(z)$ has no real zeros but has at least one zero *above* the real axis.

The method begins with the identification of all the *distinct* zeros of the polynomial $q(z)$ that lie above the real axis. They are, of course, finite in number (see Sec. 58) and may be labeled $z_1, z_2, \ldots, z_n$, where n is less than or equal to the degree of $q(z)$. We then integrate the quotient

$$f(z) = \frac{p(z)}{q(z)} \tag{8}$$

around the positively oriented boundary of the semicircular region shown in Fig. 99. That simple closed contour consists of the segment of the real axis from $z = -R$ to $z = R$ and the top half of the circle $|z| = R$, described counterclockwise and denoted by C_R. It is understood that the positive number R is large enough so that the points $z_1, z_2, \ldots, z_n$ all lie inside the closed path.

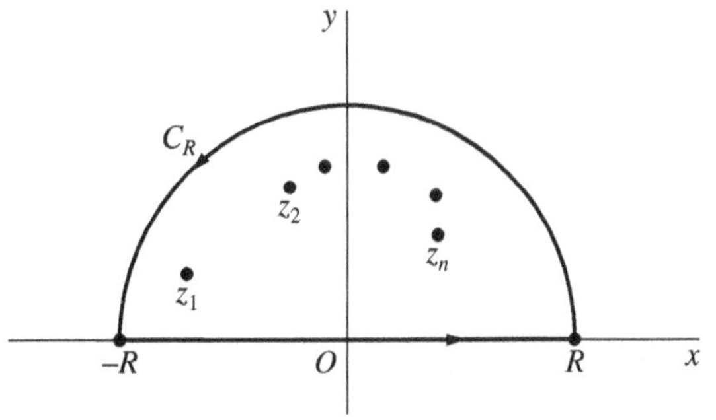

FIGURE 99

The parametric representation $z = x\ (-R \le x \le R)$ of the segment of the real axis just mentioned and Cauchy's residue theorem in Sec. 76 can be used to write

$$\int_{-R}^{R} f(x)\,dx + \int_{C_R} f(z)\,dz = 2\pi i \sum_{k=1}^{n} \operatorname*{Res}_{z=z_k} f(z),$$

or

$$\int_{-R}^{R} f(x)\,dx = 2\pi i \sum_{k=1}^{n} \operatorname*{Res}_{z=z_k} f(z) - \int_{C_R} f(z)\,dz. \tag{9}$$

If

$$\lim_{R\to\infty} \int_{C_R} f(z)\,dz = 0,$$

it then follows that

$$\text{P.V.} \int_{-\infty}^{\infty} f(x)\,dx = 2\pi i \sum_{k=1}^{n} \operatorname*{Res}_{z=z_k} f(z); \tag{10}$$

and if $f(x)$ is *even*, equations (6) and (7) tell us that

$$\int_{-\infty}^{\infty} f(x)\,dx = 2\pi i \sum_{k=1}^{n} \operatorname*{Res}_{z=z_k} f(z) \tag{11}$$

and

$$\int_{0}^{\infty} f(x)\,dx = \pi i \sum_{k=1}^{n} \operatorname*{Res}_{z=z_k} f(z). \tag{12}$$

86. EXAMPLE

We turn now to an illustration of the method described in Sec. 85 for evaluating improper integrals. In order to evaluate the integral

$$\int_0^{\infty} \frac{dx}{x^6+1},$$

we start with the observation that the function

$$f(z) = \frac{1}{z^6+1}$$

has isolated singularities at the zeros of $z^6 + 1$, which are the sixth roots of -1, and is analytic everywhere else. The method in Sec. 10 for finding roots of complex numbers reveals that the sixth roots of -1 are

$$c_k = \exp\left[i\left(\frac{\pi}{6} + \frac{2k\pi}{6}\right)\right] \qquad (k = 0, 1, 2, \ldots, 5),$$

and it is clear that none of them lies on the real axis. The first three roots,

$$c_0 = e^{i\pi/6}, \quad c_1 = i, \quad \text{and} \quad c_2 = e^{i5\pi/6},$$

lie in the upper half plane (Fig. 100) and the other three lie in the lower one. When $R > 1$, the points c_k $(k = 0, 1, 2)$ lie in the interior of the semicircular region bounded by the segment $z = x$ $(-R \le x \le R)$ of the real axis and the upper half C_R of the circle $|z| = R$ from $z = R$ to $z = -R$. Integrating $f(z)$ counterclockwise around the boundary of this semicircular region, we see that

$$\int_{-R}^{R} f(x)\,dx + \int_{C_R} f(z)\,dz = 2\pi i(B_0 + B_1 + B_2), \tag{1}$$

where B_k is the residue of $f(z)$ at c_k $(k = 0, 1, 2)$.

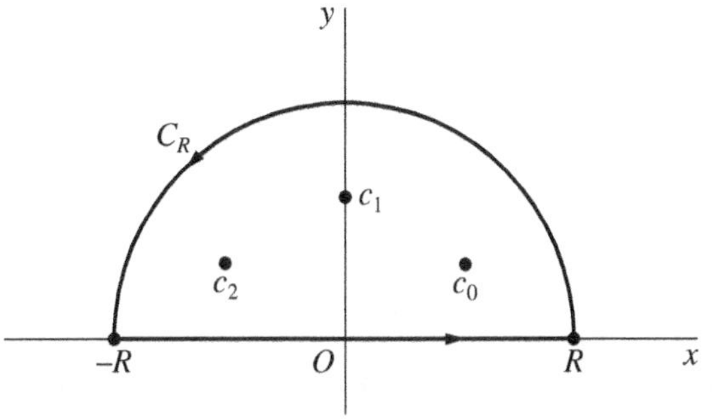

FIGURE 100

Theorem 2 in Sec. 83 tells us that the points c_k are simple poles of f and that

$$B_k = \operatorname*{Res}_{z=c_k} \frac{1}{z^6+1} = \frac{1}{6c_k^5} \cdot \frac{c_k}{c_k} = \frac{c_k}{6c_k^6} = -\frac{c_k}{6} \qquad (k = 0, 1, 2).$$

Thus

$$B_0 + B_1 + B_2 = -\frac{1}{6}(c_0 + c_1 + c_2). \tag{2}$$

If we think of the root $c_2 = e^{i5\pi/6}$ as a point on the unit circle $|z| = 1$, it is geometrically evident that c_2 can also be written $c_2 = -e^{-i\pi/6}$. Also, the definition of $\sin z$ in Sec. 37 tells us that

$$e^{i\pi/6} - e^{-i\pi/6} = 2i \sin\frac{\pi}{6} = i.$$

These two observations and equation (2) enable us to write

$$B_0 + B_1 + B_2 = -\frac{1}{6}(e^{i\pi/6} + i - e^{-i\pi/6}) = -\frac{i}{3}.$$

Equation (1) then becomes

$$\int_{-R}^{R} f(x)dx = \frac{2\pi}{3} - \int_{C_R} f(z)\,dz, \tag{3}$$

which is valid for all values of R greater than unity.

Next, we show that the integral on the right in equation (3) tends to 0 as R tends to ∞. To do this, we observe that when $R > 1$,

$$|z^6 + 1| \geq |\,|z|^6 - 1| = R^6 - 1.$$

So, if z is any point on C_R,

$$|f(z)| = \frac{1}{|z^6 + 1|} \leq M_R \quad \text{where} \quad M_R = \frac{1}{R^6 - 1};$$

and this means that

$$\left| \int_{C_R} f(z)\, dz \right| \leq M_R\, \pi R, \tag{4}$$

πR being the length of the semicircle C_R. (See Sec. 47.) Since the number

$$M_R\, \pi R = \frac{\pi R}{R^6 - 1}$$

is a quotient of polynomials in R and since the degree of the numerator is less than the degree of the denominator, that quotient must tend to zero as R tends to ∞. More precisely, if we divide both numerator and denominator by R^6 and write

$$M_R \pi R = \frac{\dfrac{\pi}{R^5}}{1 - \dfrac{1}{R^6}},$$

it is evident that $M_R \pi R$ tends to zero. Consequently, in view of inequality (4),

$$\lim_{R \to \infty} \int_{C_R} f(z)\, dz = 0.$$

It now follows from equation (3) that

$$\lim_{R \to \infty} \int_{-R}^{R} \frac{dx}{x^6 + 1} = \frac{2\pi}{3},$$

or

$$\text{P.V.} \int_{-R}^{R} \frac{dx}{x^6 + 1} = \frac{2\pi}{3}.$$

Since the integrand here is even, we know from equation (7) in Sec. 85 that

$$\int_{0}^{\infty} \frac{dx}{x^6 + 1} = \frac{\pi}{3}. \tag{5}$$

EXERCISES

Use residues to derive the integration formulas in Exercises 1 through 6.

1. $\displaystyle \int_{0}^{\infty} \frac{dx}{x^2 + 1} = \frac{\pi}{2}.$

2. $\displaystyle \int_{0}^{\infty} \frac{dx}{(x^2 + 1)^2} = \frac{\pi}{4}.$

3. $\displaystyle\int_0^\infty \frac{dx}{x^4+1} = \frac{\pi}{2\sqrt{2}}.$

4. $\displaystyle\int_0^\infty \frac{x^2\,dx}{x^6+1} = \frac{\pi}{6}.$

5. $\displaystyle\int_0^\infty \frac{x^2\,dx}{(x^2+1)(x^2+4)} = \frac{\pi}{6}.$

6. $\displaystyle\int_0^\infty \frac{x^2\,dx}{(x^2+9)(x^2+4)^2} = \frac{\pi}{200}.$

Use residues to find the Cauchy principal values of the integrals in Exercises 7 and 8.

7. $\displaystyle\int_{-\infty}^\infty \frac{dx}{x^2+2x+2}.$

8. $\displaystyle\int_{-\infty}^\infty \frac{x\,dx}{(x^2+1)(x^2+2x+2)}.$

Ans. $-\pi/5$.

9. Use a residue and the contour shown in Fig. 101, where $R > 1$, to establish the integration formula

$$\int_0^\infty \frac{dx}{x^3+1} = \frac{2\pi}{3\sqrt{3}}.$$

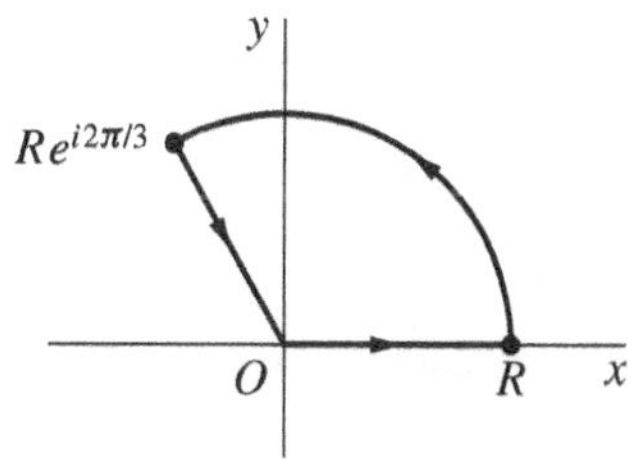

FIGURE 101

10. Let m and n be integers, where $0 \le m < n$. Follow the steps below to derive the integration formula

$$\int_0^\infty \frac{x^{2m}}{x^{2n}+1}\,dx = \frac{\pi}{2n}\csc\left(\frac{2m+1}{2n}\pi\right).$$

(*a*) Show that the zeros of the polynomial $z^{2n}+1$ lying above the real axis are

$$c_k = \exp\left[i\frac{(2k+1)\pi}{2n}\right] \qquad (k = 0, 1, 2, \ldots, n-1)$$

and that there are none on that axis.

(*b*) With the aid of Theorem 2 in Sec. 83, show that

$$\operatorname*{Res}_{z=c_k} \frac{z^{2m}}{z^{2n}+1} = -\frac{1}{2n}e^{i(2k+1)\alpha} \qquad (k = 0, 1, 2, \ldots, n-1)$$

where c_k are the zeros found in part (a) and

$$\alpha = \frac{2m+1}{2n}\pi.$$

Then use the summation formula

$$\sum_{k=0}^{n-1} z^k = \frac{1-z^n}{1-z} \qquad (z \neq 1)$$

(see Exercise 9, Sec. 9) to obtain the expression

$$2\pi i \sum_{k=0}^{n-1} \operatorname*{Res}_{z=c_k} \frac{z^{2m}}{z^{2n}+1} = \frac{\pi}{n \sin\alpha}.$$

(c) Use the final result in part (b) to complete the derivation of the integration formula.

11. The integration formula

$$\int_0^\infty \frac{dx}{[(x^2-a)^2+1]^2} = \frac{\pi}{8\sqrt{2}A^3}[(2a^2+3)\sqrt{A+a} + a\sqrt{A-a}],$$

where a is any positive number and $A = \sqrt{a^2+1}$, arises in the theory of case-hardening of steel by means of radio-frequency heating.* Follow the steps below to derive it.

(a) Point out why the four zeros of the polynomial

$$q(z) = (z^2-a)^2 + 1$$

are the square roots of the numbers $a \pm i$. Then, using the fact that the numbers

$$z_0 = \frac{1}{\sqrt{2}}(\sqrt{A+a} + i\sqrt{A-a})$$

and $-z_0$ are the square roots of $a+i$ (see Example 3 in Sec. 11), verify that $\pm\overline{z_0}$ are the square roots of $a-i$ and hence that z_0 and $-\overline{z_0}$ are the only zeros of $q(z)$ in the upper half plane $\operatorname{Im} z \geq 0$.

(b) Using the method derived in Exercise 8, Sec. 83, and keeping in mind that $z_0^2 = a+i$ for purposes of simplification, show that the point z_0 in part (a) is a pole of order 2 of the function $f(z) = 1/[q(z)]^2$ and that the residue B_1 at z_0 can be written

$$B_1 = -\frac{q''(z_0)}{[q'(z_0)]^3} = \frac{a - i(2a^2+3)}{16A^2 z_0}.$$

After observing that $q'(-\overline{z}) = -\overline{q'(z)}$ and $q''(-\overline{z}) = \overline{q''(z)}$, use the same method to show that the point $-\overline{z_0}$ in part (a) is also a pole of order 2 of the function $f(z)$, with residue

$$B_2 = \overline{\left\{\frac{q''(z_0)}{[q'(z_0)]^3}\right\}} = -\overline{B_1}.$$

*See pp. 359–364 of the book by Brown, Hoyler, and Bierwirth that is listed in Appendix 1.

Then obtain the expression

$$B_1 + B_2 = \frac{1}{8A^2 i} \operatorname{Im}\left[\frac{-a + i(2a^2 + 3)}{z_0}\right]$$

for the sum of these residues.

(*c*) Refer to part (*a*) and show that $|q(z)| \geq (R - |z_0|)^4$ if $|z| = R$, where $R > |z_0|$. Then, with the aid of the final result in part (*b*), complete the derivation of the integration formula.

87. IMPROPER INTEGRALS FROM FOURIER ANALYSIS

Residue theory can be useful in evaluating convergent improper integrals of the form

$$\text{(1)} \qquad \int_{-\infty}^{\infty} f(x) \sin ax \, dx \quad \text{or} \quad \int_{-\infty}^{\infty} f(x) \cos ax \, dx,$$

where a denotes a positive constant. As in Sec. 85, we assume that $f(x) = p(x)/q(x)$ where $p(x)$ and $q(x)$ are polynomials with real coefficients and no factors in common. Also, $q(x)$ has no zeros on the real axis and at least one zero above it. Integrals of type (1) occur in the theory and application of the Fourier integral.*

The method described in Sec. 85 and used in Sec. 86 cannot be applied directly here since (see Sec. 39)

$$|\sin az|^2 = \sin^2 ax + \sinh^2 ay$$

and

$$|\cos az|^2 = \cos^2 ax + \sinh^2 ay.$$

More precisely, since

$$\sinh ay = \frac{e^{ay} - e^{-ay}}{2},$$

the moduli $|\sin az|$ and $|\cos az|$ increase like e^{ay} as y tends to infinity. The modification illustrated in the example below is suggested by the fact that

$$\int_{-R}^{R} f(x) \cos ax \, dx + i \int_{-R}^{R} f(x) \sin ax \, dx = \int_{-R}^{R} f(x) e^{iax} \, dx,$$

together with the fact that the modulus

$$|e^{iaz}| = |e^{ia(x+iy)}| = |e^{-ay} e^{iax}| = e^{-ay}$$

is bounded in the upper half plane $y \geq 0$.

*See the authors' *Fourier Series and Boundary Value Problems*, 8th ed., Chap. 6, 2012.

EXAMPLE. Let us show that

$$\int_0^\infty \frac{\cos 2x}{(x^2+4)^2}\,dx = \frac{5\pi}{32e^4}. \tag{2}$$

We introduce the function

$$f(z) = \frac{1}{(z^2+4)^2} \tag{3}$$

and observe that the product $f(z)e^{i2z}$ is analytic everywhere on and above the real axis except at the point $z = 2i$. This singularity lies in the interior of the semicircular region whose boundary consists of the segment $-R \le x \le R$ of the real axis and the upper half C_R of the circle $|z| = R$ $(R > 2)$ from $z = R$ to $z = -R$ (Fig. 102). Integration of $f(z)e^{i2z}$ around that oriented boundary yields the equation

$$\int_{-R}^{R} \frac{e^{i2x}}{(x^2+4)^2}\,dx = 2\pi i B - \int_{C_R} f(z)e^{i2z}\,dz \tag{4}$$

where

$$B = \operatorname*{Res}_{z=2i}\,[f(z)e^{i2z}].$$

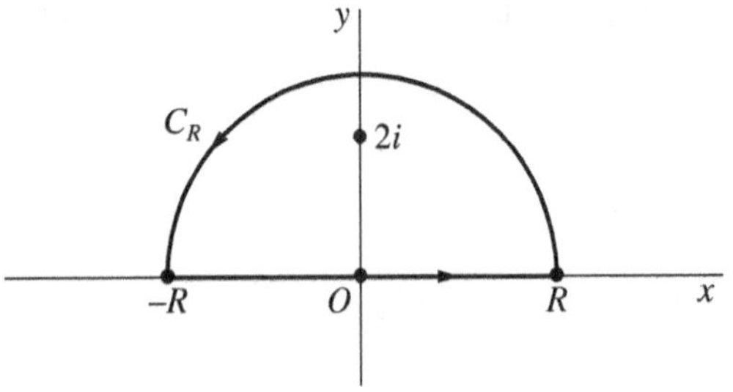

FIGURE 102

Since

$$f(z) = \frac{\phi(z)}{(z-2i)^2} \quad \text{where} \quad \phi(z) = \frac{e^{i2z}}{(z+2i)^2},$$

the point $z = 2i$ is evidently a pole of order $m = 2$ of the product $f(z)e^{i2z}$; and it is straightforward to show that

$$B = \phi'(2i) = \frac{5}{32e^4 i}.$$

By equating the real parts on each side of equation (4), then, we find that

$$\int_{-R}^{R} \frac{\cos 2x}{(x^2+4)^2}\,dx = \frac{5\pi}{16e^4} - \operatorname{Re}\int_{C_R} f(z)e^{i2z}\,dz. \tag{5}$$

Finally, we observe that when z is a point on C_R,

$$|f(z)| \le M_R \quad \text{where} \quad M_R = \frac{1}{(R^2-4)^2}$$

and that $|e^{i2z}| = e^{-2y} \leq 1$ for such a point. Consequently, in view of the property $|\text{Re}\, z| \leq |z|$ of complex numbers,

$$\left|\text{Re} \int_{C_R} f(z)e^{i2z}\, dz\right| \leq \left|\int_{C_R} f(z)e^{i2z}\, dz\right| \leq M_R \pi R. \tag{6}$$

Since the quantity

$$M_R \pi R = \frac{\pi R}{(R^2 - 4)^2} \cdot \frac{\frac{1}{R^4}}{\frac{1}{R^4}} = \frac{\frac{\pi}{R^3}}{\left(1 - \frac{4}{R^2}\right)^2}$$

tends to 0 as R tends to ∞ and because of inequalities (6), we need only let R tend to infinity in equation (5) to arrive at the equation

$$\text{P.V.} \int_{-\infty}^{\infty} \frac{\cos 2x}{(x^2 + 4)^2} dx = \frac{5\pi}{16e^4},$$

which is just another form of equation (2) since the integrand is even.

88. JORDAN'S LEMMA

In the evaluation of integrals of the type treated in Sec. 87, it is sometimes necessary to use ***Jordan's lemma***,* which is stated just below as a theorem.

Theorem. *Suppose that*

(*a*) *a function $f(z)$ is analytic at all points in the upper half plane $y \geq 0$ that are exterior to a circle $|z| = R_0$;*

(*b*) *C_R denotes a semicircle $z = Re^{i\theta}$ $(0 \leq \theta \leq \pi)$, where $R > R_0$* (Fig. 103);

(*c*) *for all points z on C_R, there is a positive constant M_R such that*

$$|f(z)| \leq M_R \quad \textit{and} \quad \lim_{R \to \infty} M_R = 0.$$

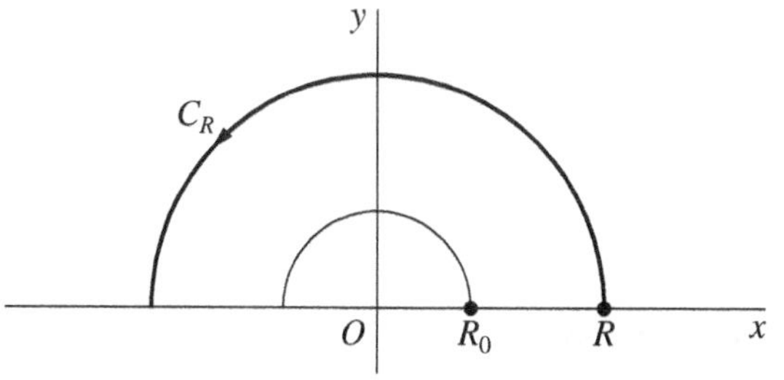

FIGURE 103

*See the first footnote in Sec. 43.

Then, for every positive constant a,

$$\lim_{R\to\infty}\int_{C_R} f(z)e^{iaz}\,dz = 0.$$

The proof is based on ***Jordan's inequality***:

$$\int_0^{\pi} e^{-R\sin\theta}\,d\theta < \frac{\pi}{R} \quad (R > 0). \tag{1}$$

To verify inequality (1), we first note from the graphs (Fig. 104) of the functions

$$y = \sin\theta \quad \text{and} \quad y = \frac{2\theta}{\pi}$$

that

$$\sin\theta \geq \frac{2\theta}{\pi} \quad \text{when} \quad 0 \leq \theta \leq \frac{\pi}{2}.$$

Consequently, since $R > 0$,

$$e^{-R\sin\theta} \leq e^{-2R\theta/\pi} \quad \text{when} \quad 0 \leq \theta \leq \frac{\pi}{2};$$

and so

$$\int_0^{\pi/2} e^{-R\sin\theta}\,d\theta \leq \int_0^{\pi/2} e^{-2R\theta/\pi}\,d\theta = \frac{\pi}{2R}(1 - e^{-R}) \quad (R > 0).$$

Hence

$$\int_0^{\pi/2} e^{-R\sin\theta}\,d\theta \leq \frac{\pi}{2R} \quad (R > 0). \tag{2}$$

But this is just another form of inequality (1), since the graph of $y = \sin\theta$ is symmetric with respect to the vertical line $\theta = \pi/2$ on the interval $0 \leq \theta \leq \pi$.

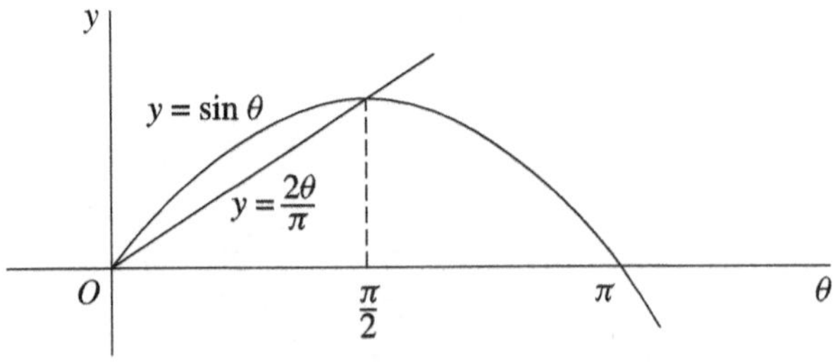

FIGURE 104

Turning now to the proof of the theorem and keeping in mind statements (*a*)–(*b*) of its hypothesis, we write

$$\int_{C_R} f(z)e^{iaz}\,dz = \int_0^{\pi} f(Re^{i\theta})\exp(iaRe^{i\theta})Rie^{i\theta}\,d\theta.$$

Since

$$\left|f(Re^{i\theta})\right| \le M_R \quad \text{and} \quad \left|\exp(iaRe^{i\theta})\right| \le e^{-aR\sin\theta}$$

and in view of Jordan's inequality (1), it follows that

$$\left|\int_{C_R} f(z)e^{iaz}\,dz\right| \le M_R R \int_0^{\pi} e^{-aR\sin\theta}\,d\theta < \frac{M_R \pi}{a}.$$

The final limit in the theorem is now evident since $M_R \to 0$ as $R \to \infty$.

EXAMPLE. Let us evaluate the improper integral

$$\int_0^{\infty} \frac{x\sin 2x}{x^2+3}\,dx. \tag{3}$$

As usual, the existence of the integral will be established by actually finding its value. We continue to use a closed semicircular path (Fig. 105) similar to the one in Sec. 87.

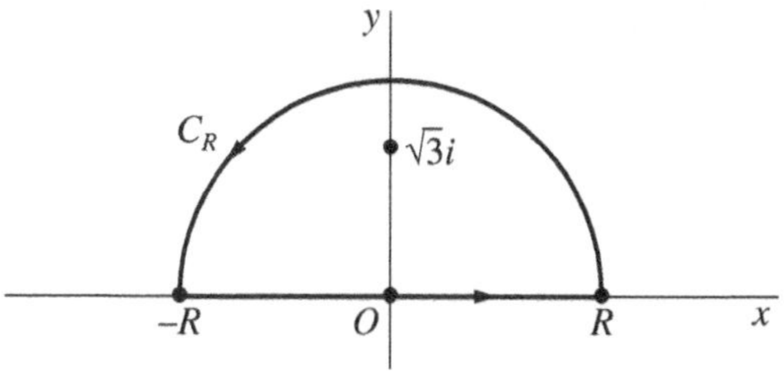

FIGURE 105

We write

$$f(z) = \frac{z}{z^2+3} = \frac{z}{(z-\sqrt{3}i)(z+\sqrt{3}i)}$$

and assume that $R > \sqrt{3}$ in Fig. 105. This ensures that the singularity $z = \sqrt{3}i$ is interior to the closed path. It is, moreover, a simple pole of the function

$$f(z)e^{i2z} = \frac{\phi(z)}{z-\sqrt{3}i} \quad \text{where} \quad \phi(z) = \frac{z\exp(i2z)}{z+\sqrt{3}i},$$

since $\phi(z)$ is analytic at $z = \sqrt{3}i$ and

$$\phi(\sqrt{3}i) = \frac{1}{2}\exp(-2\sqrt{3}) \neq 0.$$

The only other singularity $z = -\sqrt{3}i$ is, of course, outside of the path.

The residue at $z = \sqrt{3}i$ is

$$B = \phi(\sqrt{3}\,i) = \frac{1}{2}\exp(-2\sqrt{3}).$$

According to Cauchy's residue theorem, then,

$$\int_{-R}^{R} \frac{xe^{i2x}}{x^2+3}\,dx = i\pi\exp(-2\sqrt{3}) - \int_{C_R} f(z)e^{i2z}\,dz, \tag{4}$$

where C_R is the closed semicircular path shown in Fig. 105. By equating imaginary parts on each side of equation (4), we arrive at

$$\int_{-R}^{R} \frac{x \sin 2x}{x^2+3}\, dx = \pi \exp(-2\sqrt{3}) - \operatorname{Im} \int_{C_R} f(z) e^{i2z}\, dz, \tag{5}$$

Now the property $|\operatorname{Im} z| \le |z|$ of complex numbers tells us that

$$\left| \operatorname{Im} \int_{C_R} f(z) e^{i2z}\, dz \right| \le \left| \int_{C_R} f(z) e^{i2z}\, dz \right|; \tag{6}$$

and we note that when z is a point on C_R,

$$|f(z)| \le M_R \quad \text{where} \quad M_R = \frac{R}{R^2-3}$$

and that $|e^{i2z}| = e^{-2y} \le 1$ for such a point.

By proceeding as we did in Sec. 87, we *cannot* conclude that the right-hand side of inequality (6) tends to 0 as R tends to ∞. This is because the quantity

$$M_R \pi R = \frac{\pi R^2}{R^2-3} = \frac{\pi}{1 - \dfrac{3}{R^2}}$$

does not tend to zero.

The theorem at the beginning of this section does, however, provide the desired limit:

$$\lim_{R\to\infty} \int_{C_R} f(z) e^{i2z} dz = 0.$$

This is because

$$M_R = \frac{\dfrac{1}{R}}{1 - \dfrac{3}{R^2}} \to 0 \quad \text{as} \quad R \to \infty.$$

So it does, indeed, follow from inequality (6) that the left-hand side there tends to zero as R tends to infinity. Consequently, since the integrand on the left in equation (5) is even, we arrive at the result

$$\int_{-\infty}^{\infty} \frac{x \sin 2x}{x^2+3}\, dx = \pi \exp(-2\sqrt{3}),$$

or

$$\int_{0}^{\infty} \frac{x \sin 2x}{x^2+3}\, dx = \frac{\pi}{2} \exp(-2\sqrt{3}).$$

EXERCISES

Use residues to derive the integration formulas in Exercises 1 through 5.

1. $\displaystyle\int_{-\infty}^{\infty} \frac{\cos x\,dx}{(x^2+a^2)(x^2+b^2)} = \frac{\pi}{a^2-b^2}\left(\frac{e^{-b}}{b} - \frac{e^{-a}}{a}\right) \quad (a > b > 0).$

2. $\displaystyle\int_{0}^{\infty} \frac{\cos ax}{x^2+1}\,dx = \frac{\pi}{2}e^{-a} \quad (a > 0).$

3. $\displaystyle\int_{0}^{\infty} \frac{\cos ax}{(x^2+b^2)^2}\,dx = \frac{\pi}{4b^3}(1+ab)e^{-ab} \quad (a > 0, b > 0).$

4. $\displaystyle\int_{-\infty}^{\infty} \frac{x \sin ax}{x^4+4}\,dx = \frac{\pi}{2}e^{-a}\sin a \quad (a > 0).$

5. $\displaystyle\int_{-\infty}^{\infty} \frac{x^3 \sin ax}{x^4+4}\,dx = \pi e^{-a}\cos a \quad (a > 0).$

Use residues to evaluate the integrals in Exercises 6 and 7.

6. $\displaystyle\int_{-\infty}^{\infty} \frac{x \sin x\,dx}{(x^2+1)(x^2+4)}.$

7. $\displaystyle\int_{0}^{\infty} \frac{x^3 \sin x\,dx}{(x^2+1)(x^2+9)}.$

Use residues to find the Cauchy principal values of the improper integrals in Exercises 8 through 11.

8. $\displaystyle\int_{-\infty}^{\infty} \frac{\sin x\,dx}{x^2+4x+5}.$

   Ans. $\displaystyle -\frac{\pi}{e}\sin 2.$

9. $\displaystyle\int_{-\infty}^{\infty} \frac{x \sin x\,dx}{x^2+2x+2}$

   Ans. $\displaystyle \frac{\pi}{e}(\sin 1 + \cos 1).$

10. $\displaystyle\int_{-\infty}^{\infty} \frac{(x+1)\cos x}{x^2+4x+5}\,dx.$

    Ans. $\displaystyle \frac{\pi}{e}(\sin 2 - \cos 2).$

11. $\displaystyle\int_{-\infty}^{\infty} \frac{\cos x\,dx}{(x+a)^2+b^2} \quad (b > 0).$

12. Follow the steps below to evaluate the ***Fresnel integrals***, which are important in diffraction theory:

$$\int_0^{\infty} \cos(x^2)\,dx = \int_0^{\infty} \sin(x^2)\,dx = \frac{1}{2}\sqrt{\frac{\pi}{2}}.$$

(*a*) By integrating the function $\exp(iz^2)$ around the positively oriented boundary of the sector $0 \le r \le R, 0 \le \theta \le \pi/4$ (Fig. 106) and appealing to the Cauchy–Goursat theorem, show that

$$\int_0^R \cos(x^2)\,dx = \frac{1}{\sqrt{2}}\int_0^R e^{-r^2}\,dr - \text{Re}\int_{C_R} e^{iz^2}\,dz$$

and

$$\int_0^R \sin(x^2)\,dx = \frac{1}{\sqrt{2}}\int_0^R e^{-r^2}\,dr - \text{Im}\int_{C_R} e^{iz^2}\,dz,$$

where C_R is the arc $z = Re^{i\theta}$ $(0 \le \theta \le \pi/4)$.

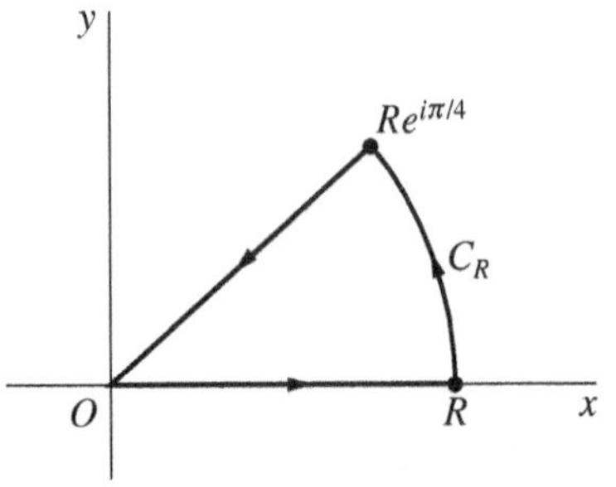

FIGURE 106

(*b*) Show that the value of the integral along the arc C_R in part (*a*) tends to zero as R tends to infinity by obtaining the inequality

$$\left|\int_{C_R} e^{iz^2}\,dz\right| \le \frac{R}{2}\int_0^{\pi/2} e^{-R^2\sin\phi}\,d\phi$$

and then referring to the form (2), Sec. 88, of Jordan's inequality.

(*c*) Use the results in parts (*a*) and (*b*), together with the known integration formula*

$$\int_0^\infty e^{-x^2}\,dx = \frac{\sqrt{\pi}}{2},$$

to complete the exercise.

89. AN INDENTED PATH

In this and the following section we illustrate the use of ***indented paths***. We begin with an important limit that will be used in this section.

Theorem. *Suppose that*

(*a*) *a function* $f(z)$ *has a simple pole at a point* $z = x_0$ *on the real axis, with a Laurent series representation in a punctured disk* $0 < |z - x_0| < R_2$ (Fig. 107) *and with residue* B_0;

*See the footnote with Exercise 4, Sec. 53.

(*b*) C_ρ *denotes the upper half of a circle* $|z - x_0| = \rho$, *where* $\rho < R_2$ *and the clockwise direction is taken.*

Then

$$\lim_{\rho \to 0} \int_{C_\rho} f(z)\,dz = -B_0 \pi i.$$

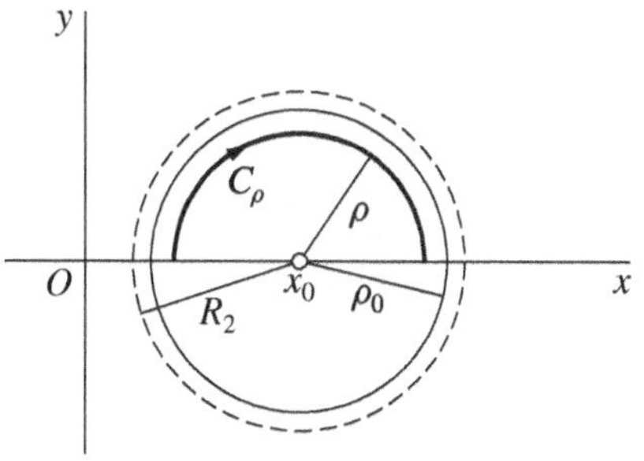

FIGURE 107

Assuming that the conditions in parts (*a*) and (*b*) are satisfied, we start the proof of the theorem by writing the Laurent series in part (*a*) as

$$f(z) = g(z) + \frac{B_0}{z - x_0} \qquad (0 < |z - x_0| < R_2)$$

where

$$g(z) = \sum_{n=0}^{\infty} a_n (z - x_0)^n \qquad (|z - x_0| < R_2).$$

Thus

(1) $$\int_{C_\rho} f(z)\,dz = \int_{C_\rho} g(z)\,dz + B_0 \int_{C_\rho} \frac{dz}{z - x_0}.$$

Now the function $g(z)$ is continuous when $|z - x_0| < R_2$, according to the theorem in Sec. 70. Hence if we choose a number ρ_0 such that $\rho < \rho_0 < R_2$ (see Fig. 107), it must be bounded on the *closed* disk $|z - x_0| \le \rho_0$, according to Sec. 18. That is, there is a nonnegative constant M such that

$$|g(z)| \le M \quad \text{whenever} \quad |z - x_0| \le \rho_0;$$

and since the length L of the path C_ρ is $L = \pi\rho$, it follows that

$$\left| \int_{C_\rho} g(z)\,dz \right| \le ML = M\pi\rho.$$

Consequently,

(2) $$\lim_{\rho \to 0} \int_{C_\rho} g(z)\,dz = 0.$$

Inasmuch as the semicircle $-C_\rho$ has parametric representation

$$z = x_0 + \rho e^{i\theta} \qquad (0 \le \theta \le \pi),$$

the second integral on the right in equation (1) has the value

$$\int_{C_\rho} \frac{dz}{z - x_0} = -\int_{-C_\rho} \frac{dz}{z - x_0} = -\int_0^\pi \frac{1}{\rho e^{i\theta}} \rho i e^{i\theta}\, d\theta = -i \int_0^\pi d\theta = -i\pi.$$

Thus

(3) $$\lim_{\rho \to 0} \int_{C_\rho} \frac{dz}{z - x_0} = -i\pi.$$

The limit in the conclusion of the theorem now follows by letting ρ tend to zero on each side of equation (1) and referring to limits (2) and (3).

EXAMPLE. We shall evaluate here ***Dirichlet's integral****

(4) $$\int_0^\infty \frac{\sin x}{x}\, dx = \frac{\pi}{2}$$

by integrating e^{iz}/z around the simple closed contour shown in Fig. 108. In that figure, ρ and R denote positive real numbers, where $\rho < R$; and L_1 and L_2 represent the intervals $\rho \le x \le R$ and $-R \le x \le -\rho$, respectively, on the real axis. The semicircles C_ρ and C_R are as shown in the figure. The semicircle C_ρ is introduced here in order to avoid passing through the singularity of the quotient e^{iz}/z.

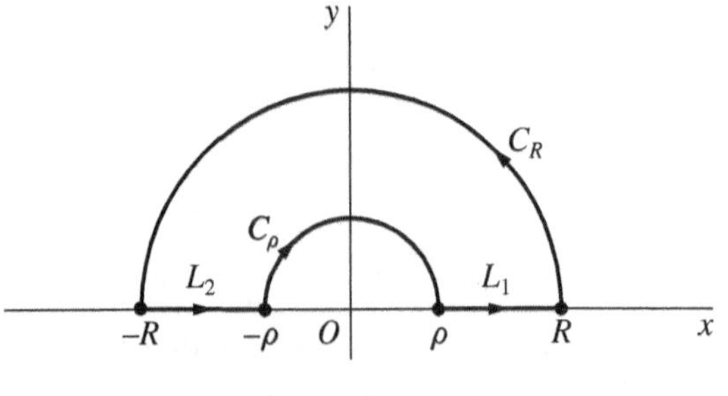

FIGURE 108

The Cauchy–Goursat theorem tells us that

$$\int_{L_1} \frac{e^{iz}}{z}\, dz + \int_{C_R} \frac{e^{iz}}{z}\, dz + \int_{L_2} \frac{e^{iz}}{z}\, dz + \int_{C_\rho} \frac{e^{iz}}{z}\, dz = 0,$$

or

(5) $$\int_{L_1} \frac{e^{iz}}{z}\, dz + \int_{L_2} \frac{e^{iz}}{z}\, dz = -\int_{C_\rho} \frac{e^{iz}}{z}\, dz - \int_{C_R} \frac{e^{iz}}{z}\, dz.$$

*This integral is important in applied mathematics and, in particular, the theory of Fourier integrals. See the authors' *Fourier Series and Boundary Value Problems*, 8th ed., pp. 163–165, 2012, where it is evaluated in a completely different way.

Moreover, since the legs L_1 and $-L_2$ have parametric representations

(6) $$z = re^{i0} = r\ (\rho \le r \le R) \quad \text{and} \quad z = re^{i\pi} = -r\ (\rho \le r \le R),$$

respectively, the left-hand side of equation (5) can be written

$$\int_{L_1} \frac{e^{iz}}{z}\,dz - \int_{-L_2} \frac{e^{iz}}{z}\,dz = \int_\rho^R \frac{e^{ir}}{r}\,dr - \int_\rho^R \frac{e^{-ir}}{r}\,dr = \int_\rho^R \frac{e^{ir} - e^{-ir}}{r}\,dr$$

$$= 2i \int_\rho^R \frac{e^{ir} - e^{-ir}}{2ir}\,dr = 2i \int_\rho^R \frac{\sin r}{r}\,dr.$$

Consequently, equation (5) reduces to

(7) $$2i \int_\rho^R \frac{\sin r}{r}\,dr = -\int_{C_\rho} \frac{e^{iz}}{z}\,dz - \int_{C_R} \frac{e^{iz}}{z} dz.$$

Now, from the Laurent series representation

$$\frac{e^{iz}}{z} = \frac{1}{z}\left[1 + \frac{(iz)}{1!} + \frac{(iz)^2}{2!} + \frac{(iz)^3}{3!} + \cdots\right] = \frac{1}{z} + \frac{i}{1!} + \frac{i^2}{2!}z + \frac{i^3}{3!}z^2 + \cdots$$
$$(0 < |z| < \infty),$$

it is clear that e^{iz}/z has a simple pole at the origin, with residue unity. So, according to the theorem at the beginning of this section,

$$\lim_{\rho\to 0} \int_{C_\rho} \frac{e^{iz}}{z}\,dz = -\pi i.$$

Also, since

$$\left|\frac{1}{z}\right| = \frac{1}{|z|} = \frac{1}{R}$$

when z is a point on C_R, we know from Jordan's lemma in Sec. 88 that

$$\lim_{R\to\infty} \int_{C_R} \frac{e^{iz}}{z}\,dz = 0.$$

Thus, by letting ρ tend to 0 in equation (7) and then letting R tend to ∞, we arrive at the result

$$2i \int_0^\infty \frac{\sin r}{r}\,dr = \pi i,$$

which is, in fact, the same as equation (4).

90. AN INDENTATION AROUND A BRANCH POINT

An indented path such as the one used in Sec. 89 can often be used to avoid a branch point (Sec. 33), as well as an isolated singularity.

EXAMPLE. Let us derive the integration formula

$$(1) \qquad \int_0^\infty \frac{x^a}{(x^2+1)^2}\,dx = \frac{(1-a)\pi}{4\cos(a\pi/2)} \qquad (-1 < a < 3)$$

where a is a real number with the indicated restriction and $x^a = \exp(a \ln x)$ when $x > 0$. To do this, we shall use the function

$$f(z) = \frac{z^a}{(z^2+1)^2} = \frac{\exp(a \log z)}{(z^2+1)^2} \qquad \left(|z| > 0, -\frac{\pi}{2} < \arg z < \frac{3\pi}{2}\right)$$

whose branch cut is the origin and the negative imaginary axis. The path of integration is shown in Fig. 109, where $\rho < 1 < R$ and the branch cut is indicated with a hollow dot and dashes.

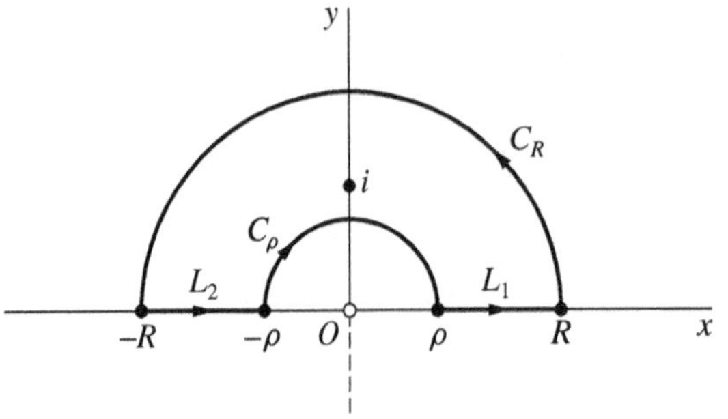

FIGURE 109

Starting with Cauchy's residue theorem, we write

$$(2) \qquad \int_{L_1} f(z)\,dz + \int_{L_2} f(z)\,dz = 2\pi i \operatorname*{Res}_{z=i} f(z) - \int_{C_\rho} f(z)\,dz - \int_{C_R} f(z)\,dz.$$

If we use the parametric equations

$$z = re^{i0} = r \ (\rho \le r \le R) \quad \text{and} \quad z = re^{i\pi} = -r \ (\rho \le r \le R)$$

for L_1 and $-L_2$, respectively, we can write the left-hand side of equation (2) as

$$\int_{L_1} f(z)\,dz - \int_{-L_2} f(z)\,dz = \int_\rho^R \frac{\exp[a(\ln r + i0)]}{(r^2+1)^2}\,dr + \int_\rho^R \frac{\exp[a(\ln r + i\pi)]}{(r^2+1)^2}\,dr$$

$$= \int_\rho^R \frac{r^a}{(r^2+1)^2}\,dr + e^{ia\pi}\int_\rho^R \frac{r^a}{(r^2+1)^2}\,dr.$$

Thus

$$(3) \qquad \int_{L_1} f(z)\,dz + \int_{L_2} f(z)\,dz = (1 + e^{ia\pi})\int_\rho^R \frac{r^a}{(r^2+1)^2}\,dr.$$

Also,

$$\text{(4)} \qquad \operatorname*{Res}_{z=i} f(z) = \phi'(i) \quad \text{where} \quad \phi(z) = \frac{z^a}{(z+i)^2}$$

since there is a pole of order $m = 2$ at the point $z = i$. Straightforward differentiation reveals that

$$\phi'(z) = e^{(a-1)\log z}\left[\frac{(a-2)z + ai}{(z+i)^3}\right]$$

and, therefore,

$$\text{(5)} \qquad \operatorname*{Res}_{z=i} f(z) = -ie^{i\,a\pi/2}\left(\frac{1-a}{4}\right).$$

Upon substituting expressions (3) and (5) into equation (2), we have

$$\text{(6)} \quad (1 + e^{i\,a\pi})\int_\rho^R \frac{r^a}{(r^2+1)^2}\,dr = \frac{\pi(1-a)}{2}e^{i\,a\pi/2} - \int_{C_\rho} f(z)\,dz - \int_{C_R} f(z)\,dz;$$

and once we have shown that

$$\text{(7)} \qquad \lim_{\rho\to 0}\int_{C_\rho} f(z)\,dz = 0 \quad \text{and} \quad \lim_{\rho\to 0}\int_{C_\rho} f(z)\,dz = 0,$$

the desired integration formula (1), with a different variable of integration, follows from equation (6):

$$\begin{aligned}\int_0^\infty \frac{r^a}{(r^2+1)^2}\,dr &= \frac{\pi(1-a)}{2}\cdot\frac{e^{ia\pi/2}}{1+e^{ia\pi}}\cdot\frac{e^{-ia\pi/2}}{e^{-ia\pi/2}}\\ &= \frac{\pi(1-a)}{4}\cdot\frac{2}{e^{ia\pi/2}+e^{-ia\pi/2}} = \frac{(1-a)\pi}{4\cos(a\pi/2)}.\end{aligned}$$

The limits (7) are found by first observing that $|z^a| = r^a$ when $z = re^{i\theta}$ is any point on the closed contour in Fig. 109. Also,

$$|z^2 + 1| \geq ||z|^2 - 1| = 1 - \rho^2$$

when z is a point on C_ρ; and

$$|z^2 + 1| \geq ||z|^2 - 1| = R^2 - 1$$

when z is on C_R. So the first of limits (7) is obtained by writing

$$\left|\int_{C_\rho} \frac{z^a}{(z^2+1)^2}\,dz\right| \leq \frac{\rho^a}{(1-\rho^2)^2}\pi\rho = \frac{\pi\rho^{a+1}}{(1-\rho^2)^2}$$

and noting that $\rho^{a+1} \to 0$ as $\rho \to 0$ since $a + 1 > 0$. As for the second of limits (7),

$$\left| \int_{C_R} \frac{z^a}{(z^2+1)^2}\, dz \right| \le \frac{R^a}{(R^2-1)^2}\pi R = \frac{\pi R^{a+1}}{(R^2-1)^2} \cdot \frac{\frac{1}{R^4}}{\frac{1}{R^4}} = \frac{\pi \frac{1}{R^{3-a}}}{\left(1 - \frac{1}{R^2}\right)^2};$$

and we see that $1/R^{3-a} \to 0$ as $R \to \infty$ since $3 - a > 0$.

91. INTEGRATION ALONG A BRANCH CUT

Cauchy's residue theorem can be useful in evaluating improper integrals from real analysis when part of the path of integration of the function $f(z)$ to which the theorem is applied lies along a branch cut of that function.

EXAMPLE. Let x^{-a}, where $x > 0$ and $0 < a < 1$, denote the principal value of the indicated power of x; that is, x^{-a} is the positive real number $\exp(-a \ln x)$. We shall evaluate here the improper real integral

$$(1) \qquad \int_0^\infty \frac{x^{-a}}{x+1}\, dx \qquad (0 < a < 1),$$

which is important in the study of the ***gamma function***.* Note that integral (1) is improper not only because of its upper limit of integration but also because its integrand has an infinite discontinuity at $x = 0$. The integral converges when $0 < a < 1$ since the integrand behaves like x^{-a} near $x = 0$ and like x^{-a-1} as x tends to infinity. We do not, however, need to establish convergence separately; for that will be contained in our evaluation of the integral.

We begin by letting C_ρ and C_R denote the circles $|z| = \rho$ and $|z| = R$, respectively, where $\rho < 1 < R$; and we assign them the orientations shown in Fig. 110. We then integrate the branch

$$(2) \qquad f(z) = \frac{z^{-a}}{z+1} \qquad (|z| > 0, 0 < \arg z < 2\pi)$$

of the multiple-valued function $z^{-a}/(z+1)$, with branch cut $\arg z = 0$, around the simple closed contour indicated in Fig. 110. That contour is traced out by a point moving from ρ to R along the top of the branch cut for $f(z)$, next around C_R and back to R, then along the bottom of the cut to ρ, and finally around C_ρ back to ρ.

Now $\theta = 0$ and $\theta = 2\pi$ along the upper and lower "edges," respectively, of the cut annulus that is formed. Since

$$f(z) = \frac{\exp(-a \log z)}{z+1} = \frac{\exp[-a(\ln r + i\theta)]}{re^{i\theta} + 1}$$

*See, for example, p. 4 of the book by Lebedev cited in Appendix 1.

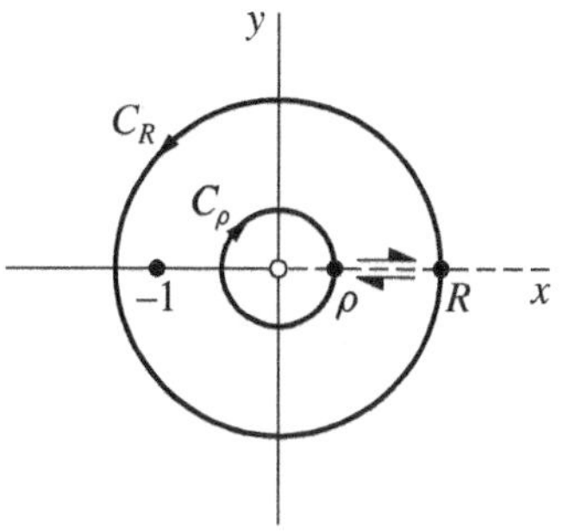

FIGURE 110

where $z = re^{i\theta}$, it follows that

$$f(z) = \frac{\exp[-a(\ln r + i0)]}{r+1} = \frac{r^{-a}}{r+1}$$

on the upper edge, where $z = re^{i0}$, and that

$$f(z) = \frac{\exp[-a(\ln r + i2\pi)]}{r+1} = \frac{r^{-a}e^{-i2a\pi}}{r+1}$$

on the lower edge, where $z = re^{i2\pi}$. The residue theorem thus suggests that

$$(3) \qquad \int_\rho^R \frac{r^{-a}}{r+1}\,dr + \int_{C_R} f(z)\,dz - \int_\rho^R \frac{r^{-a}e^{-i2a\pi}}{r+1}\,dr + \int_{C_\rho} f(z)\,dz \\ = 2\pi i \operatorname*{Res}_{z=-1} f(z).$$

Our derivation of equation (3) is, of course, only *formal* since $f(z)$ is not analytic, or even defined, on the branch cut involved. It is, nevertheless, valid and can be fully justified by an argument such as the one in Exercise 6 of this section.

The residue in equation (3) can be found by noting that the function

$$\phi(z) = z^{-a} = \exp(-a \log z) = \exp[-a(\ln r + i\theta)] \qquad (r > 0, 0 < \theta < 2\pi)$$

is analytic at $z = -1$ and that

$$\phi(-1) = \exp[-a(\ln 1 + i\pi)] = e^{-ia\pi} \neq 0.$$

This shows that the point $z = -1$ is a simple pole of the function (2) and that

$$\operatorname*{Res}_{z=-1} f(z) = e^{-ia\pi}.$$

Equation (3) can, therefore, be written as

$$(4) \qquad (1 - e^{-i2a\pi}) \int_\rho^R \frac{r^{-a}}{r+1}\,dr = 2\pi i e^{-ia\pi} - \int_{C_\rho} f(z)\,dz - \int_{C_R} f(z)\,dz.$$

According to definition (2) of $f(z)$,

$$\left|\int_{C_\rho} f(z)\,dz\right| \le \frac{\rho^{-a}}{1-\rho}\,2\pi\rho = \frac{2\pi}{1-\rho}\rho^{1-a}$$

and

$$\left|\int_{C_R} f(z)\,dz\right| \le \frac{R^{-a}}{R-1}\,2\pi R = \frac{2\pi R}{R-1}\cdot\frac{1}{R^a}.$$

Since $0 < a < 1$, the values of these two integrals evidently tend to 0 as ρ and R tend to 0 and ∞, respectively. Hence, if we let ρ tend to 0 and then R tend to ∞ in equation (4), we arrive at the result

$$(1 - e^{-i2a\pi})\int_0^\infty \frac{r^{-a}}{r+1}\,dr = 2\pi i e^{-ia\pi},$$

or

$$\int_0^\infty \frac{r^{-a}}{r+1}\,dr = 2\pi i \frac{e^{-ia\pi}}{1-e^{-i2a\pi}}\cdot\frac{e^{ia\pi}}{e^{ia\pi}} = \pi\frac{2i}{e^{ia\pi}-e^{-ia\pi}}.$$

Using the variable of integration x here, instead of r, as well as the expression

$$\sin a\pi = \frac{e^{ia\pi}-e^{-ia\pi}}{2i},$$

we arrive at the desired result:

$$(5) \qquad \int_0^\infty \frac{x^{-a}}{x+1}\,dx = \frac{\pi}{\sin a\pi} \qquad (0 < a < 1).$$

EXERCISES

1. Use the function $f(z) = (e^{iaz} - e^{ibz})/z^2$ and the indented contour in Fig. 108 (Sec. 89) to derive the integration formula

$$\int_0^\infty \frac{\cos(ax) - \cos(bx)}{x^2}\,dx = \frac{\pi}{2}(b-a) \qquad (a \ge 0, b \ge 0).$$

Then, with the aid of the trigonometric identity $1 - \cos(2x) = 2\sin^2 x$, point out how it follows that

$$\int_0^\infty \frac{\sin^2 x}{x^2}\,dx = \frac{\pi}{2}.$$

2. Derive the integration formula

$$\int_0^\infty \frac{dx}{\sqrt{x}(x^2+1)} = \frac{\pi}{\sqrt{2}}$$

by integrating the function

$$f(z) = \frac{z^{-1/2}}{z^2+1} = \frac{e^{(-1/2)\log z}}{z^2+1} \qquad \left(|z| > 0, -\frac{\pi}{2} < \arg z < \frac{3\pi}{2}\right)$$

over the indented contour appearing in Fig. 109 (Sec. 90).

3. Derive the integration formula obtained in Exercise 2 by integrating the branch

$$f(z) = \frac{z^{-1/2}}{z^2+1} = \frac{e^{(-1/2)\log z}}{z^2+1} \qquad (|z| > 0, 0 < \arg z < 2\pi)$$

of the multiple-valued function $z^{-1/2}/(z^2+1)$ over the closed contour in Fig. 110 (Sec. 91).

4. Derive the integration formula

$$\int_0^\infty \frac{\sqrt[3]{x}}{(x+a)(x+b)}\,dx = \frac{2\pi}{\sqrt{3}} \cdot \frac{\sqrt[3]{a}-\sqrt[3]{b}}{a-b} \qquad (a > b > 0)$$

using the function

$$f(z) = \frac{z^{1/3}}{(z+a)(z+b)} = \frac{e^{(1/3)\log z}}{(z+a)(z+b)} \qquad (|z| > 0, 0 < \arg z < 2\pi)$$

and a closed contour similar to the one in Fig. 110 (Sec. 91), but where

$$\rho < b < a < R.$$

5. The ***beta function*** is this function of two real variables:

$$B(p,q) = \int_0^1 t^{p-1}(1-t)^{q-1}\,dt \qquad (p > 0, q > 0).$$

Make the substitution $t = 1/(x+1)$ and use the result obtained in the example in Sec. 91 to show that

$$B(p, 1-p) = \frac{\pi}{\sin(p\pi)} \qquad (0 < p < 1).$$

6. Consider the two simple closed contours shown in Fig. 111 and obtained by dividing into two pieces the annulus formed by the circles C_ρ and C_R in Fig. 110 (Sec. 91). The legs L and $-L$ of those contours are directed line segments along any ray $\arg z = \theta_0$, where $\pi < \theta_0 < 3\pi/2$. Also, Γ_ρ and γ_ρ are the indicated portions of C_ρ, while Γ_R and γ_R make up C_R.

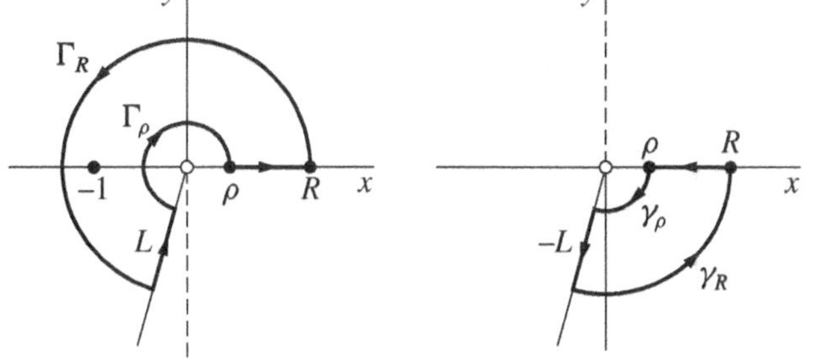

FIGURE 111

(*a*) Show how it follows from Cauchy's residue theorem that when the branch

$$f_1(z) = \frac{z^{-a}}{z+1} \qquad \left(|z| > 0, -\frac{\pi}{2} < \arg z < \frac{3\pi}{2}\right)$$

of the multiple-valued function $z^{-a}/(z+1)$ is integrated around the closed contour on the left in Fig. 111,

$$\int_{\rho}^{R} \frac{r^{-a}}{r+1}\,dr + \int_{\Gamma_R} f_1(z)\,dz + \int_{L} f_1(z)\,dz + \int_{\Gamma_\rho} f_1(z)\,dz = 2\pi i \operatorname*{Res}_{z=-1} f_1(z).$$

(*b*) Apply the Cauchy–Goursat theorem to the branch

$$f_2(z) = \frac{z^{-a}}{z+1} \qquad \left(|z| > 0, \frac{\pi}{2} < \arg z < \frac{5\pi}{2}\right)$$

of $z^{-a}/(z+1)$, integrated around the closed contour on the right in Fig. 111, to show that

$$-\int_{\rho}^{R} \frac{r^{-a}e^{-i2a\pi}}{r+1}\,dr + \int_{\gamma_\rho} f_2(z)\,dz - \int_{L} f_2(z)\,dz + \int_{\gamma_R} f_2(z)\,dz = 0.$$

(*c*) Point out why, in the last lines in parts (*a*) and (*b*), the branches $f_1(z)$ and $f_2(z)$ of $z^{-a}/(z+1)$ can be replaced by the branch

$$f(z) = \frac{z^{-a}}{z+1} \qquad (|z| > 0, 0 < \arg z < 2\pi).$$

Then, by adding corresponding sides of those two lines, derive equation (3), Sec. 91, which was obtained only formally there.

92. DEFINITE INTEGRALS INVOLVING SINES AND COSINES

The method of residues is also useful in evaluating certain definite integrals of the type

$$(1) \qquad \int_0^{2\pi} F(\sin\theta, \cos\theta)\,d\theta.$$

The fact that θ varies from 0 to 2π leads us to consider θ as an argument of a point z on a positively oriented circle C centered at the origin. Taking the radius to be unity, we use the parametric representation

$$(2) \qquad z = e^{i\theta} \qquad (0 \le \theta \le 2\pi)$$

to describe C (Fig. 112). We then refer to the differentation formula (4), Sec. 41, to write

$$\frac{dz}{d\theta} = ie^{i\theta} = iz$$

and recall (Sec. 37) that

$$\sin\theta = \frac{e^{i\theta} - e^{-i\theta}}{2i} \qquad \text{and} \qquad \cos\theta = \frac{e^{i\theta} + e^{-i\theta}}{2}.$$

These relations suggest that we make the substitutions

$$(3) \qquad \sin\theta = \frac{z - z^{-1}}{2i}, \qquad \cos\theta = \frac{z + z^{-1}}{2}, \qquad d\theta = \frac{dz}{iz},$$

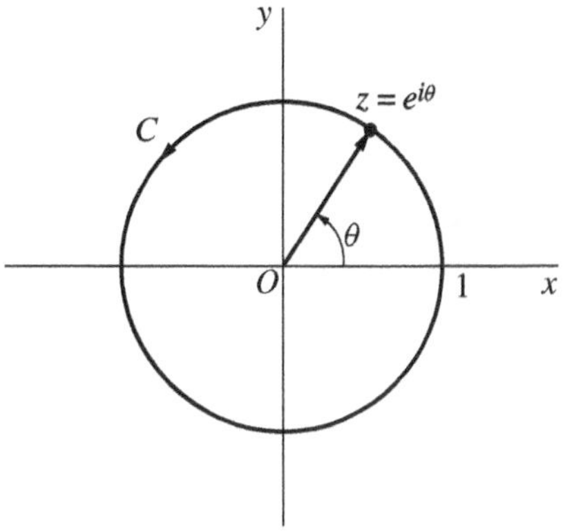

FIGURE 112

which transform integral (1) into the contour integral

$$\int_C F\left(\frac{z - z^{-1}}{2i}, \frac{z + z^{-1}}{2}\right) \frac{dz}{iz} \tag{4}$$

of a function of z around the circle C. The original integral (1) is, of course, simply a parametric form of integral (4), in accordance with expression (2), Sec. 44. When the integrand in integral (4) reduces to a rational function of z, we can evaluate that integral by means of Cauchy's residue theorem once the zeros in the denominator have been located and provided that none lie on C.

EXAMPLE 1. Let us show that

$$\int_0^{2\pi} \frac{d\theta}{1 + a\sin\theta} = \frac{2\pi}{\sqrt{1 - a^2}} \qquad (-1 < a < 1). \tag{5}$$

This integration formula is clearly valid when $a = 0$, and we exclude that case in our derivation. With substitutions (3), the integral takes the form

$$\int_C \frac{2/a}{z^2 + (2i/a)z - 1}\, dz, \tag{6}$$

where C is the positively oriented circle $|z| = 1$. The quadratic formula reveals that the denominator of the integrand here has the pure imaginary zeros

$$z_1 = \left(\frac{-1 + \sqrt{1 - a^2}}{a}\right) i, \quad z_2 = \left(\frac{-1 - \sqrt{1 - a^2}}{a}\right) i.$$

So if $f(z)$ denotes the integrand in integral (6), then

$$f(z) = \frac{2/a}{(z - z_1)(z - z_2)}.$$

Note that because $|a| < 1$,

$$|z_2| = \frac{1 + \sqrt{1 - a^2}}{|a|} > 1.$$

Also, since $|z_1 z_2| = 1$, it follows that $|z_1| < 1$. Hence there are no singular points on C, and the only one interior to it is the point z_1. The corresponding residue B_1 is found by writing

$$f(z) = \frac{\phi(z)}{z - z_1} \quad \text{where} \quad \phi(z) = \frac{2/a}{z - z_2}.$$

This shows that z_1 is a simple pole and that

$$B_1 = \phi(z_1) = \frac{2/a}{z_1 - z_2} = \frac{1}{i\sqrt{1 - a^2}}.$$

Consequently,

$$\int_C \frac{2/a}{z^2 + (2i/a)z - 1}\, dz = 2\pi i B_1 = \frac{2\pi}{\sqrt{1 - a^2}};$$

and integration formula (5) follows.

The method just illustrated applies equally well when the arguments of the sine and cosine are integral multiples of θ. One can use equation (2) to write, for example,

$$\cos 2\theta = \frac{e^{i2\theta} + e^{-i2\theta}}{2} = \frac{(e^{i\theta})^2 + (e^{i\theta})^{-2}}{2} = \frac{z^2 + z^{-2}}{2}. \tag{7}$$

EXAMPLE 2. Our goal here is to show that

$$\int_0^\pi \frac{\cos 2\theta d\theta}{1 - 2a\cos\theta + a^2} = \frac{a^2\pi}{1 - a^2} \qquad (-1 < a < 1). \tag{8}$$

Just as we did in Example 1, we exclude the possibility that $a = 0$, in which case equation (8) is obviously true. We begin with the observation that because

$$\cos(2\pi - \theta) = \cos\theta \quad \text{and} \quad \cos 2(2\pi - \theta) = \cos 2\theta,$$

the graph of the integrand is symmetric with respect to the vertical line $\theta = \pi$. This observation, together with equations (3) and (7), enables us to write

$$\int_0^\pi \frac{\cos 2\theta\, d\theta}{1 - 2a\cos\theta + a^2} = \frac{1}{2}\int_0^{2\pi} \frac{\cos 2\theta\, d\theta}{1 - 2a\cos\theta + a^2} = \frac{i}{4}\int_C \frac{z^4 + 1}{(z - a)(az - 1)z^2}\, dz,$$

where C is the positively oriented circle in Fig. 112. Evidently, then,

$$\int_0^\pi \frac{\cos 2\theta\, d\theta}{1 - 2a\cos\theta + a^2} = \frac{i}{4} 2\pi i(B_1 + B_2), \tag{9}$$

where B_1 and B_2 denote the residues of the function

$$f(z) = \frac{z^4 + 1}{(z - a)(az - 1)z^2}$$

at a and 0, respectively. The singularity $z = 1/a$ is, of course, exterior to the circle C since $|a| < 1$.

Inasmuch as

$$f(z) = \frac{\phi(z)}{z-a} \quad \text{where} \quad \phi(z) = \frac{z^4+1}{(az-1)z^2},$$

it is easy to see that

$$B_1 = \phi(a) = \frac{a^4+1}{(a^2-1)a^2}. \tag{10}$$

The residue B_2 can be found by writing

$$f(z) = \frac{\phi(z)}{z^2} \quad \text{where} \quad \phi(z) = \frac{z^4+1}{(z-a)(az-1)};$$

and straightforward differentiation reveals that

$$B_2 = \phi'(0) = \frac{a^2+1}{a^2}. \tag{11}$$

Finally, by substituting the residues (10) and (11) into expression (9), we arrive at the integration formula (8).

EXERCISES

Use residues to establish the following integration formulas:

1. $\displaystyle\int_0^{2\pi} \frac{d\theta}{5+4\sin\theta} = \frac{2\pi}{3}.$

2. $\displaystyle\int_{-\pi}^{\pi} \frac{d\theta}{1+\sin^2\theta} = \sqrt{2}\pi.$

3. $\displaystyle\int_0^{2\pi} \frac{\cos^2 3\theta\, d\theta}{5-4\cos 2\theta} = \frac{3\pi}{8}.$

4. $\displaystyle\int_0^{2\pi} \frac{d\theta}{1+a\cos\theta} = \frac{2\pi}{\sqrt{1-a^2}} \quad (-1 < a < 1).$

5. $\displaystyle\int_0^{\pi} \frac{d\theta}{(a+\cos\theta)^2} = \frac{a\pi}{\left(\sqrt{a^2-1}\right)^3} \quad (a > 1).$

6. $\displaystyle\int_0^{\pi} \sin^{2n}\theta\, d\theta = \frac{(2n)!}{2^{2n}(n!)^2}\pi \quad (n = 1, 2, \ldots).$

93. ARGUMENT PRINCIPLE

A function f is said to be ***meromorphic*** in a domain D if it is analytic throughout D except for poles. Suppose now that f is meromorphic in the domain interior to a positively oriented simple closed contour C and that it is analytic and nonzero on C.

The image Γ of C under the transformation $w = f(z)$ is a closed contour, not necessarily simple, in the w plane (Fig. 113). As a point z traverses C in the positive direction, its image w traverses Γ in a particular direction that determines the orientation of Γ. Note that since f has no zeros on C, the contour Γ does not pass through the origin in the w plane.

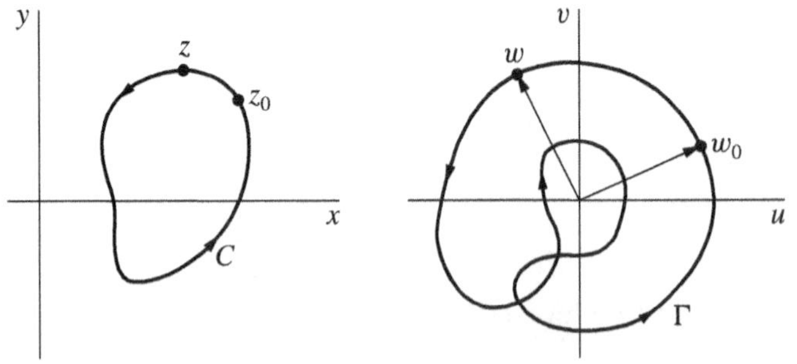

FIGURE 113

Let w_0 and w be points on Γ, where w_0 is fixed and ϕ_0 is a value of $\arg w_0$. Then let $\arg w$ vary continuously, starting with the value ϕ_0, as the point w begins at the point w_0 and traverses Γ once in the direction of orientation assigned to it by the mapping $w = f(z)$. When w returns to the point w_0, where it started, $\arg w$ assumes a particular value of $\arg w_0$, which we denote by ϕ_1. Thus the change in $\arg w$ as w describes Γ once in its direction of orientation is $\phi_1 - \phi_0$. This change is, of course, independent of the point w_0 that is chosen to determine it. Since $w = f(z)$, the number $\phi_1 - \phi_0$ is, in fact, the change in argument of $f(z)$ as z describes C once in the positive direction, starting with a point z_0; and we write

$$\Delta_C \arg f(z) = \phi_1 - \phi_0.$$

The value of $\Delta_C \arg f(z)$ is evidently an integral multiple of 2π, and the integer

$$\frac{1}{2\pi}\Delta_C \arg f(z)$$

represents the number of times the point w winds around the origin in the w plane. For that reason, this integer is sometimes called the ***winding number*** of Γ with respect to the origin $w = 0$. It is positive if Γ winds around the origin in the counterclockwise direction and negative if it winds clockwise around that point. The winding number is always zero when Γ does not enclose the origin. The verification of this fact for a special case is left to the reader (Exercise 3, Sec. 94).

The winding number can be determined from the number of zeros and poles of f interior to C. The number of poles is necessarily finite, according to Exercise 12, Sec. 83. Likewise, with the understanding that $f(z)$ is not identically equal to zero everywhere else inside C, it is easily shown (Exercise 4, Sec. 94) that the zeros of f are finite in number and are all of finite order. Suppose now that f has Z zeros and P poles in the domain interior to C. We agree that f has m_0 zeros at a point z_0 if it has a zero of order m_0 there; and if f has a pole of order m_p at z_0, that pole is to be counted

m_p times. The following theorem, which is known as the ***argument principle***, states that the winding number is simply the difference $Z - P$.

Theorem. *Let C denote a positively oriented simple closed contour, and suppose that*

(*a*) *a function $f(z)$ is meromorphic in the domain interior to C;*

(*b*) *$f(z)$ is analytic and nonzero on C;*

(*c*) *counting multiplicities, Z is the number of zeros and P the number of poles of $f(z)$ inside C.*

Then

$$\frac{1}{2\pi}\Delta_C \arg f(z) = Z - P.$$

To prove this, we evaluate the integral of $f'(z)/f(z)$ around C in two different ways. First, we let $z = z(t)$ $(a \le t \le b)$ be a parametric representation for C, so that

$$\int_C \frac{f'(z)}{f(z)}\,dz = \int_a^b \frac{f'[z(t)]z'(t)}{f[z(t)]}\,dt. \tag{1}$$

Since, under the transformation $w = f(z)$, the image Γ of C never passes through the origin in the w plane, the image of any point $z = z(t)$ on C can be expressed in exponential form as $w = \rho(t)\exp[i\phi(t)]$. Thus

$$f[z(t)] = \rho(t)e^{i\phi(t)} \qquad (a \le t \le b); \tag{2}$$

and, along each of the smooth arcs making up the contour Γ, it follows that (see Exercise 5, Sec. 43)

$$f'[z(t)]z'(t) = \frac{d}{dt}f[z(t)] = \frac{d}{dt}[\rho(t)e^{i\phi(t)}] = \rho'(t)e^{i\phi(t)} + i\rho(t)e^{i\phi(t)}\phi'(t). \tag{3}$$

Inasmuch as $\rho'(t)$ and $\phi'(t)$ are piecewise continuous on the interval $a \le t \le b$, we can now use expressions (2) and (3) to write integral (1) as follows:

$$\int_C \frac{f'(z)}{f(z)}\,dz = \int_a^b \frac{\rho'(t)}{\rho(t)}\,dt + i\int_a^b \phi'(t)\,dt = \ln\rho(t)\Big]_a^b + i\phi(t)\Big]_a^b.$$

But

$$\rho(b) = \rho(a) \quad \text{and} \quad \phi(b) - \phi(a) = \Delta_C \arg f(z).$$

Hence

$$\int_C \frac{f'(z)}{f(z)}\,dz = i\Delta_C \arg f(z). \tag{4}$$

Another way to evaluate integral (4) is to use Cauchy's residue theorem. To be specific, we observe that the integrand $f'(z)/f(z)$ is analytic inside and on C except at the points inside C at which the zeros and poles of f occur. If f has a zero of order m_0 at z_0, then (Sec. 82)

$$f(z) = (z - z_0)^{m_0} g(z), \tag{5}$$

where $g(z)$ is analytic and nonzero at z_0. Hence

$$f'(z_0) = m_0(z - z_0)^{m_0 - 1} g(z) + (z - z_0)^{m_0} g'(z),$$

or

$$\frac{f'(z)}{f(z)} = \frac{m_0}{z - z_0} + \frac{g'(z)}{g(z)}. \tag{6}$$

Since $g'(z)/g(z)$ is analytic at z_0, it has a Taylor series representation about that point; and so equation (6) tells us that $f'(z)/f(z)$ has a simple pole at z_0, with residue m_0. If, on the other hand, f has a pole of order m_p at z_0, we know from the theorem in Sec. 80 that

$$f(z) = (z - z_0)^{-m_p} \phi(z), \tag{7}$$

where $\phi(z)$ is analytic and nonzero at z_0. Because expression (7) has the same form as expression (5), with the positive integer m_0 in equation (5) replaced by $-m_p$, it is clear from equation (6) that $f'(z)/f(z)$ has a simple pole at z_0, with residue $-m_p$. Applying the residue theorem, then, we find that

$$\int_C \frac{f'(z)}{f(z)}\, dz = 2\pi i(Z - P). \tag{8}$$

The conclusion in the theorem now follows by equating the right-hand sides of equations (4) and (8).

EXAMPLE. The only zeros of the function

$$f(z) = \frac{z^3 + 2}{z} = z^2 + \frac{2}{z}$$

are exterior to the circle $|z| = 1$, since they are the cube roots of -2; and the only singularity in the finite plane is a simple pole at the origin. Hence, if C denotes the circle $|z| = 1$ in the positive direction, our theorem tells us that

$$\Delta_C \arg f(z) = 2\pi(0 - 1) = -2\pi.$$

That is, the image Γ of C under the transformation $w = f(z)$ winds around the origin $w = 0$ once in the clockwise direction.

94. ROUCHÉ'S THEOREM

The main result in this section is known as ***Rouché's theorem*** and is a consequence of the argument principle, just developed in Sec. 93. It can be useful in locating regions of the complex plane in which a given analytic function has zeros.

Theorem. *Let C denote a simple closed contour, and suppose that*

(*a*) *two functions $f(z)$ and $g(z)$ are analytic inside and on C;*

(*b*) $|f(z)| > |g(z)|$ *at each point on C.*

Then $f(z)$ and $f(z) + g(z)$ have the same number of zeros, counting multiplicities, inside C.

The orientation of C in the statement of the theorem is evidently immaterial. Thus, in the proof here, we may assume that the orientation is positive, or counterclockwise. We begin with the observation that neither the function $f(z)$ nor the sum $f(z) + g(z)$ has a zero on C, since

$$|f(z)| > |g(z)| \geq 0 \quad \text{and} \quad |f(z) + g(z)| \geq \big|\,|f(z)| - |g(z)|\,\big| > 0$$

when z is on C.

If Z_f and Z_{f+g} denote the number of zeros, counting multiplicities, of $f(z)$ and $f(z) + g(z)$, respectively, inside C, we know from the theorem in Sec. 93 that

$$Z_f = \frac{1}{2\pi}\Delta_C \arg f(z) \quad \text{and} \quad Z_{f+g} = \frac{1}{2\pi}\Delta_C \arg[f(z) + g(z)].$$

Consequently, since

$$\begin{aligned}\Delta_C \arg[f(z) + g(z)] &= \Delta_C \arg\left\{f(z)\left[1 + \frac{g(z)}{f(z)}\right]\right\}\\ &= \Delta_C \arg f(z) + \Delta_C \arg\left[1 + \frac{g(z)}{f(z)}\right],\end{aligned}$$

it is clear that

(1)
$$Z_{f+g} = Z_f + \frac{1}{2\pi}\Delta_C \arg F(z),$$

where

$$F(z) = 1 + \frac{g(z)}{f(z)}.$$

But

$$|F(z) - 1| = \frac{|g(z)|}{|f(z)|} < 1;$$

and this means that under the transformation $w = F(z)$, the image of C lies in the open disk $|w - 1| < 1$. That image does not, then, enclose the origin $w = 0$. Hence $\Delta_C \arg F(z) = 0$ and, since equation (1) reduces to $Z_{f+g} = Z_f$, Rouché's theorem is proved.

EXAMPLE 1. In order to determine the number of roots, counting multiplicities, of the equation

(2)
$$z^4 + 3z^3 + 6 = 0$$

inside the circle $|z| = 2$,write

$$f(z) = 3z^3 \quad \text{and} \quad g(z) = z^4 + 6.$$

Then observe that when $|z| = 2$,

$$|f(z)| = 3|z|^3 = 24 \quad \text{and} \quad |g(z)| \le |z|^4 + 6 = 22.$$

The conditions in Rouché's theorem are thus satisfied. Consequently, since $f(z)$ has three zeros, counting multiplicities, inside the circle $|z| = 2$, so does $f(z) + g(z)$. That is, equation (2) has three roots there, counting multiplicities.

EXAMPLE 2. Rouché's theorem can be used to give another proof of the fundamental theorem of algebra (Theorem 2, Sec. 58). To give the detals here, we consider a polynomial

(3) $$P(z) = a_0 + a_1 z + a_2 z^2 + \cdots + a_n z^n \qquad (a_n \ne 0)$$

of degree n $(n \ge 1)$ and show that it has n zeros, counting multiplicities. We write

$$f(z) = a_n z^n, \qquad g(z) = a_0 + a_1 z + a_2 z^2 + \cdots + a_{n-1} z^{n-1}$$

and let z be any point on a circle $|z| = R$, where $R > 1$. When such a point is taken, we see that

$$|f(z)| = |a_n| R^n.$$

Also,

$$|g(z)| \le |a_0| + |a_1| R + |a_2| R^2 + \cdots + |a_{n-1}| R^{n-1}.$$

Consequently, since $R > 1$,

$$|g(z)| \le |a_0| R^{n-1} + |a_1| R^{n-1} + |a_2| R^{n-1} + \cdots + |a_{n-1}| R^{n-1};$$

and it follows that

$$\frac{|g(z)|}{|f(z)|} \le \frac{|a_0| + |a_1| + |a_2| + \cdots + |a_{n-1}|}{|a_n| R} < 1$$

if, in addition to being greater than unity,

(4) $$R > \frac{|a_0| + |a_1| + |a_2| + \cdots + |a_{n-1}|}{|a_n|}.$$

That is, $|f(z)| > |g(z)|$ when $R > 1$ and inequality (4) is satisfied. Rouché's theorem then tells us that $f(z)$ and $f(z)+g(z)$ have the same number of zeros, namely n, inside C. Hence we may conclude that $P(z)$ has precisely n zeros, counting multiplicities, in the plane.

Note how Liouville's theorem in Sec. 58 only ensured the existence of at least one zero of a polynomial; but Rouché's theorem actually ensures the existence of n zeros, counting multiplicities.

EXERCISES

1. Let C denote the unit circle $|z| = 1$, described in the positive sense. Use the theorem in Sec. 93 to determine the value of $\Delta_C \arg f(z)$ when

(*a*) $f(z) = z^2$; (*b*) $f(z) = 1/z^2$; (*c*) $f(z) = (2z-1)^7/z^3$.

Ans. (*a*) 4π; (*b*) -4π; (*c*) 8π.

2. Let f be a function which is analytic inside and on a positively oriented simple closed contour C, and suppose that $f(z)$ is never zero on C. Let the image of C under the transformation $w = f(z)$ be the closed contour Γ shown in Fig. 114. Determine the value of $\Delta_C \arg f(z)$ from that figure; and, with the aid of the theorem in Sec. 93, determine the number of zeros, counting multiplicities, of f interior to C.

Ans. 6π; 3.

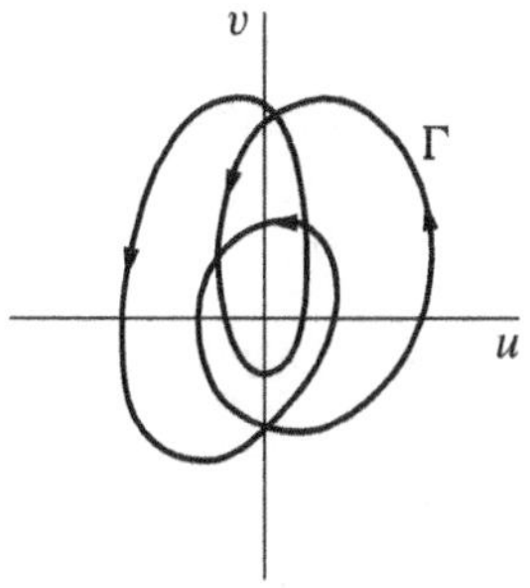

FIGURE 114

3. Using the notation in Sec. 93, suppose that Γ does not enclose the origin $w = 0$ and that there is a ray from that point which does not intersect Γ. By observing that the absolute value of $\Delta_C \arg f(z)$ must be less than 2π when a point z makes one cycle around C and recalling that $\Delta_C \arg f(z)$ is an integral multiple of 2π, point out why the winding number of Γ with respect to the origin $w = 0$ must be zero.

4. Suppose that a function f is meromorphic in the domain D interior to a simple closed contour C on which f is analytic and nonzero, and let D_0 denote the domain consisting of all points in D except for poles. Point out how it follows from the lemma in Sec. 28 and Exercise 11, Sec. 83, that if $f(z)$ is not identically equal to zero in D_0, then the zeros of f in D are all of finite order and that they are finite in number.

Suggestion: Note that if a point z_0 in D is a zero of f that is not of finite order, then there must be a neighborhood of z_0 throughout which $f(z)$ is identically equal to zero.

5. Suppose that a function f is analytic inside and on a positively oriented simple closed contour C and that it has no zeros on C. Show that if f has n zeros z_k $(k = 1, 2, \ldots, n)$ inside C, where each z_k is of multiplicity m_k, then

$$\int_C \frac{zf'(z)}{f(z)}\,dz = 2\pi i \sum_{k=1}^{n} m_k z_k.$$

[Compare with equation (8), Sec. 93, when $P = 0$ there.]

6. Determine the number of zeros, counting multiplicities, of the polynomial

(*a*) $z^6 - 5z^4 + z^3 - 2z$; (*b*) $2z^4 - 2z^3 + 2z^2 - 2z + 9$; (*c*) $z^7 - 4z^3 + z - 1$.

inside the circle $|z| = 1$.

Ans. (*a*) 4; (*b*) 0; (*c*) 3.

7. Determine the number of zeros, counting multiplicities, of the polynomial

(a) $z^4 - 2z^3 + 9z^2 + z - 1$; ($b$) $z^5 + 3z^3 + z^2 + 1$

inside the circle $|z| = 2$.

Ans. (a) 2; (b) 5.

8. Determine the number of roots, counting multiplicities, of the equation

$$2z^5 - 6z^2 + z + 1 = 0$$

in the annulus $1 \leq |z| < 2$.

Ans. 3.

9. Show that if c is a complex number such that $|c| > e$, then the equation $cz^n = e^z$ has n roots, counting multiplicities, inside the circle $|z| = 1$.

10. Let two functions f and g be as in the statement of Rouché's theorem in Sec. 94, and let the orientation of the contour C there be positive. Then define the function

$$\Phi(t) = \frac{1}{2\pi i}\int_C \frac{f'(z) + tg'(z)}{f(z) + tg(z)}\,dz \qquad (0 \leq t \leq 1)$$

and follow these steps below to give another proof of Rouché's theorem.

(a) Point out why the denominator in the integrand of the integral defining $\Phi(t)$ is never zero on C. This ensures the existence of the integral.

(b) Let t and t_0 be any two points in the interval $0 \leq t \leq 1$ and show that

$$|\Phi(t) - \Phi(t_0)| = \frac{|t - t_0|}{2\pi}\left|\int_C \frac{fg' - f'g}{(f + tg)(f + t_0g)}\,dz\right|.$$

Then, after pointing out why

$$\left|\frac{fg' - f'g}{(f + tg)(f + t_0g)}\right| \leq \frac{|fg' - f'g|}{(|f| - |g|)^2}$$

at points on C, show that there is a positive constant A, which is independent of t and t_0, such that

$$|\Phi(t) - \Phi(t_0)| \leq A|t - t_0|.$$

Conclude from this inequality that $\Phi(t)$ is continuous on the interval $0 \leq t \leq 1$.

(c) By referring to equation (8), Sec. 93, state why the value of the function Φ is, for each value of t in the interval $0 \leq t \leq 1$, an integer representing the number of zeros of $f(z) + tg(z)$ inside C. Then conclude from the fact that Φ is continuous, as shown in part (b), that $f(z)$ and $f(z) + g(z)$ have the same number of zeros, counting multiplicities, inside C.

95. INVERSE LAPLACE TRANSFORMS

Suppose that a function F of the complex variable s is analytic throughout the finite s plane except for a finite number of isolated singularities. Then let L_R denote a vertical line segment from $s = \gamma - iR$ to $s = \gamma + iR$, where the constant γ is positive and large enough that the singularities of F all lie to the left of that segment (Fig. 115). A

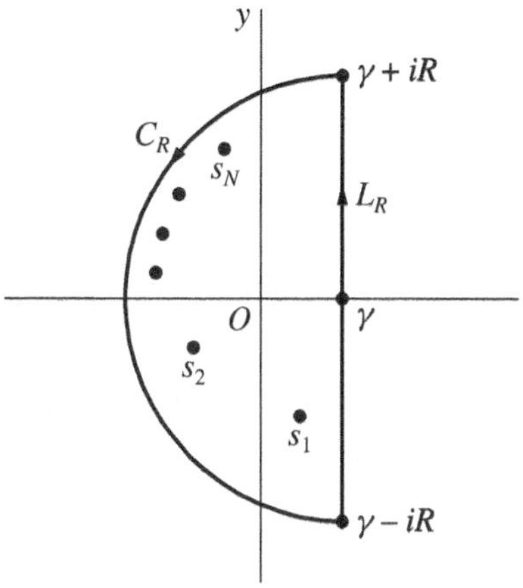

FIGURE 115

new function f of the real variable t is defined for positive values of t by means of the equation

$$f(t) = \frac{1}{2\pi i} \lim_{R\to\infty} \int_{L_R} e^{st} F(s)\, ds \qquad (t > 0), \tag{1}$$

provided this limit exists. Expression (1) is usually written

$$f(t) = \frac{1}{2\pi i} \text{ P.V.} \int_{\gamma - i\infty}^{\gamma + i\infty} e^{st} F(s)\, ds \qquad (t > 0) \tag{2}$$

[compare with equation (3), Sec. 85], and such an integral is sometimes referred to as a ***Bromwich integral***.

It can be shown that when fairly general conditions are imposed on the functions involved, the function $f(t)$ in equation (2) is the ***inverse Laplace transform*** of the function

$$F(s) = \int_0^\infty e^{-st} f(t)\, dt, \tag{3}$$

which is the familiar Laplace transform of $f(t)$. That is, if $F(s)$ is the Laplace transform of $f(t)$, then $f(t)$ is retrieved by means of equation (2).* This is done with the aid of Cauchy's residue theorem, which tells us that

$$\int_{L_R} e^{st} F(s)\, ds = 2\pi i \sum_{n=1}^{N} \operatorname*{Res}_{s=s_n} [e^{st} F(s)] - \int_{C_R} e^{st} F(s)\, ds, \tag{4}$$

*For a detailed justification of the material in this section, see, for example, Chap. 6 of the book *Operational Mathematics*, 3rd ed., 1972, by R. V. Churchill. Also, an exceptionally clear treatment of the material appears in Chap. 7 of the book *Complex Variables with Applications*, 3rd ed., 2005, by A. D. Wunsch. Both books are listed in the Bibliography.

where C_R is the semicircle shown in Fig. 115. Then, if we assume that

$$\lim_{R\to\infty} \int_{C_R} e^{st} F(s)\, ds = 0, \tag{5}$$

it follows from equation (1) that

$$f(t) = \sum_{n=1}^{N} \operatorname*{Res}_{s=s_n} [e^{st} F(s)] \qquad (t > 0). \tag{6}$$

In many applications of Laplace transforms, such as the solution of partial differential equations arising in studies of heat conduction and mechanical vibrations, the function $F(s)$ is analytic for all values of s in the finite plane except for an *infinite* set of isolated singular points s_n $(n = 1, 2, \ldots)$ that lie to the left of some vertical line $\operatorname{Re} s = \gamma$. Often the method just described for finding $f(t)$ can then be modified in such a way that the finite sum (6) is replaced by an *infinite series* of residues:

$$f(t) = \sum_{n=1}^{\infty} \operatorname*{Res}_{s=s_n} [e^{st} F(s)] \qquad (t > 0). \tag{7}$$

Our purpose here is to draw the reader's attention to the use of residues and, in particular, expression (6) in finding inverse Laplace transforms. Our discussion is brief and does not include verification that equation (1) actually gives the inverse transform $f(t)$ or describe conditions on $F(s)$ that allow limit (5) to exist. As in the example just below, only a formal treatment is expected in the exercises to follow.

EXAMPLE. The function

$$F(s) = \frac{s}{s^2+4} = \frac{s}{(s+2i)(s-2i)}$$

has isolated singularities at the points $s = \pm 2i$. According to expression (6), then,

$$f(t) = \operatorname*{Res}_{s=2i}\left[\frac{e^{st}s}{(s+2i)(s-2i)}\right] + \operatorname*{Res}_{s=-2i}\left[\frac{e^{st}s}{(s+2i)(s-2i)}\right].$$

Both singularities are simple poles; and if we write

$$f(t) = \operatorname*{Res}_{s=2i}\left[\frac{\phi_1(s)}{s-2i}\right] + \operatorname*{Res}_{s=-2i}\left[\frac{\phi_2(s)}{s+2i}\right]$$

where

$$\phi_1(s) = \frac{e^{st}s}{s+2i} \quad \text{and} \quad \phi_2(s) = \frac{e^{st}s}{s-2i},$$

we find that

$$f(t) = \phi_1(2i) + \phi_2(-2i) = \frac{e^{2it}(2i)}{4i} + \frac{e^{-2it}(-2i)}{-4i} = \frac{e^{i2t}+e^{-i2t}}{2} = \cos 2t.$$

EXERCISES

In each of the Exercises 1 through 3, use residues to find the inverse Laplace transform $f(t)$ corresponding to the given function $F(s)$. Do this in a formal way, without full justification,

1. $F(s) = \dfrac{2s^3}{s^4 - 4}$.

Ans. $f(t) = \cosh\sqrt{2}t + \cos\sqrt{2}t$.

2. $F(s) = \dfrac{2s - 2}{(s+1)(s^2 + 2s + 5)}$.

Ans. $f(t) = e^{-t}(\cos 2t + \sin 2t - 1)$.

3. $F(s) = \dfrac{12}{s^3 + 8}$.

Suggestion: After finding the three cube roots -2 and $1 \pm \sqrt{3}\,i$ of -8, it is helpful to notice that the property $z + \bar{z} = 2\,\text{Re}\,z$ of complex numbers enables one to write

$$\frac{e^{i\sqrt{3}t}}{-1 + i\sqrt{3}} + \frac{e^{-i\sqrt{3}t}}{-1 - i\sqrt{3}} = 2\,\text{Re}\left[\frac{e^{i\sqrt{3}t}}{-1 + i\sqrt{3}}\right].$$

Ans. $f(t) = e^{-2t} + e^{t}(\sqrt{3}\sin\sqrt{3}t - \cos\sqrt{3}t)$.

4. Follow the steps below to find $f(t)$ when

$$F(s) = \frac{1}{s^2} - \frac{1}{s\sinh s}.$$

Start with the observation that the isolated singularities of $F(s)$ are

$$s_0 = 0, \quad s_n = n\pi i, \quad \overline{s_n} = -n\pi i \qquad (n = 1, 2, \ldots).$$

(*a*) Use the Laurent series found in Exercise 5, Sec. 73, to show that the function $e^{st}F(s)$ has a removable singularity at $s = s_0$, with residue 0.

(*b*) Use Theorem 2 in Sec. 83 to show that

$$\operatorname*{Res}_{s=s_n}\left[e^{st}F(s)\right] = \frac{(-1)^n i \exp(in\pi t)}{n\pi}$$

and

$$\operatorname*{Res}_{s=\overline{s_n}}\left[e^{st}F(s)\right] = \frac{-(-1)^n i \exp(-in\pi t)}{n\pi}.$$

(*c*) Show how it follows from parts (*a*) and (*b*), together with series (7), Sec. 95, that

$$f(t) = \sum_{n=1}^{\infty}\left\{\operatorname*{Res}_{s=s_n}\left[e^{st}F(s)\right] + \operatorname*{Res}_{s=\overline{s_n}}\left[e^{st}F(s)\right]\right\} = \frac{2}{\pi}\sum_{n=1}^{\infty}\frac{(-1)^{n+1}}{n}\sin n\pi t.$$

CHAPTER

8

MAPPING BY ELEMENTARY FUNCTIONS

The geometric interpretation of a function of a complex variable as a mapping, or transformation, was introduced in Secs. 13 and 14 (Chap. 2). We saw there how the nature of such a function can be displayed graphically, to some extent, by the manner in which it maps certain curves and regions.

In this chapter, we shall see further examples of how various curves and regions are mapped by elementary analytic functions. Applications of such results to physical problems are illustrated in Chaps. 10 and 11.

96. LINEAR TRANSFORMATIONS

To study the mapping

$$w = Az, \tag{1}$$

where A is a nonzero complex constant and $z \neq 0$, we write A and z in exponential form:

$$A = a\exp(i\alpha), \quad z = r\exp(i\theta).$$

Then

$$w = (ar)\exp[i(\alpha + \theta)], \tag{2}$$

and we see from equation (2) that transformation (1) expands or contracts the radius vector representing z by the factor a and rotates it through the angle α about the origin. The image (Sec. 13) of a given region is, therefore, geometrically similar to that region.

The mapping

$$w = z + B, \tag{3}$$

where B is any complex constant, is a translation by means of the vector representing B. That is, if

$$w = u + iv, \quad z = x + iy, \quad \text{and} \quad B = b_1 + ib_2,$$

then the image of any point (x, y) in the z plane is the point

$$(u, v) = (x + b_1, y + b_2) \tag{4}$$

in the w plane. Since each point in any given region of the z plane is mapped into the w plane in this manner, the image region is geometrically congruent to the original one.

The general (nonconstant) ***linear transformation***

$$w = Az + B \qquad (A \neq 0) \tag{5}$$

is a composition of the transformations

$$Z = Az \quad (A \neq 0) \qquad \text{and} \qquad w = Z + B.$$

When $z \neq 0$, it is evidently an expansion or contraction and a rotation, followed by a translation.

EXAMPLE. The mapping

$$w = (1 + i)z + 2 \tag{6}$$

transforms the rectangular region in the $z = (x, y)$ plane of Fig. 116 into the rectangular region shown in the $w = (u, v)$ plane there. This is seen by expressing it as a composition of the transformations

$$Z = (1 + i)z \quad \text{and} \quad w = Z + 2. \tag{7}$$

Writing

$$1 + i = \sqrt{2}\exp\left(i\frac{\pi}{4}\right) \quad \text{and} \quad z = r\exp(i\theta),$$

one can put the first of transformations (7) in the form

$$Z = (\sqrt{2}r)\exp\left[i\left(\theta + \frac{\pi}{4}\right)\right].$$

This first transformation thus expands the radius vector for a nonzero point z by the factor $\sqrt{2}$ and rotates it counterclockwise $\pi/4$ radians about the origin. The second of transformations (7) is, of course, a translation two units to the right.

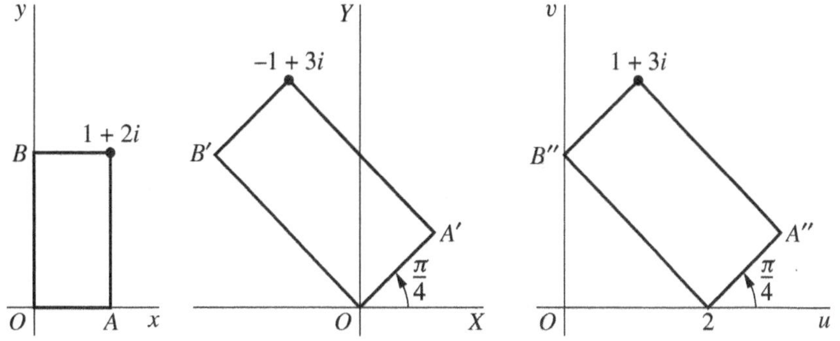

FIGURE 116
$w = (1 + i)z + 2$.

EXERCISES

1. State why the transformation $w = iz$ is a rotation in the z plane through the angle $\pi/2$. Then find the image of the infinite strip $0 < x < 1$.

   Ans. $0 < v < 1$.

2. Show that the transformation $w = iz + i$ maps the half plane $x > 0$ onto the half plane $v > 1$.

3. Find a linear transformation that maps the strip $x > 0$, $0 < y < 2$ onto the strip $-1 < u < 1$, $v > 0$, as shown in Fig. 117.

   Ans. $w = iz + 1$.

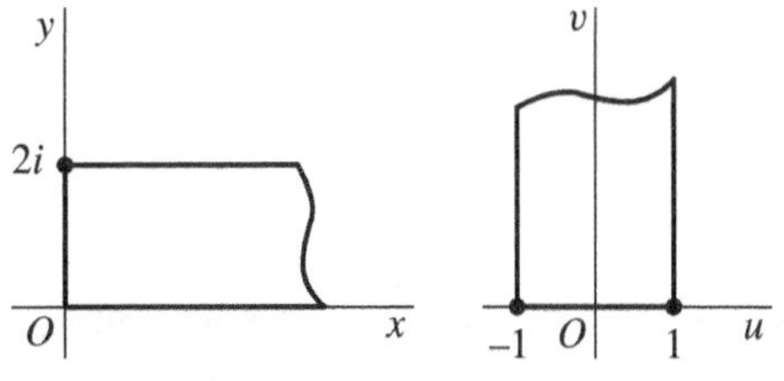

FIGURE 117

4. Find and sketch the region onto which the half plane $y > 0$ is mapped by the transformation $w = (1 + i)z$.

   Ans. $v > u$.

5. Find the image of the half plane $y > 1$ under the transformation $w = (1 - i)z$.

6. Give a geometric description of the transformation $w = A(z + B)$, where A and B are complex constants and $A \neq 0$.

97. THE TRANSFORMATION $w = 1/z$

The equation

$$w = \frac{1}{z} \tag{1}$$

establishes a one to one correspondence between the nonzero points of the z and the w planes. Since $|z|^2 = z\overline{z}$, the mapping can be described by means of the successive transformations

$$Z = \frac{z}{|z|^2}, \quad w = \overline{Z}. \tag{2}$$

The first of these transformations is an inversion with respect to the unit circle $|z| = 1$. That is, the image of a nonzero point z is the point Z with the properties

$$|Z| = \frac{1}{|z|} \quad \text{and} \quad \arg Z = \arg z.$$

Thus the points in the finite plane that are exterior to the circle are mapped onto the nonzero points interior to it (Fig. 118); and, conversely, the nonzero points interior to the circle are mapped onto the exterior points in the finite plane. Each point on this circle is mapped onto itself. The second of transformations (2) is simply a reflection in the real axis.

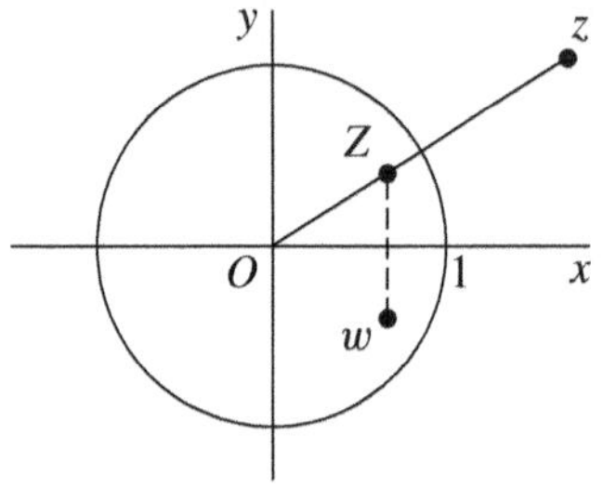

FIGURE 118

If we write transformation (1) as

$$T(z) = \frac{1}{z} \quad (z \neq 0), \tag{3}$$

we can define T at the origin and at the point at infinity so as to be continuous on the *extended* complex plane. To do this, we need only refer to Sec. 17 to see that

$$\lim_{z\to 0} T(z) = \infty \quad \text{since} \quad \lim_{z\to 0} \frac{1}{T(z)} = \lim_{z\to 0} z = 0 \tag{4}$$

and

$$\lim_{z\to \infty} T(z) = 0 \quad \text{since} \quad \lim_{z\to 0} T\left(\frac{1}{z}\right) = \lim_{z\to 0} z = 0. \tag{5}$$

In order to make T continuous on the extended plane, then, we write

$$T(0) = \infty, \quad T(\infty) = 0, \quad \text{and} \quad T(z) = \frac{1}{z} \tag{6}$$

for the remaining values of z. More precisely, limits (4) and (5) reveal that

$$\lim_{z\to z_0} T(z) = T(z_0) \tag{7}$$

for each point in the extended z plane, including $z_0 = 0$ and $z_0 = \infty$. The fact that T is continuous everywhere in the extended z plane is now a consequence of limit (7). (See Sec. 18.) Because of this continuity, we tacitly assume that $T(z)$ is intended when the function $1/z$ is referred to and the point at infinity is involved.

98. MAPPINGS BY 1/z

When a point $w = u + iv$ is the image of a nonzero point $z = x + iy$ in the finite plane under the transformation $w = 1/z$, writing

$$w = \frac{\overline{z}}{z\overline{z}} = \frac{\overline{z}}{|z|^2}$$

reveals that

$$u = \frac{x}{x^2 + y^2}, \quad v = \frac{-y}{x^2 + y^2}. \tag{1}$$

Also, since

$$z = \frac{1}{w} = \frac{\overline{w}}{w\overline{w}} = \frac{\overline{w}}{|w|^2},$$

one can see that

$$x = \frac{u}{u^2 + v^2}, \quad y = \frac{-v}{u^2 + v^2}. \tag{2}$$

The following argument, based on these relations between coordinates, shows that *the mapping $w = 1/z$ transforms circles and lines into circles and lines.* When A, B, C, and D are all real numbers satisfying the condition

$$B^2 + C^2 > 4AD, \tag{3}$$

the equation

$$A(x^2 + y^2) + Bx + Cy + D = 0 \tag{4}$$

represents an arbitrary circle or line, where $A \neq 0$ for a circle and $A = 0$ for a line. The need for condition (3) when $A \neq 0$ is evident if, by the method of completing the squares, we rewrite equation (4) as

$$\left(x + \frac{B}{2A}\right)^2 + \left(y + \frac{C}{2A}\right)^2 = \left(\frac{\sqrt{B^2 + C^2 - 4AD}}{2A}\right)^2.$$

When $A = 0$, condition (3) becomes $B^2 + C^2 > 0$, which means that B and C are not both zero. Returning to the verification of the statement in italics just above, we observe that if x and y satisfy equation (4), we can use relations (2) to substitute for those variables. After some simplifications, we find that u and v satisfy the equation (see also Exercise 14)

$$D(u^2 + v^2) + Bu - Cv + A = 0, \tag{5}$$

which also represents a circle or line. Conversely, if u and v satisfy equation (5), it follows from relations (1) that x and y satisfy equation (4).

It is now clear from equations (4) and (5) that

(*a*) a circle ($A \neq 0$) not passing through the origin ($D \neq 0$) in the z plane is transformed into a circle not passing through the origin in the w plane;

(*b*) a circle ($A \neq 0$) through the origin ($D = 0$) in the z plane is transformed into a line that does not pass through the origin in the w plane;

(*c*) a line ($A = 0$) not passing through the origin ($D \neq 0$) in the z plane is transformed into a circle through the origin in the w plane;

(*d*) a line ($A = 0$) through the origin ($D = 0$) in the z plane is transformed into a line through the origin in the w plane.

EXAMPLE 1. According to equations (4) and (5), a vertical line $x = c_1$ ($c_1 \neq 0$) is transformed by $w = 1/z$ into the circle $-c_1(u^2 + v^2) + u = 0$, or

$$\left(u - \frac{1}{2c_1}\right)^2 + v^2 = \left(\frac{1}{2c_1}\right)^2, \tag{6}$$

which is centered on the u axis and tangent to the v axis. The image of a typical point (c_1, y) on the line is, by equations (1),

$$(u, v) = \left(\frac{c_1}{c_1^2 + y^2}, \frac{-y}{c_1^2 + y^2}\right).$$

If $c_1 > 0$, the circle (6) is evidently to the right of the v axis. As the point (c_1, y) moves up the entire line, its image traverses the circle once in the clockwise direction, the point at infinity in the extended z plane corresponding to the origin in the w plane. This is illustrated in Fig. 119 when $c_1 = 1/3$. Note that $v > 0$ if $y < 0$; and as y increases through negative values to 0, one can see that u increases from 0 to $1/c_1$. Then, as y increases through positive values, v is negative and u decreases to 0.

If, on the other hand, $c_1 < 0$, the circle lies to the left of the v axis. As the point (c_1, y) moves upward, its image still makes one cycle, but in the counterclockwise direction. See Fig. 119, where the case $c_1 = -1/2$ is also shown.

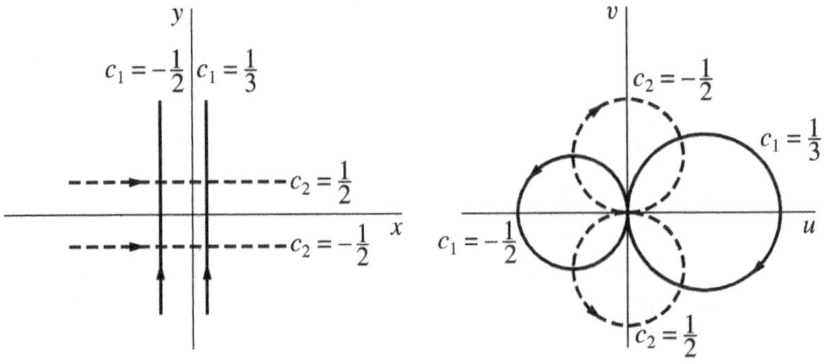

FIGURE 119
$w = 1/z$.

EXAMPLE 2. A horizontal line $y = c_2$ $(c_2 \neq 0)$ is mapped by $w = 1/z$ onto the circle

$$u^2 + \left(v + \frac{1}{2c_2}\right)^2 = \left(\frac{1}{2c_2}\right)^2, \tag{7}$$

which is centered on the v axis and tangent to the u axis. Two special cases are shown in Fig. 119, where corresponding orientations of the lines and circles are also indicated.

EXAMPLE 3. When $w = 1/z$, the half plane $x \geq c_1$ $(c_1 > 0)$ is mapped onto the disk

$$\left(u - \frac{1}{2c_1}\right)^2 + v^2 \leq \left(\frac{1}{2c_1}\right)^2. \tag{8}$$

For, according to Example 1, any line $x = c$ $(c \geq c_1)$ is transformed into the circle

$$\left(u - \frac{1}{2c}\right)^2 + v^2 = \left(\frac{1}{2c}\right)^2. \tag{9}$$

Furthermore, as c increases through all values greater than c_1, the lines $x = c$ move to the right and the image circles (9) shrink in size. (See Fig. 120.) Since the lines $x = c$ pass through all points in the half plane $x \geq c_1$ and the circles (9) pass through all points in the disk (8), the mapping is established.

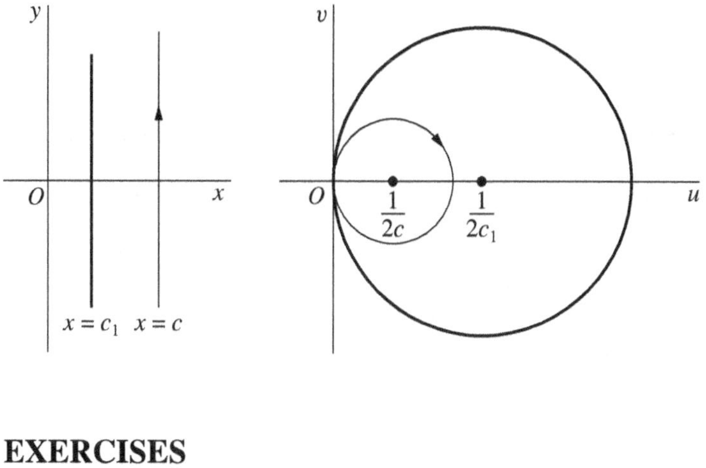

FIGURE 120
$w = 1/z$.

EXERCISES

1. In Sec. 98, point out how it follows from the first of equations (2) that when $w = 1/z$, the inequality $x \geq c_1$ $(c_1 > 0)$ is satisfied if and only if inequality (8) holds. Thus give an alternative verification of the mapping established in Example 3, Sec. 98.
2. Show that when $c_1 < 0$, the image of the half plane $x < c_1$ under the transformation $w = 1/z$ is the interior of a circle. What is the image when $c_1 = 0$?
3. Show that the image of the half plane $y > c_2$ under the transformation $w = 1/z$ is the interior of a circle when $c_2 > 0$. Find the image when $c_2 < 0$ and when $c_2 = 0$.

4. Find the image of the infinite strip $0 < y < 1/(2c)$ under the transformation $w = 1/z$. Sketch the strip and its image.

Ans. $u^2 + (v + c)^2 > c^2, \ v < 0$.

5. Find the image of the region $x > 1, y > 0$ under the transformation $w = 1/z$.

Ans. $\left(u - \frac{1}{2}\right)^2 + v^2 < \left(\frac{1}{2}\right)^2, \ v < 0$.

6. Verify the mapping, where $w = 1/z$, of the regions and parts of the boundaries indicated in (*a*) Fig. 4, Appendix 2; (*b*) Fig. 5, Appendix 2.

7. Describe geometrically the transformation $w = 1/(z - 1)$.

8. Describe geometrically the transformation $w = i/z$. State why it transforms circles and lines into circles and lines.

9. Find the image of the semi-infinite strip $x > 0, \ 0 < y < 1$ when $w = i/z$. Sketch the strip and its image.

Ans. $\left(u - \frac{1}{2}\right)^2 + v^2 > \left(\frac{1}{2}\right)^2, \ u > 0, \ v > 0$.

10. By writing $w = \rho \exp(i\phi)$, show that the mapping $w = 1/z$ transforms the hyperbola $x^2 - y^2 = 1$ into the lemniscate $\rho^2 = \cos 2\phi$. (Use Exercise 14, Sec. 6.)

11. Let the circle $|z| = 1$ have a positive, or counterclockwise, orientation. Determine the orientation of its image under the transformation $w = 1/z$.

12. Show that when a circle is transformed into a circle under the transformation $w = 1/z$, the center of the original circle is *never* mapped onto the center of the image circle.

13. Using the exponential form $z = re^{i\theta}$ of z, show that the transformation

$$w = z + \frac{1}{z},$$

which is the sum of the identity transformation and the transformation discussed in Secs. 97 and 98, maps circles $r = r_0$ onto ellipses with parametric representations

$$u = \left(r_0 + \frac{1}{r_0}\right)\cos\theta, \quad v = \left(r_0 - \frac{1}{r_0}\right)\sin\theta \qquad (0 \le \theta \le 2\pi)$$

and foci at the points $w = \pm 2$. Then show how it follows that this transformation maps the entire circle $|z| = 1$ onto the segment $-2 \le u \le 2$ of the u axis and the domain outside that circle onto the rest of the w plane.

14. (*a*) Write equation (4), Sec. 98, in the form

$$2Az\overline{z} + (B - Ci)z + (B + Ci)\overline{z} + 2D = 0,$$

where $z = x + iy$.

(*b*) Show that when $w = 1/z$, the result in part (*a*) becomes

$$2Dw\overline{w} + (B + Ci)w + (B - Ci)\overline{w} + 2A = 0.$$

Then show that if $w = u + iv$, this equation is the same as equation (5), Sec. 98.

Suggestion: In part (*a*), use the relations (see Sec. 6)

$$x = \frac{z + \overline{z}}{2} \quad \text{and} \quad y = \frac{z - \overline{z}}{2i}.$$

99. LINEAR FRACTIONAL TRANSFORMATIONS

The transformation

$$w = \frac{az+b}{cz+d} \qquad (ad - bc \neq 0), \tag{1}$$

where a, b, c, and d are complex constants, is called a ***linear fractional transformation***, or Möbius transformation. Observe that equation (1) can be written in the form

$$Azw + Bz + Cw + D = 0 \qquad (AD - BC \neq 0); \tag{2}$$

and, conversely, any equation of type (2) can be put in the form (1). Since this alternative form is linear in z and linear in w, another name for a linear fractional transformation is *bilinear transformation.*

When $c = 0$, the condition $ad - bc \neq 0$ with equation (1) becomes $ad \neq 0$; and we see that the transformation reduces to a nonconstant linear function. When $c \neq 0$, equation (1) can be written

$$w = \frac{a}{c} + \frac{bc - ad}{c} \cdot \frac{1}{cz+d} \qquad (ad - bc \neq 0). \tag{3}$$

So, once again, the condition $ad - bc \neq 0$ ensures that we do not have a constant function. The transformation $w = 1/z$ is evidently a special case of transformation (1) when $c \neq 0$.

Equation (3) reveals that when $c \neq 0$, a linear fractional transformation is a composition of the mappings.

$$Z = cz + d, \quad W = \frac{1}{Z}, \quad w = \frac{a}{c} + \frac{bc - ad}{c} W \qquad (ad - bc \neq 0).$$

It thus follows that, regardless of whether c is zero or nonzero, *any linear fractional transformation transforms circles and lines into circles and lines* because these special linear fractional transformations do. (See Secs. 96 and 98.)

Solving equation (1) for z, we find that

$$z = \frac{-dw + b}{cw - a} \qquad (ad - bc \neq 0). \tag{4}$$

When a given point w is the image of some point z under transformation (1), the point z is retrieved by means of equation (4). If $c = 0$, so that a and d are both nonzero, each point in the w plane is evidently the image of one and only one point in the z plane. The same is true if $c \neq 0$, except when $w = a/c$ since the denominator in equation (4) vanishes if w has that value. We can, however, enlarge the domain of definition of transformation (1) in order to define a linear fractional transformation T on the *extended* z plane such that the point $w = a/c$ is the image of $z = \infty$ when $c \neq 0$. We first write

$$T(z) = \frac{az+b}{cz+d} \qquad (ad - bc \neq 0). \tag{5}$$

We then write

$$T(\infty) = \infty \quad \text{if} \quad c = 0 \tag{6}$$

and

$$T(\infty) = \frac{a}{c} \quad \text{and} \quad T\left(-\frac{d}{c}\right) = \infty \quad \text{if} \quad c \neq 0. \tag{7}$$

In view of Exercise 11, Sec. 18, this makes T continuous on the extended z plane. It also agrees with the way in which we enlarged the domain of definition of the transformation $w = 1/z$ in Sec. 97.

When its domain of definition is enlarged in this way, the linear fractional transformation (5) is a *one to one* mapping of the extended z plane *onto* the extended w plane. That is, $T(z_1) \neq T(z_2)$ whenever $z_1 \neq z_2$; and, for each point w in the second plane, there is a point z in the first one such that $T(z) = w$. Hence, associated with the transformation T, there is an *inverse transformation* T^{-1}, which is defined on the extended w plane as follows:

$$T^{-1}(w) = z \quad \text{if and only if} \quad T(z) = w.$$

From equation (4), we see that

$$T^{-1}(w) = \frac{-dw + b}{cw - a} \qquad (ad - bc \neq 0). \tag{8}$$

Evidently, T^{-1} is itself a linear fractional transformation, where

$$T^{-1}(\infty) = \infty \quad \text{if} \quad c = 0 \tag{9}$$

and

$$T^{-1}\left(\frac{a}{c}\right) = \infty \quad \text{and} \quad T^{-1}(\infty) = -\frac{d}{c} \quad \text{if} \quad c \neq 0. \tag{10}$$

If T and S are two linear fractional transformations, then so is the composition $S[T(z)]$. This can be verified by combining expressions of the type (5). Note that, in particular, $T^{-1}[T(z)] = z$ for each point z in the extended plane.

There is always a linear fractional transformation that maps three given distinct points z_1, z_2, and z_3 onto three specified distinct points w_1, w_2, and w_3, respectively. Verification of this will appear in Sec. 100, where the image w of a point z under such a transformation is given implicitly in terms of z. We illustrate here a more direct approach to finding the desired transformation.

EXAMPLE 1. Let us find the special case of the general linear fractional transformation

$$w = \frac{az + b}{cz + d} \qquad (ad - bc \neq 0)$$

that maps the points

$$z_1 = 2, \quad z_2 = i, \quad \text{and} \quad z_3 = -2$$

onto the points

$$w_1 = 1, \quad w_2 = i, \quad \text{and} \quad w_3 = -1.$$

Since 1 is to be the image of 2 and -1 is to be the image of -2, we require that

$$2c + d = 2a + b \quad \text{and} \quad 2c - d = -2a + b.$$

Adding corresponding sides of these two equations reveals that $b = 2c$. The first equation then becomes $d = 2a$, and we have

$$w = \frac{az + 2c}{cz + 2a} \qquad [2(a^2 - c^2) \neq 0]. \tag{11}$$

Because i is to be transformed into i, equation (11) tells us that $c = (ai)/3$. Hence

$$w = \frac{az + \dfrac{2ai}{3}}{\dfrac{ai}{3}z + 2a} = \frac{a\left(z + \dfrac{2}{3}i\right)}{a\left(\dfrac{i}{3}z + 2\right)} \qquad (a \neq 0);$$

and we can cancel out the nonzero factor a to write

$$w = \frac{z + \dfrac{2}{3}i}{\dfrac{i}{3}z + 2},$$

which is the same as

$$w = \frac{3z + 2i}{iz + 6}. \tag{12}$$

EXAMPLE 2. Suppose that the points

$$z_1 = 1, \quad z_2 = 0, \quad \text{and} \quad z_3 = -1$$

are to be mapped onto

$$w_1 = i, \quad w_2 = \infty, \quad \text{and} \quad w_3 = 1.$$

Since $w_2 = \infty$ corresponds to $z_2 = 0$, we know from equations (6) and (7) that $c \neq 0$ and $d = 0$ in equation (1). Hence

$$w = \frac{az + b}{cz} \qquad (bc \neq 0). \tag{13}$$

Then, because 1 is to be mapped onto i and -1 onto 1, we have the relations

$$ic = a + b, \quad -c = -a + b;$$

and it follows that

$$2a = (1 + i)c, \quad 2b = (i - 1)c.$$

Finally, if we multiply numerator and denominator in the quotient (13) by 2, make these substitutions for $2a$ and $2b$, and then cancel out the nonzero number c, we arrive at

$$w = \frac{(i+1)z + (i-1)}{2z}. \tag{14}$$

100. AN IMPLICIT FORM

The equation

$$\frac{(w-w_1)(w_2-w_3)}{(w-w_3)(w_2-w_1)} = \frac{(z-z_1)(z_2-z_3)}{(z-z_3)(z_2-z_1)} \tag{1}$$

defines (implicitly) a linear fractional transformation that maps distinct points z_1, z_2, and z_3 in the finite z plane onto distinct points w_1, w_2, and w_3, respectively, in the finite w plane.* To verify this, we write equation (1) as

$$(z-z_3)(w-w_1)(z_2-z_1)(w_2-w_3) = (z-z_1)(w-w_3)(z_2-z_3)(w_2-w_1). \tag{2}$$

If $z = z_1$, the right-hand side of equation (2) is zero; and it follows that $w = w_1$. Similarly, if $z = z_3$, the left-hand side is zero and, consequently, $w = w_3$. If $z = z_2$, we have the linear equation

$$(w-w_1)(w_2-w_3) = (w-w_3)(w_2-w_1),$$

whose unique solution is $w = w_2$. One can see that the mapping defined by equation (1) is actually a linear fractional transformation by expanding the products in equation (2) and writing the result in the form (Sec. 99)

$$Azw + Bz + Cw + D = 0. \tag{3}$$

The condition $AD - BC \neq 0$, which is needed with equation (3), is clearly satisfied since, as just demonstrated, equation (1) does not define a constant function. It is left to the reader (Exercise 10) to show that equation (1) defines the *only* linear fractional transformation mapping the points z_1, z_2, and z_3 onto w_1, w_2, and w_3, respectively.

EXAMPLE 1. The transformation found in Example 1, Sec. 99, required that

$$z_1 = 2,\ z_2 = i,\ z_3 = -2 \qquad \text{and} \qquad w_1 = 1,\ w_2 = i,\ w_3 = -1.$$

Using equation (1) to write

$$\frac{(w-1)(i+1)}{(w+1)(i-1)} = \frac{(z-2)(i+2)}{(z+2)(i-2)}$$

*The two sides of equation (1) are ***cross ratios***, which play an important role in more extensive developments of linear fractional transformations than in this book. See, for instance, R. P. Boas, *Invitation to Complex Analysis*, 2d ed., pp. 171–176, 2010 or J. B. Conway, *Functions of One Complex Variable*, 2d ed., 6th printing, pp. 48–55, 1997.

and then solving for w in terms of z, we arrive at the transformation

$$w = \frac{3z + 2i}{iz + 6},$$

found earlier.

If equation (1) is modified properly, it can also be used when the point at infinity is one of the prescribed points in either the (extended) z or w plane. Suppose, for instance, that $z_1 = \infty$. Since any linear fractional transformation is continuous on the extended plane, we need only replace z_1 on the right-hand side of equation (1) by $1/z_1$, clear fractions, and let z_1 tend to zero:

$$\lim_{z_1 \to 0} \frac{(z - 1/z_1)(z_2 - z_3)}{(z - z_3)(z_2 - 1/z_1)} \cdot \frac{z_1}{z_1} = \lim_{z_1 \to 0} \frac{(z_1 z - 1)(z_2 - z_3)}{(z - z_3)(z_1 z_2 - 1)} = \frac{z_2 - z_3}{z - z_3}.$$

The desired modification of equation (1) is, then,

$$\frac{(w - w_1)(w_2 - w_3)}{(w - w_3)(w_2 - w_1)} = \frac{z_2 - z_3}{z - z_3}.$$

Note that this modification is obtained formally by simply deleting the factors involving z_1 in equation (1). It is easy to check that the same formal approach applies when any of the other prescribed points is ∞.

EXAMPLE 2. In Example 2, Sec. 99, the prescribed points were

$$z_1 = 1,\ z_2 = 0,\ z_3 = -1 \quad \text{and} \quad w_1 = i,\ w_2 = \infty,\ w_3 = 1.$$

In this case, we use the modification

$$\frac{w - w_1}{w - w_3} = \frac{(z - z_1)(z_2 - z_3)}{(z - z_3)(z_2 - z_1)}$$

of equation (1), which tells us that

$$\frac{w - i}{w - 1} = \frac{(z - 1)(0 + 1)}{(z + 1)(0 - 1)}.$$

Solving here for w, we have the transformation obtained earlier:

$$w = \frac{(i + 1)z + (i - 1)}{2z}.$$

EXERCISES

1. Find the linear fractional transformation that maps the points $z_1 = -1, z_2 = 0, z_3 = 1$ onto the points $w_1 = -i, w_2 = 1, w_3 = i$.

Suggestion: The most efficient way to find this transformation is to use equation (1) in Sec. 100.

Ans. $w = \dfrac{i - z}{i + z}$.

2. Find the linear fractional transformation that maps the points $z_1 = -i, z_2 = 0, z_3 = i$ onto the points $w_1 = -1, w_2 = i, w_3 = 1$. Into what curve is the imaginary axis $x = 0$ transformed?

3. Find the bilinear transformation that maps the points $z_1 = \infty, z_2 = i, z_3 = 0$ onto the points $w_1 = 0, w_2 = i, w_3 = \infty$.

Ans. $w = -1/z$.

4. Find the bilinear transformation that maps distinct points z_1, z_2, z_3 onto the points $w_1 = 0, w_2 = 1, w_3 = \infty$.

Ans. $w = \dfrac{(z - z_1)(z_2 - z_3)}{(z - z_3)(z_2 - z_1)}$.

5. Show that a composition of two linear fractional transformations is again a linear fractional transformation, as stated in Sec. 99. To do this, consider two such transformations

$$T(z) = \frac{a_1 z + b_1}{c_1 z + d_1} \quad (a_1 d_1 - b_1 c_1 \neq 0)$$

and

$$S(z) = \frac{a_2 z + b_2}{c_2 z + d_2} \quad (a_2 d_2 - b_2 c_2 \neq 0).$$

Then show that the composition $S[T(z)]$ has the form

$$S[T(z)] = \frac{a_3 z + b_3}{c_3 z + d_3},$$

where

$$a_3 d_3 - b_3 c_3 = (a_1 d_1 - b_1 c_1)(a_2 d_2 - b_2 c_2) \neq 0.$$

6. A ***fixed point*** of a transformation $w = f(z)$ is a point z_0 such that $f(z_0) = z_0$. Show that every linear fractional transformation, with the exception of the identity transformation $w = z$, has at most two fixed points in the extended plane.

7. Find the fixed points (see Exercise 6) of the transformation

(*a*) $w = \dfrac{z-1}{z+1}$; (*b*) $w = \dfrac{6z-9}{z}$.

Ans. (*a*) $z = \pm i$; (*b*) $z = 3$.

8. Modify equation (1), Sec. 100, for the case in which both z_2 and w_2 are the point at infinity. Then show that any linear fractional transformation must be of the form $w = az$ $(a \neq 0)$ when its fixed points (Exercise 6) are 0 and ∞.

9. Prove that if the origin is a fixed point (Exercise 6) of a linear fractional transformation, then the transformation can be written in the form

$$w = \frac{z}{cz + d} \quad (d \neq 0).$$

10. Show that there is only one linear fractional transformation which maps three given distinct points z_1, z_2, and z_3 in the extended z plane onto three specified distinct points w_1, w_2, and w_3 in the extended w plane.

Suggestion: Let T and S be two such linear fractional transformations. Then, after pointing out why $S^{-1}[T(z_k)] = z_k$ $(k = 1, 2, 3)$, use the results in Exercises 5 and 6 to show that $S^{-1}[T(z)] = z$ for all z. Thus show that $T(z) = S(z)$ for all z.

11. With the aid of equation (1), Sec. 100, prove that if a linear fractional transformation maps the points of the x axis onto points of the u axis, then the coefficients in the transformation are all real, except possibly for a common complex factor. The converse statement is evident.

12. Let

$$T(z) = \frac{az+b}{cz+d} \qquad (ad - bc \neq 0)$$

be any linear fractional transformation other than $T(z) = z$. Show that

$$T^{-1} = T \quad \text{if and only if} \quad d = -a.$$

Suggestion: Write the equation $T^{-1}(z) = T(z)$ as

$$(a+d)[cz^2 + (d-a)z - b] = 0.$$

101. MAPPINGS OF THE UPPER HALF PLANE

This section is devoted to the construction of the most general linear fractional transformation having the following property:

(a) it maps the upper half plane $\operatorname{Im} z > 0$ onto the open disk $|w| < 1$ and the boundary $\operatorname{Im} z = 0$ of the half plane onto the boundary $|w| = 1$ of the disk (Fig. 121).

We will show that any such linear fractional transformation must be of the following type, and conversely:

(b) it must be of the form

$$w = e^{i\alpha}\left(\frac{z - z_0}{z - \overline{z_0}}\right) \qquad (\operatorname{Im} z_0 > 0),$$

where α is any real number.

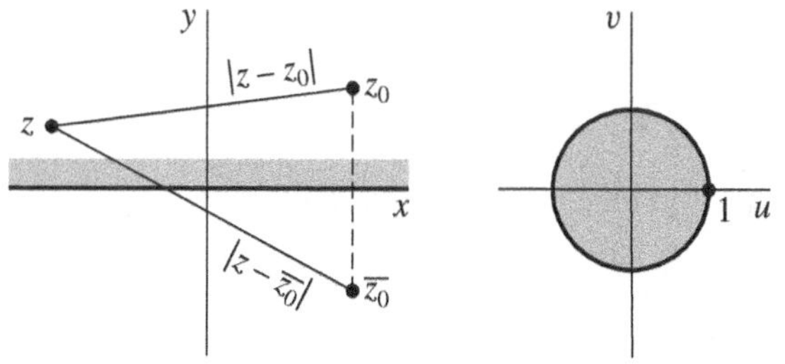

FIGURE 121
$w = e^{i\alpha}\left(\frac{z - z_0}{z - \overline{z_0}}\right) \quad (\operatorname{Im} z_0 > 0).$

In order to show that statements (a) and (b) are equivalent, we first assume that statement (a) is true and obtain statement (b). Once that is done, we assume that statement (b) is true and obtain statement (a),

(*a*) implies (*b*)

Keeping in mind that points on the line $\text{Im}\, z = 0$ are to be transformed into points on the circle $|w| = 1$, we start by selecting the points $z = 0$, $z = 1$, and $z = \infty$ on the line and determining conditions on a linear fractional transformation

$$w = \frac{az + b}{cz + d} \qquad (ad - bc \neq 0) \tag{1}$$

which are necessary in order for the images of those points to have unit modulus.

We note from equation (1) that if $|w| = 1$ when $z = 0$, then $|b/d| = 1$; that is,

$$|b| = |d| \neq 0. \tag{2}$$

Furthermore, statements (6) and (7) in Sec. 99 tell us that the image of the point $z = \infty$ is a *finite* number only if $c \neq 0$, that finite number being $w = a/c$. So the requirement that $|w| = 1$ when $z = \infty$ means that $|a/c| = 1$, or

$$|a| = |c| \neq 0; \tag{3}$$

and the fact that a and c are nonzero enables us to rewrite equation (1) as

$$w = \frac{a}{c} \cdot \frac{z + (b/a)}{z + (d/c)}. \tag{4}$$

Then, since $|a/c| = 1$ and

$$\left|\frac{b}{a}\right| = \left|\frac{d}{c}\right| \neq 0,$$

according to relations (2) and (3), equation (4) can be put in the form

$$w = e^{i\alpha}\left(\frac{z - z_0}{z - z_1}\right) \qquad (|z_1| = |z_0| \neq 0), \tag{5}$$

where α is a real constant and z_0 and z_1 are (nonzero) complex constants.

Next, we impose on transformation (5) the condition that $|w| = 1$ when $z = 1$. This tells us that

$$|1 - z_1| = |1 - z_0|,$$

or

$$(1 - z_1)(1 - \overline{z_1}) = (1 - z_0)(1 - \overline{z_0}).$$

But $z_1\overline{z_1} = z_0\overline{z_0}$ since $|z_1| = |z_0|$, and the above relation reduces to

$$z_1 + \overline{z_1} = z_0 + \overline{z_0};$$

that is, $\text{Re}\, z_1 = \text{Re}\, z_0$. It follows that either

$$z_1 = z_0 \quad \text{or} \quad z_1 = \overline{z_0},$$

again since $|z_1| = |z_0|$. If $z_1 = z_0$, transformation (5) becomes the constant function $w = \exp(i\alpha)$; hence $z_1 = \overline{z_0}$.

Transformation (5), with $z_1 = \overline{z_0}$, maps the point z_0 onto the origin $w = 0$; and, since points interior to the circle $|w| = 1$ are to be the images of points *above* the real axis in the z plane, we may conclude that $\text{Im}\, z_0 > 0$. Any linear fractional transformation having property (a) must, therefore, have the form (b).

(b) implies (a)

It remains to show that, conversely, any linear fractional transformation of the form (b) has the mapping property (a). This is easily done by taking the modulus of each side of the equation in statement (b) and interpreting the resulting equation,

$$|w| = \frac{|z - z_0|}{|z - \overline{z_0}|},$$

geometrically. If a point z lies above the real axis, both it and the point z_0 lie on the same side of that axis, which is the perpendicular bisector of the line segment joining z_0 and $\overline{z_0}$. It follows that the distance $|z - z_0|$ is less than the distance $|z - \overline{z_0}|$ (Fig. 121); that is, $|w| < 1$. Likewise, if z lies below the real axis, the distance $|z - z_0|$ is greater than the distance $|z - \overline{z_0}|$; and so $|w| > 1$. Finally, if z is on the real axis, $|w| = 1$ because then $|z - z_0| = |z - \overline{z_0}|$. Since any linear fractional transformation is a one to one mapping of the extended z plane onto the extended w plane, this shows that *the transformation in statement* (b) *maps the half plane* $\text{Im}\, z > 0$ *onto the disk* $|w| < 1$ *and the boundary of the half plane onto the boundary of the disk.*

102. EXAMPLES

Our first example here illustrates the linear fractional transformation obtained in the preceding section, namely

$$(1) \qquad w = e^{i\alpha}\left(\frac{z - z_0}{z - \overline{z_0}}\right) \qquad (\text{Im}\, z_0 > 0),$$

where α is any real number.

EXAMPLE 1. The transformation

$$w = \frac{i - z}{i + z}$$

can be put in the form

$$w = e^{i\pi}\left(\frac{z - i}{z - \overline{i}}\right),$$

which is a special case of transformation (1). Inasmuch as transformation (1) is simply a restatement of the transformation that is of the form (b) in Sec. 101, it follows that this special case also has property (a) in Sec. 101. (See Exercise 1, Sec. 100, as well as Fig. 13 in Appendix 2, where corresponding points in the z and w planes are indicated.)

Images of the upper half plane $\text{Im}\, z \geq 0$ under other types of linear fractional transformations are often fairly easy to determine by examining the particular transformation in question, as is done in the next example.

EXAMPLE 2. By writing $z = x + iy$ and $w = u + iv$, we can readily show that the transformation

$$w = \frac{z-1}{z+1} \tag{2}$$

maps the half plane $y > 0$ onto the half plane $v > 0$ and the x axis onto the u axis. We first note that when the number z is real, so is the number w. Consequently, since the image of the real axis $y = 0$ is either a circle or a line, it must be the real axis $v = 0$. Furthermore, for any point w in the finite w plane,

$$v = \operatorname{Im} w = \operatorname{Im} \frac{(z-1)(\overline{z}+1)}{(z+1)(\overline{z+1})} = \frac{2y}{|z+1|^2} \qquad (z \neq -1).$$

The numbers y and v thus have the same sign, and this means that points above the x axis correspond to points above the u axis and points below the x axis correspond to points below the u axis. Finally, since points on the x axis correspond to points on the u axis and since a linear fractional transformation is a one to one mapping of the extended plane onto the extended plane (Sec. 99), the stated mapping property of transformation (2) is established.

Our final example involves a composite function and uses the mapping discussed in Example 2.

EXAMPLE 3. The transformation

$$w = \operatorname{Log} \frac{z-1}{z+1}, \tag{3}$$

where the principal branch of the logarithmic function is used, is a composition of the functions

$$Z = \frac{z-1}{z+1} \quad \text{and} \quad w = \operatorname{Log} Z. \tag{4}$$

According to Example 2, the first of transformations (4) maps the upper half plane $y > 0$ onto the upper half plane $Y > 0$, where $z = x + iy$ and $Z = X + iY$. Furthermore, it is easy to see from Fig. 122 that the second of transformations (4) maps the half plane $Y > 0$ onto the strip $0 < v < \pi$, where $w = u + iv$. More precisely, by writing $Z = R\exp(i\Theta)$ and

$$\operatorname{Log} Z = \ln R + i\Theta \qquad (R > 0, -\pi < \Theta < \pi),$$

we see that as a point $Z = R\exp(i\Theta_0)$ $(0 < \Theta_0 < \pi)$ moves outward from the origin along the ray $\Theta = \Theta_0$, its image is the point whose *rectangular* coordinates in the w plane are $(\ln R, \Theta_0)$. That image evidently moves to the right along the entire length of the horizontal line $v = \Theta_0$. Since these lines fill the strip $0 < v < \pi$ as the choice of Θ_0 varies between $\Theta_0 = 0$ to $\Theta_0 = \pi$, the mapping of the half plane $Y > 0$ onto the strip is, in fact, one to one.

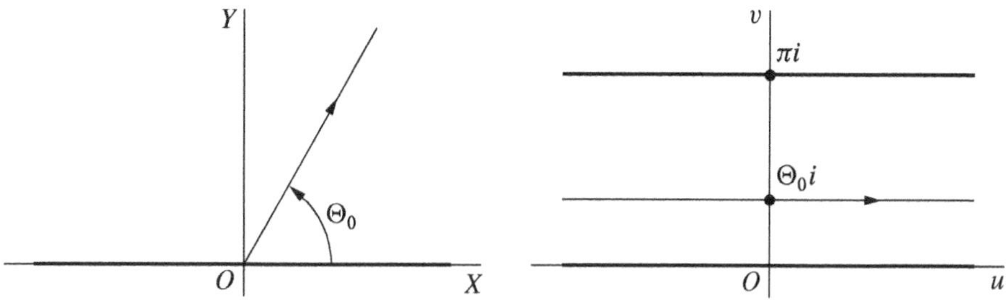

FIGURE 122
$w = \text{Log } Z$.

This shows that the composition (3) of the mappings (4) transforms the plane $y > 0$ onto the strip $0 < v < \pi$. Corresponding boundary points are shown in Fig. 19 of Appendix 2.

EXERCISES

1. Recall from Example 1 in Sec. 102 that the transformation

$$w = \frac{i - z}{i + z}$$

maps the half plane $\text{Im } z > 0$ onto the disk $|w| < 1$ and the boundary of the half plane onto the boundary of the disk. Show that a point $z = x$ is mapped onto the point

$$w = \frac{1 - x^2}{1 + x^2} + i\frac{2x}{1 + x^2},$$

and then complete the verification of the mapping illustrated in Fig. 13, Appendix 2, by showing that segments of the x axis are mapped as indicated there.

2. Verify the mapping shown in Fig. 12, Appendix 2, where

$$w = \frac{z - 1}{z + 1}.$$

Suggestion: Write the given transformation as a composition of the mappings

$$Z = iz, \quad W = \frac{i - Z}{i + Z}, \quad w = -W.$$

Then refer to the mapping whose verification was completed in Exercise 1.

3. (*a*) By finding the inverse of the transformation

$$w = \frac{i - z}{i + z}$$

and appealing to Fig. 13, Appendix 2, whose verification was completed in Exercise 1, show that the transformation

$$w = i\frac{1 - z}{1 + z}$$

maps the disk $|z| \le 1$ onto the half plane $\text{Im } w \ge 0$.

(*b*) Show that the linear fractional transformation

$$w = \frac{z-2}{z}$$

can be written

$$Z = z - 1, \quad W = i\frac{1-Z}{1+Z}, \quad w = iW.$$

Then, with the aid of the result in part (*a*), verify that it maps the disk $|z-1| \le 1$ onto the left half plane $\text{Re}\, w \le 0$.

4. Transformation (1), Sec. 102, maps the point $z = \infty$ onto the point $w = \exp(i\alpha)$, which lies on the boundary of the disk $|w| \le 1$. Show that if $0 < \alpha < 2\pi$ and the points $z = 0$ and $z = 1$ are to be mapped onto the points $w = 1$ and $w = \exp(i\alpha/2)$, respectively, the transformation can be written

$$w = e^{i\alpha}\left[\frac{z + \exp(-i\alpha/2)}{z + \exp(i\alpha/2)}\right].$$

5. Note that when $\alpha = \pi/2$, the transformation in Exercise 4 becomes

$$w = \frac{iz + \exp(i\pi/4)}{z + \exp(i\pi/4)}.$$

Verify that this special case maps points on the x axis as indicated in Fig. 123.

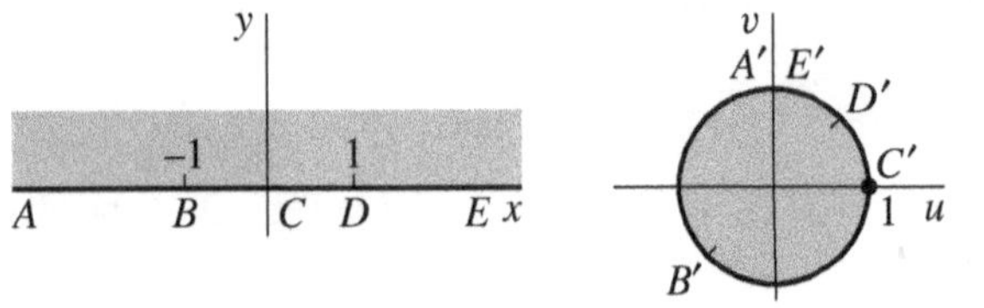

FIGURE 123
$$w = \frac{iz + \exp(i\pi/4)}{z + \exp(i\pi/4)}.$$

6. Show that if $\text{Im}\, z_0 < 0$, transformation (1), Sec. 102, maps the lower half plane $\text{Im}\, z \le 0$ onto the unit disk $|w| \le 1$.

7. The equation $w = \log(z-1)$ can be written

$$Z = z - 1, \quad w = \log Z.$$

Find a branch of $\log Z$ such that the cut z plane consisting of all points except those on the segment $x \ge 1$ of the real axis is mapped by $w = \log(z-1)$ onto the strip $0 < v < 2\pi$ in the w plane.

103. MAPPINGS BY THE EXPONENTIAL FUNCTION

The object of this section is to provide the reader with some examples of mappings by the exponential function e^z that was introduced in Chap. 3 (Sec. 30). Our examples are reasonably simple, and we begin here by examining the images of vertical and horizontal lines.

EXAMPLE 1. We know from Sec. 30 that the transformation

$$w = e^z \tag{1}$$

can be written $w = e^x e^{iy}$, where $z = x + iy$. Thus, if $w = \rho e^{i\phi}$,

$$\rho = e^x, \quad \phi = y. \tag{2}$$

The image of a typical point $z = (c_1, y)$ on a vertical line $x = c_1$ has polar coordinates $\rho = \exp c_1$ and $\phi = y$ in the w plane. That image moves counterclockwise around the circle shown in Fig. 124 as z moves up the line. The image of the line is evidently the entire circle; and each point on the circle is the image of an infinite number of points, spaced 2π units apart, along the line.

A horizontal line $y = c_2$ is mapped in a one to one manner onto the ray $\phi = c_2$. To see that this is so, we note that the image of a point $z = (x, c_2)$ has polar coordinates $\rho = e^x$ and $\phi = c_2$. Consequently, as that point z moves along the entire line from left to right, its image moves outward along the entire ray $\phi = c_2$, as indicated in Fig. 124.

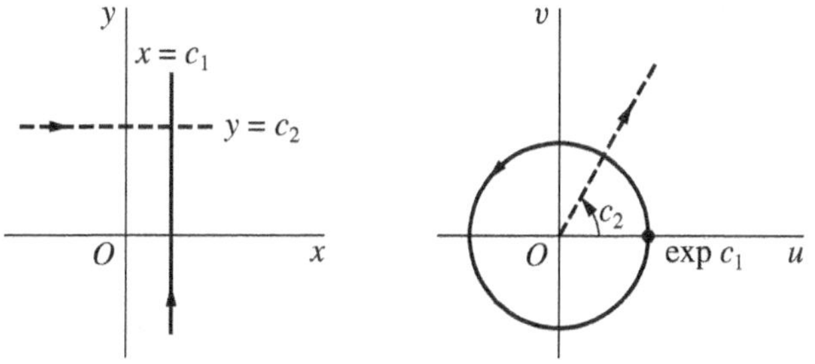

FIGURE 124
$w = \exp z$.

Vertical and horizontal line *segments* are mapped onto portions of circles and rays, respectively, and images of various regions are readily obtained from observations made in Example 1. This is illustrated in the following example.

EXAMPLE 2. Let us show that the transformation $w = e^z$ maps the rectangular region $a \le x \le b, c \le y \le d$ onto the region $e^a \le \rho \le e^b, c \le \phi \le d$. The two regions and corresponding parts of their boundaries are indicated in Fig. 125.

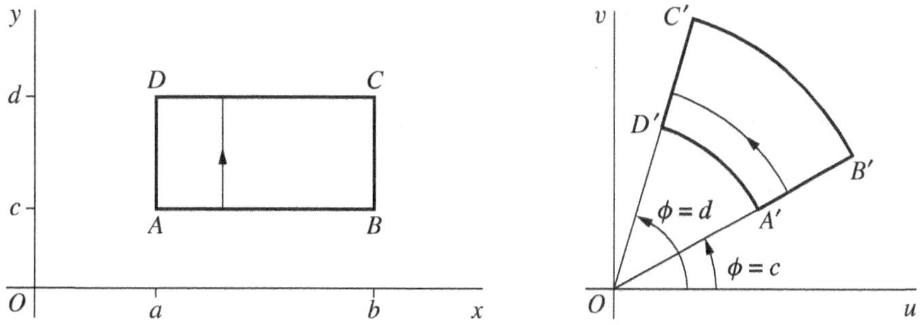

FIGURE 125
$w = \exp z$.

The vertical line segment AD is mapped onto the arc $\rho = e^a, c \le \phi \le d$, which is labeled $A'D'$. The images of vertical line segments to the right of AD and joining the horizontal parts of the boundary are larger arcs; eventually, the image of the line segment BC is the arc $\rho = e^b, c \le \phi \le d$, labeled $B'C'$. The mapping is one to one if $d - c < 2\pi$. In particular, if $c = 0$ and $d = \pi$, then $0 \le \phi \le \pi$; and the rectangular region is mapped onto half of a circular ring, as shown in Fig. 8, Appendix 2.

Our final example here uses the images of *horizontal* lines to find the image of a horizontal strip.

EXAMPLE 3. When $w = e^z$, the image of the infinite strip $0 \le y \le \pi$ is the upper half $v \ge 0$ of the w plane (Fig. 126). This is seen by recalling from Example 1 how a horizontal line $y = c$ is transformed into a ray $\phi = c$ from the origin. As the real number c increases from $c = 0$ to $c = \pi$, the y intercepts of the lines increase from 0 to π and the angles of inclination of the rays increase from $\phi = 0$ to $\phi = \pi$. This mapping is also shown in Fig. 6 of Appendix 2, where corresponding points on the boundaries of the two regions are indicated.

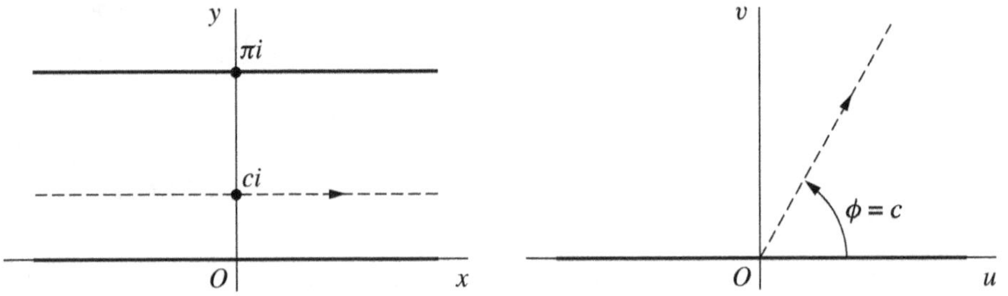

FIGURE 126
$w = \exp z$.

104. MAPPING VERTICAL LINE SEGMENTS BY $w = \sin z$

Since (Sec. 37) $\sin z = \sin x \cosh y + i \cos x \sinh y$, where $z = x + iy$, the transformation $w = \sin z$, where $w = u + iv$, can be written

$$u = \sin x \cosh y, \quad v = \cos x \sinh y. \tag{1}$$

One method that is often useful in finding images of regions under this transformation is to examine images of vertical lines $x = c_1$. If $0 < c_1 < \pi/2$, points on the line $x = c_1$ are transformed into points on the curve

$$u = \sin c_1 \cosh y, \quad v = \cos c_1 \sinh y \qquad (-\infty < y < \infty), \tag{2}$$

which is the right-hand branch of the hyperbola

$$\frac{u^2}{\sin^2 c_1} - \frac{v^2}{\cos^2 c_1} = 1 \tag{3}$$

with foci at the points

$$w = \pm\sqrt{\sin^2 c_1 + \cos^2 c_1} = \pm 1.$$

The second of equations (2) shows that as a point (c_1, y) moves upward along the entire length of the line, its image moves upward along the entire length of the hyperbola's branch. Such a line and its image are shown in Fig. 127, where corresponding points are labeled. Note that, in particular, there is a one to one mapping of the top half ($y > 0$) of the line onto the top half ($v > 0$) of the hyperbola's branch. If $-\pi/2 < c_1 < 0$, the line $x = c_1$ is mapped onto the left-hand branch of the same hyperbola. As before, corresponding points are indicated in Fig. 127.

The line $x = 0$, or the y axis, needs to be considered separately. According to equations (1), the image of each point $(0, y)$ is $(0, \sinh y)$. Hence the y axis is mapped onto the v axis in a one to one manner, the positive y axis corresponding to the positive v axis.

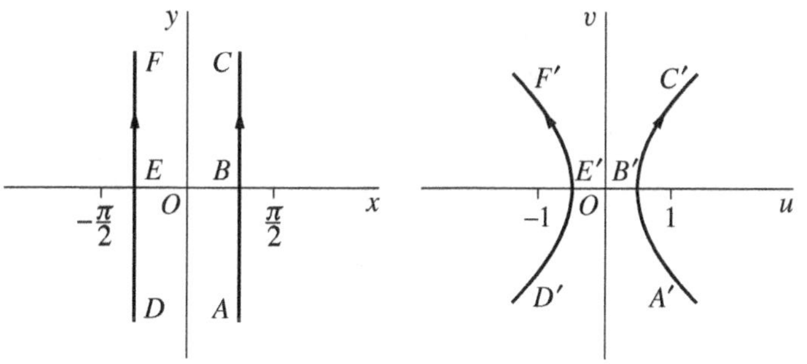

FIGURE 127
$w = \sin z$.

We now illustrate how these observations can be used to establish the images of certain regions.

EXAMPLE. Here we show that the transformation $w = \sin z$ is a one to one mapping of the semi-infinite strip $-\pi/2 \le x \le \pi/2$, $y \ge 0$ in the z plane onto the upper half $v \ge 0$ of the w plane.

To do this, we first show that the boundary of the strip is mapped in a one to one manner onto the real axis in the w plane, as indicated in Fig. 128. The image of the line segment BA there is found by writing $x = \pi/2$ in equations (1) and restricting y to be nonnegative. Since $u = \cosh y$ and $v = 0$ when $x = \pi/2$, a typical point $(\pi/2, y)$ on BA is mapped onto the point $(\cosh y, 0)$ in the w plane; and that image must move to the right from B' along the u axis as $(\pi/2, y)$ moves upward from B. Points $(x, 0)$ on the horizontal segment DB have images $(\sin x, 0)$, which move to the right from D' to B' as x increases from $x = -\pi/2$ to $x = \pi/2$, or as $(x, 0)$ goes from D to B. Finally, as points $(-\pi/2, y)$ on the line segment DE move upward from D, their images $(-\cosh y, 0)$ move left from D'.

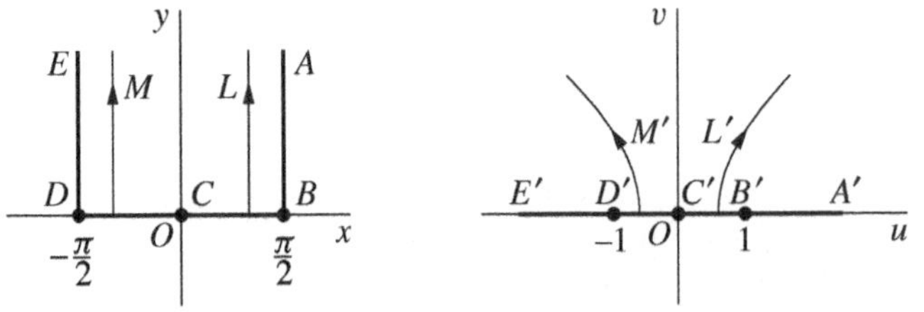

FIGURE 128
$w = \sin z$.

Now each point in the interior $-\pi/2 < x < \pi/2, y > 0$ of the strip lies on one of the vertical half lines $x = c_1, y > 0$ $(-\pi/2 < c_1 < \pi/2)$ that are shown in Fig. 128. Also, it is important to notice that the images of those half lines are distinct and constitute the entire half plane $v > 0$. More precisely, if the upper half L of a line $x = c_1$ $(0 < c_1 < \pi/2)$ is thought of as moving to the left toward the positive y axis, the right-hand branch of the hyperbola containing its image L' is opening up wider and its vertex $(\sin c_1, 0)$ is tending toward the origin $w = 0$. Hence L' tends to become the positive v axis, which we saw just prior to this example is the image of the positive y axis. On the other hand, as L approaches the segment BA of the boundary of the strip, the branch of the hyperbola closes down around the segment $B'A'$ of the u axis and its vertex $(\sin c_1, 0)$ tends toward the point $w = 1$. Similar statements can be made regarding the half line M and its image M' in Fig. 128. We may conclude that the image of each point in the interior of the strip lies in the upper half plane $v > 0$ and, furthermore, that each point in the half plane is the image of exactly one point in the interior of the strip.

This completes our demonstration that the transformation $w = \sin z$ is a one to one mapping of the strip $-\pi/2 \leq x \leq \pi/2, y \geq 0$ onto the half plane $v \geq 0$. The final result is shown in Fig. 9, Appendix 2. The right-hand half of the strip is evidently mapped onto the first quadrant of the w plane, as shown in Fig. 10, Appendix 2.

105. MAPPING HORIZONTAL LINE SEGMENTS BY $w = \sin z$

Another convenient way to find the images of certain regions when $w = \sin z$ is to consider the images of *horizontal* line segments $y = c_2$ $(-\pi \leq x \leq \pi)$, where $c_2 > 0$. According to equations (1) in Sec. 104, the image of such a line segment is the curve with parametric representation

$$u = \sin x \cosh c_2, \quad v = \cos x \sinh c_2 \qquad (-\pi \leq x \leq \pi). \tag{1}$$

That curve is readily seen to be the ellipse

$$\frac{u^2}{\cosh^2 c_2} + \frac{v^2}{\sinh^2 c_2} = 1, \tag{2}$$

whose foci lie at the points

$$w = \pm\sqrt{\cosh^2 c_2 - \sinh^2 c_2} = \pm 1.$$

The image of a point (x, c_2) moving to the right from point A to point E in Fig. 129 makes one circuit around the ellipse in the clockwise direction. Note that when smaller values of the positive number c_2 are taken, the ellipse becomes smaller but retains the same foci $(\pm 1, 0)$. In the limiting case $c_2 = 0$, equations (1) become

$$u = \sin x, \quad v = 0 \qquad (-\pi \le x \le \pi);$$

and we find that the interval $-\pi \le x \le \pi$ of the x axis is mapped onto the interval $-1 \le u \le 1$ of the u axis. The mapping is not, however, one to one, as it is when $c_2 > 0$.

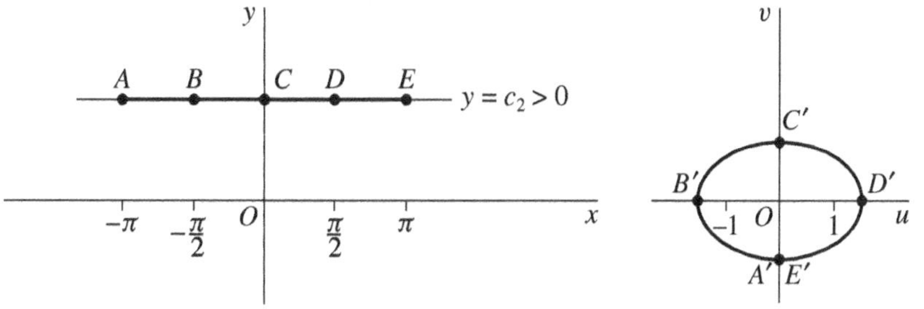

FIGURE 129
$w = \sin z$.

EXAMPLE. The rectangular region $-\pi/2 \le x \le \pi/2,\ 0 \le y \le b$ is mapped by $w = \sin z$ in a one to one manner onto the semi-elliptical region that is shown in Fig. 130, where corresponding boundary points are also indicated. For if L is a line segment $y = c_2\ (-\pi/2 \le x \le \pi/2)$, where $0 < c_2 \le b$, its image L' is the top half of the ellipse (2). As c_2 decreases, L moves downward toward the x axis and the semi-ellipse L' also moves downward and tends to become the line segment $E'F'A'$ from $w = -1$ to $w = 1$. In fact, when $c_2 = 0$, equations (1) become

$$u = \sin x, \quad v = 0 \qquad \left(-\frac{\pi}{2} \le x \le \frac{\pi}{2}\right);$$

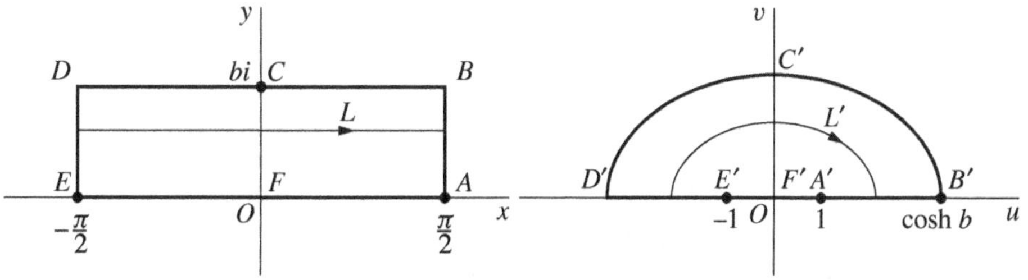

FIGURE 130
$w = \sin z$.

and this is clearly a one to one mapping of the segment *EFA* onto $E'F'A'$. Inasmuch as any point in the semi-elliptical region in the w plane lies on one and only one of the semi-ellipses, or on the limiting case $E'F'A'$, that point is the image of exactly one point in the rectangular region in the z plane. The desired mapping, which is also shown in Fig. 11 of Appendix 2, is now established.

106. SOME RELATED MAPPINGS

Mappings by various other functions closely related to the sine function are easily obtained once mappings by the sine function are known.

EXAMPLE 1. One need only recall the identity (Sec. 37)

$$\sin\left(z+\frac{\pi}{2}\right) = \cos z$$

to see that the transformation $w = \cos z$ can be written successively as

$$Z = z + \frac{\pi}{2}, \quad w = \sin Z.$$

Hence the cosine transformation is the same as the sine transformation preceded by a translation to the right through $\pi/2$ units.

EXAMPLE 2. According to Sec. 39, the transformation $w = \sinh z$ can be written $w = -i\sin(iz)$, or

$$Z = iz, \quad W = \sin Z, \quad w = -iW.$$

It is, therefore, a combination of the sine transformation and rotations through right angles. The transformation $w = \cosh z$ is, likewise, essentially a cosine transformation since $\cosh z = \cos(iz)$.

EXAMPLE 3. With the aid of the identities

$$\sin\left(z+\frac{\pi}{2}\right) = \cos z \quad \text{and} \quad \cos(iz) = \cosh z$$

that were used in the two examples just above, one can write the transformation $w = \cosh z$ as

$$(1) \qquad Z = iz + \frac{\pi}{2}, \quad w = \sin Z.$$

Let us now use transformations (1) to find the image of the horizontal semi-infinite strip

$$x \geq 0,\ 0 \leq y \leq \pi/2$$

under the transformation $w = \cosh z$.

The first of transformations (1) is a rotation of the given strip through a right angle in the positive direction followed by a translation $\pi/2$ units to the right, as shown in Fig. 131. The transformation $w = \sin Z$ then maps the resulting strip onto the first

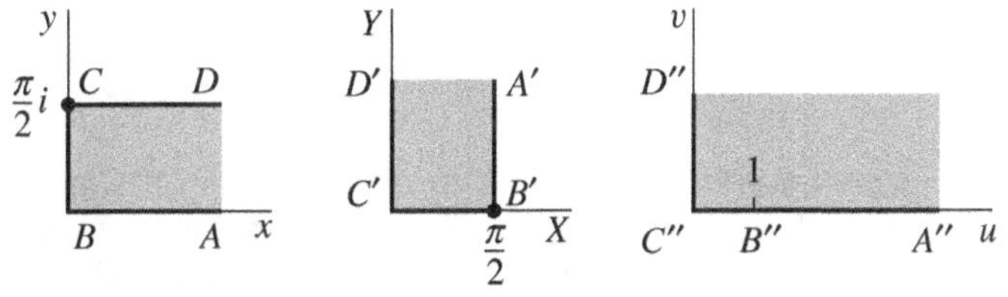

FIGURE 131
$w = \cosh z$.

quadrant of the w plane, as pointed out at the end of Sec. 104 and shown in Fig. 10, Appendix 2. It is left to the reader to verify corresponding boundary points of the given strip and the first quadrant that are labeled in Fig. 131.

EXERCISES

1. Show that the lines $ay = x$ $(a \neq 0)$ are mapped onto the spirals $\rho = \exp(a\phi)$ under the transformation $w = \exp z$, where $w = \rho \exp(i\phi)$.

2. By considering the images of *horizontal* line segments, verify that the image of the rectangular region $a \leq x \leq b, c \leq y \leq d$ under the transformation $w = \exp z$ is the region $e^a \leq \rho \leq e^b, c \leq \phi \leq d$, as shown in Fig. 125 (Sec. 103).

3. Verify the mapping of the region and boundary shown in Fig. 7 of Appendix 2, where the transformation is $w = \exp z$.

4. Find the image of the semi-infinite strip $x \geq 0, 0 \leq y \leq \pi$ under the transformation $w = \exp z$, and label corresponding portions of the boundaries.

5. Show that the transformation $w = \sin z$ maps the top half $(y > 0)$ of the vertical line $x = c_1$ $(-\pi/2 < c_1 < 0)$ in a one to one manner onto the top half $(v > 0)$ of the left-hand branch of hyperbola (3), Sec. 104, as indicated in Fig. 128 of that section.

6. Show that under the transformation $w = \sin z$, a line $x = c_1$ $(\pi/2 < c_1 < \pi)$ is mapped onto the right-hand branch of hyperbola (3), Sec. 104. Note that the mapping is one to one and that the upper and lower halves of the line are mapped onto the *lower* and *upper* halves, respectively, of the branch.

7. Vertical half lines were used in the example in Sec. 104 to show that the transformation $w = \sin z$ is a one to one mapping of the open region $-\pi/2 < x < \pi/2, y > 0$ onto the half plane $v > 0$. Verify that result by using, instead, the *horizontal* line segments $y = c_2$ $(-\pi/2 < x < \pi/2)$, where $c_2 > 0$.

8. (*a*) Show that under the transformation $w = \sin z$, the images of the line segments forming the boundary of the rectangular region $0 \leq x \leq \pi/2, 0 \leq y \leq 1$ are the line segments and the arc $D'E'$ shown in Fig. 132. The arc $D'E'$ is a quarter of the

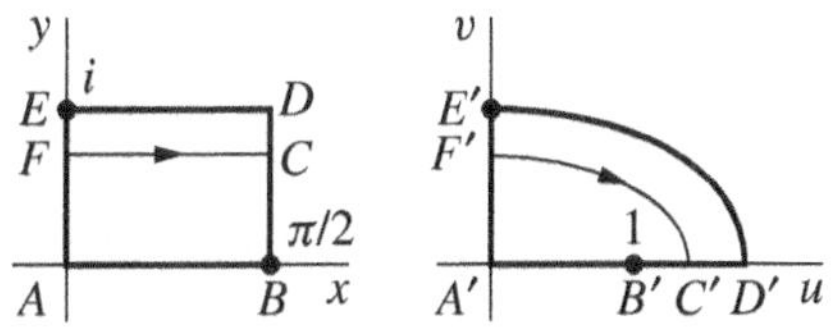

FIGURE 132
$w = \sin z$.

ellipse

$$\frac{u^2}{\cosh^2 1} + \frac{v^2}{\sinh^2 1} = 1.$$

(*b*) Complete the mapping indicated in Fig. 132 by using images of horizontal line segments to prove that the transformation $w = \sin z$ establishes a one to one correspondence between the interior points of the regions $ABDE$ and $A'B'D'E'$.

9. Verify that the interior of a rectangular region $-\pi \le x \le \pi, a \le y \le b$ lying above the x axis is mapped by $w = \sin z$ onto the interior of an elliptical ring which has a cut along the segment $-\sinh b \le v \le -\sinh a$ of the negative imaginary axis, as indicated in Fig. 133. Note that while the mapping of the interior of the rectangular region is one to one, the mapping of its boundary is *not*.

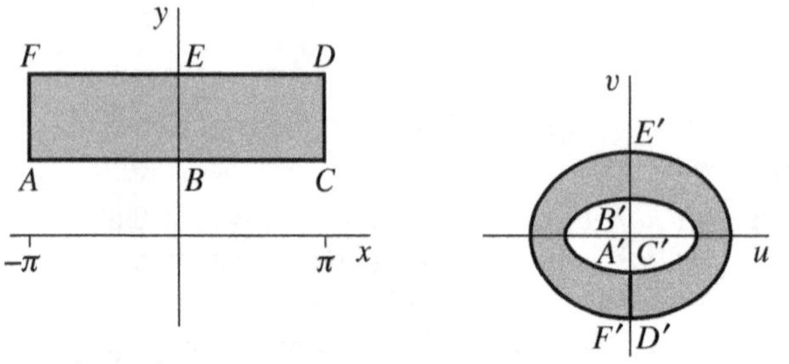

FIGURE 133
$w = \sin z$.

10. Observe that the transformation $w = \cosh z$ can be expressed as a composition of the mappings

$$Z = e^z, \quad W = Z + \frac{1}{Z}, \quad w = \frac{1}{2}W.$$

Then, by referring to Figs. 7 and 16 in Appendix 2, show that when $w = \cosh z$, the semi-infinite strip $x \le 0, 0 \le y \le \pi$ in the z plane is mapped onto the lower half $v \le 0$ of the w plane. Indicate corresponding parts of the boundaries.

11. (*a*) Verify that the equation $w = \sin z$ can be written

$$Z = i\left(z + \frac{\pi}{2}\right), \quad W = \cosh Z, \quad w = -W.$$

(*b*) Use the result in part (*a*) here and the one in Exercise 10 to show that the transformation $w = \sin z$ maps the semi-infinite strip $-\pi/2 \le x \le \pi/2, y \ge 0$ onto the half plane $v \ge 0$, as shown in Fig. 9, Appendix 2. (This mapping was verified in a different way in the example in Sec. 104 and in Exercise 7.)

107. MAPPINGS BY z^2

In Chap 2 (Sec. 14), we considered some fairly simple mappings under the transformation $w = z^2$, written in the form

$$u = x^2 - y^2, \quad v = 2xy. \tag{1}$$

We turn now to a less elementary example and then (Sec. 108) examine related mappings $w = z^{1/2}$, where specific branches of the square root function are taken.

EXAMPLE 1. Let us use equations (1) to show that the image of the vertical strip $0 \le x \le 1$, $y \ge 0$, shown in Fig. 134, is the closed semiparabolic region indicated there.

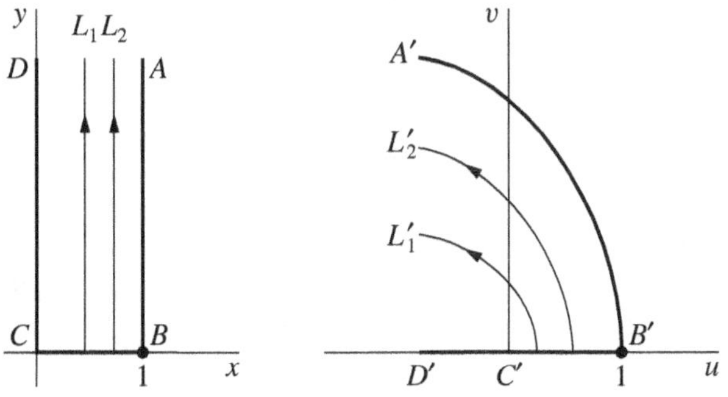

FIGURE 134
$w = z^2$.

When $0 < x_1 < 1$, the point (x_1, y) moves up a vertical half line, labeled L_1 in Fig. 134, as y increases from $y = 0$. The image traced out in the uv plane has, according to equations (1), the parametric representation

$$(2) \qquad u = x_1^2 - y^2, \quad v = 2x_1 y \qquad (0 \le y < \infty).$$

Using the second of these equations to substitute for y in the first one, we see that the image points (u, v) must lie on the parabola

$$(3) \qquad v^2 = -4x_1^2(u - x_1^2),$$

with vertex at $(x_1^2, 0)$ and focus at the origin. Since v increases with y from $v = 0$, according to the second of equations (2), we also see that as the point (x_1, y) moves up L_1 from the x axis, its image moves up the top half L_1' of the parabola from the u axis. Furthermore, when a number x_2 larger than x_1 but less than 1 is taken, the corresponding half line L_2 has an image L_2' that is a half parabola to the right of L_1', as indicated in Fig. 134. We note, in fact, that the image of the half line BA in that figure is the top half of the parabola $v^2 = -4(u - 1)$, labeled $B'A'$.

The image of the half line CD is found by observing from equations (1) that a typical point $(0, y)$, where $y \ge 0$, on CD is transformed into the point $(-y^2, 0)$ in the uv plane. So, as a point moves up from the origin along CD, its image moves left from the origin along the u axis. Evidently, then, as the vertical half lines in the xy plane move to the left, the half parabolas that are their images in the uv plane shrink down to become the half line $C'D'$.

It is now clear that the images of all the half lines between and including CD and BA fill up the closed semiparabolic region bounded by $A'B'C'D'$. Also, each point in that region is the image of only one point in the closed strip bounded by $ABCD$. Hence we may conclude that the semiparabolic region is the image of the strip and that there is a one to one correspondence between points in those closed regions. (Compare with Fig. 3 in Appendix 2, where the strip has arbitrary width.)

Mappings that are compositions of z^2 and other elementary functions are often interesting and useful.

EXAMPLE 2. Let us show that the transformation $w = \sin^2 z$ maps the semi-infinite vertical strip $0 \le x \le \pi/2$, $y \ge 0$ onto the upper half plane $v \ge 0$. We do this by writing

$$Z = \sin z, \quad w = Z^2 \tag{4}$$

and noting that the first of these transformations maps the given region in the z plane into the Z plane as shown in Fig. 135. (See the last paragraph in Sec. 104 and also Fig. 10 in Appendix 2.) The second of transformations (4) then maps the first quadrant in the Z plane onto the upper half of the w plane. This second mapping is evident from the discussion of the transformation $w = z^2$ in Sec. 14 (Chap. 2).

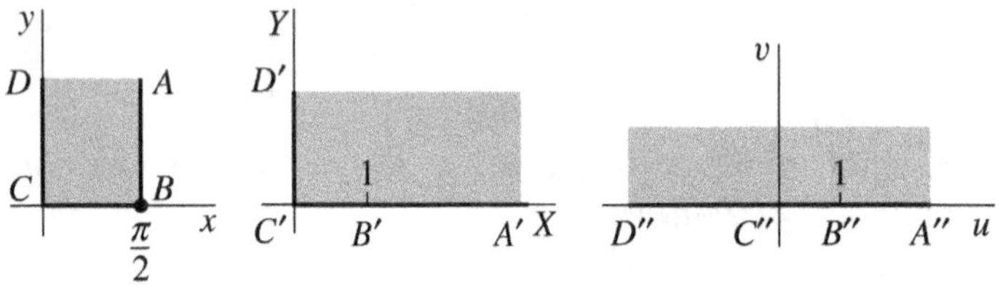

FIGURE 135
$w = \sin^2 z$.

108. MAPPINGS BY BRANCHES OF $z^{1/2}$

We turn now to mappings by branches of the square root function and recall from Sec. 10 in Chap. 1 how the square roots of $z^{1/2}$ were defined when $z \neq 0$. According to that section, if polar coordinates are used and

$$z = r\exp(i\Theta) \qquad (r > 0, -\pi < \Theta \le \pi),$$

then

$$z^{1/2} = \sqrt{r}\exp\frac{i(\Theta + 2k\pi)}{2} \qquad (k = 0, 1), \tag{1}$$

the principal root occurring when $k = 0$. In Sec. 34, we saw that $z^{1/2}$ can also be written

$$z^{1/2} = \exp\left(\frac{1}{2}\log z\right) \qquad (z \neq 0). \tag{2}$$

The ***principal branch*** $F_0(z)$ of the double-valued function $z^{1/2}$ is then obtained by taking the principal branch of $\log z$ and writing (see Sec. 35)

$$F_0(z) = \exp\left(\frac{1}{2}\operatorname{Log} z\right) \qquad (|z| > 0, -\pi < \operatorname{Arg} z < \pi).$$

Since

$$\frac{1}{2}\operatorname{Log} z = \frac{1}{2}(\ln r + i\Theta) = \ln\sqrt{r} + \frac{i\Theta}{2}$$

when $z = r\exp(i\Theta)$, this becomes

$$F_0(z) = \sqrt{r}\exp\frac{i\Theta}{2} \qquad (r > 0, -\pi < \Theta < \pi). \tag{3}$$

The right-hand side of this equation is, of course, the same as the right-hand side of equation (1) when $k = 0$ and $-\pi < \Theta < \pi$ there. The origin and the ray $\Theta = \pi$ form the branch cut for F_0, and the origin is the branch point.

Images of curves and regions under the transformation $w = F_0(z)$ may be obtained by writing $w = \rho\exp(i\phi)$, where $\rho = \sqrt{r}$ and $\phi = \Theta/2$. Arguments are evidently halved by this transformation, and it is understood that $w = 0$ when $z = 0$.

EXAMPLE. It is easy to verify that $w = F_0(z)$ is a one to one mapping of the quarter disk $0 \le r \le 2, 0 \le \theta \le \pi/2$ onto the sector $0 \le \rho \le \sqrt{2}, 0 \le \phi \le \pi/4$ in the w plane (Fig. 136). To do this, we observe that as a point $z = r\exp(i\theta_1)$ moves outward from the origin along a radius R_1 of length 2 and with angle of inclination θ_1 $(0 \le \theta_1 \le \pi/2)$, its image $w = \sqrt{r}\exp(i\theta_1/2)$ moves outward from the origin in the w plane along a radius R_1' whose length is $\sqrt{2}$ and angle of inclination is $\theta_1/2$. See Fig. 136, where another radius R_2 and its image R_2' are also shown. It is now clear from the figure that if the region in the z plane is thought of as being swept out by a radius, starting with DA and ending with DC, then the region in the w plane is swept out by the corresponding radius, starting with $D'A'$ and ending with $D'C'$. This establishes a one to one correspondence between points in the two regions.

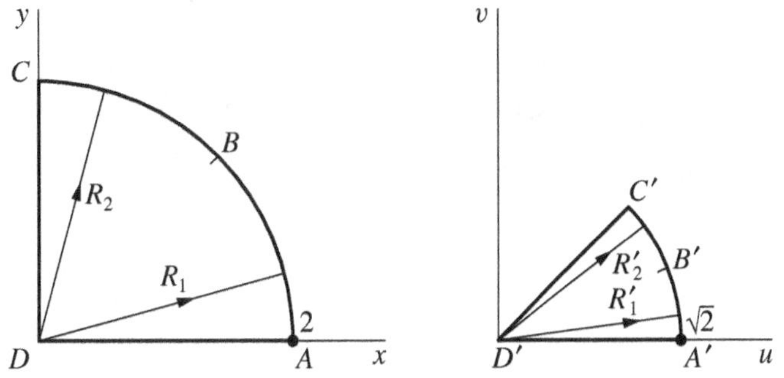

FIGURE 136
$w = F_0(z)$.

When $-\pi < \Theta < \pi$ and the branch

$$\log z = \ln r + i(\Theta + 2\pi)$$

of the logarithmic function is used, equation (2) yields the branch

$$F_1(z) = \sqrt{r}\exp\frac{i(\Theta + 2\pi)}{2} \qquad (r > 0, -\pi < \Theta < \pi) \tag{4}$$

of $z^{1/2}$, which corresponds to $k = 1$ in equation (1). Since $\exp(i\pi) = -1$, it follows that $F_1(z) = -F_0(z)$. The values $\pm F_0(z)$ thus represent the totality of values of $z^{1/2}$

at all points in the domain $r > 0, -\pi < \Theta < \pi$. If, by means of expression (3), we extend the domain of definition of F_0 to include the ray $\Theta = \pi$ and if we write $F_0(0) = 0$, then the values $\pm F_0(z)$ represent the totality of values of $z^{1/2}$ in the entire z plane.

Other branches of $z^{1/2}$ are obtained by using other branches of $\log z$ in expression (2). A branch where the ray $\theta = \alpha$ is used to form the branch cut is given by the equation

$$(5) \qquad f_\alpha(z) = \sqrt{r}\exp\frac{i\theta}{2} \qquad (r > 0, \alpha < \theta < \alpha + 2\pi).$$

Observe that when $\alpha = -\pi$, we have the branch $F_0(z)$ and that when $\alpha = \pi$, we have the branch $F_1(z)$. Just as in the case of F_0, the domain of definition of f_α can be extended to the entire complex plane by using expression (5) to define f_α at the nonzero points on the branch cut and by writing $f_\alpha(0) = 0$. Such extensions are, however, never continuous on the entire complex plane.

Finally, suppose that n is any positive integer, where $n \geq 2$. The values of $z^{1/n}$ are the nth roots of z when $z \neq 0$; and, according to Sec. 34, the multiple-valued function $z^{1/n}$ can be written

$$(6) \quad z^{1/n} = \exp\left(\frac{1}{n}\log z\right) = \sqrt[n]{r}\exp\frac{i(\Theta + 2k\pi)}{n} \qquad (k = 0, 1, 2, \ldots, n-1),$$

where $r = |z|$ and $\Theta = \operatorname{Arg} z$. The case $n = 2$ has just been considered. In the general case, each of the n functions

$$(7) \qquad F_k(z) = \sqrt[n]{r}\exp\frac{i(\Theta + 2k\pi)}{n} \qquad (k = 0, 1, 2, \ldots, n-1)$$

is a branch of $z^{1/n}$, defined on the domain $r > 0, -\pi < \Theta < \pi$. When $w = \rho e^{i\phi}$, the transformation $w = F_k(z)$ is a one to one mapping of that domain onto the domain

$$\rho > 0, \quad \frac{(2k-1)\pi}{n} < \phi < \frac{(2k+1)\pi}{n}.$$

These n branches of $z^{1/n}$ yield the n distinct nth roots of z at any point z in the domain $r > 0, -\pi < \Theta < \pi$. The principal branch occurs when $k = 0$, and further branches of the type (5) are readily constructed.

EXERCISES

1. Show, indicating corresponding orientations, that the mapping $w = z^2$ transforms horizontal lines $y = y_1$ $(y_1 > 0)$ into parabolas $v^2 = 4y_1^2(u + y_1^2)$, all with foci at the origin $w = 0$. (Compare with Example 1, Sec. 107.)

2. Use the result in Exercise 1 to show that the transformation $w = z^2$ is a one to one mapping of a horizontal strip $a \leq y \leq b$ above the x axis onto the closed region between the two parabolas

$$v^2 = 4a^2(u + a^2), \quad v^2 = 4b^2(u + b^2).$$

3. Point out how it follows from the discussion in Example 1, Sec. 107, that the transformation $w = z^2$ maps a vertical strip $0 \le x \le c, y \ge 0$ of arbitrary width onto a closed semiparabolic region, as shown in Fig. 3, Appendix 2.

4. Modify the discussion in Example 1, Sec. 107, to show that when $w = z^2$, the image of the closed triangular region formed by the lines $y = \pm x$ and $x = 1$ is the closed parabolic region bounded on the left by the segment $-2 \le v \le 2$ of the v axis and on the right by a portion of the parabola $v^2 = -4(u - 1)$. Verify the corresponding points on the two boundaries shown in Fig. 137.

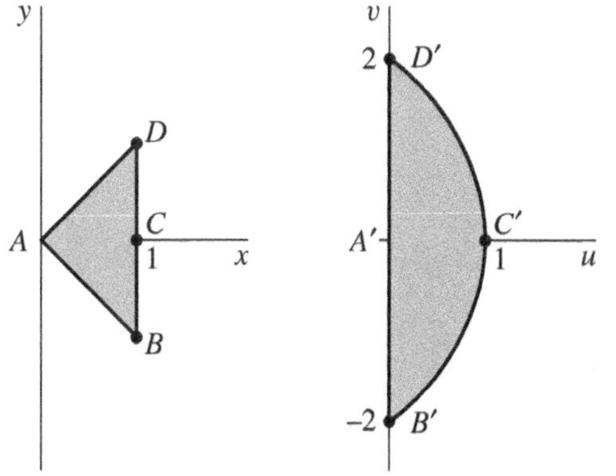

FIGURE 137
$w = z^2$.

5. Write the transformation $w = F_0(\sin z)$ as

$$Z = \sin z, \quad w = F_0(Z) \qquad (|Z| > 0, \ -\pi < \operatorname{Arg} z < \pi).$$

With the understanding that $F_0(0) = 0$, show that $w = F_0(\sin z)$ maps the vertical semi-infinite strip $0 \le x \le \pi/2, \ y \ge 0$ onto the octant in the w plane that is shown on the far right in Fig. 138. (Compare this exercise with Example 2 in Sec. 107.)

Suggestion: See the last sentence in Sec. 104.

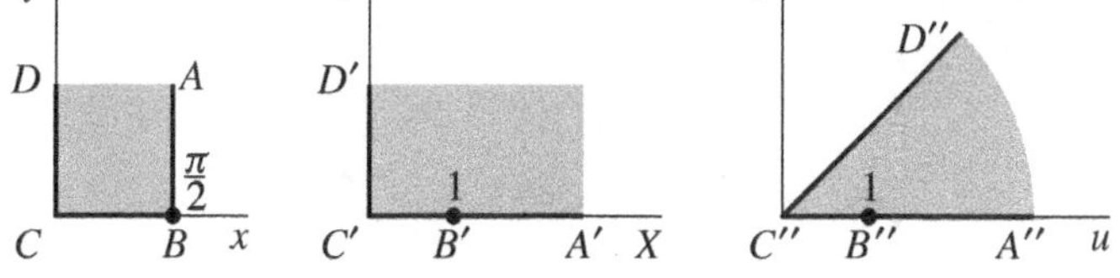

FIGURE 138
$w = F_0(\sin z)$.

6. Use Fig. 9, Appendix 2, to show that if $w = (\sin z)^{1/4}$ and the principal branch of the fractional power is taken, then the semi-infinite strip $-\pi/2 < x < \pi/2, y > 0$ is mapped onto the part of the first quadrant lying between the line $v = u$ and the u axis. Label corresponding parts of the boundaries.

7. According to Example 2, Sec. 102, the linear fractional transformation

$$Z = \frac{z - 1}{z + 1}$$

maps the x axis onto the X axis and the half planes $y > 0$ and $y < 0$ onto the half planes $Y > 0$ and $Y < 0$, respectively. Show that, in particular, it maps the segment $-1 \le x \le 1$ of the x axis onto the segment $X \le 0$ of the X axis. Then show that when the principal branch of the square root is used, the composite function

$$w = Z^{1/2} = \left(\frac{z-1}{z+1}\right)^{1/2}$$

maps the z plane, except for the segment $-1 \le x \le 1$ of the x axis, onto the right half plane $u > 0$.

8. Determine the image of the domain $r > 0$, $-\pi < \Theta < \pi$ in the z plane under each of the transformations $w = F_k(z)$ $(k = 0, 1, 2, 3)$, where $F_k(z)$ are the four branches of $z^{1/4}$ given by equation (7), Sec. 108, when $n = 4$. Use these branches to determine the fourth roots of i.

109. SQUARE ROOTS OF POLYNOMIALS

The remaining three sections of this chapter deal with aspects of multiple-valued functions that will not be used to any extent in the chapters that follow, and the reader may skip to Chap. 9 without serious disruption.

EXAMPLE 1. Branches of the double-valued function $(z - z_0)^{1/2}$ can be obtained by noting that it is a composition of the translation $Z = z - z_0$ and the double-valued function $Z^{1/2}$. Each branch of $Z^{1/2}$ yields a branch of $(z-z_0)^{1/2}$. More precisely, when $Z = Re^{i\theta}$, branches of $Z^{1/2}$ are

$$Z^{1/2} = \sqrt{R}\exp\frac{i\theta}{2} \qquad (R > 0, \alpha < \theta < \alpha + 2\pi),$$

according to equation (5) in Sec. 108. Hence if we write

$$R = |z - z_0|, \quad \Theta = \text{Arg}\,(z - z_0), \quad \text{and} \quad \theta = \arg(z - z_0),$$

two branches of $(z - z_0)^{1/2}$ are

$$G_0(z) = \sqrt{R}\exp\frac{i\Theta}{2} \qquad (R > 0, -\pi < \Theta < \pi) \tag{1}$$

and

$$g_0(z) = \sqrt{R}\exp\frac{i\theta}{2} \qquad (R > 0, 0 < \theta < 2\pi). \tag{2}$$

The branch of $Z^{1/2}$ that was used in writing $G_0(z)$ is defined at all points in the Z plane except for the origin and points on the ray $\text{Arg}\, Z = \pi$. The transformation $w = G_0(z)$ is, therefore, a one to one mapping of the domain

$$|z - z_0| > 0, \quad -\pi < \text{Arg}\,(z - z_0) < \pi$$

onto the right half Re $w > 0$ of the w plane (Fig. 139). The transformation $w = g_0(z)$ maps the domain

$$|z - z_0| > 0, \quad 0 < \arg(z - z_0) < 2\pi$$

in a one to one manner onto the upper half plane Im $w > 0$.

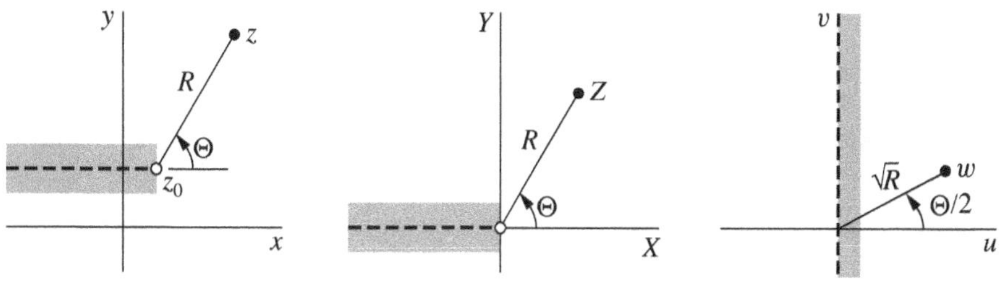

FIGURE 139
$w = G_0(z)$.

EXAMPLE 2. For an instructive but less elementary example, we now consider the double-valued function $(z^2 - 1)^{1/2}$. Using established properties of logarithms, one can write

$$(z^2 - 1)^{1/2} = \exp\left[\frac{1}{2}\log(z^2 - 1)\right] = \exp\left[\frac{1}{2}\log(z - 1) + \frac{1}{2}\log(z + 1)\right],$$

or

$$(z^2 - 1)^{1/2} = (z - 1)^{1/2}(z + 1)^{1/2} \qquad (z \neq \pm 1). \tag{3}$$

Consequently, if $f_1(z)$ is a branch of $(z - 1)^{1/2}$ defined on a domain D_1 and $f_2(z)$ is a branch of $(z + 1)^{1/2}$ defined on a domain D_2, the product $f(z) = f_1(z)f_2(z)$ is a branch of $(z^2 - 1)^{1/2}$ defined at all points lying in both D_1 and D_2.

In order to obtain a specific branch of $(z^2 - 1)^{1/2}$, we use the branch of $(z - 1)^{1/2}$ and the branch of $(z + 1)^{1/2}$ given by equation (2). If we write

$$r_1 = |z - 1| \quad \text{and} \quad \theta_1 = \arg(z - 1),$$

that branch of $(z - 1)^{1/2}$ is

$$f_1(z) = \sqrt{r_1}\exp\frac{i\theta_1}{2} \qquad (r_1 > 0, 0 < \theta_1 < 2\pi).$$

The branch of $(z + 1)^{1/2}$ given by equation (2) is

$$f_2(z) = \sqrt{r_2}\exp\frac{i\theta_2}{2} \qquad (r_2 > 0, 0 < \theta_2 < 2\pi),$$

where

$$r_2 = |z+1| \quad \text{and} \quad \theta_2 = \arg(z+1).$$

The product of these two branches is, therefore, the branch f of $(z^2-1)^{1/2}$ defined by means of the equation

$$f(z) = \sqrt{r_1 r_2} \exp \frac{i(\theta_1+\theta_2)}{2}, \tag{4}$$

where

$$r_k > 0, \quad 0 < \theta_k < 2\pi \qquad (k = 1, 2).$$

As illustrated in Fig. 140, the branch f is defined everywhere in the z plane except on the ray $r_2 \geq 0, \theta_2 = 0$, which is the portion $x \geq -1$ of the x axis.

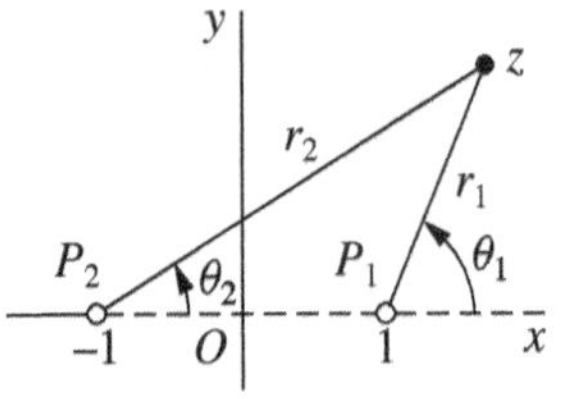

FIGURE 140

The branch f of $(z^2-1)^{1/2}$ given in equation (4) can be extended to a function

$$F(z) = \sqrt{r_1 r_2} \exp \frac{i(\theta_1+\theta_2)}{2}, \tag{5}$$

where

$$r_k > 0, \quad 0 \leq \theta_k < 2\pi \quad (k = 1, 2) \qquad \text{and} \qquad r_1 + r_2 > 2.$$

As we shall now see, this function is analytic everywhere in its domain of definition, which is the entire z plane except for the segment $-1 \leq x \leq 1$ of the x axis.

Since $F(z) = f(z)$ for all z in the domain of definition of F except on the ray $r_1 > 0, \theta_1 = 0$, we need only show that F is analytic on that ray. To do this, we form the product of the branches of $(z-1)^{1/2}$ and $(z+1)^{1/2}$ which are given by equation (1). That is, we consider the function

$$G(z) = \sqrt{r_1 r_2} \exp \frac{i(\Theta_1+\Theta_2)}{2},$$

where

$$r_1 = |z-1|, \quad r_2 = |z+1|, \quad \Theta_1 = \text{Arg}\,(z-1), \quad \Theta_2 = \text{Arg}\,(z+1)$$

and where

$$r_k > 0, \quad -\pi < \Theta_k < \pi \qquad (k = 1, 2).$$

Observe that G is analytic in the entire z plane except for the ray $r_1 \geq 0, \Theta_1 = \pi$. Now $F(z) = G(z)$ when the point z lies above or on the ray $r_1 > 0, \Theta_1 = 0$; for then $\theta_k = \Theta_k$ $(k = 1, 2)$. When z lies below that ray, $\theta_k = \Theta_k + 2\pi$ $(k = 1, 2)$.

Consequently, $\exp(i\theta_k/2) = -\exp(i\Theta_k/2)$; and this means that

$$\exp\frac{i(\theta_1+\theta_2)}{2} = \left(\exp\frac{i\theta_1}{2}\right)\left(\exp\frac{i\theta_2}{2}\right) = \exp\frac{i(\Theta_1+\Theta_2)}{2}.$$

So again, $F(z) = G(z)$. Since $F(z)$ and $G(z)$ are the same in a domain containing the ray $r_1 > 0, \Theta_1 = 0$ and since G is analytic in that domain, F is analytic there. Hence *F is analytic everywhere except on the line segment P_2P_1 in* Fig. 140.

The function F defined by equation (5) cannot itself be extended to a function which is analytic at points on the line segment P_2P_1. This is because the value on the right in equation (5) jumps from $i\sqrt{r_1 r_2}$ to numbers near $-i\sqrt{r_1 r_2}$ as the point z moves downward across that line segment, and the extension would not even be continuous there.

The transformation $w = F(z)$ is, as we shall see, a one to one mapping of the domain D_z consisting of all points in the z plane except those on the line segment P_2P_1 onto the domain D_w consisting of the entire w plane with the exception of the segment $-1 \le v \le 1$ of the v axis (Fig. 141).

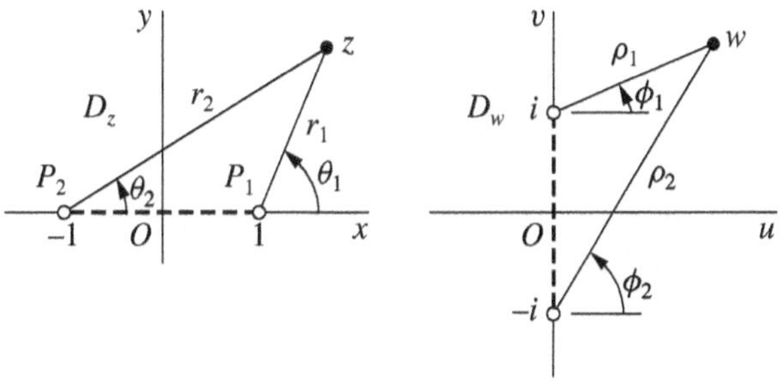

FIGURE 141
$w = F(z)$.

Before verifying this, we note that if $z = iy\ (y > 0)$, then

$$r_1 = r_2 > 1 \quad \text{and} \quad \theta_1 + \theta_2 = \pi;$$

hence the positive y axis is mapped by $w = F(z)$ onto that part of the v axis for which $v > 1$. The negative y axis is, moreover, mapped onto that part of the v axis for which $v < -1$. Each point in the upper half $y > 0$ of the domain D_z is mapped into the upper half $v > 0$ of the w plane, and each point in the lower half $y < 0$ of the domain D_z is mapped into the lower half $v < 0$ of the w plane. Also, the ray $r_1 > 0, \theta_1 = 0$ is mapped onto the positive real axis in the w plane, and the ray $r_2 > 0, \theta_2 = \pi$ is mapped onto the negative real axis there.

To show that the transformation $w = F(z)$ is *one to one*, we observe that if $F(z_1) = F(z_2)$, then $z_1^2 - 1 = z_2^2 - 1$. From this, it follows that $z_1 = z_2$ or $z_1 = -z_2$. However, because of the manner in which F maps the upper and lower halves of the domain D_z, as well as the portions of the real axis lying in D_z, the case $z_1 = -z_2$ is impossible. Thus, if $F(z_1) = F(z_2)$, then $z_1 = z_2$; and F is one to one.

We can show that F maps the domain D_z *onto* the domain D_w by finding a function H mapping D_w into D_z with the property that if $z = H(w)$, then $w = F(z)$. This will show that for any point w in D_w, there exists a point z in D_z such that $F(z) = w$; that is, the mapping F is onto. The mapping H will be the inverse of F.

To find H, we first note that if w is a value of $(z^2 - 1)^{1/2}$ for a specific z, then $w^2 = z^2 - 1$; and z is, therefore, a value of $(w^2 + 1)^{1/2}$ for that w. The function H will be a branch of the double-valued function

$$(w^2 + 1)^{1/2} = (w - i)^{1/2}(w + i)^{1/2} \qquad (w \neq \pm i).$$

Following our procedure for obtaining the function $F(z)$, we write $w - i = \rho_1 \exp(i\phi_1)$ and $w + i = \rho_2 \exp(i\phi_2)$. (See Fig. 141.) With the restrictions

$$\rho_k > 0, \ -\frac{\pi}{2} \leq \phi_k < \frac{3\pi}{2} \quad (k = 1, 2) \qquad \text{and} \qquad \rho_1 + \rho_2 > 2,$$

we then write

$$(6) \qquad H(w) = \sqrt{\rho_1 \rho_2} \exp \frac{i(\phi_1 + \phi_2)}{2},$$

the domain of definition being D_w. The transformation $z = H(w)$ maps points of D_w lying above or below the u axis onto points above or below the x axis, respectively. It maps the positive u axis into that part of the x axis where $x > 1$ and the negative u axis into that part of the negative x axis where $x < -1$. If $z = H(w)$, then $z^2 = w^2 + 1$; and so $w^2 = z^2 - 1$. Since z is in D_z and since $F(z)$ and $-F(z)$ are the two values of $(z^2 - 1)^{1/2}$ for a point in D_z, we see that $w = F(z)$ or $w = -F(z)$. But it is evident from the manner in which F and H map the upper and lower halves of their domains of definition, including the portions of the real axes lying in those domains, that $w = F(z)$.

Mappings by branches of double-valued functions

$$(7) \qquad w = (z^2 + Az + B)^{1/2} = \left[(z - z_0)^2 - z_1^2\right]^{1/2} \qquad (z_1 \neq 0),$$

where $A = -2z_0$ and $B = z_0^2 = z_1^2$, can be treated with the aid of the results found for the function F in Example 2 just above and the successive transformations

$$(8) \qquad Z = \frac{z - z_0}{z_1}, \quad W = (Z^2 - 1)^{1/2}, \quad w = z_1 W.$$

EXERCISES

1. The branch F of $(z^2 - 1)^{1/2}$ in Example 2, Sec. 109, was defined in terms of the coordinates $r_1, r_2, \theta_1, \theta_2$. Explain geometrically why the conditions $r_1 > 0, 0 < \theta_1 + \theta_2 < \pi$ describe the first quadrant $x > 0, y > 0$ of the z plane. Then show that $w = F(z)$ maps that quadrant onto the first quadrant $u > 0, v > 0$ of the w plane.

Suggestion: To show that the quadrant $x > 0, y > 0$ in the z plane is described, note that $\theta_1 + \theta_2 = \pi$ at each point on the positive y axis and that $\theta_1 + \theta_2$ decreases as a point z moves to the right along a ray $\theta_2 = c \ (0 < c < \pi/2)$.

2. For the mapping $w = F(z)$ of the first quadrant in the z plane onto the first quadrant in the w plane in Exercise 1, show that

$$u = \frac{1}{\sqrt{2}}\sqrt{r_1 r_2 + x^2 - y^2 - 1} \quad \text{and} \quad v = \frac{1}{\sqrt{2}}\sqrt{r_1 r_2 - x^2 + y^2 + 1},$$

where

$$(r_1 r_2)^2 = (x^2 + y^2 + 1)^2 - 4x^2,$$

and that the image of the portion of the hyperbola $x^2 - y^2 = 1$ in the first quadrant is the ray $v = u$ $(u > 0)$.

3. Show that in Exercise 2 the domain D that lies under the hyperbola and in the first quadrant of the z plane is described by the conditions $r_1 > 0, 0 < \theta_1 + \theta_2 < \pi/2$. Then show that the image of D is the octant $0 < v < u$. Sketch the domain D and its image.

4. Let F be the branch of $(z^2 - 1)^{1/2}$ that was defined in Example 2, Sec. 109, and let $z_0 = r_0 \exp(i\theta_0)$ be a fixed complex number, where $r_0 > 0$ and $0 \le \theta_0 < 2\pi$. Show that a branch F_0 of $(z^2 - z_0^2)^{1/2}$ whose branch cut is the line segment between the points z_0 and $-z_0$ can be written $F_0(z) = z_0 F(Z)$, where $Z = z/z_0$.

5. Write $z - 1 = r_1 \exp(i\theta_1)$ and $z + 1 = r_2 \exp(i\Theta_2)$, where

$$0 < \theta_1 < 2\pi \quad \text{and} \quad -\pi < \Theta_2 < \pi,$$

to define a branch of the function

(*a*) $(z^2 - 1)^{1/2}$;

(*b*) $\left(\dfrac{z-1}{z+1}\right)^{1/2}$.

In each case, the branch cut should consist of the two rays $\theta_1 = 0$ and $\Theta_2 = \pi$.

6. Using the notation in Sec. 109, show that the function

$$w = \left(\frac{z-1}{z+1}\right)^{1/2} = \sqrt{\frac{r_1}{r_2}} \exp \frac{i(\theta_1 - \theta_2)}{2}$$

is a branch with the same domain of definition D_z and the same branch cut as the function $w = F(z)$ in that section. Show that this transformation maps D_z onto the right half plane $\rho > 0, -\pi/2 < \phi < \pi/2$, where the point $w = 1$ is the image of the point $z = \infty$. Also, show that the inverse transformation is

$$z = \frac{1 + w^2}{1 - w^2} \qquad (\operatorname{Re} w > 0).$$

(Compare with Exercise 7, Sec. 108.)

7. Show that the transformation in Exercise 6 maps the region outside the unit circle $|z| = 1$ in the upper half of the z plane onto the region in the first quadrant of the w plane between the line $v = u$ and the u axis. Sketch the two regions.

8. Write $z = r\exp(i\Theta)$, $z - 1 = r_1 \exp(i\Theta_1)$, and $z + 1 = r_2 \exp(i\Theta_2)$, where the values of all three arguments lie between $-\pi$ and π. Then define a branch of the function $[z(z^2 - 1)]^{1/2}$ whose branch cut consists of the two segments $x \le -1$ and $0 \le x \le 1$ of the x axis.

110. RIEMANN SURFACES

This and the following section constitute a brief introduction to the concept of a mapping defined on a ***Riemann surface***, which is a generalization of the complex plane consisting of more than one sheet. The theory rests on the fact that at each point on such a surface only one value of a given multiple-valued function is assigned.

Once a Riemann surface is devised for a given function, the function is single-valued on the surface and the theory of single-valued functions applies there. Complexities arising because the function is multiple-valued are thus relieved by a geometric device. However, the description of those surfaces and the arrangement of proper connections between the sheets can become quite involved. We limit our attention to fairly simple examples and begin with a surface for $\log z$.

EXAMPLE 1. Corresponding to each nonzero number z, the multiple-valued function

$$\log z = \ln r + i\theta \tag{1}$$

has infinitely many values. To describe $\log z$ as a single-valued function, we replace the z plane, with the origin deleted, by a surface on which a new point is located whenever the argument of the number z is increased or decreased by 2π, or an integral multiple of 2π.

We treat the z plane, with the origin deleted, as a thin sheet R_0 which is cut along the positive half of the real axis. On that sheet, let θ range from 0 to 2π. Let a second sheet R_1 be cut in the same way and placed in front of the sheet R_0. The lower edge of the slit in R_0 is then joined to the upper edge of the slit in R_1. On R_1, the angle θ ranges from 2π to 4π; so, when z is represented by a point on R_1, the imaginary component of $\log z$ ranges from 2π to 4π.

A sheet R_2 is then cut in the same way and placed in front of R_1. The lower edge of the slit in R_1 is joined to the upper edge of the slit in this new sheet, and similarly for sheets $R_3, R_4, \ldots$. A sheet R_{-1} on which θ varies from 0 to -2π is cut and placed behind R_0, with the lower edge of its slit connected to the upper edge of the slit in R_0; the sheets $R_{-2}, R_{-3}, \ldots$ are constructed in like manner. The coordinates r and θ of a point on any sheet can be considered as polar coordinates of the projection of the point onto the original z plane, the angular coordinate θ being restricted to a definite range of 2π radians on each sheet.

Consider any continuous curve on this connected surface of infinitely many sheets. As a point z describes that curve, the values of $\log z$ vary continuously since θ, in addition to r, varies continuously; and $\log z$ now assumes just one value corresponding to each point on the curve. For example, as the point makes a complete cycle around the origin on the sheet R_0 over the path indicated in Fig. 142, the angle changes from 0 to 2π. As it moves across the ray $\theta = 2\pi$, the point passes to the sheet R_1 of the surface. As the point completes a cycle in R_1, the angle θ varies from 2π to 4π; and as it crosses the ray $\theta = 4\pi$, the point passes to the sheet R_2.

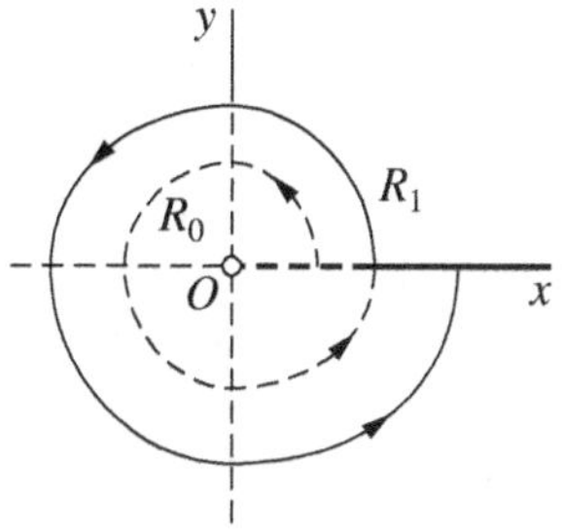

FIGURE 142

The surface described here is a Riemann surface for $\log z$. It is a connected surface of infinitely many sheets, arranged so that $\log z$ is a single-valued function of points on it.

The transformation $w = \log z$ maps the whole Riemann surface in a one to one manner onto the entire w plane. The image of the sheet R_0 is the strip $0 \le v \le 2\pi$ (see Example 3, Sec. 102). As a point z moves onto the sheet R_1 over the arc shown in Fig. 143, its image w moves upward across the line $v = 2\pi$, as indicated in that figure.

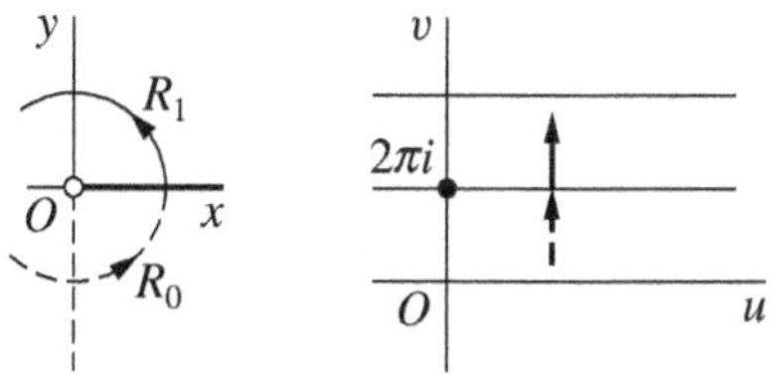

FIGURE 143

Note that $\log z$, defined on the sheet R_1, represents the analytic continuation (Sec. 28) of the single-valued analytic function

$$f(z) = \ln r + i\theta \qquad (0 < \theta < 2\pi)$$

upward across the positive real axis. In this sense, $\log z$ is not only a single-valued function of all points z on the Riemann surface but also an *analytic* function at all points there.

The sheets could, of course, be cut along the negative real axis or along any other ray from the origin, and properly joined along the slits, to form other Riemann surfaces for $\log z$.

EXAMPLE 2. Corresponding to each point in the z plane other than the origin, the square root function

$$z^{1/2} = \sqrt{r}e^{i\theta/2} \tag{2}$$

has two values. A Riemann surface for $z^{1/2}$ is obtained by replacing the z plane with a surface made up of two sheets R_0 and R_1, each cut along the positive real axis and with R_1 placed in front of R_0. The lower edge of the slit in R_0 is joined to the upper edge of the slit in R_1, and the lower edge of the slit in R_1 is joined to the upper edge of the slit in R_0.

As a point z starts from the upper edge of the slit in R_0 and describes a continuous circuit around the origin in the counterclockwise direction (Fig. 144), the angle θ increases from 0 to 2π. The point then passes from the sheet R_0 to the sheet R_1, where θ increases from 2π to 4π. As the point moves still further, it passes back to the sheet R_0, where the values of θ can vary from 4π to 6π or from 0 to 2π, a choice that does not affect the value of $z^{1/2}$, etc. Note that the value of $z^{1/2}$ at a point where the circuit passes from the sheet R_0 to the sheet R_1 is different from the value of $z^{1/2}$ at a point where the circuit passes from the sheet R_1 to the sheet R_0.

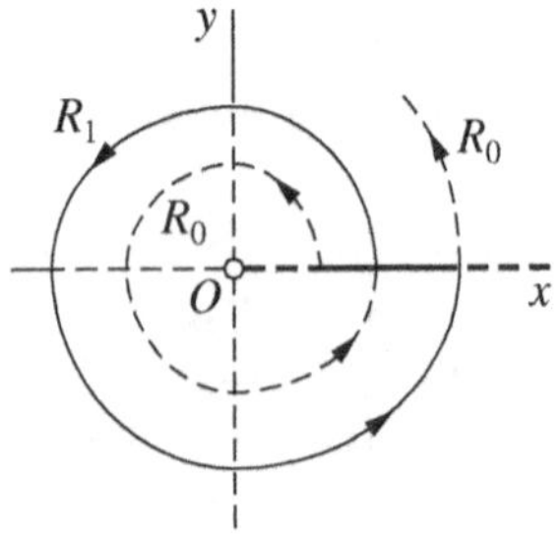

FIGURE 144

We have thus constructed a Riemann surface on which $z^{1/2}$ is single-valued for each nonzero z. In that construction, the edges of the sheets R_0 and R_1 are joined in pairs in such a way that the resulting surface is closed and connected. The points where two of the edges are joined are distinct from the points where the other two edges are joined. Thus it is physically impossible to build a model of that Riemann surface. In visualizing a Riemann surface, it is important to understand how we are to proceed when we arrive at an edge of a slit.

The origin is a special point on this Riemann surface. It is common to both sheets, and a curve around the origin on the surface must wind around it twice in order to be a closed curve. A point of this kind on a Riemann surface is called a ***branch point.***

The image of the sheet R_0 under the transformation $w = z^{1/2}$ is the upper half of the w plane since the argument of w is $\theta/2$ on R_0, where $0 \le \theta/2 \le \pi$. Likewise, the image of the sheet R_1 is the lower half of the w plane. As defined on either sheet, the function is the analytic continuation, across the cut, of the function defined on the other sheet. In this respect, the single-valued function $z^{1/2}$ of points on the Riemann surface is analytic at all points except the origin.

EXERCISES

1. Describe the Riemann surface for $\log z$ obtained by cutting the z plane along the negative real axis. Compare this Riemann surface with the one obtained in Example 1, Sec. 110.

2. Determine the image under the transformation $w = \log z$ of the sheet R_n, where n is an arbitrary integer, of the Riemann surface for $\log z$ given in Example 1, Sec. 110.

3. Verify that under the transformation $w = z^{1/2}$, the sheet R_1 of the Riemann surface for $z^{1/2}$ given in Example 2, Sec. 110, is mapped onto the lower half of the w plane.

4. Describe the curve, on a Riemann surface for $z^{1/2}$, whose image is the entire circle $|w| = 1$ under the transformation $w = z^{1/2}$.

5. Let C denote the positively oriented circle $|z-2| = 1$ on the Riemann surface described in Example 2, Sec. 110, for $z^{1/2}$, where the upper half of that circle lies on the sheet R_0 and the lower half on R_1. Note that for each point z on C, one can write

$$z^{1/2} = \sqrt{r}e^{i\theta/2} \quad \text{where} \quad 4\pi - \frac{\pi}{2} < \theta < 4\pi + \frac{\pi}{2}.$$

State why it follows that

$$\int_C z^{1/2}\,dz = 0.$$

Generalize this result to fit the case of the other simple closed curves that cross from one sheet to another without enclosing the branch points. Generalize to other functions, thus extending the Cauchy–Goursat theorem to integrals of multiple-valued functions.

111. SURFACES FOR RELATED FUNCTIONS

We consider here Riemann surfaces for two composite functions involving simple polynomials and the square root function.

EXAMPLE 1. Let us describe a Riemann surface for the double-valued function

$$(1) \qquad f(z) = (z^2-1)^{1/2} = \sqrt{r_1 r_2}\exp\frac{i(\theta_1+\theta_2)}{2},$$

where $z - 1 = r_1\exp(i\theta_1)$ and $z + 1 = r_2\exp(i\theta_2)$. A branch of this function, with the line segment P_2P_1 between the branch points $z = \pm 1$ serving as a branch cut (Fig. 145), was described in Example 2, Sec. 109. That branch is as written above, with the restrictions $r_k > 0$, $0 \le \theta_k < 2\pi$ $(k = 1, 2)$ and $r_1 + r_2 > 2$. The branch is not defined on the segment P_2P_1.

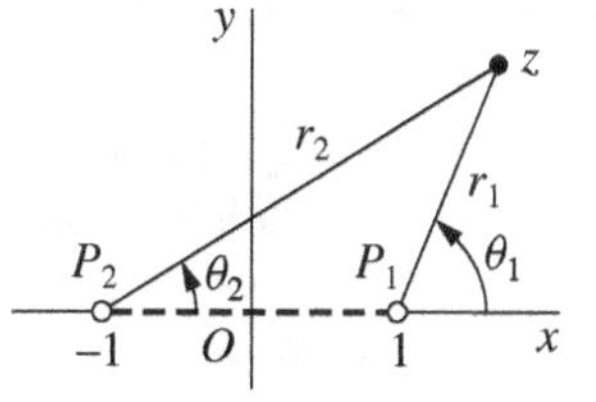

FIGURE 145

A Riemann surface for the double-valued function (1) must consist of two sheets R_0 and R_1. Let both sheets be cut along the segment P_2P_1. The lower edge of the slit in R_0 is then joined to the upper edge of the slit in R_1, and the lower edge in R_1 is joined to the upper edge in R_0.

On the sheet R_0, let the angles θ_1 and θ_2 range from 0 to 2π. If a point on the sheet R_0 describes a simple closed curve that encloses the segment P_2P_1 once in the counterclockwise direction, then both θ_1 and θ_2 change by the amount 2π upon the return of the point to its original position. The change in $(\theta_1+\theta_2)/2$ is also 2π, and the value of f is unchanged. If a point starting on the sheet R_0 describes a path that passes twice around just the branch point $z = 1$, it crosses from the sheet R_0 onto the sheet R_1 and then back onto the sheet R_0 before it returns to its original position. In this case, the value of θ_1 changes by the amount 4π, while the value of θ_2 does not change at all. Similarly, for a circuit twice around the point $z = -1$, the value of θ_2 changes by 4π, while the value of θ_1 remains unchanged. Again, the change in $(\theta_1 + \theta_2)/2$ is 2π; and the value of f is unchanged. Thus, on the sheet R_0, the range of the angles θ_1 and θ_2 may be extended by changing both θ_1 and θ_2 by the same integral multiple of 2π or by changing just one of the angles by a multiple of 4π. In either case, the total change in both angles is an even integral multiple of 2π.

To obtain the range of values for θ_1 and θ_2 on the sheet R_1, we note that if a point starts on the sheet R_0 and describes a path around just one of the branch points once, it crosses onto the sheet R_1 and does not return to the sheet R_0. In this case, the value of one of the angles is changed by 2π, while the value of the other remains unchanged. Hence, on the sheet R_1, one angle can range from 2π to 4π, while the other ranges from 0 to 2π. Their sum then ranges from 2π to 4π, and the value of $(\theta_1 + \theta_2)/2$, which is the argument of $f(z)$, ranges from π to 2π. Again, the range of the angles is extended by changing the value of just one of the angles by an integral multiple of 4π or by changing the value of both angles by the same integral multiple of 2π.

The double-valued function (1) may now be considered as a single-valued function of the points on the Riemann surface just constructed. The transformation $w = f(z)$ maps each of the sheets used in the construction of that surface onto the entire w plane.

EXAMPLE 2. Consider the double-valued function

$$f(z) = [z(z^2-1)]^{1/2} = \sqrt{rr_1r_2}\exp\frac{i(\theta+\theta_1+\theta_2)}{2} \tag{2}$$

(Fig. 146). The points $z = 0, \pm 1$ are branch points of this function. We note that if the point z describes a circuit that includes all three of those points, the argument of $f(z)$ changes by the angle 3π and the value of the function thus changes. Consequently, a branch cut must run from one of those branch points to the point at infinity in order to describe a single-valued branch of f. Hence the point at infinity is also a branch point, as one can show by noting that the function $f(1/z)$ has a branch point at $z = 0$.

Let two sheets be cut along the line segment L_2 from $z = -1$ to $z = 0$ and along the part L_1 of the real axis to the right of the point $z = 1$. We specify that each of

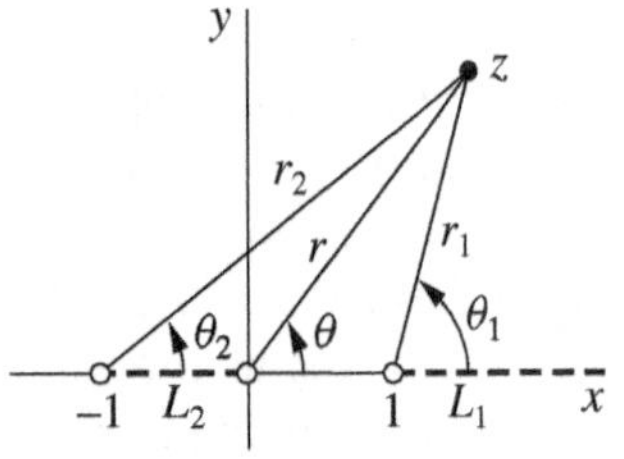

FIGURE 146

the three angles θ, θ_1, and θ_2 may range from 0 to 2π on the sheet R_0 and from 2π to 4π on the sheet R_1. We also specify that the angles corresponding to a point on either sheet may be changed by integral multiples of 2π in such a way that the sum of the three angles changes by an integral multiple of 4π. The value of the function f is, therefore, unaltered.

A Riemann surface for the double-valued function (2) is obtained by joining the lower edges in R_0 of the slits along L_1 and L_2 to the upper edges in R_1 of the slits along L_1 and L_2, respectively. The lower edges in R_1 of the slits along L_1 and L_2 are then joined to the upper edges in R_0 of the slits along L_1 and L_2, respectively. It is readily verified with the aid of Fig. 146 that one branch of the function is represented by its values at points on R_0 and the other branch at points on R_1.

EXERCISES

1. Describe a Riemann surface for the triple-valued function $w = (z-1)^{1/3}$, and point out which third of the w plane represents the image of each sheet of that surface.

2. Corresponding to each point on the Riemann surface described in Example 2, Sec. 111, for the function $w = f(z)$ in that example, there is just one value of w. Show that corresponding to each value of w, there are, in general, three points on the surface.

3. Describe a Riemann surface for the multiple-valued function

$$f(z) = \left(\frac{z-1}{z}\right)^{1/2}.$$

4. Note that the Riemann surface described in Example 1, Sec. 111, for $(z^2-1)^{1/2}$ is also a Riemann surface for the function

$$g(z) = z + (z^2-1)^{1/2}.$$

Let f_0 denote the branch of $(z^2-1)^{1/2}$ defined on the sheet R_0, and show that the branches g_0 and g_1 of g on the two sheets are given by the equations

$$g_0(z) = \frac{1}{g_1(z)} = z + f_0(z).$$

5. In Exercise 4, the branch f_0 of $(z^2-1)^{1/2}$ can be described by means of the equation

$$f_0(z) = \sqrt{r_1 r_2}\left(\exp\frac{i\theta_1}{2}\right)\left(\exp\frac{i\theta_2}{2}\right),$$

where θ_1 and θ_2 range from 0 to 2π and

$$z-1 = r_1\exp(i\theta_1), \quad z+1 = r_2\exp(i\theta_2).$$

Note that

$$2z = r_1\exp(i\theta_1) + r_2\exp(i\theta_2),$$

and show that the branch g_0 of the function $g(z) = z + (z^2 - 1)^{1/2}$ can be written in the form

$$g_0(z) = \frac{1}{2}\left(\sqrt{r_1}\exp\frac{i\theta_1}{2} + \sqrt{r_2}\exp\frac{i\theta_2}{2}\right)^2.$$

Find $g_0(z)\overline{g_0(z)}$ and note that $r_1 + r_2 \geq 2$ and $\cos[(\theta_1 - \theta_2)/2] \geq 0$ for all z, to prove that $|g_0(z)| \geq 1$. Then show that the transformation $w = z + (z^2 - 1)^{1/2}$ maps the sheet R_0 of the Riemann surface onto the region $|w| \geq 1$, the sheet R_1 onto the region $|w| \leq 1$, and the branch cut between the points $z = \pm 1$ onto the circle $|w| = 1$. Note that the transformation used here is an inverse of the transformation

$$z = \frac{1}{2}\left(w + \frac{1}{w}\right).$$

CHAPTER 9

CONFORMAL MAPPING

In this chapter, we introduce and develop the concept of a conformal mapping, with emphasis on connections between such mappings and harmonic functions (Sec. 27). Applications to physical problems will follow in Chap. 10.

112. PRESERVATION OF ANGLES AND SCALE FACTORS

Let C be a smooth arc (Sec. 43), represented by the equation

$$z = z(t) \qquad (a \le t \le b),$$

and let $f(z)$ be a function defined at all points z on C. The equation

$$w = f[z(t)] \qquad (a \le t \le b)$$

is a parametric representation of the image Γ of C under the transformation $w = f(z)$.

Suppose that C passes through a point $z_0 = z(t_0)(a < t_0 < b)$ at which f is analytic and that $f'(z_0) \ne 0$. According to the chain rule, verified in Exercise 5, Sec. 43, if $w(t) = f[z(t)]$, then

$$w'(t_0) = f'[z(t_0)]z'(t_0); \tag{1}$$

and this means that (see Sec. 9)

$$\arg w'(t_0) = \arg f'[z(t_0)] + \arg z'(t_0). \tag{2}$$

Statement (2) is useful in relating the directions of C and Γ at the points z_0 and $w_0 = f(z_0)$, respectively.

To be specific, let θ_0 denote a value of arg $z'(t_0)$ and let ϕ_0 be a value of arg $w'(t_0)$. According to the discussion of unit tangent vectors **T** near the end of Sec. 43, the number θ_0 is the angle of inclination of a directed line tangent to C at z_0 and ϕ_0 is the angle of inclination of a directed line tangent to Γ at the point $w_0 = f(z_0)$. (See Fig. 147.) In view of statement (2), there is a value ψ_0 of arg $f'[z(t_0)]$ such that

$$\phi_0 = \psi_0 + \theta_0. \tag{3}$$

Thus $\phi_0 - \theta_0 = \psi_0$, and we find that the angles ϕ_0 and θ_0 differ by the ***angle of rotation***

$$\psi_0 = \arg f'(z_0). \tag{4}$$

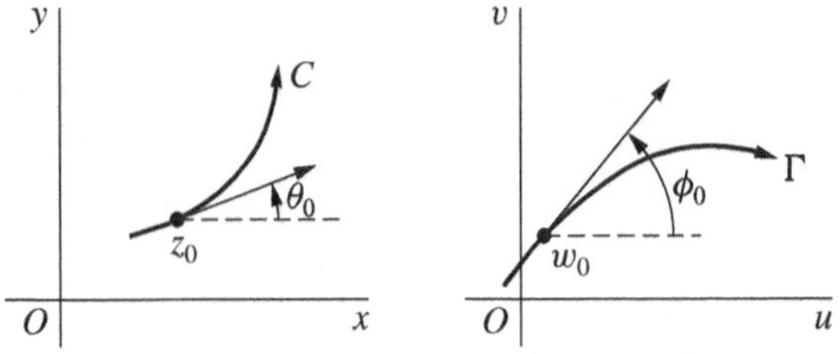

FIGURE 147
$\phi_0 = \psi_0 + \theta_0$.

Now let C_1 and C_2 be two smooth arcs passing through z_0, and let θ_1 and θ_2 be angles of inclination of directed lines tangent to C_1 and C_2, respectively, at z_0. We know from the preceding paragraph that the quantities

$$\phi_1 = \psi_0 + \theta_1 \quad \text{and} \quad \phi_2 = \psi_0 + \theta_2$$

are angles of inclination of directed lines tangent to the image curves Γ_1 and Γ_2, respectively, at the point $w_0 = f(z_0)$. Thus $\phi_2 - \phi_1 = \theta_2 - \theta_1$; that is, the angle $\phi_2 - \phi_1$ from Γ_1 to Γ_2 is the same in *magnitude* and *sense* as the angle $\theta_2 - \theta_1$ from C_1 to C_2. Those angles are denoted by α in Fig. 148.

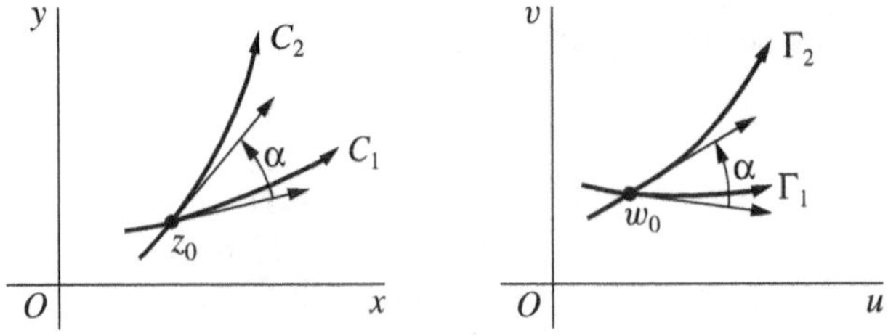

FIGURE 148

Because of this angle-preserving property, a transformation $w = f(z)$ is said to be ***conformal*** at a point z_0 if f is analytic there and $f'(z_0) \neq 0$. Such a transformation is actually conformal at each point in some neighborhood of z_0. For it must be analytic in a neighborhood of z_0 (Sec. 25); and since its derivative f' is continuous in that neighborhood (Sec. 57), Theorem 2 in Sec. 18 tells us that there is also a neighborhood of z_0 throughout which $f'(z) \neq 0$.

A transformation $w = f(z)$, defined on a domain D, is referred to as a conformal transformation, or a ***conformal mapping,*** when it is conformal at each point in D. That is, the mapping is conformal in D if f is analytic in D and its derivative f' has no zeros there. Each of the elementary functions studied in Chap. 3 can be used to define a transformation that is conformal in some domain.

EXAMPLE 1. The mapping $w = e^z$ is conformal throughout the entire z plane since $(e^z)' = e^z \neq 0$ for each z. Consider any two lines $x = c_1$ and $y = c_2$ in the z plane, the first directed upward and the second directed to the right. According to Example 1 in Sec. 103, their images under the mapping $w = e^z$ are a positively oriented circle centered at the origin and a ray from the origin, respectively. As illustrated in Fig. 124 (Sec. 103), the angle between the lines at their point of intersection is a right angle in the negative direction, and the same is true of the angle between the circle and the ray at the corresponding point in the w plane. The conformality of the mapping $w = e^z$ is also illustrated in Figs. 7 and 8 of Appendix 2.

EXAMPLE 2. Consider two smooth arcs which are level curves $u(x, y) = c_1$ and $v(x, y) = c_2$ of the real and imaginary components, respectively, of a function

$$f(z) = u(x, y) + iv(x, y),$$

and suppose that they intersect at a point z_0 where f is analytic and $f'(z_0) \neq 0$. The transformation $w = f(z)$ is conformal at z_0 and maps these arcs into the lines $u = c_1$ and $v = c_2$, which are orthogonal at the point $w_0 = f(z_0)$. According to our theory, then, the arcs must be orthogonal at z_0. This has already been verified and illustrated in Exercises 2 through 6 of Sec. 27.

A mapping that preserves the magnitude of the angle between two smooth arcs but not necessarily the sense is called an ***isogonal mapping.***

EXAMPLE 3. The transformation $w = \overline{z}$, which is a reflection in the real axis, is isogonal but not conformal. If it is followed by a conformal transformation, the resulting transformation $w = f(\overline{z})$ is also isogonal but not conformal.

Suppose that f is not a constant function and is analytic at a point z_0. If, in addition, $f'(z_0) = 0$, then z_0 is called a ***critical point*** of the transformation $w = f(z)$.

EXAMPLE 4. The point $z_0 = 0$ is a critical point of the transformation

$$w = 1 + z^2,$$

which is a composition of the mappings

$$Z = z^2 \quad \text{and} \quad w = 1 + Z.$$

A ray $\theta = \alpha$ from the point $z_0 = 0$ is evidently mapped onto the ray from the point $w_0 = 1$ whose angle of inclination is 2α, and the angle between any two rays drawn from $z_0 = 0$ is *doubled* by the transformation.

More generally, it can be shown that if z_0 is a critical point of a transformation $w = f(z)$, there is an integer m ($m \geq 2$) such that the angle between any two smooth arcs passing through z_0 is multiplied by m under that transformation. The integer m is the smallest positive integer such that $f^{(m)}(z_0) \neq 0$. Verification of these facts is left to the exercises.

Another property of a transformation $w = f(z)$ that is conformal at a point z_0 is obtained by considering the modulus of $f'(z_0)$. From the definition of derivative and a property of limits involving moduli that was derived in Exercise 7, Sec. 18, we know that

$$(5) \qquad |f'(z_0)| = \left| \lim_{z \to z_0} \frac{f(z) - f(z_0)}{z - z_0} \right| = \lim_{z \to z_0} \frac{|f(z) - f(z_0)|}{|z - z_0|}.$$

Now $|z - z_0|$ is the length of a line segment joining z_0 and z, and $|f(z) - f(z_0)|$ is the length of the line segment joining the points $f(z_0)$ and $f(z)$ in the w plane. Evidently, then, if z is near the point z_0, the ratio

$$\frac{|f(z) - f(z_0)|}{|z - z_0|}$$

of the two lengths is approximately the number $|f'(z_0)|$. Note that $|f'(z_0)|$ represents an expansion if it is greater than unity and a contraction if it is less than unity.

Although the angle of rotation $\arg f'(z)$ and the **scale factor** $|f'(z_0)|$ vary, in general, from point to point, it follows from the continuity of f' (see Sec. 57) that their values are approximately $\arg f'(z_0)$ and $|f'(z_0)|$ at points z near z_0. Hence the image of a small region in a neighborhood of z_0 *conforms* to the original region in the sense that it has approximately the same shape. A large region may, however, be transformed into a region that bears no resemblance to the original one.

113. FURTHER EXAMPLES

The two examples that follow are closely related; and, in addition to illustrating the material in the preceding section, they emphasize how the preservation of angles and scale factors can change from point to point in the z plane.

EXAMPLE 1. The function

$$f(z) = z^2 = x^2 - y^2 + i2xy$$

is entire, and its derivative $f'(z) = 2z$ is zero only at the origin. Hence the transformation $w = f(z)$ is conformal at the point $z_0 = 1 + i$, where the half lines

$$(1) \qquad y = x \ (x \geq 0) \quad \text{and} \quad x = 1 \ (y \geq 0)$$

intersect. We denote those half lines by C_1 and C_2, respectively, as shown in Fig. 149, and we agree that their positive sense is upward. Observe that the angle from C_1 to C_2 is $\pi/4$ at their point of intersection.

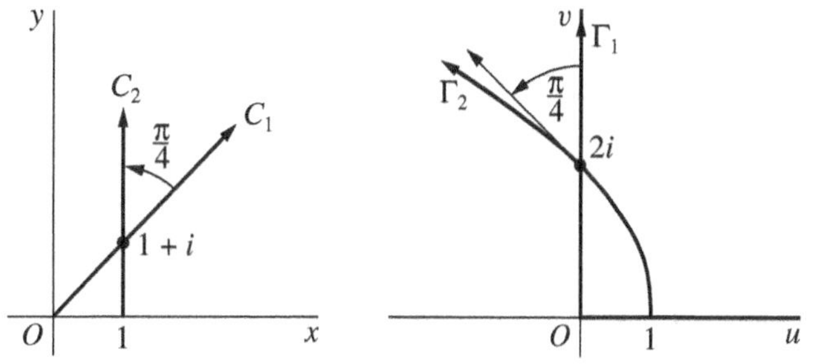

FIGURE 149
$w = z^2$.

Since the image of a point $z = (x, y)$ is a point in the w plane whose rectangular coordinates are

$$u = x^2 - y^2 \quad \text{and} \quad v = 2xy, \tag{2}$$

the half line C_1 is transformed into the curve Γ_1 with parametric representation

$$u = 0, \quad v = 2x^2 \qquad (0 \le x < \infty). \tag{3}$$

Thus Γ_1 is the upper half $v \ge 0$ of the v axis. The half line C_2 is transformed into the curve Γ_2 represented by the equations

$$u = 1 - y^2, \quad v = 2y \qquad (0 \le y < \infty). \tag{4}$$

By eliminating the variable y in equations (3), we find that Γ_2 is the upper half of the parabola $v^2 = -4(u-1)$. Note that in each case, the positive sense of the image curve is upward.

If u and v are the variables in representation (4) for the image curve Γ_2, then

$$\frac{dv}{du} = \frac{dv/dy}{du/dy} = \frac{2}{-2y} = -\frac{2}{v}.$$

In particular, $dv/du = -1$ when $v = 2$. Consequently, the angle from the image curve Γ_1 to the image curve Γ_2 at the point $w = f(1+i) = 2i$ is $\pi/4$, as required by the conformality of the mapping at $z = 1+i$. The angle of rotation $\pi/4$ at the point $z = 1+i$ is, of course, a value of

$$\arg f'(1+i) = \arg[2(1+i)] = \frac{\pi}{4} + 2n\pi \qquad (n = 0, \pm 1, \pm 2, \ldots).$$

The scale factor at that point is the number

$$|f'(1+i)| = |2(1+i)| = 2\sqrt{2}.$$

EXAMPLE 2. Turning now to Fig. 150, we consider the same half line C_2 used in Example 1 and the new one C_3 that is shown in the figure. Those half lines intersect at the point $z_0 = 1$, and their positive directions are as shown.

We also use the same transformation $w = z^2$ as in Example 1. Thus the image of C_2 remains the same as in Example 1. In view of equations (2), and since $y = 0$ on

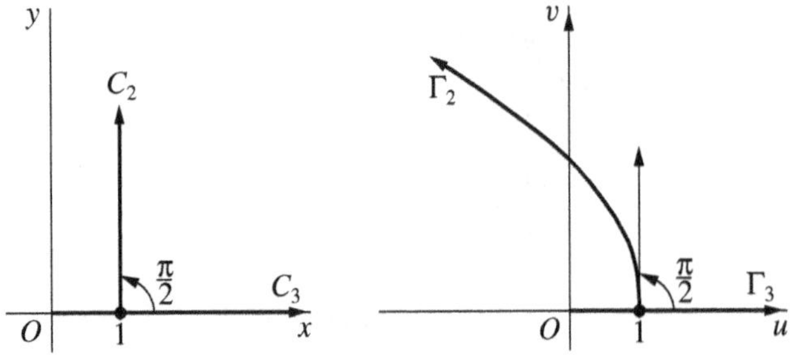

FIGURE 150
$w = z^2$.

C_3, the image Γ_3 of C_3 is

$$u = x^2, \quad v = 0 \qquad (0 \le x < \infty).$$

This tells us that the right angle between C_2 and C_3 in the z plane is preserved in the w plane.

Finally, we observe that the scale factor at the point of intersection $z_0 = 1$ of the curves C_2 and C_3 in Fig. 150 is $|f'(1)| = 2$.

114. LOCAL INVERSES

A transformation $w = f(z)$ that is conformal at a point z_0 has a ***local inverse*** there. That is, if $w_0 = f(z_0)$, then there exists a unique transformation $z = g(w)$, which is defined and analytic in a neighborhood N of w_0, such that $g(w_0) = z_0$ and $f[g(w)] = w$ for all points w in N. The derivative of $g(w)$ is, moreover,

$$g'(w) = \frac{1}{f'(z)}. \tag{1}$$

We note from expression (1) that the transformation $z = g(w)$ is itself conformal at w_0.

Assuming that $w = f(z)$ is, in fact, conformal at z_0, let us verify the existence of such an inverse, which is a direct consequence of results in advanced calculus.* As noted in Sec. 112, the conformality of the transformation $w = f(z)$ at z_0 implies that there is some neighborhood of z_0 throughout which f is analytic. Hence if we write

$$z = x + iy, \quad z_0 = x_0 + iy_0, \quad \text{and} \quad f(z) = u(x, y) + iv(x, y),$$

we know that there is a neighborhood of the point (x_0, y_0) throughout which the functions $u(x, y)$ and $v(x, y)$, along with their partial derivatives of all orders, are continuous (see Sec. 57).

*The results from advanced calculus to be used here appear in, for instance, A. E. Taylor and W. R. Mann, *Advanced Calculus*, 3d ed., pp. 241–247, 1983.

Now the pair of equations

(2) $$u = u(x, y), \quad v = v(x, y)$$

represents a transformation from the neighborhood just mentioned into the uv plane. Moreover, the determinant

$$J = \begin{vmatrix} u_x & u_y \\ v_x & v_y \end{vmatrix} = u_x v_y - v_x u_y,$$

which is known as the ***Jacobian*** of the transformation, is nonzero at the point (x_0, y_0). For, in view of the Cauchy–Riemann equations $u_x = v_y$ and $u_y = -v_x$, one can write J as

$$J = (u_x)^2 + (v_x)^2 = |f'(z)|^2;$$

and $f'(z_0) \neq 0$ since the transformation $w = f(z)$ is conformal at z_0. The above continuity conditions on the functions $u(x, y)$ and $v(x, y)$ and their derivatives, together with this condition on the Jacobian, are sufficient to ensure the existence of a local inverse of transformation (2) at (x_0, y_0). That is, if

(3) $$u_0 = u(x_0, y_0) \quad \text{and} \quad v_0 = v(x_0, y_0),$$

then there is a unique continuous transformation

(4) $$x = x(u, v), \quad y = y(u, v),$$

defined on a neighborhood N of the point (u_0, v_0) and mapping that point onto (x_0, y_0), such that equations (2) hold when equations (4) hold. Also, in addition to being continuous, the functions (4) have continuous first-order partial derivatives satisfying the equations

(5) $$x_u = \frac{1}{J} v_y, \quad x_v = -\frac{1}{J} u_y, \quad y_u = -\frac{1}{J} v_x, \quad y_v = \frac{1}{J} u_x$$

throughout N.

If we write $w = u + iv$ and $w_0 = u_0 + iv_0$, as well as

(6) $$g(w) = x(u, v) + iy(u, v),$$

the transformation $z = g(w)$ is evidently the local inverse of the original transformation $w = f(z)$ at z_0. Transformations (2) and (4) can be written

$$u + iv = u(x, y) + iv(x, y) \quad \text{and} \quad x + iy = x(u, v) + iy(u, v);$$

and these last two equations are the same as

$$w = f(z) \quad \text{and} \quad z = g(w),$$

where g has the desired properties. Equations (5) can be used to show that g is analytic in N. Details are left to the exercises, where expression (1) for $g'(w)$ is also derived.

EXAMPLE. We know from Example 1 in Sec. 112, that if $f(z) = e^z$, the transformation $w = f(z)$ is conformal everywhere in the z plane and, in particular, at the point $z_0 = 2\pi i$. The image of this choice of z_0 is the point $w_0 = 1$. When points in the w plane are expressed in the form $w = \rho \exp(i\phi)$, the local inverse at z_0 can be obtained by writing $g(w) = \log w$, where $\log w$ denotes the branch

$$\log w = \ln \rho + i\phi \qquad (\rho > 0, \pi < \theta < 3\pi)$$

of the logarithmic function, restricted to any neighborhood of w_0 that does not contain the origin. Observe that

$$g(1) = \ln 1 + i2\pi = 2\pi i$$

and that when w is in the neighborhood,

$$f[g(w)] = \exp(\log w) = w.$$

Also

$$g'(w) = \frac{d}{dw} \log w = \frac{1}{w} = \frac{1}{\exp z},$$

in accordance with equation (1).

Note that if the point $z_0 = 0$ is chosen, one can use the principal branch

$$\text{Log } w = \ln \rho + i\phi \qquad (\rho > 0, -\pi < \phi < \pi)$$

of the logarithmic function to define g. In this case, $g(1) = 0$.

EXERCISES

1. Determine the angle of rotation at the point $z_0 = 2 + i$ when $w = z^2$, and illustrate it for some particular curve. Show that the scale factor at that point is $2\sqrt{5}$.

2. What angle of rotation is produced by the transformation $w = 1/z$ at the point

   (*a*) $z_0 = 1$; (*b*) $z_0 = i$?

   Ans. (*a*) π; (*b*) 0.

3. Show that under the transformation $w = 1/z$, the images of the lines $y = x - 1$ and $y = 0$ are the circle $u^2 + v^2 - u - v = 0$ and the line $v = 0$, respectively. Sketch all four curves, determine corresponding directions along them, and verify the conformality of the mapping at the point $z_0 = 1$.

4. Show that the angle of rotation at a nonzero point $z_0 = r_0 \exp(i\theta_0)$ under the transformation $w = z^n$ $(n = 1, 2, \ldots)$ is $(n - 1)\theta_0$. Determine the scale factor of the transformation at that point.

   Ans. nr_0^{n-1}.

5. Show that the transformation $w = \sin z$ is conformal at all points except

$$z = \frac{\pi}{2} + n\pi \qquad (n = 0, \pm 1, \pm 2, \ldots).$$

Note that this is in agreement with the mapping of directed line segments shown in Figs. 9, 10, and 11 of Appendix 2.

6. Find the local inverse of the transformation $w = z^2$ at the point
(a) $z_0 = 2$; (b) $z_0 = -2$; (c) $z_0 = -i$.

Ans. (a) $w^{1/2} = \sqrt{\rho}\, e^{i\phi/2}$ $(\rho > 0, -\pi < \phi < \pi)$;

(c) $w^{1/2} = \sqrt{\rho}\, e^{i\phi/2}$ $(\rho > 0, 2\pi < \phi < 4\pi)$.

7. In Sec. 114, it was pointed out that the components $x(u, v)$ and $y(u, v)$ of the inverse function $g(w)$ defined by equation (6) there are continuous and have continuous first-order partial derivatives in a neighborhood N. Use equations (5), Sec. 114, to show that the Cauchy–Riemann equations $x_u = y_v$, $x_v = -y_u$ hold in N. Then conclude that $g(w)$ is analytic in that neighborhood.

8. Show that if $z = g(w)$ is the local inverse of a conformal transformation $w = f(z)$ at a point z_0, then

$$g'(w) = \frac{1}{f'(z)}$$

at points w in a neighborhood N where g is analytic (Exercise 7).

Suggestion: Start with the fact that $f[g(w)] = w$, and apply the chain rule for differentiating composite functions.

9. Let C be a smooth arc lying in a domain D throughout which a transformation $w = f(z)$ is conformal, and let Γ denote the image of C under that transformation. Show that Γ is also a smooth arc.

10. Suppose that a function f is analytic at z_0 and that

$$f'(z_0) = f''(z_0) = \cdots = f^{(m-1)}(z_0) = 0, \qquad f^{(m)}(z_0) \neq 0$$

for some positive integer m $(m \geq 1)$. Also, write $w_0 = f(z_0)$.

(a) Use the Taylor series for f about the point z_0 to show that there is a neighborhood of z_0 in which the difference $f(z) - w_0$ can be written

$$f(z) - w_0 = (z - z_0)^m \frac{f^{(m)}(z_0)}{m!}\,[1 + g(z)],$$

where $g(z)$ is continuous at z_0 and $g(z_0) = 0$.

(b) Let Γ be the image of a smooth arc C under the transformation $w = f(z)$, as shown in Fig. 147 (Sec. 112), and note that the angles of inclination θ_0 and ϕ_0 in that figure are limits of $\arg(z - z_0)$ and $\arg[f(z) - w_0]$, respectively, as z approaches z_0 along the arc C. Then use the result in part (a) to show that θ_0 and ϕ_0 are related by the equation

$$\phi_0 = m\theta_0 + \arg f^{(m)}(z_0).$$

(c) Let α denote the angle between two smooth arcs C_1 and C_2 passing through z_0, as shown on the left in Fig. 148 (Sec. 112). Show how it follows from the relation obtained in part (b) that the corresponding angle between the image curves Γ_1 and Γ_2 at the point $w_0 = f(z_0)$ is $m\alpha$. (Note that the transformation is conformal at z_0 when $m = 1$ and that z_0 is a critical point when $m \geq 2$.)

115. HARMONIC CONJUGATES

We saw in Sec. 27 that if a function

$$f(z) = u(x, y) + iv(x, y)$$

is analytic in a domain D, then the real-valued functions u and v are harmonic in that domain. That is, they have continuous partial derivatives of the first and second order in D and satisfy Laplace's equation there:

$$u_{xx} + u_{yy} = 0, \quad v_{xx} + v_{yy} = 0. \tag{1}$$

Suppose now that two given functions $u(x, y)$ and $v(x, y)$ are harmonic in a domain D and that their first-order partial derivatives satisfy the Cauchy–Riemann equations

$$u_x = v_y, \quad u_y = -v_x \tag{2}$$

throughout D. Then v is said to be a ***harmonic conjugate*** of u. The meaning of the word conjugate here is, of course, different from that in Sec. 6, where $\bar{z}$ is defined.

The theorem just below connects the concepts of analytic functions and harmonic conjugates.

Theorem. *A function $f(z) = u(x, y) + iv(x, y)$ is analytic in a domain D if and only if v is a harmonic conjugate of u.*

The proof is easy. If v is a harmonic conjugate of u in D, the Cauchy–Riemann equations (2) must be satisfied. According to the theorem in Sec. 23, then, f is analytic in D. Conversely, if f is analytic in D, we know from the first paragraph in this section that u and v are harmonic in D; furthermore, in view of the theorem in Sec. 21, the Cauchy–Riemann equations (2) are satisfied in D.

The following example shows that if v is a harmonic conjugate of u in some domain, it is *not*, in general, true that u is a harmonic conjugate of v there. (See also Exercises 3 and 4.)

EXAMPLE 1. Suppose that

$$u(x, y) = x^2 - y^2 \quad \text{and} \quad v(x, y) = 2xy.$$

Since these are the real and imaginary components, respectively, of the entire function $f(z) = z^2$, we know that v is a harmonic conjugate of u throughout the plane. But u cannot be a harmonic conjugate of v since, as verified in Exercise 2(*b*), Sec. 26, the function $2xy + i(x^2 - y^2)$ is not analytic anywhere.

We now illustrate one method for finding a harmonic conjugate of a given harmonic function.

EXAMPLE 2. The function

$$u(x, y) = 2x(1 - y) = 2x - 2xy \tag{3}$$

is readily seen to be harmonic throughout the entire xy plane. Since a harmonic conjugate $v(x, y)$ is related to $u(x, y)$ by means of the Cauchy–Riemann equations (2), the first of those equations, namely $u_x = v_y$, tells us that $2 - 2y = v_y$. That is,

$$v_y(x, y) = 2 - 2y.$$

Holding x fixed and integrating each side here with respect to y, we find that

$$v(x, y) = 2y - y^2 + g(x), \tag{4}$$

where g is, at present, an *arbitrary* differentiable function of x.

Turning now to the relation $u_y = -v_x$, which is the second of equations (2), we see that $-2x = -g'(x)$, or $g'(x) = 2x$. Consequently, $g(x) = x^2 + C$, where C is an arbitrary real number. According to expression (4), then, the function

$$v(x, y) = 2y - y^2 + x^2 + C \tag{5}$$

is a harmonic conjugate of $u(x, y)$.

The corresponding analytic function is

$$f(z) = 2x(1 - y) + i(2y - y^2 + x^2 + C). \tag{6}$$

The form $f(z) = 2z + i(z^2 + C)$ of this function is easily verified and is suggested by noting that when $y = 0$, expression (6) becomes $f(x) = 2x + i(x^2 + C)$. Inasmuch as $v(x, y)$ is unique except for an arbitrary constant (see Exercise 5), it is customary to write $C = 0$, so that $f(z) = 2z + iz^2$.

The following theorem ensures the existence of a harmonic conjugate of any given harmonic function $u(x, y)$ that is defined on a *simply connected domain* (Sec. 52). Thus, in such domains, every harmonic function is the real part of an analytic function $f(z)$.

Theorem. *If a harmonic function $u(x, y)$ is defined on a simply connected domain D, it always has a harmonic conjugate $v(x, y)$ in D.*

In order to prove this theorem, we first recall some important facts about line integrals arising in advanced calculus.* Suppose that $P(x, y)$ and $Q(x, y)$ have continuous first-order partial derivatives in a simply connected domain D of the xy plane, and let (x_0, y_0) and (x, y) be any two points in D. If $P_y = Q_x$ everywhere in D, then the line integral

$$\int_C P(s, t)\,ds + Q(s, t)\,dt$$

from (x_0, y_0) to (x, y) is independent of the contour C that is taken as long as the contour lies entirely in D. Furthermore, when the point (x_0, y_0) is kept fixed and (x, y)

*See, for example, W. Kaplan, *Advanced Mathematics for Engineers*, pp. 546–550, 1992.

is allowed to vary throughout D, the integral represents a single-valued function

$$F(x, y) = \int_{(x_0, y_0)}^{(x, y)} P(s, t)\, ds + Q(s, t)\, dt \tag{7}$$

of x and y whose first-order partial derivatives are given by the equations

$$F_x(x, y) = P(x, y), \quad F_y(x, y) = Q(x, y). \tag{8}$$

Note that the value of F is changed by an additive constant when a different starting point (x_0, y_0) is taken.

Returning to the given harmonic function $u(x, y)$, observe how it follows from Laplace's equation $u_{xx} + u_{yy} = 0$ that

$$(-u_y)_y = (u_x)_x$$

everywhere in D. Also, the second-order partial derivatives of u are continuous in D; and this means that the first-order partial derivatives of $-u_y$ and u_x are continuous there. Thus, if (x_0, y_0) is a fixed point in D, the function

$$v(x, y) = \int_{(x_0, y_0)}^{(x, y)} -u_t(s, t)\, ds + u_s(s, t)\, dt \tag{9}$$

is well defined for all (x, y) in D; and, according to equations (8),

$$v_x(x, y) = -u_y(x, y), \quad v_y(x, y) = u_x(x, y). \tag{10}$$

These are the Cauchy–Riemann equations. Since the first-order partial derivatives of u are continuous, it is evident from equations (10) that those derivatives of v are also continuous. Hence (Sec. 23) $u(x, y) + iv(x, y)$ is an analytic function in D; and v is, therefore, a harmonic conjugate of u.

The function v defined by equation (9) is, of course, not the only harmonic conjugate of u, since the more general function $v(x, y) + C$, where C is any real constant, is also one. But, just as we did in Example 2, we may write $C = 0$.

EXAMPLE 3. Consider the harmonic function

$$u(x, y) = 2x - 2xy,$$

whose harmonic conjugate has already been found in Example 2. According to expression (9), the function

$$v(x, y) = \int_{(0,0)}^{(x, y)} 2s\, ds + (2 - 2t) dt$$

is a harmonic conjugate of $u(x, y)$ throughout the entire *xy* plane. The integral here is readily evaluated by inspection. It can also be evaluated first along the horizontal path from the origin (0, 0) to the point $(x, 0)$ and then along the vertical path from $(x, 0)$ to the point (x, y) The result is

$$v(x, y) = x^2 + (2y - y^2) = 2y - y^2 + x^2,$$

which, along with an arbitrary constant, was obtained in Example 2.

EXERCISES

1. Show that $u(x, y)$ is harmonic in some domain and follow the steps used in Example 2, Sec. 115, to find a harmonic conjugate $v(x, y)$ when

(a) $u(x, y) = 2x - x^3 + 3xy^2$; (b) $u(x, y) = \sinh x \sin y$; (c) $u(x, y) = \dfrac{y}{x^2 + y^2}$.

Ans. (a) $v(x, y) = 2y - 3x^2y + y^3$;
(b) $v(x, y) = -\cosh x \cos y$;
(c) $v(x, y) = \dfrac{x}{x^2 + y^2}$.

2. In each case, show that the function $u(x, y)$ is harmonic throughout the xy plane. Then, using expression (9), Sec. 115, find its harmonic conjugate. Also, write the corresponding function

$$f(z) = u(x, y) + iv(x, y)$$

in terms of z:

(a) $u(x, y) = xy$; (b) $u(x, y) = y^3 - 3x^2y$.

Ans. (a) $v(x, y) = -\frac{1}{2}(x^2 - y^2)$, $f(z) = -\frac{i}{2}z^2$;
(b) $v(x, y) = -3xy^2 + x^3$, $f(z) = iz^3$.

3. Suppose that v is a harmonic conjugate of u in a domain D and also that u is a harmonic conjugate of v in D. Show how it follows that both $u(x, y)$ and $v(x, y)$ must be constant throughout D.

4. Use the theorem in Sec. 115 to show that v is a harmonic conjugate of u in a domain D if and only if $-u$ is a harmonic conjugate of v in D. (Compare with the result obtained in Exercise 3.)

Suggestion: Observe that the function $f(z) = u(x, y) + iv(x, y)$ is analytic in D if and only if $-if(z)$ is analytic there.

5. Show that if v and V are harmonic conjugates of $u(x, y)$ in a domain D, then $v(x, y)$ and $V(x, y)$ can differ at most by an additive constant.

6. Verify that the function $u(r, \theta) = \ln r$ is harmonic in the domain $r > 0, 0 < \theta < 2\pi$ by showing that it satisfies the polar form of Laplace's equation, obtained in Exercise 1, Sec. 27. Then use the technique in Example 2, Sec. 115, but involving the Cauchy–Riemann equations in polar form (Sec. 24), to derive the harmonic conjugate $v(r, \theta) = \theta$. (Compare with Exercise 6, Sec. 26.)

7. Let $u(x, y)$ be harmonic in a simply connected domain D. By appealing to results in Secs. 115 and 57, show that its partial derivatives of all orders are continuous throughout that domain.

116. TRANSFORMATIONS OF HARMONIC FUNCTIONS

The problem of finding a function that is harmonic in a specified domain and satisfies prescribed conditions on the boundary of the domain is prominent in applied mathematics. If the values of the function are prescribed along the boundary, the problem is known as a boundary value problem of the first kind, or a ***Dirichlet problem***.

If the values of the normal derivative of the function are prescribed on the boundary, the boundary value problem is one of the second kind, or a ***Neumann problem***. Modifications and combinations of those types of boundary conditions also arise.

The domains most frequently encountered in the applications are simply connected; and, since a function that is harmonic in a simply connected domain always has a harmonic conjugate (Sec. 115), solutions of boundary value problems for such domains are the real or imaginary components of analytic functions.

EXAMPLE 1. In Example 1, Sec. 27, we saw that the function

$$T(x, y) = e^{-y} \sin x$$

satisfies a certain Dirichlet problem for the strip $0 < x < \pi$, $y > 0$ and noted that it represents a solution of a temperature problem. The function $T(x, y)$, which is actually harmonic throughout the xy plane, is the real component of the entire function

$$-ie^{iz} = e^{-y} \sin x - ie^{-y} \cos x.$$

It is also the imaginary component of the entire function e^{iz}.

Sometimes a solution of a given boundary value problem can be discovered by identifying it as the real or imaginary component of an analytic function. But the success of that procedure depends on the simplicity of the problem and on one's familiarity with the real and imaginary components of a variety of analytic functions. The following theorem is an important aid.

Theorem. *Suppose that*

(*a*) *an analytic function*

$$w = f(z) = u(x, y) + iv(x, y)$$

maps a domain D_z *in the* z *plane onto a domain* D_w *in the* w *plane;*

(*b*) $h(u, v)$ *is a harmonic function defined on* D_w.

It follows that the function

$$H(x, y) = h[u(x, y), v(x, y)]$$

is harmonic in D_z.

We first prove the theorem for the case in which the domain D_w is simply connected. According to Sec. 104, that property of D_w ensures that the given harmonic function $h(u, v)$ has a harmonic conjugate $g(u, v)$. Hence the function

$$\Phi(w) = h(u, v) + ig(u, v) \tag{1}$$

is analytic in D_w. Since the function $f(z)$ is analytic in D_z, the composite function $\Phi[f(z)]$ is also analytic in D_z. Consequently, the real part $h[u(x, y), v(x, y)]$ of this composition is harmonic in D_z.

If D_w is *not* simply connected, we observe that each point w_0 in D_w has a neighborhood $|w - w_0| < \varepsilon$ lying entirely in D_w. Since that neighborhood is simply connected, a function of the type (1) is analytic in it. Furthermore, since f is continuous at a point z_0 in D_z whose image is w_0, there is a neighborhood $|z-z_0| < \delta$ whose image is contained in the neighborhood $|w - w_0| < \varepsilon$. Hence it follows that the composition $\Phi[f(z)]$ is analytic in the neighborhood $|z - z_0| < \delta$, and we may conclude that $h[u(x, y), v(x, y)]$ is harmonic there. Finally, since w_0 was arbitrarily chosen in D_w and since each point in D_z is mapped onto such a point under the transformation $w = f(z)$, the function $h[u(x, y), v(x, y)]$ must be harmonic throughout D_z.

The proof of the theorem for the general case in which D_w is not necessarily simply connected can also be accomplished directly by means of the chain rule for partial derivatives. The computations are, however, somewhat involved (see Exercise 8, Sec. 117).

EXAMPLE 2. The transformation

$$w = e^z = e^x \cos y + i e^x \sin y$$

maps the horizontal strip $0 < y < \pi$ onto the upper half plane $v > 0$, as we saw in Example 3 in Sec. 103. Also, since w^2 is analytic in that half plane, the function

$$h(u, v) = \text{Re}(w^2) = u^2 - v^2$$

is harmonic there. According to our theorem, then, the following function is harmonic throughout the strip $0 < y < \pi$:

$$H(x, y) = (e^x \cos y)^2 - (e^x \sin y)^2 = e^{2x}(\cos^2 y - \sin^2 y);$$

and this simplifies to

$$H(x, y) = e^{2x} \cos 2y.$$

EXAMPLE 3. For another example, consider the transformation

$$w = \text{Log}\, z = \ln r + i\Theta \quad \left(r > 0,\ -\frac{\pi}{2} < \Theta < \frac{\pi}{2}\right).$$

In rectangular coordinates, it takes the form

$$w = \text{Log}\, z = \ln \sqrt{x^2 + y^2} + i \arctan\left(\frac{y}{x}\right),$$

where $-\pi/2 < \arctan t < \pi/2$. This transformation maps the right half plane onto the horizontal strip $-\pi/2 < v < \pi/2$ (see Exercise 3, Sec. 117). Finally, since the function

$$h(u, v) = \text{Im}\, w = v$$

is harmonic in that strip, our theorem tells us that the function

$$H(x, y) = \arctan\left(\frac{y}{x}\right)$$

is harmonic in the half plane $x > 0$.

117. TRANSFORMATIONS OF BOUNDARY CONDITIONS

The conditions that a function or its normal derivative have prescribed values along the boundary of a domain in which it is harmonic are the most common, although not the only, important types of boundary conditions. In this section, we show that certain of these conditions remain unaltered under the change of variables associated with a conformal transformation. These results will be used in Chap. 10 to solve boundary value problems. The basic technique there is to transform a given boundary value problem in the xy plane into a simpler one in the uv plane and then to use the theorems of this and Sec. 116 to write the solution of the original problem in terms of the solution obtained for the simpler one.

Theorem. *Suppose that*

(*a*) *a transformation*

$$w = f(z) = u(x, y) + iv(x, y)$$

is conformal at each point of a smooth arc C and that Γ is the image of C under that transformation;

(*b*) *$h(u, v)$ is a function that satisfies one of the conditions*

$$h = h_0 \quad \text{and} \quad \frac{dh}{dn} = 0$$

at points on Γ, where h_0 is a real constant and dh/dn denotes directional derivatives of h normal to Γ.

It follows that the function

$$H(x, y) = h[u(x, y), v(x, y)]$$

satisfies the corresponding condition

$$H = h_0 \quad \text{or} \quad \frac{dH}{dN} = 0$$

at points on C, where dH/dN denotes directional derivatives of H normal to C.

It should be emphasized that in the applications, C may be the entire boundary of a domain or just part of it.

To show that the condition $h = h_0$ on Γ implies that $H = h_0$ on C, we note from the expression for $H(x, y)$ in the statement of the theorem that the value of H at any point (x, y) on C is the same as the value of h at the image (u, v) of (x, y) under the transformation $w = f(z)$. Since the image point (u, v) lies on Γ and since $h = h_0$ along that curve, it follows that $H = h_0$ along C.

Suppose, on the other hand, that $dh/dn = 0$ on Γ. From calculus, we know that

$$\frac{dh}{dn} = (\text{grad } h) \cdot \mathbf{n}, \tag{1}$$

where grad h denotes the gradient of h at a point (u, v) on Γ and $\mathbf{n}$ is a unit vector normal to Γ at (u, v). Since $dh/dn = 0$ at (u, v), equation (1) tells us that grad h is orthogonal to $\mathbf{n}$ at (u, v). That is, grad h is tangent to Γ there (Fig. 151). But gradients are orthogonal to level curves; and, because grad h is tangent to Γ, we see that Γ is orthogonal to a level curve $h(u, v) = c$ passing through (u, v).

Now, according to the expression for $H(x, y)$ in the theorem, the level curve $H(x, y) = c$ in the z plane can be written

$$h[u(x, y), v(x, y)] = c.$$

Hence it is transformed into the level curve $h(u, v) = c$ under the transformation $w = f(z)$. Furthermore, since C is transformed into Γ and since Γ is orthogonal to the level curve $h(u, v) = c$, as demonstrated in the preceding paragraph, it follows from the conformality of the transformation $w = f(z)$ that C is orthogonal to the level curve $H(x, y) = c$ at the point (x, y) corresponding to (u, v). Because gradients are orthogonal to level curves, this means that grad H is tangent to C at (x, y) (see Fig. 151). Consequently, if $\mathbf{N}$ denotes a unit vector normal to C at (x, y), grad H is orthogonal to $\mathbf{N}$. That is,

$$(\text{grad } H) \cdot \mathbf{N} = 0. \tag{2}$$

Finally, since

$$\frac{dH}{dN} = (\text{grad } H) \cdot \mathbf{N},$$

we may conclude from equation (2) that $dH/dN = 0$ at points on C.

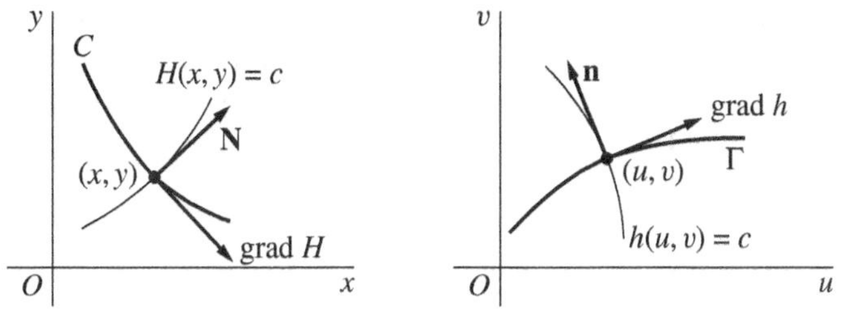

FIGURE 151

In this discussion, we have tacitly assumed that grad $h \neq \mathbf{0}$. If grad $h = \mathbf{0}$, it follows from the identity

$$|\text{grad } H(x, y)| = |\text{grad } h(u, v)||f'(z)|,$$

derived in Exercise 10(a) of this section, that grad $H = \mathbf{0}$; hence dh/dn and the corresponding normal derivative dH/dN are both zero. We have also assumed that

(a) grad h and grad H always exist;

(b) the level curve $H(x, y) = c$ is smooth when grad $h \neq \mathbf{0}$ at (u, v).

Condition (b) ensures that angles between arcs are preserved by the transformation $w = f(z)$ in the theorem when it is conformal. In all of our applications, both conditions (a) and (b) will be satisfied.

EXAMPLE. Consider, for instance, the function $h(u, v) = v + 2$. The transformation

$$w = iz^2 = i(x + iy)^2 = -2xy + i(x^2 - y^2)$$

is conformal when $z \neq 0$. It maps the half line $y = x$ $(x > 0)$ onto the negative u axis, where $h = 2$, and the positive x axis onto the positive v axis, where the normal derivative h_u is 0 (Fig. 152). According to the above theorem, the function

$$H(x, y) = x^2 - y^2 + 2$$

must satisfy the condition $H = 2$ along the half line $y = x$ $(x > 0)$ and $H_y = 0$ along the positive x axis, as one can verify directly.

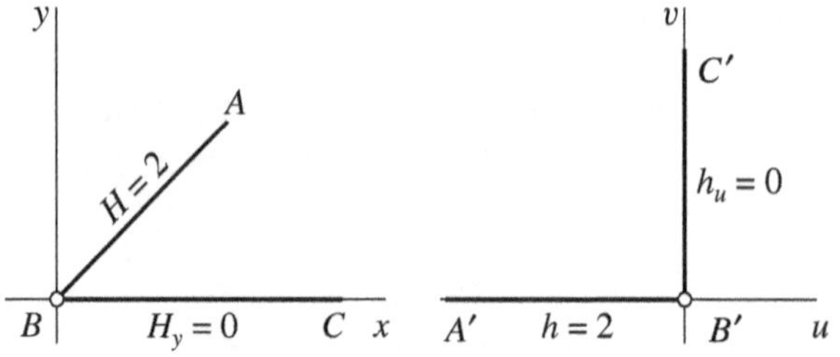

FIGURE 152

A boundary condition that is not of one of the two types mentioned in the theorem may be transformed into a condition that is substantially different from the original one (see Exercise 6). New boundary conditions for the transformed problem can be obtained for a particular transformation in any case. It is interesting to note that under a conformal transformation, the ratio of a directional derivative of H along a smooth arc C in the z plane to the directional derivative of h along the image curve Γ at the corresponding point in the w plane is $|f'(z)|$; usually, this ratio is not constant along a given arc. (See Exercise 10.)

EXERCISES

1. In Example 2, Sec. 116, we used the theorem in that section to show that the function

$$H(x, y) = e^{2x} \cos 2y$$

is harmonic in the horizontal strip $0 < y < \pi$ of the z plane. Verify this result directly.

2. The function $h(u, v) = e^{-v} \sin u$ is harmonic throughout the entire uv plane and, in particular, in the upper half plane

$$D_w\colon v > 0$$

(see Example 1 in Sec. 116). Using the theorem in Sec. 116, together with the fact that the function $w = z^2$ maps the quadrant

$$D_z\colon x > 0,\ y > 0$$

onto that half plane (see Example 2, Sec. 14), point out how it follows that the function

$$H(x, y) = e^{-2xy} \sin(x^2 - y^2)$$

is harmonic in the quadrant D_z.

3. Example 3, Sec. 116, used the fact that the transformation $w = \operatorname{Log} z$ maps the right half plane onto the horizontal strip $-\pi/2 < v < \pi/2$. Verify this fact with the aid of Fig. 153.

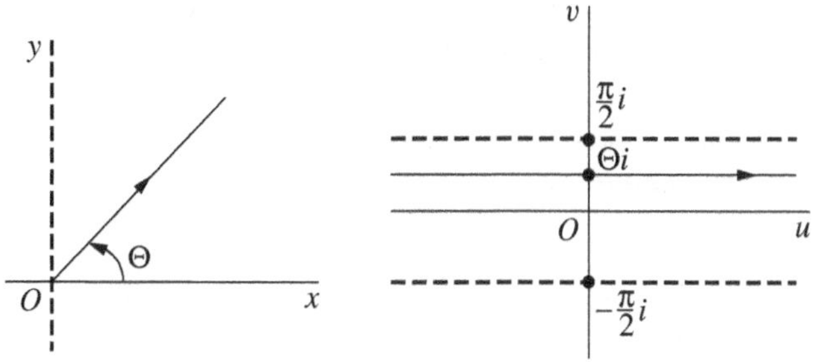

FIGURE 153
$w = \operatorname{Log} z$.

4. Under the transformation $w = \exp z$, the image of the segment $0 \le y \le \pi$ of the y axis is the semicircle $u^2 + v^2 = 1$, $v \ge 0$ (see Sec. 103). Also, the function

$$h(u, v) = \operatorname{Re}\left(2 - w + \frac{1}{w}\right) = 2 - u + \frac{u}{u^2 + v^2}$$

is harmonic everywhere in the w plane except for the origin; and it assumes the value $h = 2$ on the semicircle. Write an explicit expression for the function $H(x, y)$ in the theorem of Sec. 117. Then illustrate the theorem by showing directly that $H = 2$ along the segment $0 \le y \le \pi$ of the y axis.

5. The transformation $w = z^2$ maps the positive x and y axes and the origin in the z plane onto the u axis in the w plane. Consider the harmonic function

$$h(u, v) = \operatorname{Re}(e^{-w}) = e^{-u} \cos v,$$

and observe that its normal derivative h_v along the u axis is zero. Then illustrate the theorem in Sec. 117 when $f(z) = z^2$ by showing directly that the normal derivative of the function $H(x, y)$ defined in that theorem is zero along both positive axes in the z plane. (Note that the transformation $w = z^2$ is not conformal at the origin.)

6. Replace the function $h(u, v)$ in Exercise 5 by the harmonic function

$$h(u, v) = \operatorname{Re}(-2iw + e^{-w}) = 2v + e^{-u} \cos v.$$

Then show that $h_v = 2$ along the u axis but that $H_y = 4x$ along the positive x axis and $H_x = 4y$ along the positive y axis. This illustrates how a condition of the type

$$\frac{dh}{dn} = h_0 \ne 0$$

is *not necessarily* transformed into a condition of the type $dH/dN = h_0$.

7. Show that if a function $H(x, y)$ is a solution of a Neumann problem (Sec. 116), then $H(x, y) + A$, where A is any real constant, is also a solution of that problem.

8. Suppose that an analytic function $w = f(z) = u(x, y) + iv(x, y)$ maps a domain D_z in the z plane onto a domain D_w in the w plane; and let a function $h(u, v)$, with continuous partial derivatives of the first and second order, be defined on D_w. Use the chain rule for partial derivatives to show that if $H(x, y) = h[u(x, y), v(x, y)]$, then

$$H_{xx}(x, y) + H_{yy}(x, y) = [h_{uu}(u, v) + h_{vv}(u, v)]\,|f'(z)|^2.$$

Conclude that the function $H(x, y)$ is harmonic in D_z when $h(u, v)$ is harmonic in D_w. This is an alternative proof of the theorem in Sec. 116, even when the domain D_w is multiply connected.

Suggestion: In the simplifications, it is important to note that since f is analytic, the Cauchy–Riemann equations $u_x = v_y, u_y = -v_x$ hold and that the functions u and v both satisfy Laplace's equation. Also, the continuity conditions on the derivatives of h ensure that $h_{vu} = h_{uv}$.

9. Let $p(u, v)$ be a function that has continuous partial derivatives of the first and second order and satisfies ***Poisson's equation***

$$p_{uu}(u, v) + p_{vv}(u, v) = \Phi(u, v)$$

in a domain D_w of the w plane, where Φ is a prescribed function. Show how it follows from the identity obtained in Exercise 8 that if an analytic function

$$w = f(z) = u(x, y) + iv(x, y)$$

maps a domain D_z onto the domain D_w, then the function

$$P(x, y) = p[u(x, y), v(x, y)]$$

satisfies the Poisson equation

$$P_{xx}(x, y) + P_{yy}(x, y) = \Phi[u(x, y), v(x, y)]\,|f'(z)|^2$$

in D_z.

10. Suppose that $w = f(z) = u(x, y) + iv(x, y)$ is a conformal mapping of a smooth arc C onto a smooth arc Γ in the w plane. Let the function $h(u, v)$ be defined on Γ, and write

$$H(x, y) = h[u(x, y), v(x, y)].$$

(*a*) From calculus, we know that the x and y components of grad H are the partial derivatives H_x and H_y, respectively; likewise, grad h has components h_u and h_v. By applying the chain rule for partial derivatives and using the Cauchy–Riemann equations, show that if (x, y) is a point on C and (u, v) is its image on Γ, then

$$|\text{grad } H(x, y)| = |\text{grad } h(u, v)|\,|f'(z)|.$$

(*b*) Show that the angle from the arc C to grad H at a point (x, y) on C is equal to the angle from Γ to grad h at the image (u, v) of the point (x, y).

(*c*) Let s and σ denote distance along the arcs C and Γ, respectively; and let $\mathbf{t}$ and $\boldsymbol{\tau}$ denote unit tangent vectors at a point (x, y) on C and its image (u, v), in the direction of increasing distance. With the aid of the results in parts (*a*) and (*b*) and using the fact that

$$\frac{dH}{ds} = (\text{grad } H) \cdot \mathbf{t} \quad \text{and} \quad \frac{dh}{d\sigma} = (\text{grad } h) \cdot \boldsymbol{\tau},$$

show that the directional derivative along the arc Γ is transformed as follows:

$$\frac{dH}{ds} = \frac{dh}{d\sigma}\,|f'(z)|.$$

CHAPTER 10

APPLICATIONS OF CONFORMAL MAPPING

We now use conformal mapping to solve a number of physical problems involving Laplace's equation in two independent variables. Problems in heat conduction, electrostatic potential, and fluid flow will be treated. Since these problems are intended to illustrate methods, they will be kept on a fairly elementary level.

118. STEADY TEMPERATURES

In the theory of heat conduction, the ***flux*** across a surface within a solid body at a point on that surface is the quantity of heat flowing in a specified direction normal to the surface per unit time per unit area at the point. Flux is, therefore, measured in such units as calories per second per square centimeter. It is denoted here by Φ, and it varies with the normal derivative of the temperature T at the point on the surface:

$$\Phi = -K\frac{dT}{dN} \qquad (K > 0). \tag{1}$$

Relation (1) is known as ***Fourier's law*** and the constant K is called the ***thermal conductivity*** of the material of the solid, which is assumed to be homogeneous.*

*The law is named for the French mathematical physicist Joseph Fourier (1768–1830). His book, cited in Appendix 1, is a classic in the theory of heat conduction.

The points in the solid can be assigned rectangular coordinates in three-dimensional space, and we restrict our attention to those cases in which the temperature T varies with only the x and y coordinates. Since T does not vary with the coordinate along the axis perpendicular to the xy plane, the flow of heat is, then, two-dimensional and parallel to that plane. We agree, moreover, that the flow is in a steady state; that is, T does not vary with time.

It is assumed that no thermal energy is created or destroyed within the solid. That is, no heat sources or sinks are present there. Also, the temperature function $T(x, y)$ and its partial derivatives of the first and second order are continuous at each point interior to the solid. This statement and expression (1) for the flux of heat are postulates in the mathematical theory of heat conduction, postulates that also apply at points within a solid containing a continuous distribution of sources or sinks.

Consider now an element of volume that is interior to the solid and has the shape of a rectangular prism of unit height perpendicular to the xy plane, with base Δx by Δy in the plane (Fig. 154). The time rate of flow of heat toward the right across the left-hand face is $-KT_x(x, y)\Delta y$; and toward the right across the right-hand face, it is $-KT_x(x + \Delta x, y)\Delta y$. Subtracting the first rate from the second, we obtain the net rate of heat loss from the element through those two faces. This resultant rate can be written

$$-K\left[\frac{T_x(x + \Delta x, y) - T_x(x, y)}{\Delta x}\right]\Delta x\Delta y,$$

or

$$(2) \qquad -KT_{xx}(x, y)\Delta x\Delta y$$

if Δx is very small. Expression (2) is, of course, an approximation whose accuracy increases as Δx and Δy are made smaller.

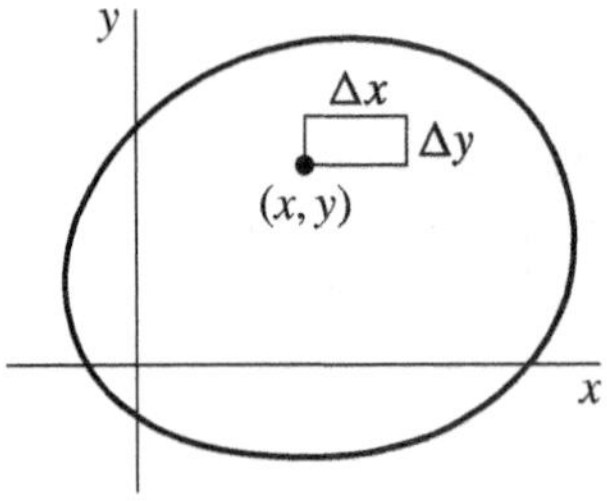

FIGURE 154

In like manner, the resultant rate of heat loss through the other two faces perpendicular to the xy plane is found to be

$$(3) \qquad -KT_{yy}(x, y)\Delta x\Delta y.$$

Heat enters or leaves the element only through these four faces, and the temperatures within the element are steady. Hence the sum of expressions (2) and (3) is zero; that is,

$$(4) \qquad T_{xx}(x, y) + T_{yy}(x, y) = 0.$$

The temperature function thus satisfies Laplace's equation at each interior point of the solid.

In view of equation (4) and the continuity of the temperature function and its partial derivatives, T *is a harmonic function of* x *and* y in the domain representing the interior of the solid body.

The surfaces $T(x, y) = c_1$, where c_1 is any real constant, are the ***isotherms*** within the solid. They can also be considered as curves in the xy plane; then $T(x, y)$ can be interpreted as the temperature at a point (x, y) in a thin sheet of material in that plane, with the faces of the sheet thermally insulated. The isotherms are the level curves of the function T.

The gradient of T is perpendicular to an isotherm at each point on it, and the maximum flux at such a point is in the direction of the gradient there. If $T(x, y)$ denotes temperatures in a thin sheet and if S is a harmonic conjugate of the function T, then a curve $S(x, y) = c_2$ has the gradient of T as a tangent vector at each point where the analytic function $T(x, y) + iS(x, y)$ is conformal (see Exercise 2, Sec. 27). The curves $S(x, y) = c_2$ are called ***lines of flow***.

If the normal derivative dT/dN is zero along any part of the boundary of the sheet, then the flux of heat across that part is zero. That is, the part is thermally insulated and is, therefore, a line of flow.

The function T may also denote the concentration of a substance that is diffusing through a solid. In that case, K is the diffusion constant. The above discussion and the derivation of equation (4) apply as well to steady-state diffusion.

119. STEADY TEMPERATURES IN A HALF PLANE

Let us find an expression for the steady temperatures $T(x, y)$ in a thin semi-infinite plate $y \geq 0$ whose faces are insulated and whose edge $y = 0$ is kept at temperature zero except for the segment $-1 < x < 1$, where it is kept at temperature unity (Fig. 155). The function $T(x, y)$ is to be bounded; this condition is natural if we consider the given plate as the limiting case of the plate $0 \leq y \leq y_0$ whose upper edge is kept at a fixed temperature as y_0 is increased. In fact, it would be physically reasonable to stipulate that $T(x, y)$ approach zero as y tends to infinity.

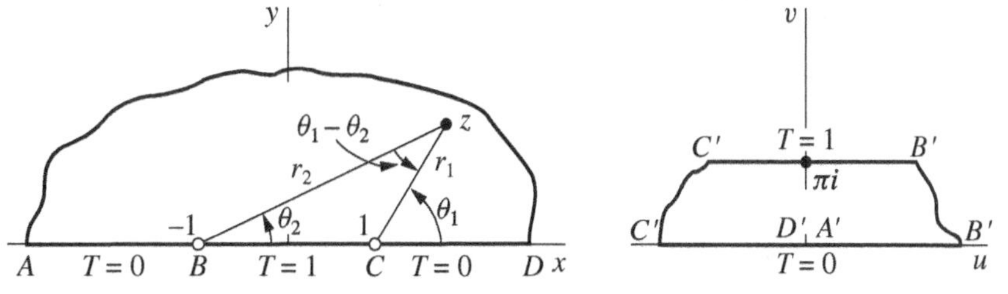

FIGURE 155

$$w = \log \frac{z-1}{z+1} \left(\frac{r_1}{r_2} > 0, -\frac{\pi}{2} < \theta_1 - \theta_2 < \frac{3\pi}{2} \right).$$

The boundary value problem to be solved can be written

$$(1) \qquad T_{xx}(x, y) + T_{yy}(x, y) = 0 \qquad (-\infty < x < \infty, y > 0),$$

$$(2) \qquad T(x, 0) = \begin{cases} 1 & \text{when } |x| < 1, \\ 0 & \text{when } |x| > 1; \end{cases}$$

also, $|T(x, y)| < M$ where M is some positive constant. This is a Dirichlet problem (Sec. 116) for the upper half plane $y \geq 0$. Our method of solution will be to obtain a new Dirichlet problem for a region in the uv plane. That region will be the image of the half plane under a transformation $w = f(z)$ that is analytic in the domain $y > 0$ and conformal along the boundary $y = 0$ except at the points $(\pm 1, 0)$, where $f(z)$ is undefined. It will be a simple matter to discover a bounded harmonic function satisfying the new problem. The two theorems in Chap. 9 will then be applied to transform the solution of the problem in the uv plane into a solution of the original problem in the xy plane. Specifically, a harmonic function of u and v will be transformed into a harmonic function of x and y, and the boundary conditions in the uv plane will be preserved on corresponding portions of the boundary in the xy plane. There should be no confusion if we use the same symbol T to denote the different temperature functions in the two planes.

Let us write

$$z - 1 = r_1 \exp(i\theta_1) \quad \text{and} \quad z + 1 = r_2 \exp(i\theta_2),$$

where $0 \leq \theta_k \leq \pi$ $(k = 1, 2)$. The transformation

$$(3) \quad w = \log \frac{z-1}{z+1} = \ln \frac{r_1}{r_2} + i(\theta_1 - \theta_2) \qquad \left(\frac{r_1}{r_2} > 0, -\frac{\pi}{2} < \theta_1 - \theta_2 < \frac{3\pi}{2} \right)$$

is defined on the upper half plane $y \geq 0$, except for the two points $z = \pm 1$, since $0 \leq \theta_1 - \theta_2 \leq \pi$ when $y \geq 0$. (See Fig. 155.) Now the value of the logarithm is the principal value when $0 \leq \theta_1 - \theta_2 \leq \pi$, and we recall from Example 3 in Sec. 102 that the upper half plane $y > 0$ is then mapped onto the horizontal strip $0 < v < \pi$ in the w plane. As already noted in that example, the mapping is shown with corresponding boundary points in Fig. 19 of Appendix 2. Indeed, it was that figure which suggested transformation (3) here. The segment of the x axis between $z = -1$ and $z = 1$, where $\theta_1 - \theta_2 = \pi$, is mapped onto the upper edge of the strip; and the rest of the x axis, where $\theta_1 - \theta_2 = 0$, is mapped onto the lower edge. The required analyticity and conformality conditions are evidently satisfied by transformation (3).

A bounded harmonic function of u and v that is zero on the edge $v = 0$ of the strip and unity on the edge $v = \pi$ is clearly

$$(4) \qquad T = \frac{1}{\pi} v;$$

it is harmonic since it is the imaginary component of the entire function $(1/\pi)w$. Changing to x and y coordinates by means of the equation

$$(5) \qquad w = \ln \left| \frac{z-1}{z+1} \right| + i \arg \left(\frac{z-1}{z+1} \right),$$

we find that

$$v = \arg\left[\frac{(z-1)(\overline{z}+1)}{(z+1)(\overline{z+1})}\right] = \arg\left[\frac{x^2+y^2-1+i2y}{(x+1)^2+y^2}\right],$$

or

$$v = \arctan\left(\frac{2y}{x^2+y^2-1}\right).$$

The range of the arctangent function here is from 0 to π since

$$\arg\left(\frac{z-1}{z+1}\right) = \theta_1 - \theta_2$$

and $0 \le \theta_1 - \theta_2 \le \pi$. Expression (4) now takes the form

$$T = \frac{1}{\pi}\arctan\left(\frac{2y}{x^2+y^2-1}\right) \qquad (0 \le \arctan t \le \pi). \tag{6}$$

Since the function (4) is harmonic in the strip $0 < v < \pi$ and since transformation (3) is analytic in the half plane $y > 0$, we may apply the theorem in Sec. 116 to conclude that the function (6) is harmonic in that half plane. The boundary conditions for the two harmonic functions are the same on corresponding parts of the boundaries because they are of the type $h = h_0$, treated in the theorem of Sec. 117. The bounded function (6) is, therefore, the desired solution of the original problem. One can, of course, verify directly that the function (6) satisfies Laplace's equation and has the values tending to those indicated on the left in Fig. 155 as the point (x, y) approaches the x axis from above.

The isotherms $T(x, y) = c_1$ $(0 < c_1 < 1)$ are arcs of the circles

$$x^2 + (y - \cot \pi c_1)^2 = \csc^2 \pi c_1,$$

passing through the points $(\pm 1, 0)$ and with centers on the y axis.

Finally, we note that since the product of a harmonic function by a constant is also harmonic, the function

$$T = \frac{T_0}{\pi}\arctan\left(\frac{2y}{x^2+y^2-1}\right) \qquad (0 \le \arctan t \le \pi)$$

represents steady temperatures in the given half plane when the temperature $T = 1$ along the segment $-1 < x < 1$ of the x axis is replaced by any constant temperature $T = T_0$.

120. A RELATED PROBLEM

Consider a semi-infinite slab in the three-dimensional space bounded by the planes $x = \pm\pi/2$ and $y = 0$ when the first two surfaces are kept at temperature zero and the third at temperature unity. We wish to find a formula for the temperature $T(x, y)$ at any interior point of the slab. The problem is also that of finding temperatures in a thin plate having the form of a semi-infinite strip $-\pi/2 \le x \le \pi/2$, $y \ge 0$ when the faces of the plate are perfectly insulated (Fig. 156).

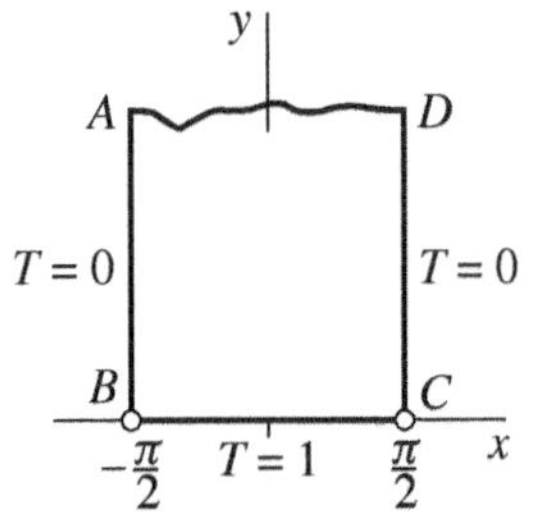

FIGURE 156

The boundary value problem here is

$$T_{xx}(x, y) + T_{yy}(x, y) = 0 \qquad \left(-\frac{\pi}{2} < x < \frac{\pi}{2}, y > 0\right), \tag{1}$$

$$T\left(-\frac{\pi}{2}, y\right) = T\left(\frac{\pi}{2}, y\right) = 0 \qquad (y > 0), \tag{2}$$

$$T(x, 0) = 1 \qquad \left(-\frac{\pi}{2} < x < \frac{\pi}{2}\right), \tag{3}$$

where $T(x, y)$ is bounded.

In view of the example in Sec. 104, as well as Fig. 9 of Appendix 2, the mapping

$$w = \sin z \tag{4}$$

transforms this boundary value problem into the one posed in Sec. 119 (Fig. 155). Hence, according to solution (6) in that section,

$$T = \frac{1}{\pi} \arctan\left(\frac{2v}{u^2 + v^2 - 1}\right) \qquad (0 \le \arctan t \le \pi). \tag{5}$$

The change of variables indicated in equation (4) can be written (see Sec. 37)

$$u = \sin x \cosh y, \quad v = \cos x \sinh y;$$

and the harmonic function (5) becomes

$$T = \frac{1}{\pi} \arctan\left(\frac{2 \cos x \sinh y}{\sin^2 x \cosh^2 y + \cos^2 x \sinh^2 y - 1}\right).$$

Since the denominator here reduces to $\sinh^2 y - \cos^2 x$, the quotient can be put in the form

$$\frac{2 \cos x \sinh y}{\sinh^2 y - \cos^2 x} = \frac{2(\cos x / \sinh y)}{1 - (\cos x / \sinh y)^2} = \tan 2\alpha,$$

where $\tan \alpha = \cos x / \sinh y$. Hence $T = (2/\pi)\alpha$; that is,

$$T = \frac{2}{\pi} \arctan\left(\frac{\cos x}{\sinh y}\right) \qquad \left(0 \le \arctan t \le \frac{\pi}{2}\right). \tag{6}$$

This arctangent function has the range 0 to $\pi/2$ because its argument is nonnegative.

Since $\sin z$ is entire and the function (5) is harmonic in the half plane $v > 0$, the function (6) is harmonic in the strip $-\pi/2 < x < \pi/2$, $y > 0$. Also, the function (5) satisfies the boundary condition $T = 1$ when $|u| < 1$ and $v = 0$, as well as the condition $T = 0$ when $|u| > 1$ and $v = 0$. The function (6) thus satisfies boundary conditions (2) and (3). Moreover, $|T(x, y)| \leq 1$ throughout the strip. Expression (6) is, therefore, the temperature formula that is sought.

The isotherms $T(x, y) = c_1$ $(0 < c_1 < 1)$ are the portions of the surfaces

$$\cos x = \tan\left(\frac{\pi c_1}{2}\right) \sinh y$$

within the slab, each surface passing through the points $(\pm\pi/2, 0)$ in the xy plane. If K is the thermal conductivity, the flux of heat into the slab through the surface lying in the plane $y = 0$ is

$$-KT_y(x, 0) = \frac{2K}{\pi \cos x} \qquad \left(-\frac{\pi}{2} < x < \frac{\pi}{2}\right).$$

The flux outward through the surface lying in the plane $x = \pi/2$ is

$$-KT_x\left(\frac{\pi}{2}, y\right) = \frac{2K}{\pi \sinh y} \qquad (y > 0).$$

The boundary value problem posed in this section can also be solved by the *method of separation of variables*. That method is more direct, but it gives the solution in the form of an infinite series.*

121. TEMPERATURES IN A QUADRANT

Let us find the steady temperatures in a thin plate having the form of a quadrant if a segment at the end of one edge is insulated, if the rest of that edge is kept at a fixed temperature, and if the second edge is kept at another fixed temperature. The surfaces are insulated, and so the problem is two-dimensional.

The temperature scale and the unit of length can be chosen so that the boundary value problem for the temperature function T becomes

(1) $$T_{xx}(x, y) + T_{yy}(x, y) = 0 \qquad (x > 0, y > 0),$$

(2) $$\begin{cases} T_y(x, 0) = 0 & \text{when } 0 < x < 1, \\ T(x, 0) = 1 & \text{when } x > 1, \end{cases}$$

(3) $$T(0, y) = 0 \qquad (y > 0),$$

where $T(x, y)$ is bounded in the quadrant. The plate and its boundary conditions are shown on the left in Fig. 157. Conditions (2) prescribe the values of the normal

*A similar problem is treated in the authors' *Fourier Series and Boundary Value Problems*, 8th ed., pp. 133–134, 2012. Also, a short discussion of the uniqueness of solutions to boundary value problems can be found in Chap. 11 of that book.

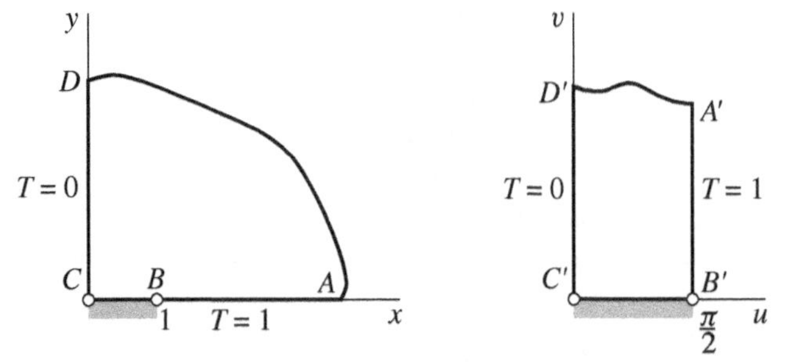

FIGURE 157

derivative of the function T over a part of a boundary line and the values of the function itself over another part of that line. The separation of variables method mentioned at the end of Sec. 120 is not adapted to such problems with different types of conditions along the same boundary line.

As indicated in Fig. 10 of Appendix 2, the transformation

$$z = \sin w \tag{4}$$

is a one to one mapping of the semi-infinite strip $0 \le u \le \pi/2, v \ge 0$ onto the quadrant $x \ge 0, y \ge 0$. Observe that the existence of an inverse is ensured by the fact that the given transformation is both one to one and onto. Since transformation (4) is conformal throughout the strip except at the point $w = \pi/2$, the inverse transformation must be conformal throughout the quadrant except at the point $z = 1$. That inverse transformation maps the segment $0 < x < 1$ of the x axis onto the base of the strip and the rest of the boundary onto the sides of the strip as shown in Fig. 157.

Since the inverse of transformation (4) is conformal in the quadrant, except when $z = 1$, the solution to the given problem can be obtained by finding a function that is harmonic in the strip and satisfies the boundary conditions shown on the right in Fig. 157. Observe that these boundary conditions are of the types $h = h_0$ and $dh/dn = 0$ in the theorem of Sec. 117.

The required temperature function T for the new boundary value problem is clearly

$$T = \frac{2}{\pi}u, \tag{5}$$

the function $(2/\pi)u$ being the real component of the entire function $(2/\pi)w$. We must now express T in terms of x and y.

To obtain u in terms of x and y, we first note that according to equation (4) and Sec. 37,

$$x = \sin u \cosh v, \quad y = \cos u \sinh v. \tag{6}$$

When $0 < u < \pi/2$, both $\sin u$ and $\cos u$ are nonzero; and, consequently,

$$\frac{x^2}{\sin^2 u} - \frac{y^2}{\cos^2 u} = 1. \tag{7}$$

Now it is convenient to observe that for each fixed u, hyperbola (7) has foci at the points

$$z = \pm\sqrt{\sin^2 u + \cos^2 u} = \pm 1$$

and that the length of the transverse axis, which is the line segment joining the two vertices $(\pm \sin u, 0)$, is $2 \sin u$. Thus the absolute value of the difference of the distances between the foci and a point (x, y) lying on the part of the hyperbola in the first quadrant is

$$\sqrt{(x+1)^2 + y^2} - \sqrt{(x-1)^2 + y^2} = 2 \sin u.$$

It follows directly from equations (6) that this relation also holds when $u = 0$ or $u = \pi/2$. In view of equation (5), then, the required temperature function is

$$T = \frac{2}{\pi} \arcsin \left[\frac{\sqrt{(x+1)^2 + y^2} - \sqrt{(x-1)^2 + y^2}}{2} \right] \tag{8}$$

where, since $0 \le u \le \pi/2$, the arcsine function has the range 0 to $\pi/2$.

If we wish to verify that this function satisfies boundary conditions (2), we must remember that $\sqrt{(x-1)^2}$ denotes $x - 1$ when $x > 1$ and $1 - x$ when $0 < x < 1$, the square roots being positive. Note, too, that the temperature at any point along the insulated part of the lower edge of the plate is

$$T(x, 0) = \frac{2}{\pi} \arcsin x \qquad (0 < x < 1).$$

It can be seen from equation (5) that the isotherms $T(x, y) = c_1$ $(0 < c_1 < 1)$ are the parts of the confocal hyperbolas (7), where $u = \pi c_1/2$, which lie in the first quadrant. Since the function $(2/\pi)v$ is a harmonic conjugate of the function (5), the lines of flow are quarters of the confocal ellipses obtained by holding v constant in equations (6).

EXERCISES

1. Use the function Log z to find an expression for the bounded steady temperatures in a plate having the form of a quadrant $x \ge 0$, $y \ge 0$ (Fig. 158) if its faces are perfectly insulated and its edges have temperatures $T(x, 0) = 0$ and $T(0, y) = 1$. Find the isotherms and lines of flow, and draw some of them.

Ans. $T = \dfrac{2}{\pi} \arctan\left(\dfrac{y}{x}\right)$.

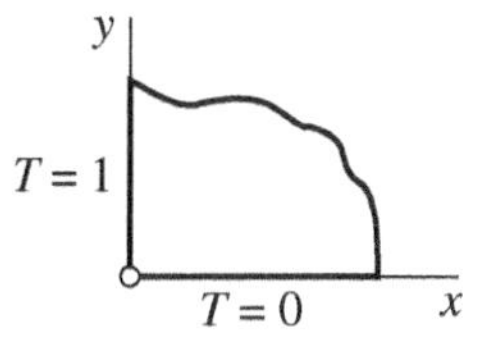

FIGURE 158

2. Solve the following Dirichlet problem for a semi-infinite strip (Fig. 159):

$$H_{xx}(x, y) + H_{yy}(x, y) = 0 \qquad (0 < x < \pi/2,\ y > 0),$$
$$H(x, 0) = 0 \qquad (0 < x < \pi/2),$$
$$H(0, y) = 1, \quad H(\pi/2, y) = 0 \qquad (y > 0),$$

where $0 \le H(x, y) \le 1$.

Suggestion: This problem can be transformed into the one in Exercise 1.

Ans. $H = \dfrac{2}{\pi} \arctan\left(\dfrac{\tanh y}{\tan x}\right).$

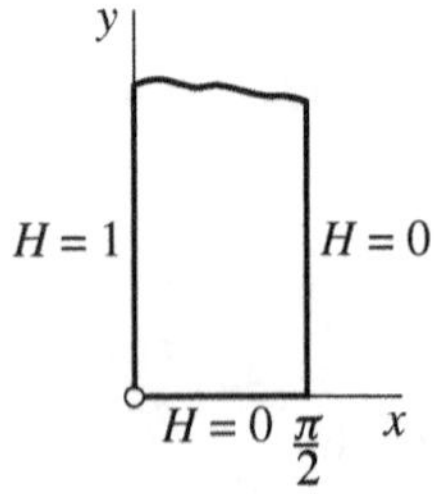

FIGURE 159

3. Derive an expression for temperatures $T(r, \theta)$ in a semicircular plate $r \le 1, 0 \le \theta \le \pi$ with insulated faces if $T = 1$ along the radial edge $\theta = 0$ $(0 < r < 1)$ and $T = 0$ on the rest of the boundary.

Suggestion: This problem can be transformed into the one in Exercise 2.

Ans. $T = \dfrac{2}{\pi} \arctan\left(\dfrac{1 - r}{1 + r} \cot \dfrac{\theta}{2}\right).$

4. Find the steady temperatures in a solid whose shape is that of a long cylindrical wedge if its boundary planes $\theta = 0$ and $\theta = \theta_0$ $(0 < r < r_0)$ are kept at constant temperatures zero and T_0, respectively, and if its surface $r = r_0$ $(0 < \theta < \theta_0)$ is perfectly insulated (Fig. 160).

Ans. $T = \dfrac{T_0}{\theta_0} \arctan\left(\dfrac{y}{x}\right).$

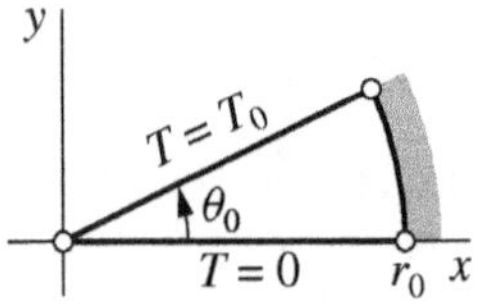

FIGURE 160

5. Find the bounded steady temperatures $T(x, y)$ in the semi-infinite solid $y \ge 0$ if $T = 0$ on the part $x < -1$ $(y = 0)$ of the boundary, if $T = 1$ on the part $x > 1$ $(y = 0)$, and if the strip $-1 < x < 1$ $(y = 0)$ of the boundary is insulated (Fig. 161).

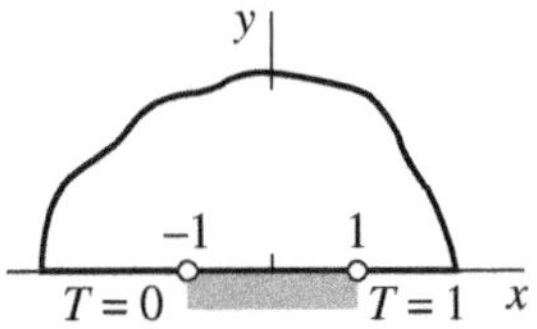

FIGURE 161

$$\textit{Ans. } T = \frac{1}{2} + \frac{1}{\pi}\arcsin\left[\frac{\sqrt{(x+1)^2+y^2} - \sqrt{(x-1)^2+y^2}}{2}\right]$$

$(-\pi/2 \le \arcsin t \le \pi/2)$.

6. The portions $x < 0\ (y = 0)$ and $x < 0\ (y = \pi)$ of the edges of an infinite horizontal plate $0 \le y \le \pi$ are thermally insulated, as are the faces of the plate. Also, the conditions $T(x, 0) = 1$ and $T(x, \pi) = 0$ are maintained when $x > 0$ (Fig. 162). Find the steady temperatures in the plate.

Suggestion: This problem can be transformed into the one in Exercise 5.

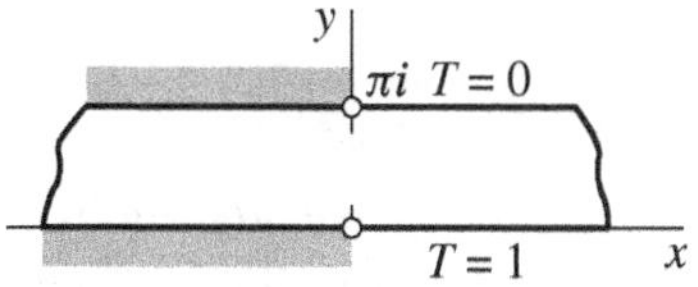

FIGURE 162

7. Find the bounded steady temperatures in the solid $x \ge 0, y \ge 0$ when the boundary surfaces are kept at fixed temperatures except for insulated strips of equal width at the corner, as shown in Fig. 163.

Suggestion: This problem can be transformed into the one in Exercise 5.

$$\textit{Ans. } T = \frac{1}{2} + \frac{1}{\pi}\arcsin\left[\frac{\sqrt{(x^2-y^2+1)^2+(2xy)^2} - \sqrt{(x^2-y^2-1)^2+(2xy)^2}}{2}\right]$$

$(-\pi/2 \le \arctan t \le \pi/2)$.

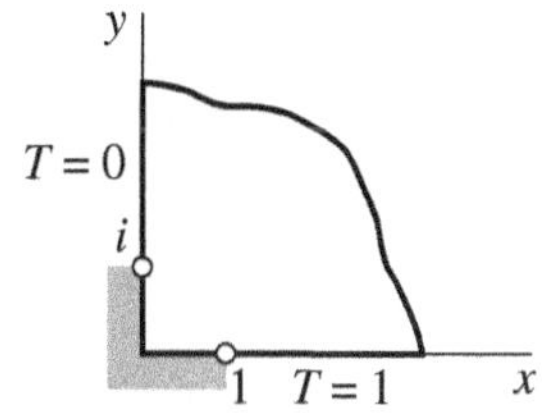

FIGURE 163

8. Solve the boundary value problem for the plate $x \ge 0, y \ge 0$ in the z plane when the faces are insulated and the boundary conditions are those indicated in Fig. 164.

Suggestion: Use the mapping

$$w = \frac{i}{z} = \frac{i\bar{z}}{|z|^2}$$

to transform this problem into the one posed in Sec. 121 (Fig. 157).

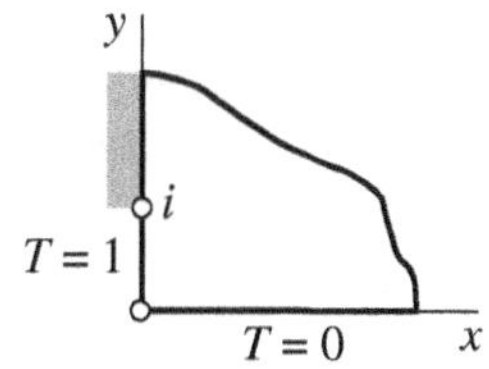

FIGURE 164

9. In the problem of the semi-infinite plate shown on the left in Fig. 155 (Sec. 119), obtain a harmonic conjugate of the temperature function $T(x, y)$ from equation (5), Sec. 119, and find the lines of flow of heat. Show that those lines of flow consist of the upper half of the y axis and the upper halves of certain circles on either side of that axis, the centers of the circles lying on the segment AB or CD of the x axis.

10. Show that if the function T in Sec. 119 is not required to be bounded, the harmonic function (4) in that section can be replaced by the harmonic function

$$T = \operatorname{Im}\left(\frac{1}{\pi}w + A\cosh w\right) = \frac{1}{\pi}v + A\sinh u \sin v,$$

where A is an arbitrary real constant. Conclude that the solution of the Dirichlet problem for the strip in the uv plane (Fig. 155) would not, then, be unique.

11. Suppose that the condition that T be bounded is omitted from the problem for temperatures in the semi-infinite slab of Sec. 120 (Fig. 156). Show that an infinite number of solutions are then possible by noting the effect of adding to the solution found there the imaginary part of the function $A \sin z$, where A is an arbitrary real constant.

12. Consider a thin plate, with insulated faces, whose shape is the upper half of the region enclosed by an ellipse with foci $(\pm 1, 0)$. The temperature on the elliptical part of its boundary is $T = 1$. The temperature along the segment $-1 < x < 1$ of the x axis is $T = 0$, and the rest of the boundary along the x axis is insulated. With the aid of Fig. 11 in Appendix 2, find the lines of flow of heat.

13. According to Sec. 59 and Exercise 5 of that section, if $f(z) = u(x, y) + iv(x, y)$ is continuous on a closed bounded region R and analytic and not constant in the interior of R, then the function $u(x, y)$ reaches its maximum and minimum values on the boundary of R, and never in the interior. By interpreting $u(x, y)$ as a steady temperature, state a physical reason why that property of maximum and minimum values should hold true.

122. ELECTROSTATIC POTENTIAL

In an electrostatic force field, the ***field intensity*** at a point is a vector representing the force exerted on a unit positive charge placed at that point. The electrostatic ***potential*** is a scalar function of the space coordinates such that, at each point, its directional derivative in any direction is the negative of the component of the field intensity in that direction.

For two stationary charged particles, the magnitude of the force of attraction or repulsion exerted by one particle on the other is directly proportional to the product of the charges and inversely proportional to the square of the distance between those particles. From this inverse-square law, it can be shown that the potential at a point due to a single particle in space is inversely proportional to the distance between the point and the particle. In any region free of charges, the potential due to a distribution of charges outside that region can be shown to satisfy Laplace's equation for three-dimensional space.

If conditions are such that the potential V is the same in all planes parallel to the xy plane, then in regions free of charges V is a harmonic function of just the two variables x and y:

$$V_{xx}(x, y) + V_{yy}(x, y) = 0.$$

The field intensity vector at each point is parallel to the xy plane, with x and y components $-V_x(x, y)$ and $-V_y(x, y)$, respectively. That vector is, therefore, the negative of the gradient of $V(x, y)$.

A surface along which $V(x, y)$ is constant is an equipotential surface. The tangential component of the field intensity vector at a point on a conducting surface is zero in the static case since charges are free to move on such a surface. Hence $V(x, y)$ is constant along the surface of a conductor, and that surface is an ***equipotential***.

If U is a harmonic conjugate of V, the curves $U(x, y) = c_2$ in the xy plane are called ***flux lines***. When such a curve intersects an equipotential curve $V(x, y) = c_1$ at a point where the derivative of the analytic function $V(x, y) + iU(x, y)$ is not zero, the two curves are orthogonal at that point and the field intensity is tangent to the flux line there.

Boundary value problems for the potential V are the same mathematical problems as those for steady temperatures T; and, as in the case of steady temperatures, the methods of complex variables are limited to two-dimensional problems. The problem posed in Sec. 120 (see Fig. 156), for instance, can be interpreted as that of finding the two-dimensional electrostatic potential in the empty space

$$-\frac{\pi}{2} < x < \frac{\pi}{2}, y > 0$$

bounded by the conducting planes $x = \pm\pi/2$ and $y = 0$, insulated at their intersections, when the first two surfaces are kept at potential zero and the third at potential unity.

The potential in the steady flow of electricity in a conducting sheet lying in a plane is also a harmonic function at points free from sources and sinks. Gravitational potential is a further example of a harmonic function in physics.

123. EXAMPLES

The two examples here illustrate how conformal mappings can often be used in solving potential problems.

EXAMPLE 1. A long hollow circular cylinder is made out of a thin sheet of conducting material, and the cylinder is split lengthwise to form two equal parts. Those parts are separated by slender strips of insulating material and are used as electrodes, one of which is grounded at potential zero and the other kept at a different fixed potential. We take the coordinate axes and units of length and potential difference as indicated on the left in Fig. 165. We then interpret the electrostatic potential $V(x, y)$ over any cross section of the enclosed space that is distant from the ends of the cylinder as a harmonic function inside the circle $x^2 + y^2 = 1$ in the xy plane. Note that $V = 0$ on the upper half of the circle and that $V = 1$ on the lower half.

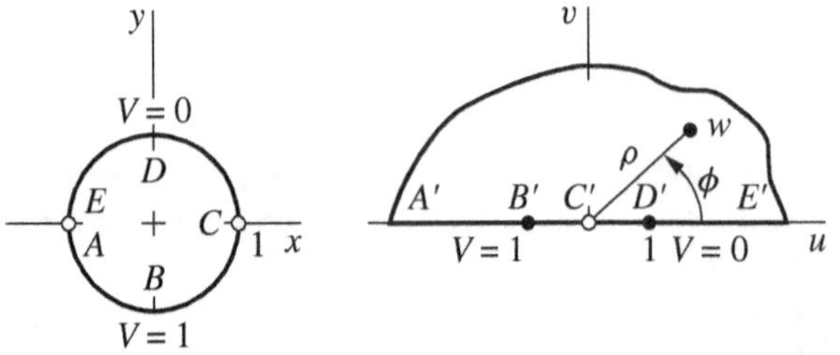

FIGURE 165
$w = i\dfrac{1-z}{1+z}$

A linear fractional transformation that maps the upper half plane onto the interior of the unit circle centered at the origin, the positive real axis onto the upper half of the circle, and the negative real axis onto the lower half of the circle is verified in Exercise 1, Sec. 102. The result is given in Fig. 13 of Appendix 2; interchanging z and w there, we find that the inverse of the transformation

$$z = \frac{i-w}{i+w} \tag{1}$$

gives us a new problem for V in a half plane, indicated on the right in Fig. 165.

Now the imaginary component of

$$\frac{1}{\pi}\text{Log}\, w = \frac{1}{\pi}\ln\rho + i\frac{1}{\pi}\phi \qquad (\rho > 0, 0 \le \phi \le \pi) \tag{2}$$

is a bounded function of u and v that assumes the required constant values on the two parts $\phi = 0$ and $\phi = \pi$ of the u axis. Hence the desired harmonic function for the half plane is

$$V = \frac{1}{\pi}\arctan\left(\frac{v}{u}\right), \tag{3}$$

where the values of the arctangent function range from 0 to π.

The inverse of transformation (1) is

$$w = i\frac{1-z}{1+z}, \tag{4}$$

from which u and v can be expressed in terms of x and y. Equation (3) then becomes

$$V = \frac{1}{\pi}\arctan\left(\frac{1-x^2-y^2}{2y}\right) \qquad (0 \le \arctan t \le \pi). \tag{5}$$

The function (5) is the potential function for the space enclosed by the cylindrical electrodes since it is harmonic inside the circle and assumes the required values on the semicircles. If we wish to verify this solution, we must note that

$$\lim_{\substack{t\to 0\\ t>0}} \arctan t = 0 \quad \text{and} \quad \lim_{\substack{t\to 0\\ t<0}} \arctan t = \pi.$$

The equipotential curves $V(x, y) = c_1$ $(0 < c_1 < 1)$ in the circular region are arcs of the circles

$$x^2 + (y + \tan \pi c_1)^2 = \sec^2 \pi c_1,$$

with each circle passing through the points $(\pm 1, 0)$. Also, the segment of the x axis between those points is the equipotential $V(x, y) = 1/2$. A harmonic conjugate U of V is $-(1/\pi) \ln \rho$, or the imaginary part of the function $-(i/\pi)\text{Log}\, w$. In view of equation (4), U may be written

$$U = -\frac{1}{\pi} \ln \left| \frac{1-z}{1+z} \right|.$$

From this equation, it can be seen that the flux lines $U(x, y) = c_2$ are arcs of circles with centers on the x axis. The segment of the y axis between the electrodes is also a flux line.

EXAMPLE 2. Let r_0 denote any real number greater than unity. The Dirichlet problem shown on the left in Fig. 166 can be solved using the solution of the one on the right in that figure. The following series solution of the one on the right can be found by the method of separation of variables, mentioned in Sec. 120:*

$$V = \frac{4}{\pi} \sum_{n=1}^{\infty} \frac{\sinh(\alpha_n v)}{\sinh(\alpha_n \pi)} \cdot \frac{\sin(\alpha_n u)}{2n-1} \tag{6}$$

where

$$\alpha_n = \frac{(2n-1)\pi}{\ln r_0} \qquad (n = 1, 2, \ldots). \tag{7}$$

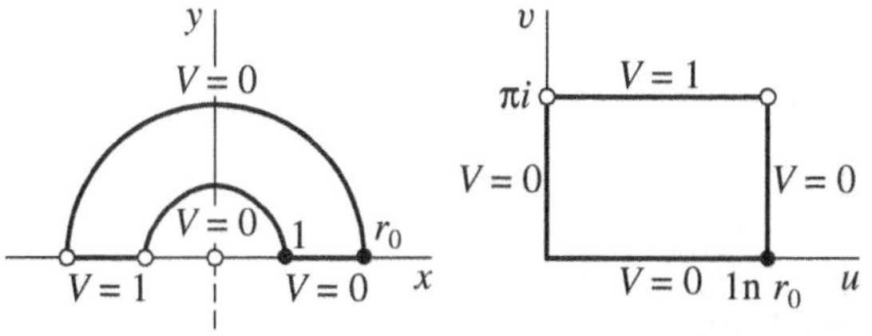

FIGURE 166
$w = \log z \quad \left(r > 0, -\frac{\pi}{2} < \theta < \frac{3\pi}{2}\right).$

In order to solve the first boundary value problem in Fig. 166, we now introduce the branch

$$\log z = \ln r + i\theta \qquad \left(r > 0, -\frac{\pi}{2} < \theta < \frac{3\pi}{2}\right) \tag{8}$$

of the logarithmic function. By examining the images of appropriate portions of rays from the origin in the z plane, one can readily see that transformation (8) is a one to

*See the authors' *Fourier Series and Boundary Value Problems*, 8th ed., pp. 131–133, 2012.

one mapping of the semicircular region in Fig. 166 onto the rectangular region there. Also, corresponding points on the two boundaries are as indicated.

The theorems in Secs. 116 and 117 now tell us that since the real and imaginary parts u and v of the function (8) are harmonic in the rectangle in the w plane,

$$V(r, \theta) = \frac{4}{\pi}\sum_{n=1}^{\infty} \frac{\sinh(\alpha_n \theta)}{\sinh(\alpha_n \pi)} \cdot \frac{\sin(\alpha_n \ln r)}{2n-1} \tag{9}$$

where the numbers α_n are defined by equation (7).

EXERCISES

1. The harmonic function (3) of Sec. 123 is bounded in the half plane $v \geq 0$ and satisfies the boundary conditions indicated on the right in Fig. 165. Show that if the imaginary component of Ae^w, where A is any real constant, is added to that function, then the resulting function satisfies all the requirements except for the boundedness condition.

2. Show that transformation (4) of Sec. 123 maps the upper half of the circular region shown on the left in Fig. 165 onto the first quadrant of the w plane and the diameter CE onto the positive v axis. Then find the electrostatic potential V in the space enclosed by the half cylinder $x^2 + y^2 = 1$, $y \geq 0$ and the plane $y = 0$ when $V = 0$ on the cylindrical surface and $V = 1$ on the planar surface (Fig. 167).

   Ans. $V = \dfrac{2}{\pi}\arctan\left(\dfrac{1 - x^2 - y^2}{2y}\right)$.

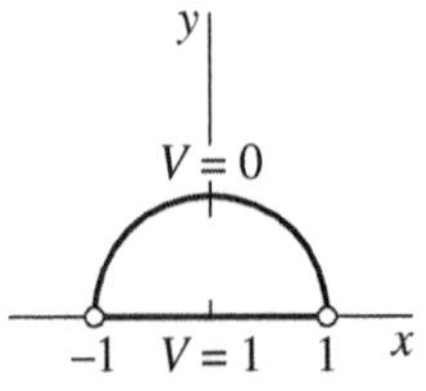

FIGURE 167

3. Find the electrostatic potential $V(r, \theta)$ in the space $0 < r < 1, 0 < \theta < \pi/4$, bounded by the half planes $\theta = 0$ and $\theta = \pi/4$ and the portion $0 \leq \theta \leq \pi/4$ of the cylindrical surface $r = 1$, when $V = 1$ on the planar surfaces and $V = 0$ on the cylindrical one. (See Exercise 2.) Verify that the function obtained satisfies the boundary conditions.

4. Note that all branches of $\log z$ have the same real component, which is harmonic everywhere except at the origin. Then write an expression for the electrostatic potential $V(x, y)$ in the space between two coaxial conducting cylindrical surfaces $x^2 + y^2 = 1$ and $x^2 + y^2 = r_0^2$ $(r_0 \neq 1)$ when $V = 0$ on the first surface and $V = 1$ on the second.

   Ans. $V = \dfrac{\ln(x^2 + y^2)}{2 \ln r_0}$.

5. Find the bounded electrostatic potential $V(x, y)$ in the space $y > 0$ bounded by an infinite conducting plane $y = 0$ one strip $(-a < x < a, y = 0)$ of which is insulated from the rest of the plane and kept at potential $V = 1$, while $V = 0$ on the rest (Fig. 168). Verify that the function obtained satisfies the stated boundary conditions.

$$\textit{Ans. } V = \frac{1}{\pi}\arctan\left(\frac{2ay}{x^2+y^2-a^2}\right) \quad (0 \le \arctan t \le \pi).$$

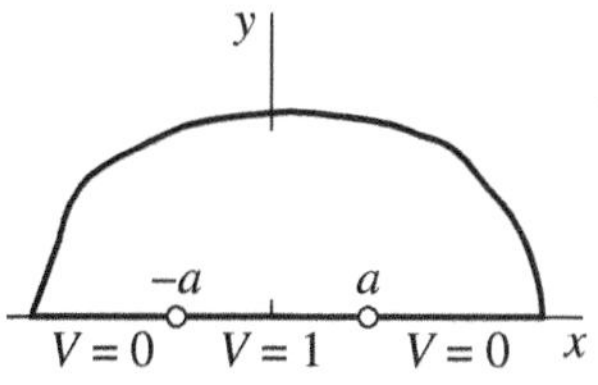

FIGURE 168

6. Derive an expression for the electrostatic potential in a semi-infinite space that is bounded by two half planes and a half cylinder, as shown in Fig. 169, when $V = 1$ on the cylindrical surface and $V = 0$ on the planar surfaces. Draw some of the equipotential curves in the xy plane.

$$\textit{Ans. } V = \frac{2}{\pi}\arctan\left(\frac{2y}{x^2+y^2-1}\right).$$

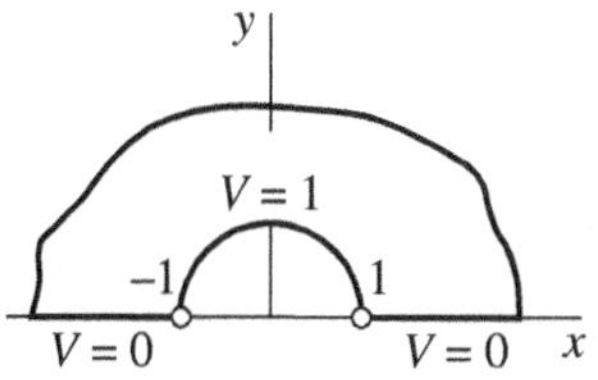

FIGURE 169

7. Find the potential V in the space between the planes $y = 0$ and $y = \pi$ when $V = 0$ on the parts of those planes where $x > 0$ and $V = 1$ on the parts where $x < 0$ (Fig. 170). Verify that the result satisfies the boundary conditions.

$$\textit{Ans. } V = \frac{1}{\pi}\arctan\left(\frac{\sin y}{\sinh x}\right) \quad (0 \le \arctan t \le \pi).$$

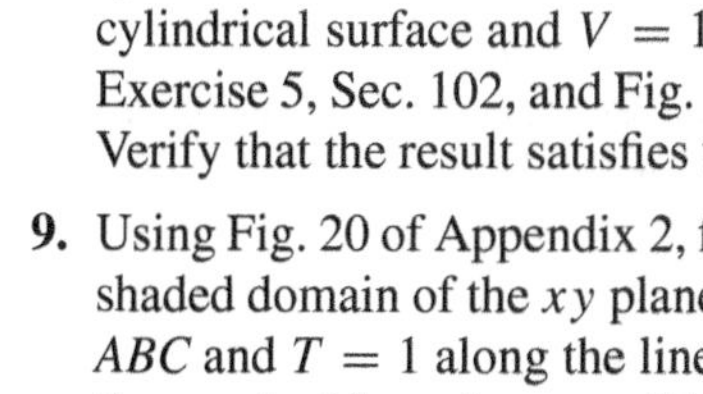

FIGURE 170

8. Derive an expression for the electrostatic potential V in the space interior to a long cylinder $r = 1$ when $V = 0$ on the first quadrant ($r = 1, 0 < \theta < \pi/2$) of the cylindrical surface and $V = 1$ on the rest ($r = 1, \pi/2 < \theta < 2\pi$) of that surface. (See Exercise 5, Sec. 102, and Fig. 123 there.) Show that $V = 3/4$ on the axis of the cylinder. Verify that the result satisfies the boundary conditions.

9. Using Fig. 20 of Appendix 2, find a temperature function $T(x, y)$ that is harmonic in the shaded domain of the xy plane shown there and assumes the values $T = 0$ along the arc ABC and $T = 1$ along the line segment DEF. Verify that the function obtained satisfies the required boundary conditions. (See Exercise 2.)

10. The solution of the Dirichlet problem on the right in Fig. 171 is*

$$V = \frac{4}{\pi}\sum_{n=1}^{\infty} \frac{\sinh mu}{m \sinh(m \ln r_0)} \sin mv$$

where $m = 2n - 1$. By using the branch

$$\log = \ln r + i\theta \quad \left(r > 0, \ -\frac{\pi}{2} < \theta < \frac{3\pi}{2}\right)$$

of the logarithmic function, derive the following solution of the Dirichlet problem on the left in Fig. 171:

$$V(r, \theta) = \frac{4}{\pi}\sum_{n=1}^{\infty} \left(\frac{r^m - r^{-m}}{r_0^m - r_0^{-m}}\right) \frac{\sin m\theta}{m}$$

where $m = 2n - 1$.

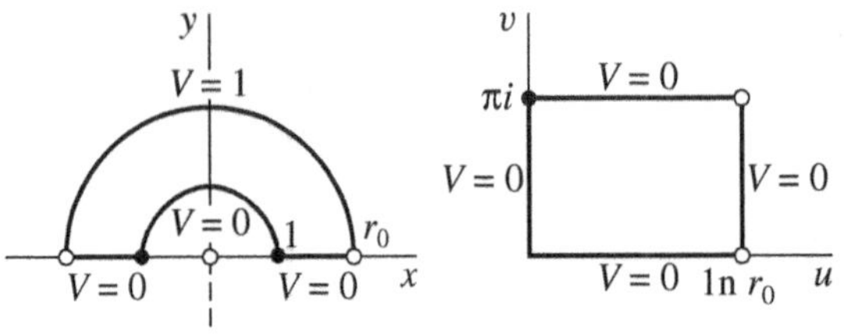

FIGURE 171
$w = \log z \quad \left(r > 0, -\frac{\pi}{2} < \theta < \frac{3\pi}{2}\right).$

124. TWO-DIMENSIONAL FLUID FLOW

Harmonic functions play an important role in hydrodynamics and aerodynamics. Again, we consider only the two-dimensional steady-state type of problem. That is, the motion of the fluid is assumed to be the same in all planes parallel to the xy plane, the velocity being parallel to that plane and independent of time. It is, then, sufficient to consider the motion of a sheet of fluid in the xy plane.

We let the vector representing the complex number

$$V = p + iq$$

denote the velocity of a particle of the fluid at any point (x, y); hence the x and y components of the velocity vector are $p(x, y)$ and $q(x, y)$, respectively. At points interior to a region of flow in which no sources or sinks of the fluid occur, the real-valued functions $p(x, y)$ and $q(x, y)$ and their first-order partial derivatives are assumed to be continuous.

The ***circulation*** of the fluid along any contour C is defined as the line integral with respect to arc length σ of the tangential component $V_T(x, y)$ of the velocity vector

*See the reference to the authors' book in the footnote with Example 2, Sec. 123.

along C:

$$\int_C V_T(x, y)\, d\sigma. \tag{1}$$

The ratio of the circulation along C to the length of C is, therefore, a mean speed of the fluid along that contour. It is shown in advanced calculus that such an integral can be written*

$$\int_C V_T(x, y)\, d\sigma = \int_C p(x, y)\, dx + q(x, y)\, dy. \tag{2}$$

When C is a positively oriented simple closed contour lying in a simply connected domain of flow containing no sources or sinks, Green's theorem (see Sec. 50) enables us to write

$$\int_C p(x, y)\, dx + q(x, y)\, dy = \iint_R [q_x(x, y) - p_y(x, y)]\, dA,$$

where R is the closed region consisting of points interior to and on C. Thus

$$\int_C V_T(x, y)\, d\sigma = \iint_R [q_x(x, y) - p_y(x, y)]\, dA \tag{3}$$

for such a contour

A physical interpretation of the integrand on the right in expression (3) for the circulation along the simple closed contour C is readily given. We let C denote a circle of radius r which is centered at a point (x_0, y_0) and taken counterclockwise. The mean speed along C is then found by dividing the circulation by the circumference $2\pi r$, and the corresponding mean angular speed of the fluid about the center of the circle is obtained by dividing that mean speed by r:

$$\frac{1}{\pi r^2} \iint_R \frac{1}{2}[q_x(x, y) - p_y(x, y)]\, dA.$$

Now this is also an expression for the mean value of the function

$$\omega(x, y) = \frac{1}{2}[q_x(x, y) - p_y(x, y)] \tag{4}$$

over the circular region R bounded by C. Its limit as r tends to zero is the value of ω at the point (x_0, y_0). Hence the function $\omega(x, y)$, called the ***rotation*** of the fluid, represents the limiting angular speed of a circular element of the fluid as the circle shrinks to its center (x, y), the point at which ω is evaluated.

If $\omega(x, y) = 0$ at each point in some simply connected domain, the flow is ***irrotational*** in that domain. We consider only irrotational flows here, and we also assume that the fluid is ***incompressible*** and ***free from viscosity***. Under our assumption of steady irrotational flow of fluids with uniform density ρ, it can be shown that the

*Properties of line integrals in advanced calculus that are used in this and the following section are to be found in, for instance, W. Kaplan, *Advanced Mathematics for Engineers*, Chap. 10, 1992.

fluid pressure $P(x, y)$ satisfies the following special case of ***Bernoulli's equation***:

$$\frac{P}{\rho} + \frac{1}{2}|V|^2 = c,$$

where c is a constant. Note that the pressure is greatest where the speed $|V|$ is least.

Let D be a simply connected domain in which the flow is irrotational. According to equation (4), $p_y = q_x$ throughout D. This relation between partial derivatives implies that the line integral

$$\int_C p(s,t)\,ds + q(s,t)\,dt$$

along a contour C lying entirely in D and joining any two points (x_0, y_0) and (x, y) in D is actually independent of path. Thus, if (x_0, y_0) is fixed, the function

$$\phi(x, y) = \int_{(x_0,y_0)}^{(x,y)} p(s,t)\,ds + q(s,t)\,dt \tag{5}$$

is well defined on D; and, by taking partial derivatives on each side of this equation, we find that

$$\phi_x(x, y) = p(x, y), \quad \phi_y(x, y) = q(x, y). \tag{6}$$

From equations (6), we see that the velocity vector $V = p + iq$ is the gradient of ϕ; and the directional derivative of ϕ in any direction represents the component of the velocity of flow in that direction.

The function $\phi(x, y)$ is called the ***velocity potential***. From equation (5), it is evident that $\phi(x, y)$ changes by an additive constant when the reference point (x_0, y_0) is changed. The level curves $\phi(x, y) = c_1$ are called ***equipotentials***. Because it is the gradient of $\phi(x, y)$, the velocity vector V is normal to an equipotential at any point where V is not the zero vector.

Just as in the case of the flow of heat, the condition that the incompressible fluid enter or leave an element of volume only by flowing through the boundary of that element requires that $\phi(x, y)$ must satisfy Laplace's equation

$$\phi_{xx}(x, y) + \phi_{yy}(x, y) = 0$$

in a domain where the fluid is free from sources or sinks. In view of equations (6) and the continuity of the functions p and q and their first-order partial derivatives, it follows that the partial derivatives of the first and second order of ϕ are continuous in such a domain. Hence the velocity potential ϕ is a harmonic function in that domain.

125. THE STREAM FUNCTION

According to Sec. 124, the velocity vector

$$V = p(x, y) + iq(x, y) \tag{1}$$

for a simply connected domain in which the flow is irrotational can be written

$$V = \phi_x(x, y) + i\phi_y(x, y) = \text{grad}\,\phi(x, y), \tag{2}$$

where ϕ is the velocity potential. When the velocity vector is not the zero vector, it is normal to an equipotential passing through the point (x, y). If, moreover, $\psi(x, y)$ denotes a harmonic conjugate of $\phi(x, y)$ (see Sec. 115), the velocity vector is tangent to a curve $\psi(x, y) = c_2$. The curves $\psi(x, y) = c_2$ are called the ***streamlines*** of the flow, and the function ψ is the ***stream function.*** In particular, a boundary across which fluid cannot flow is a streamline.

The analytic function

$$F(z) = \phi(x, y) + i\psi(x, y)$$

is called the ***complex potential*** of the flow. Note that

$$F'(z) = \phi_x(x, y) + i\psi_x(x, y)$$

and, in view of the Cauchy–Riemann equations,

$$F'(z) = \phi_x(x, y) - i\phi_y(x, y).$$

Expression (2) for the velocity thus becomes

$$V = \overline{F'(z)}. \tag{3}$$

The speed, or magnitude of the velocity, is obtained by writing

$$|V| = |F'(z)|.$$

According to equation (9), Sec. 115, if ϕ is harmonic in a simply connected domain D, a harmonic conjugate of ϕ there can be written

$$\psi(x, y) = \int_{(x_0, y_0)}^{(x, y)} -\phi_t(s, t)\,ds + \phi_s(s, t)\,dt,$$

where the integration is independent of path. With the aid of equations (6), Sec. 124, we can, therefore, write

$$\psi(x, y) = \int_C -q(s, t)\,ds + p(s, t)\,dt, \tag{4}$$

where C is any contour in D from (x_0, y_0) to (x, y).

Now it is shown in advanced calculus that the right-hand side of equation (4) represents the integral with respect to arc length σ along C of the normal component $V_N(x, y)$ of the vector whose x and y components are $p(x, y)$ and $q(x, y)$, respectively. So expression (4) can be written

$$\psi(x, y) = \int_C V_N(s, t)\,d\sigma. \tag{5}$$

Physically, then, $\psi(x, y)$ represents the time rate of flow of the fluid across C. More precisely, $\psi(x, y)$ denotes the rate of flow, by volume, across a surface of unit height standing perpendicular to the xy plane on the curve C.

EXAMPLE. When the complex potential is the function

$$F(z) = Az, \tag{6}$$

where A is a positive real constant,

$$\phi(x, y) = Ax \quad \text{and} \quad \psi(x, y) = Ay. \tag{7}$$

The streamlines $\psi(x, y) = c_2$ are the horizontal lines $y = c_2/A$, and the velocity at any point is

$$V = \overline{F'(z)} = A.$$

Here a point (x_0, y_0) at which $\psi(x, y) = 0$ is any point on the x axis. If the point (x_0, y_0) is taken as the origin, then $\psi(x, y)$ is the rate of flow across any contour drawn from the origin to the point (x, y) (Fig. 172). The flow is uniform and to the right. It can be interpreted as the uniform flow in the upper half plane bounded by the x axis, which is a streamline, or as the uniform flow between two parallel lines $y = y_1$ and $y = y_2$.

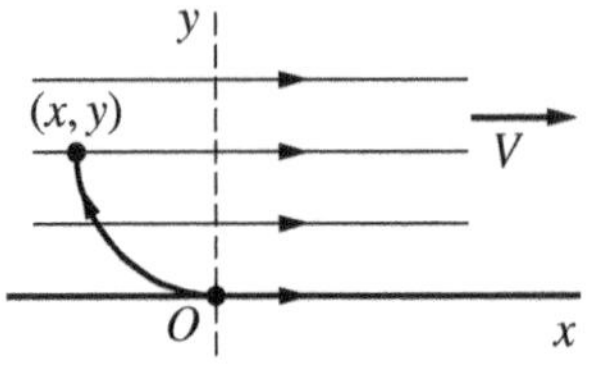

FIGURE 172

The stream function ψ characterizes a definite flow in a region. The question of whether just one such function exists corresponding to a given region, except possibly for a constant factor or an additive constant, is not examined here. Sometimes, when the velocity is uniform far from the obstruction or when sources and sinks are involved (Chap. 11), the physical situation indicates that the flow is uniquely determined by the conditions given in the problem.

A harmonic function is not always uniquely determined, even up to a constant factor, by simply prescribing its values on the boundary of a region. In the example above, the function $\psi(x, y) = Ay$ is harmonic in the half plane $y > 0$ and has zero values on the boundary. The function $\psi_1(x, y) = Be^x \sin y$ also satisfies those conditions. However, the streamline $\psi_1(x, y) = 0$ consists not only of the line $y = 0$ but also of the lines $y = n\pi$ $(n = 1, 2, \ldots)$. Here the function $F_1(z) = Be^z$ is the complex potential for the flow in the strip between the lines $y = 0$ and $y = \pi$, both lines making up the streamline $\psi(x, y) = 0$; if $B > 0$, the fluid flows to the right along the lower line and to the left along the upper one.

126. FLOWS AROUND A CORNER AND AROUND A CYLINDER

In analyzing a flow in the xy, or z, plane, it is often simpler to consider a corresponding flow in the uv, or w, plane. Then, if ϕ is a velocity potential and ψ a stream function for the flow in the uv plane, results in Secs. 116 and 117 can be applied to these harmonic functions. That is, when the domain of flow D_w in the uv plane is the image of a domain D_z under a transformation

$$w = f(z) = u(x, y) + iv(x, y),$$

where f is analytic, the functions

$$\phi[u(x, y), v(x, y)] \quad \text{and} \quad \psi[u(x, y), v(x, y)]$$

are harmonic in D_z. These new functions may be interpreted as velocity potential and stream function in the xy plane. A streamline or natural boundary $\psi(u, v) = c_2$ in the uv plane corresponds to a streamline or natural boundary $\psi[u(x, y), v(x, y)] = c_2$ in the xy plane.

In using this technique, it is often most efficient to first write the complex potential function for the region in the w plane and then obtain from that the velocity potential and stream function for the corresponding region in the xy plane. More precisely, if the potential function in the uv plane is

$$F(w) = \phi(u, v) + i\psi(u, v),$$

the composite function

$$F[f(z)] = \phi[u(x, y), v(x, y)] + i\psi[u(x, y), v(x, y)]$$

is the desired complex potential in the xy plane.

In order to avoid an excess of notation, we use the same symbols F, ϕ, and ψ for the complex potential, etc., in both the xy and the uv planes.

EXAMPLE 1. Consider a flow in the first quadrant $x > 0, y > 0$ that comes in downward parallel to the y axis but is forced to turn a corner near the origin, as shown in Fig. 173. To determine the flow, we recall (Example 2, Sec. 14) that the transformation

$$w = z^2 = x^2 - y^2 + i2xy$$

maps the first quadrant onto the upper half of the uv plane and the boundary of the quadrant onto the entire u axis.

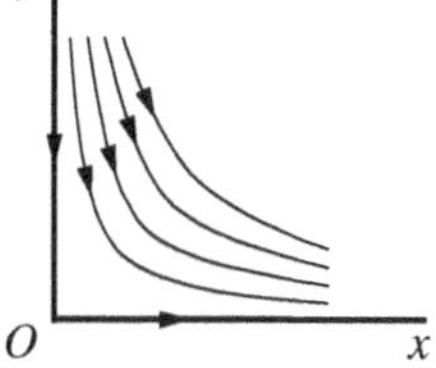

FIGURE 173

From the example in Sec. 125, we know that the complex potential for a uniform flow to the right in the upper half of the w plane is $F = Aw$, where A is a positive real constant. The potential in the quadrant is, therefore,

$$F = Az^2 = A(x^2 - y^2) + i2Axy; \tag{1}$$

and it follows that the stream function for the flow there is

$$\psi = 2Axy. \tag{2}$$

This stream function is, of course, harmonic in the first quadrant, and it vanishes on the boundary.

The streamlines are branches of the rectangular hyperbolas

$$2Axy = c_2.$$

According to equation (3), Sec. 125, the velocity of the fluid is

$$V = \overline{2Az} = 2A(x - iy).$$

Observe that the speed

$$|V| = 2A\sqrt{x^2 + y^2}$$

of a particle is directly proportional to its distance from the origin. The value of the stream function (2) at a point (x, y) can be interpreted as the rate of flow across a line segment extending from the origin to that point.

EXAMPLE 2. Let a long circular cylinder of unit radius be placed in a large body of fluid flowing with a uniform velocity, the axis of the cylinder being perpendicular to the direction of flow. To determine the steady flow around the cylinder, we represent the cylinder by the circle $x^2 + y^2 = 1$ and let the flow distant from it be parallel to the x axis and to the right (Fig. 174). Symmetry shows that points on the x axis exterior to the circle may be treated as boundary points, and so we need to consider only the upper part of the figure as the region of flow.

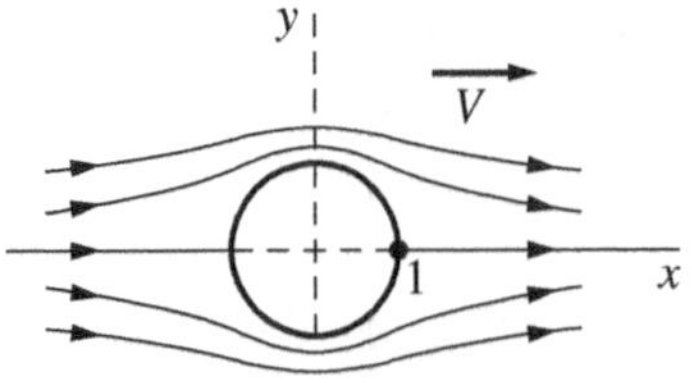

FIGURE 174

The boundary of this region of flow, consisting of the upper semicircle and the parts of the x axis exterior to the circle, is mapped onto the entire u axis by the transformation

$$w = z + \frac{1}{z}.$$

The region itself is mapped onto the upper half plane $v \geq 0$, as indicated in Fig. 17, Appendix 2. The complex potential for the corresponding uniform flow in that half plane is $F = Aw$, where A is a positive real constant. Hence the complex potential for the region exterior to the circle and above the x axis is

$$F = A\left(z + \frac{1}{z}\right). \tag{3}$$

The velocity

$$V = A\left(1 - \frac{1}{\overline{z}^2}\right) \tag{4}$$

approaches A as $|z|$ increases. Thus the flow is nearly uniform and parallel to the x axis at points distant from the circle, as one would expect. From expression (4), we see that $V(\overline{z}) = \overline{V(z)}$; hence that expression also represents velocities of flow in the lower region, the lower semicircle being a streamline.

According to equation (3), the stream function for the given problem is, in polar coordinates,

$$\psi = A\left(r - \frac{1}{r}\right)\sin\theta. \tag{5}$$

The streamlines

$$A\left(r - \frac{1}{r}\right)\sin\theta = c_2$$

are symmetric to the y axis and have asymptotes parallel to the x axis. Note that when $c_2 = 0$, the streamline consists of the circle $r = 1$ and the parts of the x axis exterior to the circle.

EXERCISES

1. State why the components of velocity can be obtained from the stream function by means of the equations

$$p(x, y) = \psi_y(x, y), \quad q(x, y) = -\psi_x(x, y).$$

2. At an interior point of a region of flow and under the conditions that we have assumed, the fluid pressure cannot be less than the pressure at all other points in a neighborhood of that point. Justify this statement with the aid of statements in Secs. 124, 125, and 59.

3. For the flow around a corner described in Example 1, Sec. 126, at what point of the region $x \geq 0$, $y \geq 0$ is the fluid pressure greatest?

4. Show that the speed of the fluid at points on the cylindrical surface in Example 2, Sec. 126, is $2A|\sin\theta|$ and also that the fluid pressure on the cylinder is greatest at the points $z = \pm 1$ and least at the points $z = \pm i$.

5. Write the complex potential for the flow around a cylinder $r = r_0$ when the velocity V at a point z approaches a real constant A as the point recedes from the cylinder.

6. Obtain the stream function $\psi = Ar^4 \sin 4\theta$ for a flow in the angular region

$$r \geq 0,\ 0 \leq \theta \leq \frac{\pi}{4}$$

that is shown in Fig. 175. Sketch a few of the streamlines in the interior of that region.

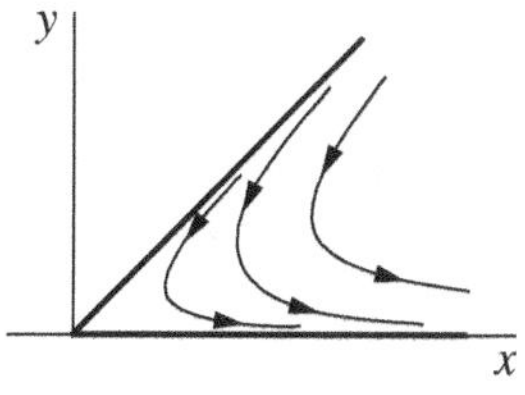

FIGURE 175

7. Obtain the complex potential $F = A \sin z$ for a flow inside the semi-infinite region

$$-\frac{\pi}{2} \le x \le \frac{\pi}{2}, \; y \ge 0$$

that is shown in Fig. 176. Write the equations of the streamlines.

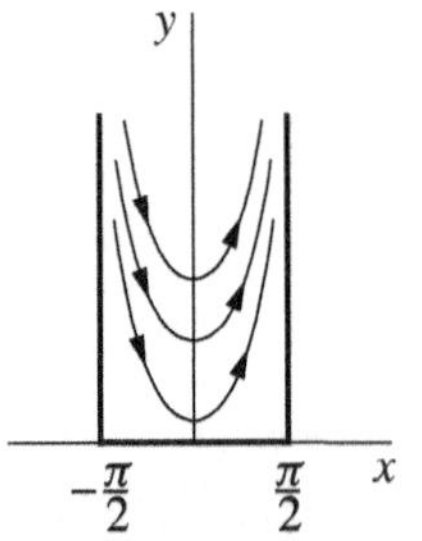

FIGURE 176

8. Show that if the velocity potential is $\phi = A \ln r \; (A > 0)$ for flow in the region $r \ge r_0$, then the streamlines are the half lines $\theta = c \; (r \ge r_0)$ and the rate of flow outward through each complete circle about the origin is $2\pi A$, corresponding to a source of that strength at the origin.

9. Obtain the complex potential

$$F = A\left(z^2 + \frac{1}{z^2}\right)$$

for a flow in the region $r \ge 1, 0 \le \theta \le \pi/2$. Write expressions for V and ψ. Note how the speed $|V|$ varies along the boundary of the region, and verify that $\psi(x, y) = 0$ on the boundary.

10. Suppose that the flow at an infinite distance from the cylinder of unit radius in Example 2, Sec. 126, is uniform in a direction making an angle α with the x axis; that is,

$$\lim_{|z|\to\infty} V = Ae^{i\alpha} \qquad (A > 0).$$

Find the complex potential.

Ans. $F = A\left(ze^{-i\alpha} + \frac{1}{z}e^{i\alpha}\right)$.

11. Write

$$z - 2 = r_1 \exp(i\theta_1), \quad z + 2 = r_2 \exp(i\theta_2),$$

and

$$(z^2 - 4)^{1/2} = \sqrt{r_1 r_2} \exp\left(i\frac{\theta_1 + \theta_2}{2}\right),$$

where

$$0 \le \theta_1 < 2\pi \quad \text{and} \quad 0 \le \theta_2 < 2\pi.$$

The function $(z^2 - 4)^{1/2}$ is then single-valued and analytic everywhere except on the branch cut consisting of the segment of the x axis joining the points $z = \pm 2$. We know, moreover, from Exercise 13, Sec. 98, that the transformation

$$z = w + \frac{1}{w}$$

maps the circle $|w| = 1$ onto the line segment from $z = -2$ to $z = 2$ and that it maps the domain outside the circle onto the rest of the z plane. Use all of the observations above to show that the inverse transformation, where $|w| > 1$ for every point not on the branch cut, can be written

$$w = \frac{1}{2}[z + (z^2 - 4)^{1/2}] = \frac{1}{4}\left(\sqrt{r_1}\exp\frac{i\theta_1}{2} + \sqrt{r_2}\exp\frac{i\theta_2}{2}\right)^2.$$

The transformation and this inverse establish a one to one correspondence between points in the two domains.

12. With the aid of the results found in Exercises 10 and 11, derive the expression

$$F = A[z\cos\alpha - i(z^2 - 4)^{1/2}\sin\alpha]$$

for the complex potential of the steady flow around a long plate whose width is 4 and whose cross section is the line segment joining the two points $z = \pm 2$ in Fig. 177, assuming that the velocity of the fluid at an infinite distance from the plate is $A\exp(i\alpha)$ where $A > 0$. The branch of $(z^2 - 4)^{1/2}$ that is used is the one described in Exercise 11.

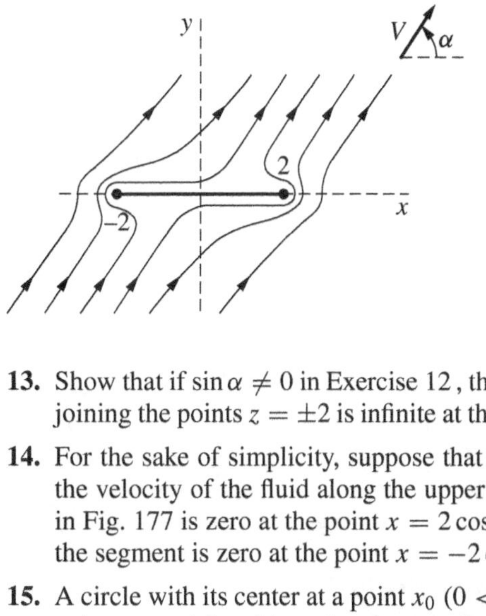

FIGURE 177

13. Show that if $\sin\alpha \neq 0$ in Exercise 12, then the speed of the fluid along the line segment joining the points $z = \pm 2$ is infinite at the ends and is equal to $A|\cos\alpha|$ at the midpoint.

14. For the sake of simplicity, suppose that $0 < \alpha \leq \pi/2$ in Exercise 12. Then show that the velocity of the fluid along the upper side of the line segment representing the plate in Fig. 177 is zero at the point $x = 2\cos\alpha$ and that the velocity along the lower side of the segment is zero at the point $x = -2\cos\alpha$.

15. A circle with its center at a point x_0 $(0 < x_0 < 1)$ on the x axis and passing through the point $z = -1$ is subjected to the transformation

$$w = z + \frac{1}{z}.$$

Individual nonzero points z can be mapped geometrically by adding the vectors representing

$$z = re^{i\theta} \quad \text{and} \quad \frac{1}{z} = \frac{1}{r}e^{-i\theta}.$$

Indicate by mapping some points that the image of the circle is a profile of the type shown in Fig. 178 and that points exterior to the circle map onto points exterior to the profile. This is a special case of the profile of a ***Joukowski airfoil***. (See also Exercises 16 and 17 below.)

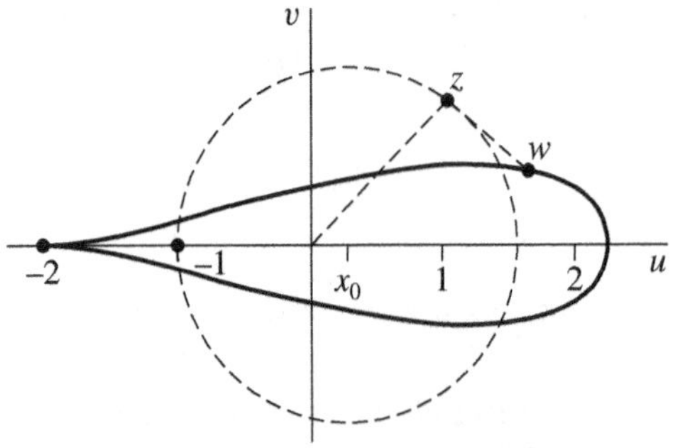

FIGURE 178

16. (*a*) Show that the mapping of the circle in Exercise 15 is conformal except at $z = -1$.

(*b*) Let the complex numbers

$$t = \lim_{\Delta z \to 0} \frac{\Delta z}{|\Delta z|} \quad \text{and} \quad \tau = \lim_{\Delta w \to 0} \frac{\Delta w}{|\Delta w|}$$

represent unit vectors tangent to a smooth directed arc at $z = -1$ and that arc's image, respectively, under the transformation

$$w = z + \frac{1}{z}.$$

Show that $\tau = -t^2$ and hence that the Joukowski profile in Fig. 178 has a cusp at the point $w = -2$, the angle between the tangents at the cusp being zero.

17. Find the complex potential for the flow around the airfoil in Exercise 15 when the velocity V of the fluid at an infinite distance from the origin is a real constant A. Recall that the inverse of the transformation

$$w = z + \frac{1}{z}$$

used in Exercise 15 is given, with z and w interchanged, in Exercise 11.

18. Note that under the transformation $w = e^z + z$, both halves, where $x \geq 0$ and $x \leq 0$, of the line $y = \pi$ are mapped onto the half line $v = \pi$ $(u \leq -1)$. Similarly, the line $y = -\pi$ is mapped onto the half line $v = -\pi$ $(u \leq -1)$; and the strip $-\pi \leq y \leq \pi$ is mapped onto the w plane. Also, note that the change of directions, $\arg(dw/dz)$, under this transformation approaches zero as x tends to $-\infty$. Show that the streamlines of a fluid flowing through the open channel formed by the half lines in the w plane (Fig. 179) are the images of the lines $y = c_2$ in the strip. These streamlines also represent the equipotential curves of the electrostatic field near the edge of a parallel-plate capacitor.

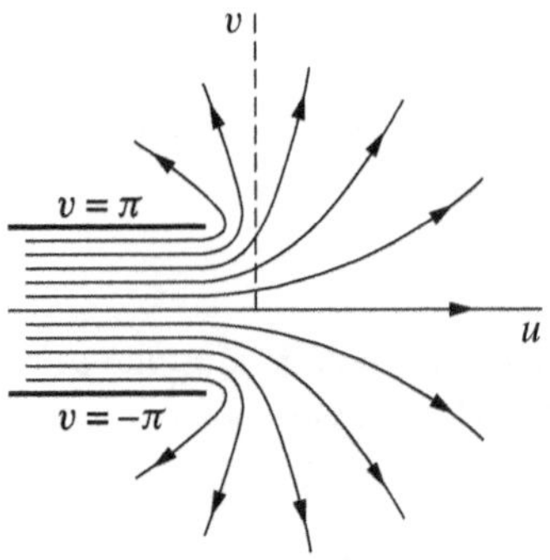

FIGURE 179

CHAPTER 11

THE SCHWARZ–CHRISTOFFEL TRANSFORMATION

In this chapter, we construct a transformation, known as the Schwarz–Christoffel transformation, which maps the x axis and the upper half of the z plane onto a given simple closed polygon and its interior in the w plane. Applications are made to the solution of problems in fluid flow and electrostatic potential theory.

127. MAPPING THE REAL AXIS ONTO A POLYGON

We represent the unit vector which is tangent to a smooth arc C at a point z_0 by the complex number t, and we let the number τ denote the unit vector tangent to the image Γ of C at the corresponding point w_0 under a transformation $w = f(z)$. We assume that f is analytic at z_0 and that $f'(z_0) \neq 0$. According to Sec. 112,

$$\arg \tau = \arg f'(z_0) + \arg t. \tag{1}$$

In particular, if C is a segment of the x axis with positive sense to the right, then $t = 1$ and $\arg t = 0$ at each point $z_0 = x$ on C. In that case, equation (1) becomes

$$\arg \tau = \arg f'(x). \tag{2}$$

If $f'(z)$ has a constant argument along that segment, it follows that $\arg \tau$ is constant. Hence the image Γ of C is also a segment of a straight line.

Let us now construct a transformation $w = f(z)$ that maps the whole x axis onto a polygon of n sides, where $x_1, x_2, \ldots, x_{n-1}$, and ∞ are the points on that axis whose images are to be the vertices of the polygon and where

$$x_1 < x_2 < \cdots < x_{n-1}.$$

The vertices are the n points $w_j = f(x_j)$ $(j = 1, 2, \ldots, n-1)$ and $w_n = f(\infty)$. The function f should be such that $\arg f'(z)$ jumps from one constant value to another at the points $z = x_j$ as the point z traces out the x axis (Fig. 180).

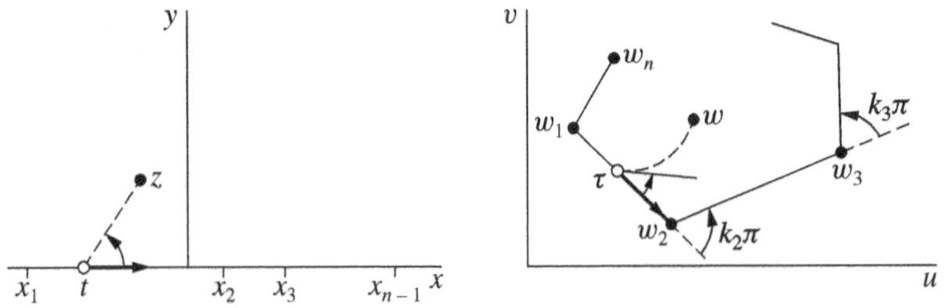

FIGURE 180

If the function f is chosen such that

$$f'(z) = A(z - x_1)^{-k_1}(z - x_2)^{-k_2} \cdots (z - x_{n-1})^{-k_{n-1}}, \tag{3}$$

where A is a complex constant and each k_j is a real constant, then the argument of $f'(z)$ changes in the prescribed manner as z describes the real axis. This is seen by writing the argument of the derivative (3) as

$$\begin{aligned} \arg f'(z) = {} & \arg A - k_1 \arg(z - x_1) \\ & - k_2 \arg(z - x_2) - \cdots - k_{n-1} \arg(z - x_{n-1}). \end{aligned} \tag{4}$$

When $z = x$ and $x < x_1$,

$$\arg(z - x_1) = \arg(z - x_2) = \cdots = \arg(z - x_{n-1}) = \pi.$$

When $x_1 < x < x_2$, the argument $\arg(z - x_1)$ is 0 and each of the other arguments is π. According to equation (4), then, $\arg f'(z)$ increases abruptly by the angle $k_1\pi$ as z moves to the right through the point $z = x_1$. It again jumps in value, by the amount $k_2\pi$, as z passes through the point x_2, etc.

In view of equation (2), the unit vector τ is constant in direction as z moves from x_{j-1} to x_j; the point w thus moves in that fixed direction along a straight line. The direction of τ changes abruptly, by the angle $k_j\pi$, at the image point w_j of x_j, as shown in Fig. 180. Those angles $k_j\pi$ are the exterior angles of the polygon described by the point w.

The exterior angles can be limited to angles between $-\pi$ and π, in which case $-1 < k_j < 1$. We assume that the sides of the polygon never cross one another and that the polygon is given a positive, or counterclockwise, orientation. The sum of the exterior angles of a *closed* polygon is, then, 2π; and the exterior angle at the vertex w_n, which is the image of the point $z = \infty$, can be written

$$k_n\pi = 2\pi - (k_1 + k_2 + \cdots + k_{n-1})\pi.$$

Thus the numbers k_j must necessarily satisfy the conditions

$$(5) \qquad k_1 + k_2 + \cdots + k_{n-1} + k_n = 2, \qquad -1 < k_j < 1 \qquad (j = 1, 2, \ldots, n).$$

Note that $k_n = 0$ if

$$(6) \qquad k_1 + k_2 + \cdots + k_{n-1} = 2.$$

This means that the direction of τ does not change at the point w_n. So w_n is not a vertex, and the polygon has $n - 1$ sides.

The existence of a mapping function f whose derivative is given by equation (3) will be established in the next section.

128. SCHWARZ–CHRISTOFFEL TRANSFORMATION

In our expression (Sec. 127)

$$(1) \qquad f'(z) = A(z - x_1)^{-k_1}(z - x_2)^{-k_2} \cdots (z - x_{n-1})^{-k_{n-1}}$$

for the derivative of a function that is to map the x axis onto a polygon, let the factors $(z - x_j)^{-k_j}$ $(j = 1, 2, \ldots, n - 1)$ represent branches of power functions with branch cuts extending below that axis. To be specific, write

$$(z - x_j)^{-k_j} = \exp[-k_j \log(z - x_j)] = \exp[-k_j(\ln|z - x_j| + i\theta_j)]$$

and then

$$(2) \qquad (z - x_j)^{-k_j} = |z - x_j|^{-k_j} \exp(-ik_j\theta_j) \qquad \left(-\frac{\pi}{2} < \theta_j < \frac{3\pi}{2}\right),$$

where $\theta_j = \arg(z - x_j)$ and $j = 1, 2, \ldots, n - 1$. This makes $f'(z)$ analytic everywhere in the half plane $y \geq 0$ except at the $n - 1$ branch points x_j.

If z_0 is a point in that region of analyticity, denoted here by R, then the function

$$(3) \qquad F(z) = \int_{z_0}^{z} f'(s)\, ds$$

is single-valued and analytic throughout the same region, where the path of integration from z_0 to z is any contour lying within R. Moreover, $F'(z) = f'(z)$ (see Sec. 48).

To define the function F at the point $z = x_1$ so that it is continuous there, we note that $(z - x_1)^{-k_1}$ is the only factor in expression (1) that is not analytic at x_1. Hence if $\phi(z)$ denotes the product of the rest of the factors in that expression, $\phi(z)$ is analytic at the point x_1 and is represented throughout an open disk $|z - x_1| < R_1$ by its Taylor series about x_1. So we can write

$$f'(z) = (z - x_1)^{-k_1}\phi(z)$$
$$= (z - x_1)^{-k_1}\left[\phi(x_1) + \frac{\phi'(x_1)}{1!}(z - x_1) + \frac{\phi''(x_1)}{2!}(z - x_1)^2 + \cdots\right],$$

or

$$f'(z) = \phi(x_1)(z - x_1)^{-k_1} + (z - x_1)^{1-k_1}\psi(z), \tag{4}$$

where ψ is analytic and therefore continuous throughout the entire open disk. Since $1 - k_1 > 0$, the last term on the right in equation (4) thus represents a continuous function of z throughout the upper half of the disk, where $\operatorname{Im} z \geq 0$, if we assign it the value zero at $z = x_1$. It follows that the integral

$$\int_{Z_1}^{z} (s - x_1)^{1-k_1}\psi(s)\,ds$$

of that last term along a contour from Z_1 to z, where Z_1 and the contour lie in the half disk, is a continuous function of z at $z = x_1$. The integral

$$\int_{Z_1}^{z} (s - x_1)^{-k_1}\,ds = \frac{1}{1 - k_1}\left[(z - x_1)^{1-k_1} - (Z_1 - x_1)^{1-k_1}\right]$$

along the same path also represents a continuous function of z at x_1 if we define the value of the integral there as its limit as z approaches x_1 in the half disk. The integral of the function (4) along the stated path from Z_1 to z is, then, continuous at $z = x_1$; and the same is true of integral (3) since it can be written as an integral along a contour in R from z_0 to Z_1 plus the integral from Z_1 to z.

The above argument applies at each of the $n - 1$ points x_j to make F continuous throughout the region $y \geq 0$.

From equation (1), we can show that for a sufficiently large positive number R, a positive constant M exists such that if $\operatorname{Im} z \geq 0$, then

$$|f'(z)| < \frac{M}{|z|^{2-k_n}} \qquad \text{whenever} \qquad |z| > R. \tag{5}$$

Since $2 - k_n > 1$, this order property of the integrand in equation (3) ensures the existence of the limit of the integral there as z tends to infinity; that is, a number W_n exists such that

$$\lim_{z\to\infty} F(z) = W_n \qquad (\operatorname{Im} z \geq 0). \tag{6}$$

Details of the argument are left to Exercises 1 and 2.

Our mapping function, whose derivative is given by equation (1), can be written $f(z) = F(z) + B$, where B is a complex constant. The resulting transformation,

$$w = A\int_{z_0}^{z} (s - x_1)^{-k_1}(s - x_2)^{-k_2}\cdots(s - x_{n-1})^{-k_{n-1}}\,ds + B, \tag{7}$$

is the ***Schwarz–Christoffel transformation***, named in honor of the two German mathematicians H. A. Schwarz (1843–1921) and E. B. Christoffel (1829–1900) who discovered it independently.

Transformation (7) is continuous throughout the half plane $y \geq 0$ and is conformal there except for the points x_j. We have assumed that the numbers k_j satisfy conditions (5), Sec. 127. In addition, we suppose that the constants x_j and k_j are such that the sides of the polygon do not cross, so that it is a simple closed contour. Then, according to Sec. 127, as the point z describes the x axis in the positive direction, its image w describes the polygon P in the positive sense; and there is a one to one correspondence between points on that axis and points on P. According to condition (6), the image w_n of the point $z = \infty$ exists and $w_n = W_n + B$.

If z is an interior point of the upper half plane $y \geq 0$ and x_0 is any point on the x axis other than one of the x_j, then the angle from the vector t at x_0 up to the line segment joining x_0 and z is positive and less than π (Fig. 180). At the image w_0 of x_0, the corresponding angle from the vector τ to the image of the line segment joining x_0 and z has that same value. Thus the images of interior points in the half plane lie to the left of the sides of the polygon, taken counterclockwise. A proof that the transformation establishes a one to one correspondence between the interior points of the half plane and the points within the polygon is left to the reader (Exercise 3).

Given a specific polygon P, let us examine the number of constants in the Schwarz–Christoffel transformation that must be determined in order to map the x axis onto P. For this purpose, we may write $z_0 = 0$, $A = 1$, and $B = 0$ and simply require that the x axis be mapped onto some polygon P' similar to P. The size and position of P' can then be adjusted to match those of P by introducing the appropriate constants A and B.

The numbers k_j are all determined from the exterior angles at the vertices of P. The $n - 1$ constants x_j remain to be chosen. The image of the x axis is some polygon P' that has the same angles as P. But if P' is to be similar to P, then $n - 2$ connected sides must have a common ratio to the corresponding sides of P; this condition is expressed by means of $n - 3$ equations in the $n - 1$ real unknowns x_j. Thus *two of the numbers x_j, or two relations between them, can be chosen arbitrarily,* provided those $n - 3$ equations in the remaining $n - 3$ unknowns have real-valued solutions.

When a finite point $z = x_n$ on the x axis, instead of the point at infinity, represents the point whose image is the vertex w_n, it follows from Sec. 127 that the Schwarz–Christoffel transformation takes the form

$$w = A \int_{z_0}^{z} (s - x_1)^{-k_1} (s - x_2)^{-k_2} \cdots (s - x_n)^{-k_n} \, ds + B, \tag{8}$$

where $k_1 + k_2 + \cdots + k_n = 2$. The exponents k_j are determined from the exterior angles of the polygon. But, in this case, there are n real constants x_j that must satisfy the $n - 3$ equations noted above. Thus *three of the numbers x_j, or three conditions on those n numbers, can be chosen arbitrarily* when transformation (8) is used to map the x axis onto a given polygon.

EXERCISES

1. Obtain inequality (5), Sec. 128.

Suggestion: Let R be larger than the numbers $|x_j|$ $(j = 1, 2, \ldots, n-1)$. Note that if R is sufficiently large, the inequalities $|z|/2 < |z - x_j| < 2|z|$ hold for each x_j when $|z| > R$. Then use expression (1), Sec. 128, along with conditions (5), Sec. 127.

2. Use condition (5), Sec. 128, and sufficient conditions for the existence of improper integrals of real-valued functions to show that $F(x)$ has some limit W_n as x tends to infinity, where $F(z)$ is defined by equation (3) in that section. Also, show that the integral of $f'(z)$ over each arc of a semicircle $|z| = R$ $(\text{Im } z \geq 0)$ approaches 0 as R tends to ∞. Then deduce that

$$\lim_{z\to\infty} F(z) = W_n \qquad (\text{Im } z \geq 0),$$

as stated in equation (6) of Sec. 128.

3. According to Sec. 93, the expression

$$N = \frac{1}{2\pi i}\int_C \frac{g'(z)}{g(z)}\,dz$$

can be used to determine the number (N) of zeros of a function g interior to a positively oriented simple closed contour C when $g(z) \neq 0$ on C and when C lies in a simply connected domain D throughout which g is analytic and $g'(z)$ is never zero. In that expression, write $g(z) = f(z) - w_0$, where $f(z)$ is the Schwarz–Christoffel mapping function (7), Sec. 128, and the point w_0 is either interior to or exterior to the polygon P that is the image of the x axis; thus $f(z) \neq w_0$. Let the contour C consist of the upper half of a circle $|z| = R$ and a segment $-R < x < R$ of the x axis that contains all $n-1$ points x_j, except that a small segment about each point x_j is replaced by the upper half of a circle $|z - x_j| = \rho_j$ with that segment as its diameter. Then the number of points z interior to C such that $f(z) = w_0$ is

$$N_C = \frac{1}{2\pi i}\int_C \frac{f'(z)}{f(z) - w_0}\,dz.$$

Note that $f(z) - w_0$ approaches the nonzero point $W_n - w_0$ when $|z| = R$ and R tends to ∞, and recall the order property (5), Sec. 128, for $|f'(z)|$. Let the ρ_j tend to zero, and prove that the number of points in the upper half of the z plane at which $f(z) = w_0$ is

$$N = \frac{1}{2\pi i}\lim_{R\to\infty}\int_{-R}^{R} \frac{f'(x)}{f(x) - w_0}\,dx.$$

Deduce that since

$$\int_P \frac{dw}{w - w_0} = \lim_{R\to\infty}\int_{-R}^{R} \frac{f'(x)}{f(x) - w_0}\,dx,$$

$N = 1$ if w_0 is interior to P and that $N = 0$ if w_0 is exterior to P. Thus show that the mapping of the half plane $\text{Im } z > 0$ onto the interior of P is one to one.

129. TRIANGLES AND RECTANGLES

The Schwarz–Christoffel transformation is written in terms of the points x_j and not in terms of their images, which are the vertices of the polygon. No more than three of those points can be chosen arbitrarily; so, when the given polygon has more than three sides, some of the points x_j must be determined in order to make the given polygon, or any polygon similar to it, be the image of the x axis. The selection of conditions for the determination of those constants that are convenient to use often requires ingenuity.

Another limitation in using the transformation is due to the integration that is involved. Often the integral cannot be evaluated in terms of a finite number of elementary functions. In such cases, the solution of problems by means of the transformation can become quite involved.

If the polygon is a triangle with vertices at the points w_1, w_2, and w_3 (Fig. 181), the transformation can be written

$$w = A \int_{z_0}^{z} (s - x_1)^{-k_1} (s - x_2)^{-k_2} (s - x_3)^{-k_3}\, ds + B, \tag{1}$$

where $k_1 + k_2 + k_3 = 2$. In terms of the interior angles θ_j,

$$k_j = 1 - \frac{1}{\pi}\theta_j \qquad (j = 1, 2, 3).$$

Here we have taken all three points x_j as finite points on the x axis. Arbitrary values can be assigned to each of them. The complex constants A and B, which are associated with the size and position of the triangle, can be determined so that the upper half plane is mapped onto the given triangular region.

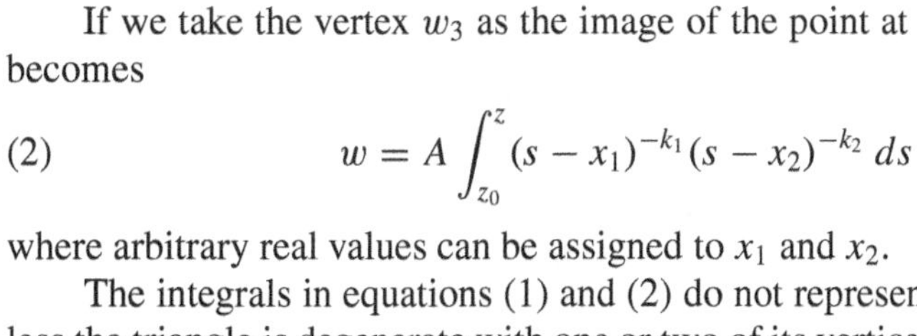

FIGURE 181

If we take the vertex w_3 as the image of the point at infinity, the transformation becomes

$$w = A \int_{z_0}^{z} (s - x_1)^{-k_1} (s - x_2)^{-k_2}\, ds + B, \tag{2}$$

where arbitrary real values can be assigned to x_1 and x_2.

The integrals in equations (1) and (2) do not represent elementary functions unless the triangle is degenerate with one or two of its vertices at infinity. The integral in equation (2) becomes an *elliptic integral* when the triangle is equilateral or when it is a right triangle with one of its angles equal to either $\pi/3$ or $\pi/4$.

EXAMPLE 1. For an equilateral triangle, $k_1 = k_2 = k_3 = 2/3$. It is convenient to write $x_1 = -1$, $x_2 = 1$, and $x_3 = \infty$ and to use equation (2), with $z_0 = 1$, $A = 1$, and $B = 0$. The transformation then becomes

$$w = \int_1^z (s+1)^{-2/3}(s-1)^{-2/3}\,ds. \tag{3}$$

The image of the point $z = 1$ is clearly $w = 0$; that is, $w_2 = 0$. If $z = -1$ in this integral, one can write $s = x$, where $-1 < x < 1$. Then

$$x + 1 > 0 \quad \text{and} \quad \arg(x+1) = 0,$$

while

$$|x - 1| = 1 - x \quad \text{and} \quad \arg(x-1) = \pi.$$

Hence

$$\begin{aligned} w &= \int_1^{-1} (x+1)^{-2/3}(1-x)^{-2/3}\exp\left(-\frac{2\pi i}{3}\right)dx \\ &= \exp\left(\frac{\pi i}{3}\right)\int_0^1 \frac{2\,dx}{(1-x^2)^{2/3}} \end{aligned} \tag{4}$$

when $z = -1$. With the substitution $x = \sqrt{t}$, the last integral here reduces to a special case of the one used in defining the beta function (Exercise 5, Sec. 91). Let b denote its value, which is positive:

$$b = \int_0^1 \frac{2\,dx}{(1-x^2)^{2/3}} = \int_0^1 t^{-1/2}(1-t)^{-2/3}\,dt = B\left(\frac{1}{2}, \frac{1}{3}\right). \tag{5}$$

The vertex w_1 is, therefore, the point (Fig. 182)

$$w_1 = b\exp\frac{\pi i}{3}. \tag{6}$$

The vertex w_3 is on the positive u axis because

$$w_3 = \int_1^\infty (x+1)^{-2/3}(x-1)^{-2/3}\,dx = \int_1^\infty \frac{dx}{(x^2-1)^{2/3}}.$$

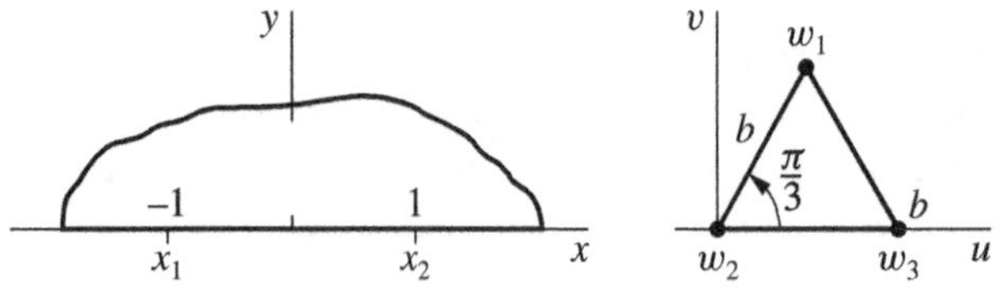

FIGURE 182

But the value of w_3 is also represented by integral (3) when z tends to infinity along the negative x axis; that is,

$$w_3 = \int_1^{-1} (|x+1||x-1|)^{-2/3} \exp\left(-\frac{2\pi i}{3}\right) dx + \int_{-1}^{-\infty} (|x+1||x-1|)^{-2/3} \exp\left(-\frac{4\pi i}{3}\right) dx.$$

In view of the first of expressions (4) for w_1, then,

$$w_3 = w_1 + \exp\left(-\frac{4\pi i}{3}\right) \int_{-1}^{-\infty} (|x+1||x-1|)^{-2/3} dx = b \exp\frac{\pi i}{3} + \exp\left(-\frac{\pi i}{3}\right) \int_1^{\infty} \frac{dx}{(x^2-1)^{2/3}},$$

or

$$w_3 = b \exp\frac{\pi i}{3} + w_3 \exp\left(-\frac{\pi i}{3}\right).$$

Solving for w_3, we find that

$$w_3 = b. \tag{7}$$

We have thus verified that the image of the x axis is the equilateral triangle of side b shown in Fig. 182. We can also see that

$$w = \frac{b}{2} \exp\frac{\pi i}{3} \quad \text{when} \quad z = 0.$$

When the polygon is a rectangle, each $k_j = 1/2$. If we choose ± 1 and $\pm a$ as the points x_j whose images are the vertices and write

$$g(z) = (z+a)^{-1/2}(z+1)^{-1/2}(z-1)^{-1/2}(z-a)^{-1/2}, \tag{8}$$

where $0 \le \arg(z - x_j) \le \pi$, the Schwarz–Christoffel transformation becomes

$$w = -\int_0^z g(s)\, ds, \tag{9}$$

except for a transformation $W = Aw + B$ to adjust the size and position of the rectangle. Integral (9) is a constant times the elliptic integral

$$\int_0^z (1-s^2)^{-1/2}(1-k^2s^2)^{-1/2}\, ds \qquad \left(k = \frac{1}{a}\right),$$

but the form (8) of the integrand indicates more clearly the appropriate branches of the power functions involved.

EXAMPLE 2. Let us locate the vertices of the rectangle when $a > 1$. As shown in Fig. 183, $x_1 = -a$, $x_2 = -1$, $x_3 = 1$, and $x_4 = a$. All four vertices can be described in terms of two positive numbers b and c that depend on the value of a in the following manner:

$$b = \int_0^1 |g(x)|\,dx = \int_0^1 \frac{dx}{\sqrt{(1-x^2)(a^2-x^2)}}, \tag{10}$$

$$c = \int_1^a |g(x)|\,dx = \int_1^a \frac{dx}{\sqrt{(x^2-1)(a^2-x^2)}}. \tag{11}$$

If $-1 < x < 0$, then

$$\arg(x+a) = \arg(x+1) = 0 \qquad \text{and} \qquad \arg(x-1) = \arg(x-a) = \pi;$$

hence

$$g(x) = \left[\exp\left(-\frac{\pi i}{2}\right)\right]^2 |g(x)| = -|g(x)|.$$

If $-a < x < -1$, then

$$g(x) = \left[\exp\left(-\frac{\pi i}{2}\right)\right]^3 |g(x)| = i|g(x)|.$$

Thus

$$\begin{aligned} w_1 &= -\int_0^{-a} g(x)\,dx = -\int_0^{-1} g(x)\,dx - \int_{-1}^{-a} g(x)\,dx \\ &= \int_0^{-1} |g(x)|\,dx - i\int_{-1}^{-a} |g(x)|\,dx = -b + ic. \end{aligned}$$

It is left to the exercises to show that

$$w_2 = -b, \qquad w_3 = b, \qquad w_4 = b + ic. \tag{12}$$

The position and dimensions of the rectangle are shown in Fig. 183.

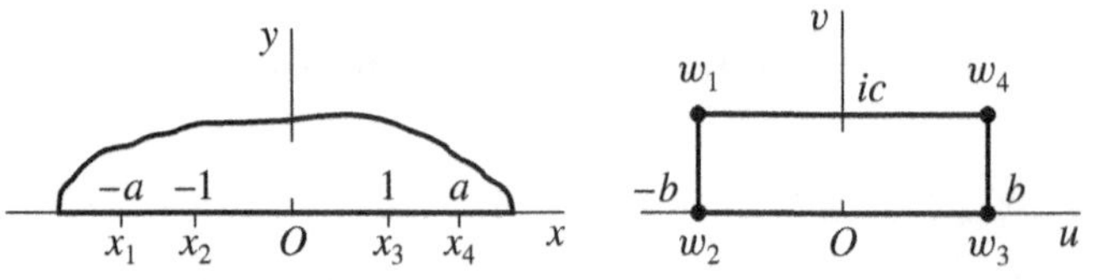

FIGURE 183

130. DEGENERATE POLYGONS

We now apply the Schwarz–Christoffel transformation to some degenerate polygons whose integrals represent elementary functions. For purposes of illustration, the examples here result in transformations that we have already seen in Chap. 8.

EXAMPLE 1. Let us map the half plane $y \geq 0$ onto the semi-infinite strip

$$-\frac{\pi}{2} \leq u \leq \frac{\pi}{2}, \quad v \geq 0.$$

We consider the strip as the limiting form of a triangle with vertices w_1, w_2, and w_3 (Fig. 184) as the imaginary part of w_3 tends to infinity.

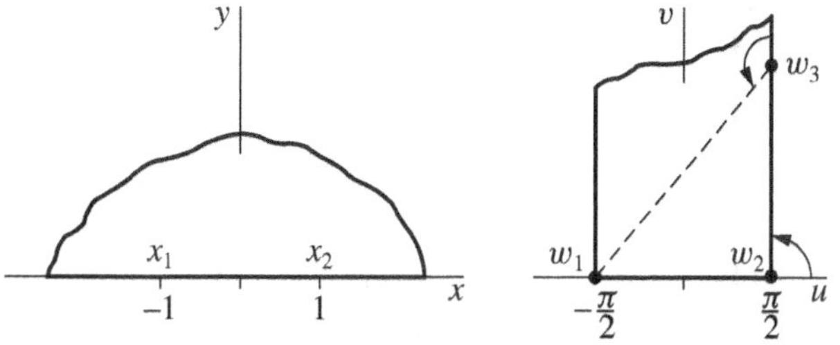

FIGURE 184

The limiting values of the exterior angles are

$$k_1\pi = k_2\pi = \frac{\pi}{2} \qquad \text{and} \qquad k_3\pi = \pi.$$

We choose the points $x_1 = -1$, $x_2 = 1$, and $x_3 = \infty$ as the points whose images are the vertices. Then the derivative of the mapping function can be written

$$\frac{dw}{dz} = A(z+1)^{-1/2}(z-1)^{-1/2} = A'(1-z^2)^{-1/2}.$$

Hence $w = A' \sin^{-1} z + B$. If we write $A' = 1/a$ and $B = b/a$, it follows that

$$z = \sin(aw - b).$$

This transformation from the w to the z plane satisfies the conditions $z = -1$ when $w = -\pi/2$ and $z = 1$ when $w = \pi/2$ if $a = 1$ and $b = 0$. The resulting transformation is

$$z = \sin w,$$

which we have already verified (Sec. 104), with the z and w planes interchanged, as one that maps the strip onto the half plane.

EXAMPLE 2. Consider the strip $0 < v < \pi$ as the limiting form of a rhombus with vertices at the points $w_1 = \pi i$, w_2, $w_3 = 0$, and w_4 as the points w_2 and w_4 are moved infinitely far to the left and right, respectively (Fig. 185). In the limit, the

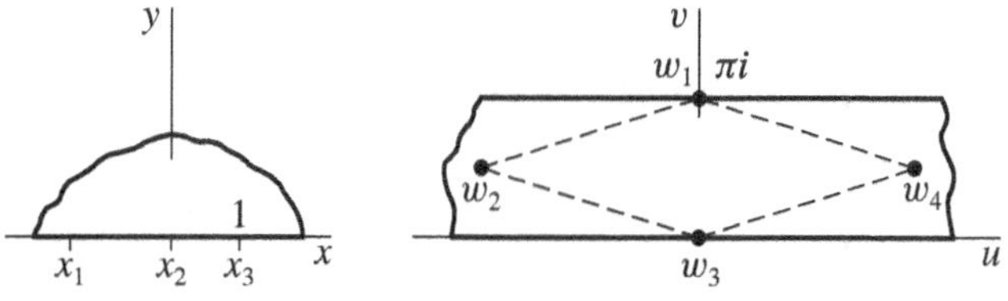

FIGURE 185

exterior angles become

$$k_1\pi = 0, \quad k_2\pi = \pi, \quad k_3\pi = 0, \quad k_4\pi = \pi.$$

We leave x_1 to be determined and choose the values $x_2 = 0$, $x_3 = 1$, and $x_4 = \infty$. The derivative of the Schwarz–Christoffel mapping function then becomes

$$\frac{dw}{dz} = A(z - x_1)^0 z^{-1}(z - 1)^0 = \frac{A}{z};$$

thus

$$w = A \operatorname{Log} z + B.$$

Now $B = 0$ because $w = 0$ when $z = 1$. The constant A must be real because the point w lies on the real axis when $z = x$ and $x > 0$. The point $w = \pi i$ is the image of the point $z = x_1$, where x_1 is a negative number; consequently,

$$\pi i = A \operatorname{Log} x_1 = A \ln |x_1| + A\pi i.$$

By identifying real and imaginary parts here, we see that $|x_1| = 1$ and $A = 1$. Hence the transformation becomes

$$w = \operatorname{Log} z;$$

also, $x_1 = -1$. We already know from Example 3 in Sec. 102 that this transformation maps the half plane onto the strip.

The procedure used in these two examples is not rigorous because limiting values of angles and coordinates were not introduced in an orderly way. Limiting values were used whenever it seemed expedient to do so. But if we verify the mapping obtained, it is not essential that we justify the steps in our derivation of the mapping function. The formal method used here is shorter and less tedious than rigorous methods.

EXERCISES

1. In transformation (1), Sec. 129, write $z_0 = 0$, $B = 0$, and

$$A = \exp\frac{3\pi i}{4}, \qquad x_1 = -1, \qquad x_2 = 0, \qquad x_3 = 1,$$

$$k_1 = \frac{3}{4}, \qquad k_2 = \frac{1}{2}, \qquad k_3 = \frac{3}{4}$$

to map the x axis onto an *isosceles right triangle*. Show that the vertices of that triangle are the points

$$w_1 = bi, \qquad w_2 = 0, \qquad \text{and} \qquad w_3 = b,$$

where b is the positive constant

$$b = \int_0^1 (1 - x^2)^{-3/4} x^{-1/2}\, dx.$$

Also, show that

$$2b = B\left(\frac{1}{4}, \frac{1}{4}\right),$$

where B is the beta function that was defined in Exercise 5, Sec. 91.

2. Obtain expressions (12) in Sec. 129 for the rest of the vertices of the rectangle shown in Fig. 183.

3. Show that when $0 < a < 1$ in expression (8), Sec. 129, the vertices of the rectangle are those shown in Fig. 183, where b and c now have the values

$$b = \int_0^a |g(x)|\, dx, \qquad c = \int_a^1 |g(x)|\, dx.$$

4. Show that the special case

$$w = i\int_0^z (s+1)^{-1/2}(s-1)^{-1/2}s^{-1/2}\, ds$$

of the Schwarz–Christoffel transformation (7), Sec. 128, maps the x axis onto the *square* with vertices

$$w_1 = bi, \qquad w_2 = 0, \qquad w_3 = b, \qquad w_4 = b + ib,$$

where the (positive) number b is related to the beta function, used in Exercise 1:

$$2b = B\left(\frac{1}{4}, \frac{1}{2}\right).$$

5. Use the Schwarz–Christoffel transformation to arrive at the transformation

$$w = z^m \quad (0 < m < 1),$$

which maps the half plane $y \geq 0$ onto the wedge $|w| \geq 0, 0 \leq \arg w \leq m\pi$ and transforms the point $z = 1$ into the point $w = 1$. Consider the wedge as the limiting case of the triangular region shown in Fig. 186 as the angle α there tends to 0.

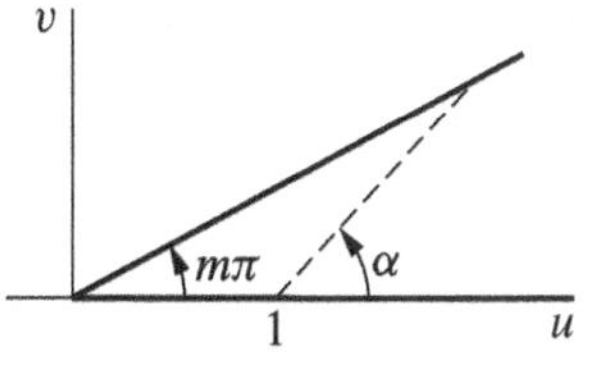

FIGURE 186

6. Refer to Fig. 26 in Appendix 2. As a point z moves to the right along the negative real axis, its image point w is to move to the right along the entire u axis. As z describes the segment $0 \leq x \leq 1$ of the real axis, its image point w is to move to the left along the half line $v = \pi i$ $(u \geq 1)$; and, as z moves to the right along that part of the positive real axis where $x \geq 1$, its image point w is to move to the right along the same half line $v = \pi i$ $(u \geq 1)$. Note the changes in direction of the motion of w at the images of the points $z = 0$ and $z = 1$. These changes suggest that the derivative of a mapping function should be

$$f'(z) = A(z-0)^{-1}(z-1),$$

where A is some constant; thus obtain formally the mapping function

$$w = \pi i + z - \text{Log}\, z,$$

which can be verified as one that maps the half plane $\text{Re}\, z > 0$ as indicated in the figure.

7. As a point z moves to the right along that part of the negative real axis where $x \leq -1$, its image point is to move to the right along the negative real axis in the w plane. As z moves on the real axis to the right along the segment $-1 \leq x \leq 0$ and then along the segment $0 \leq x \leq 1$, its image point w is to move in the direction of increasing v along the segment $0 \leq v \leq 1$ of the v axis and then in the direction of decreasing v along the same segment. Finally, as z moves to the right along that part of the positive real axis where $x \geq 1$, its image point is to move to the right along the positive real axis in the w plane. Note the changes in direction of the motion of w at the images of the points $z = -1$, $z = 0$, and $z = 1$. A mapping function whose derivative is

$$f'(z) = A(z+1)^{-1/2}(z-0)^1(z-1)^{-1/2},$$

where A is some constant, is thus indicated. Obtain formally the mapping function

$$w = \sqrt{z^2 - 1},$$

where $0 < \arg \sqrt{z^2 - 1} < \pi$. By considering the successive mappings

$$Z = z^2, \quad W = Z - 1, \quad \text{and} \quad w = \sqrt{W},$$

verify that the resulting transformation maps the right half plane $\text{Re}\, z > 0$ onto the upper half plane $\text{Im}\, w > 0$, with a cut along the segment $0 < v \leq 1$ of the v axis.

8. The inverse of the linear fractional transformation

$$Z = \frac{i - z}{i + z}$$

maps the unit disk $|Z| \leq 1$ conformally, except at the point $Z = -1$, onto the half plane $\text{Im}\, z \geq 0$. (See Fig. 13, Appendix 2.) Let Z_j be points on the circle $|Z| = 1$ whose images are the points $z = x_j$ $(j = 1, 2, \ldots, n)$ that are used in the Schwarz–Christoffel transformation (8), Sec. 128. Show formally, without determining the branches of the power functions, that

$$\frac{dw}{dZ} = A'(Z - Z_1)^{-k_1}(Z - Z_2)^{-k_2} \cdots (Z - Z_n)^{-k_n},$$

where A' is a constant. Thus show that *the transformation*

$$w = A' \int_0^Z (S - Z_1)^{-k_1}(S - Z_2)^{-k_2} \cdots (S - Z_n)^{-k_n}\, dS + B$$

maps the interior of the circle $|Z| = 1$ *onto the interior of a polygon,* the vertices of the polygon being the images of the points Z_j on the circle.

9. In the integral of Exercise 8, let the numbers Z_j $(j = 1, 2, \ldots, n)$ be the nth roots of unity. Write $\omega = \exp(2\pi i/n)$ and $Z_1 = 1$, $Z_2 = \omega, \ldots, Z_n = \omega^{n-1}$ (see Sec. 10). Let each of the numbers k_j $(j = 1, 2, \ldots, n)$ have the value $2/n$. The integral in Exercise 8 then becomes

$$w = A' \int_0^Z \frac{dS}{(S^n - 1)^{2/n}} + B.$$

Show that when $A' = 1$ and $B = 0$, this transformation maps the interior of the unit circle $|Z| = 1$ onto the interior of a regular polygon of n sides and that the center of the polygon is the point $w = 0$.

Suggestion: The image of each of the points Z_j $(j = 1, 2, \ldots, n)$ is a vertex of some polygon with an exterior angle of $2\pi/n$ at that vertex. Write

$$w_1 = \int_0^1 \frac{dS}{(S^n - 1)^{2/n}},$$

where the path of the integration is along the positive real axis from $Z = 0$ to $Z = 1$ and the principal value of the nth root of $(S^n - 1)^2$ is to be taken. Then show that the images of the points $Z_2 = \omega, \ldots, Z_n = \omega^{n-1}$ are the points $\omega w_1, \ldots, \omega^{n-1} w_1$, respectively. Thus verify that the polygon is regular and is centered at $w = 0$.

131. FLUID FLOW IN A CHANNEL THROUGH A SLIT

We now present a further example of the idealized steady flow treated in Chap. 10, an example that will help show how sources and sinks can be accounted for in problems of fluid flow. In this and the following two sections, the problems are posed in the uv plane, rather than the xy plane. That allows us to refer directly to earlier results in this chapter without interchanging the planes.

Consider the two-dimensional steady flow of fluid between two parallel planes $v = 0$ and $v = \pi$ when the fluid is entering through a narrow slit along the line in the first plane that is perpendicular to the uv plane at the origin (Fig. 187). Let the rate of flow of fluid into the channel through the slit be Q units of volume per unit time for each unit of depth of the channel, where the depth is measured perpendicular to the uv plane. The rate of flow out at either end is, then, $Q/2$.

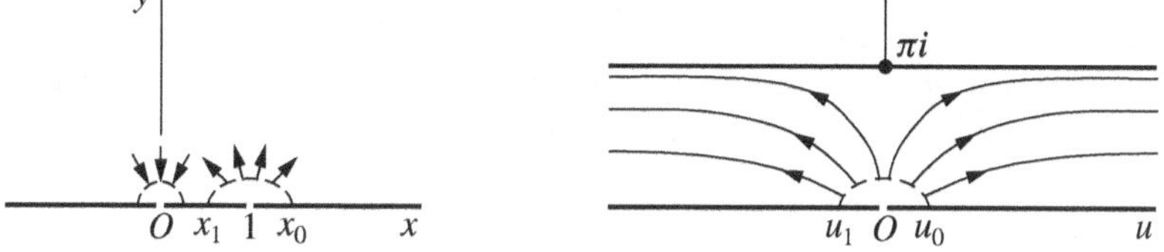

FIGURE 187

The transformation $w = \text{Log}\, z$ is a one to one mapping of the upper half $y > 0$ of the z plane onto the strip $0 < v < \pi$ in the w plane (see Example 2 in Sec. 130). The inverse transformation

$$z = e^w = e^u e^{iv} \tag{1}$$

maps the strip onto the half plane (see Example 3, Sec. 103). Under transformation (1), the image of the u axis is the positive half of the x axis, and the image of the line $v = \pi$

is the negative half of the x axis. Hence the boundary of the strip is transformed into the boundary of the half plane.

The image of the point $w = 0$ is the point $z = 1$. The image of a point $w = u_0$, where $u_0 > 0$, is a point $z = x_0$, where $x_0 > 1$. The rate of flow of fluid across a curve joining the point $w = u_0$ to a point (u, v) within the strip is a stream function $\psi(u, v)$ for the flow (Sec. 125). If u_1 is a negative real number, then the rate of flow into the channel through the slit can be written

$$\psi(u_1, 0) = Q.$$

Now, under a conformal transformation, the function ψ is transformed into a function of x and y that represents the stream function for the flow in the corresponding region of the z plane; that is, the rate of flow is the same across corresponding curves in the two planes. As in Chap. 10, the same symbol ψ is used to represent the different stream functions in the two planes. Since the image of the point $w = u_1$ is a point $z = x_1$, where $0 < x_1 < 1$, the rate of flow across any curve connecting the points $z = x_0$ and $z = x_1$ and lying in the upper half of the z plane is also equal to Q. Hence there is a source at the point $z = 1$ equal to the source at $w = 0$.

The same argument applies in general to show that *under a conformal transformation, a source or sink at a given point corresponds to an equal source or sink at the image of that point.*

As Re w tends to $-\infty$, the image of w approaches the point $z = 0$. A sink of strength $Q/2$ at the latter point corresponds to the sink infinitely far to the left in the strip. To apply the argument in this case, we consider the rate of flow across a curve connecting the boundary lines $v = 0$ and $v = \pi$ of the left-hand part of the strip and the rate of flow across the image of that curve in the z plane.

The sink at the right-hand end of the strip is transformed into a sink at infinity in the z plane.

The stream function ψ for the flow in the upper half of the z plane in this case must be a function whose values are constant along each of the three parts of the x axis. Moreover, its value must increase by Q as the point z moves around the point $z = 1$ from the position $z = x_0$ to the position $z = x_1$, and its value must decrease by $Q/2$ as z moves about the origin in the corresponding manner. We see that the function

$$\psi = \frac{Q}{\pi}\left[\operatorname{Arg}(z-1) - \frac{1}{2}\operatorname{Arg} z\right]$$

satisfies those requirements. Furthermore, this function is harmonic in the half plane Im $z > 0$ because it is the imaginary component of the function

$$F = \frac{Q}{\pi}\left[\operatorname{Log}(z-1) - \frac{1}{2}\operatorname{Log} z\right] = \frac{Q}{\pi}\operatorname{Log}(z^{1/2} - z^{-1/2}).$$

The function F is a complex potential function for the flow in the upper half of the z plane. Since $z = e^w$, a complex potential function $F(w)$ for the flow in the channel is

$$F(w) = \frac{Q}{\pi}\text{Log}\,(e^{w/2} - e^{-w/2}).$$

By dropping an additive constant, one can write

$$(2)\qquad F(w) = \frac{Q}{\pi}\text{Log}\left(\sinh\frac{w}{2}\right).$$

We have used the same symbol F to denote three distinct functions, once in the z plane and twice in the w plane.

The velocity vector is

$$(3)\qquad V = \overline{F'(w)} = \frac{Q}{2\pi}\coth\frac{\overline{w}}{2}.$$

From this, it can be seen that

$$\lim_{|u|\to\infty} V = \frac{Q}{2\pi}.$$

Also, the point $w = \pi i$ is a ***stagnation point***; that is, the velocity is zero there. Hence the fluid pressure along the wall $v = \pi$ of the channel is greatest at points opposite the slit.

The stream function $\psi(u, v)$ for the channel is the imaginary component of the function $F(w)$ given by equation (2). The streamlines $\psi(u, v) = c_2$ are, therefore, the curves

$$\frac{Q}{\pi}\text{Arg}\left(\sinh\frac{w}{2}\right) = c_2.$$

This equation reduces to

$$(4)\qquad \tan\frac{v}{2} = c\tanh\frac{u}{2},$$

where c is any real constant. Some of these streamlines are indicated in Fig. 187.

132. FLOW IN A CHANNEL WITH AN OFFSET

To further illustrate the use of the Schwarz–Christoffel transformation, let us find the complex potential for the flow of a fluid in a channel with an abrupt change in its breadth (Fig. 188). We take our unit of length such that the breadth of the wide part of the channel is π units; then $h\pi$, where $0 < h < 1$, represents the breadth of the narrow part. Let the real constant V_0 denote the velocity of the fluid far from the offset in the wide part; thus

$$\lim_{u\to-\infty} V = V_0,$$

where the complex variable V represents the velocity vector. The rate of flow per unit depth through the channel, or the strength of the source on the left and of the sink on

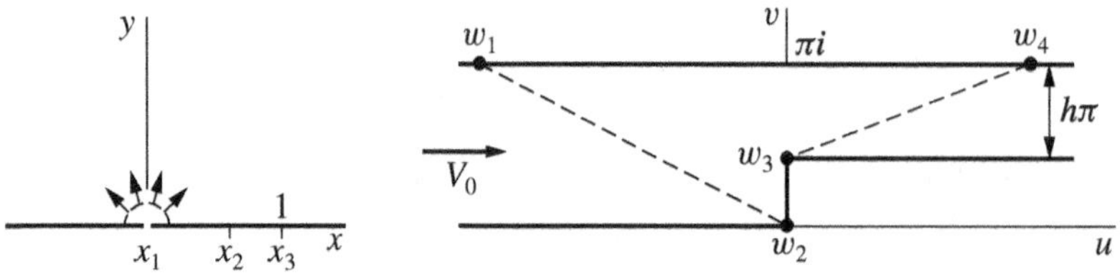

FIGURE 188

the right, is then

$$Q = \pi V_0. \tag{1}$$

The cross section of the channel can be considered as the limiting case of the quadrilateral with the vertices w_1, w_2, w_3, and w_4 shown in Fig. 188 as the first and last of these vertices are moved infinitely far to the left and right, respectively. In the limit, the exterior angles become

$$k_1\pi = \pi, \qquad k_2\pi = \frac{\pi}{2}, \qquad k_3\pi = -\frac{\pi}{2}, \qquad k_4\pi = \pi.$$

As before, we proceed formally, using limiting values whenever it is convenient to do so. If we write $x_1 = 0$, $x_3 = 1$, $x_4 = \infty$ and leave x_2 to be determined, where $0 < x_2 < 1$, the derivative of the mapping function becomes

$$\frac{dw}{dz} = Az^{-1}(z - x_2)^{-1/2}(z-1)^{1/2}. \tag{2}$$

To simplify the determination of the constants A and x_2 here, we proceed at once to the complex potential of the flow. The source of the flow in the channel infinitely far to the left corresponds to an equal source at $z = 0$ (Sec. 131). The entire boundary of the cross section of the channel is the image of the x axis. In view of equation (1), then, the function

$$F = V_0 \operatorname{Log} z = V_0 \ln r + i V_0 \theta \tag{3}$$

is the potential for the flow in the upper half of the z plane, with the required source at the origin. Here the stream function is $\psi = V_0 \theta$. It increases in value from 0 to $V_0\pi$ over each semicircle $z = Re^{i\theta}\,(0 \le \theta \le \pi)$ as θ varies from 0 to π. [Compare with equation (5), Sec. 125, and Exercise 8, Sec. 126.]

The complex conjugate of the velocity V in the w plane can be written

$$\overline{V(w)} = \frac{dF}{dw} = \frac{dF}{dz}\frac{dz}{dw}.$$

Thus, by referring to equations (2) and (3), we can see that

$$\overline{V(w)} = \frac{V_0}{A}\left(\frac{z - x_2}{z-1}\right)^{1/2}. \tag{4}$$

At the limiting position of the point w_1, which corresponds to $z = 0$, the velocity is the real constant V_0. So it follows from equation (4) that

$$V_0 = \frac{V_0}{A}\sqrt{x_2}.$$

At the limiting position of w_4, which corresponds to $z = \infty$, let the real number V_4 denote the velocity. Now it seems plausible that as a vertical line segment spanning the narrow part of the channel is moved infinitely far to the right, V approaches V_4 at each point on that segment. We could establish this conjecture as a fact by first finding w as the function of z from equation (2); but, to shorten our discussion, we assume that this is true, Then, since the flow is steady,

$$\pi h V_4 = \pi V_0 = Q,$$

or $V_4 = V_0/h$. Letting z tend to infinity in equation (4), we find that

$$\frac{V_0}{h} = \frac{V_0}{A}.$$

Thus

(5) $$A = h, \qquad x_2 = h^2$$

and

(6) $$\overline{V(w)} = \frac{V_0}{h}\left(\frac{z - h^2}{z - 1}\right)^{1/2}.$$

From equation (6), we know that the magnitude $|V|$ of the velocity becomes infinite at the corner w_3 of the offset since it is the image of the point $z = 1$. Also, the corner w_2 is a stagnation point, a point where $V = 0$. Hence, along the boundary of the channel, the fluid pressure is greatest at w_2 and least at w_3.

To write the relation between the potential and the variable w, we must integrate equation (2), which can now be written

(7) $$\frac{dw}{dz} = \frac{h}{z}\left(\frac{z - 1}{z - h^2}\right)^{1/2}.$$

By substituting a new variable s, where

$$\frac{z - h^2}{z - 1} = s^2,$$

one can show that equation (7) reduces to

$$\frac{dw}{ds} = 2h\left(\frac{1}{1 - s^2} - \frac{1}{h^2 - s^2}\right).$$

Hence

(8) $$w = h \operatorname{Log}\frac{1 + s}{1 - s} - \operatorname{Log}\frac{h + s}{h - s}.$$

The constant of integration here is zero because when $z = h^2$, the quantity s is zero and so, therefore, is w.

In terms of s, the potential F of equation (3) becomes

$$F = V_0 \operatorname{Log} \frac{h^2 - s^2}{1 - s^2};$$

consequently,

$$s^2 = \frac{\exp(F/V_0) - h^2}{\exp(F/V_0) - 1}. \tag{9}$$

By substituting s from this equation into equation (8), we obtain an implicit relation that defines the potential F as a function of w.

133. ELECTROSTATIC POTENTIAL ABOUT AN EDGE OF A CONDUCTING PLATE

Two parallel conducting plates of infinite extent are kept at the electrostatic potential $V = 0$, and a parallel semi-infinite plate, placed midway between them, is kept at the potential $V = 1$. The coordinate system and the unit of length are chosen so that the plates lie in the planes $v = 0$, $v = \pi$, and $v = \pi/2$ (Fig. 189). Let us determine the potential function $V(u, v)$ in the region between those plates.

The cross section of that region in the uv plane has the limiting form of the quadrilateral bounded by the dashed lines in Fig. 189 as the points w_1 and w_3 move out to the right and w_4 to the left. In applying the Schwarz–Christoffel transformation here, we let the point x_4, corresponding to the vertex w_4, be the point at infinity. We choose the points $x_1 = -1$, $x_3 = 1$ and leave x_2 to be determined. The limiting values of the exterior angles of the quadrilateral are

$$k_1\pi = \pi, \qquad k_2\pi = -\pi, \qquad k_3\pi = k_4\pi = \pi.$$

Thus

$$\frac{dw}{dz} = A(z+1)^{-1}(z - x_2)(z-1)^{-1} = A\left(\frac{z - x_2}{z^2 - 1}\right) = \frac{A}{2}\left(\frac{1 + x_2}{z+1} + \frac{1 - x_2}{z - 1}\right),$$

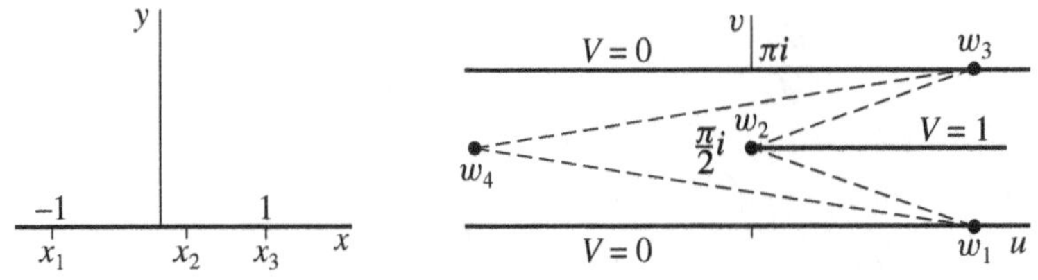

FIGURE 189

and so the transformation of the upper half of the z plane into the divided strip in the w plane has the form

$$(1)\qquad w = \frac{A}{2}[(1 + x_2)\,\mathrm{Log}\,(z + 1) + (1 - x_2)\,\mathrm{Log}\,(z - 1)] + B.$$

Let A_1, A_2 and B_1, B_2 denote the real and imaginary parts of the constants A and B. When $z = x$, the point w lies on the boundary of the divided strip; and, according to equation (1),

$$(2)\qquad u + iv = \frac{A_1 + iA_2}{2}\{(1 + x_2)[\ln|x + 1| + i\arg(x + 1)] + (1 - x_2)[\ln|x - 1| + i\arg(x - 1)]\} + B_1 + iB_2.$$

To determine the constants here, we first note that the limiting position of the line segment joining the points w_1 and w_4 is the u axis. That segment is the image of the part of the x axis to the left of the point $x_1 = -1$; this is because the line segment joining w_3 and w_4 is the image of the part of the x axis to the right of $x_3 = 1$, and the other two sides of the quadrilateral are the images of the remaining two segments of the x axis. Hence when $v = 0$ and u tends to infinity through positive values, the corresponding point x approaches the point $z = -1$ from the left. Thus

$$\arg(x + 1) = \pi, \qquad \arg(x - 1) = \pi,$$

and $\ln|x + 1|$ tends to $-\infty$. Also, since $-1 < x_2 < 1$, the real part of the quantity inside the braces in equation (2) tends to $-\infty$. Since $v = 0$, it readily follows that $A_2 = 0$; for, otherwise, the imaginary part on the right would become infinite. By equating imaginary parts on the two sides, we now see that

$$0 = \frac{A_1}{2}[(1 + x_2)\pi + (1 - x_2)\pi] + B_2.$$

Hence

$$(3)\qquad -\pi A_1 = B_2, \qquad A_2 = 0.$$

The limiting position of the line segment joining the points w_1 and w_2 is the half line $v = \pi/2$ $(u \geq 0)$. Points on that half line are images of the points $z = x$, where $-1 < x \leq x_2$; consequently,

$$\arg(x + 1) = 0, \qquad \arg(x - 1) = \pi.$$

Identifying the imaginary parts on the two sides of equation (2), we thus arrive at the relation

$$(4)\qquad \frac{\pi}{2} = \frac{A_1}{2}(1 - x_2)\pi + B_2.$$

Finally, the limiting positions of the points on the line segment joining w_3 to w_4 are the points $u + \pi i$, which are the images of the points x when $x > 1$. By identifying, for those points, the imaginary parts in equation (2), we find that

$$\pi = B_2.$$

Then, in view of equations (3) and (4),

$$A_1 = -1, \qquad x_2 = 0.$$

Thus $x = 0$ is the point whose image is the vertex $w = \pi i/2$; and, upon substituting these values into equation (2) and identifying real parts, we see that $B_1 = 0$.

Transformation (1) now becomes

$$w = -\frac{1}{2}[\text{Log}(z+1) + \text{Log}(z-1)] + \pi i, \tag{5}$$

or

$$z^2 = 1 + e^{-2w}. \tag{6}$$

Under this transformation, the required harmonic function $V(u, v)$ becomes a harmonic function of x and y in the half plane $y > 0$; and the boundary conditions indicated in Fig. 190 are satisfied. Note that $x_2 = 0$ now. The harmonic function in that half plane which assumes those values on the boundary is the imaginary component of the analytic function

$$\frac{1}{\pi}\text{Log}\frac{z-1}{z+1} = \frac{1}{\pi}\ln\frac{r_1}{r_2} + \frac{i}{\pi}(\theta_1 - \theta_2),$$

where θ_1 and θ_2 range from 0 to π. Writing the tangents of these angles as functions of x and y and simplifying, we find that

$$\tan\pi V = \tan(\theta_1 - \theta_2) = \frac{2y}{x^2 + y^2 - 1}. \tag{7}$$

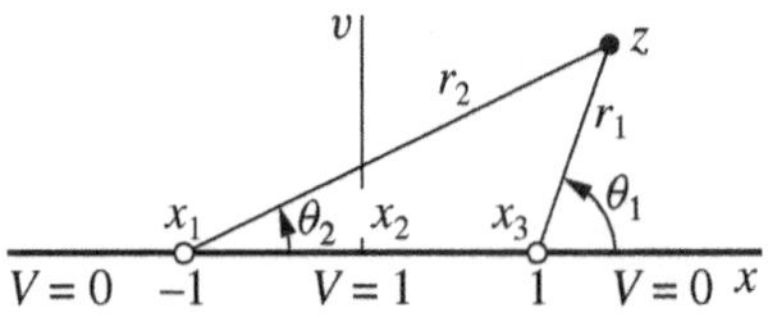

FIGURE 190

Equation (6) furnishes expressions for $x^2 + y^2$ and $x^2 - y^2$ in terms of u and v. Then, from equation (7), we find that the relation between the potential V and the coordinates u and v can be written

$$\tan\pi V = \frac{1}{s}\sqrt{e^{-4u} - s^2}, \tag{8}$$

where

$$s = -1 + \sqrt{1 + 2e^{-2u}\cos 2v + e^{-4u}}.$$

EXERCISES

1. Use the Schwarz–Christoffel transformation to obtain formally the mapping function given with Fig. 22, Appendix 2.

2. Explain why the solution of the problem of flow in a channel with a semi-infinite rectangular obstruction (Fig. 191) is included in the solution of the problem treated in Sec. 121.

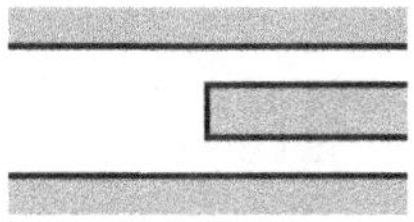

FIGURE 191

3. Refer to Fig. 29, Appendix 2. As a point z moves to the right along the negative part of the real axis where $x \le -1$, its image point w is to move to the right along the half line $v = h\ (u \le 0)$. As the point z moves to the right along the segment $-1 \le x \le 1$ of the x axis, its image point w is to move in the direction of decreasing v along the segment $0 \le v \le h$ of the v axis. Finally, as z moves to the right along the positive part of the real axis where $x \ge 1$, its image point w is to move to the right along the positive real axis. Note the changes in the direction of motion of w at the images of the points $z = -1$ and $z = 1$. These changes indicate that the derivative of a mapping function might be

$$\frac{dw}{dz} = A\left(\frac{z+1}{z-1}\right)^{1/2},$$

where A is some constant. Thus obtain formally the transformation given with the figure. Verify that the transformation, written in the form

$$w = \frac{h}{\pi}\{(z+1)^{1/2}(z-1)^{1/2} + \text{Log}\,[z + (z+1)^{1/2}(z-1)^{1/2}]\}$$

where $0 \le \arg(z \pm 1) \le \pi$, maps the boundary in the manner indicated in the figure.

4. Let $T(u, v)$ denote the bounded steady-state temperatures in the shaded region of the w plane in Fig. 29, Appendix 2, with the boundary conditions $T(u, h) = 1$ when $u < 0$ and $T = 0$ on the rest $(B'C'D')$ of the boundary. Using the parameter α, where $0 < \alpha < \pi/2$, show that the image of each point $z = i \tan\alpha$ on the positive y axis is the point

$$w = \frac{h}{\pi}\left[\ln(\tan\alpha + \sec\alpha) + i\left(\frac{\pi}{2} + \sec\alpha\right)\right]$$

(see Exercise 3) and that the temperature at that point w is

$$T(u, v) = \frac{\alpha}{\pi} \qquad \left(0 < \alpha < \frac{\pi}{2}\right).$$

5. Let $F(w)$ denote the complex potential function for the flow of a fluid over a step in the bed of a deep stream represented by the shaded region of the w plane in Fig. 29, Appendix 2, where the fluid velocity V approaches a real constant V_0 as $|w|$ tends to infinity in that region. The transformation that maps the upper half of the z plane onto the region is noted in Exercise 3. Use the chain rule

$$\frac{dF}{dw} = \frac{dF}{dz}\frac{dz}{dw}$$

to show that

$$\overline{V(w)} = V_0(z-1)^{1/2}(z+1)^{-1/2};$$

and, in terms of the points $z = x$ whose images are the points along the bed of the stream, show that

$$|V| = |V_0| \sqrt{\left|\frac{x-1}{x+1}\right|}.$$

Note that the speed increases from $|V_0|$ along $A'B'$ until $|V| = \infty$ at B', then diminishes to zero at C', and increases toward $|V_0|$ from C' to D'; note, too, that the speed is $|V_0|$ at the point

$$w = i\left(\frac{1}{2} + \frac{1}{\pi}\right)h,$$

between B' and C'.

CHAPTER 12

INTEGRAL FORMULAS OF THE POISSON TYPE

In this chapter, we develop a theory that enables us to solve a variety of boundary value problems whose solutions are expressed in terms of definite or improper integrals. Many of the integrals occurring are then readily evaluated.

134. POISSON INTEGRAL FORMULA

Let C_0 denote a positively oriented circle, centered at the origin, and suppose that a function f is analytic inside and on C_0. The Cauchy integral formula (Sec. 54)

$$f(z) = \frac{1}{2\pi i}\int_{C_0} \frac{f(s)\,ds}{s-z} \tag{1}$$

expresses the value of f at any point z interior to C_0 in terms of the values of f at points s on C_0. In this section, we shall obtain from formula (1) a corresponding one for the real component of the function f; and, in Sec. 135, we shall use that result to solve the Dirichlet problem (Sec. 116) for the disk bounded by C_0.

We let r_0 denote the radius of C_0 and write $z = r\exp(i\theta)$, where $0 < r < r_0$ (Fig. 192). The ***inverse*** of the nonzero point z with respect to the circle is the point z_1 lying on the same ray from the origin as z and satisfying the condition $|z_1||z| = r_0^2$. (Such inverse points, when $r_0 = 1$, have already been used in Sec. 97.) Because

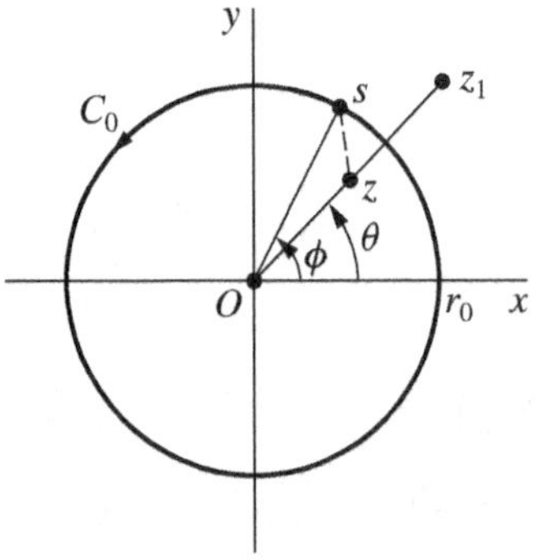

FIGURE 192

$(r_0/r) > 1$,

$$|z_1| = \frac{r_0^2}{|z|} = \left(\frac{r_0}{r}\right) r_0 > r_0;$$

and this means that z_1 is exterior to the circle C_0. According to the Cauchy–Goursat theorem (Sec. 50), then,

$$\int_{C_0} \frac{f(s)\,ds}{s - z_1} = 0.$$

Hence

$$f(z) = \frac{1}{2\pi i} \int_{C_0} \left(\frac{1}{s-z} - \frac{1}{s-z_1}\right) f(s)\,ds;$$

and, using the parametric representation $s = r_0 \exp(i\phi)$ $(0 \le \phi \le 2\pi)$ for C_0, we have

$$f(z) = \frac{1}{2\pi} \int_0^{2\pi} \left(\frac{s}{s-z} - \frac{s}{s-z_1}\right) f(s)\,d\phi \tag{2}$$

where, for convenience, we retain the s to denote $r_0 \exp(i\phi)$. Now

$$z_1 = \frac{r_0^2}{r} e^{i\theta} = \frac{r_0^2}{re^{-i\theta}} = \frac{s\overline{s}}{\overline{z}};$$

and, in view of this expression for z_1, the quantity inside the parentheses in equation (2) can be written

$$\frac{s}{s-z} - \frac{s}{s - s(\overline{s}/\overline{z})} = \frac{s}{s-z} + \frac{\overline{z}}{\overline{s}-\overline{z}} = \frac{r_0^2 - r^2}{|s-z|^2}. \tag{3}$$

An alternative form of the Cauchy integral formula (1) is, therefore,

$$f(re^{i\theta}) = \frac{r_0^2 - r^2}{2\pi} \int_0^{2\pi} \frac{f(r_0 e^{i\phi})}{|s-z|^2}\,d\phi \tag{4}$$

when $0 < r < r_0$. This form is also valid when $r = 0$; in that case, it reduces directly to

$$f(0) = \frac{1}{2\pi} \int_0^{2\pi} f(r_0 e^{i\phi})\,d\phi,$$

which is just the parametric form of equation (1) when $z = 0$.

The quantity $|s - z|$ is the distance between the points s and z, and the law of cosines can be used to write (see Fig. 192)

$$|s - z|^2 = r_0^2 - 2r_0 r\cos(\phi - \theta) + r^2. \tag{5}$$

Hence, if u is the real component of the analytic function f, it follows from formula (4) that

$$u(r, \theta) = \frac{1}{2\pi}\int_0^{2\pi} \frac{(r_0^2 - r^2)u(r_0, \phi)}{r_0^2 - 2r_0 r\cos(\phi - \theta) + r^2}\, d\phi \qquad (r < r_0). \tag{6}$$

This is the ***Poisson integral formula*** for the harmonic function u in the open disk bounded by the circle $r = r_0$.

Formula (6) defines a linear integral transformation of $u(r_0, \phi)$ into $u(r, \theta)$. The kernel of the transformation is, except for the factor $1/(2\pi)$, the real-valued function

$$P(r_0, r, \phi - \theta) = \frac{r_0^2 - r^2}{r_0^2 - 2r_0 r\cos(\phi - \theta) + r^2}, \tag{7}$$

which is known as the ***Poisson kernel.*** In view of equation (5), we can also write

$$P(r_0, r, \phi - \theta) = \frac{r_0^2 - r^2}{|s - z|^2}. \tag{8}$$

Let us now verify the following properties of P, where $r < r_0$:

(a) P is a positive function;

(b) $P(r_0, r, \phi - \theta) = \text{Re}\left(\dfrac{s + z}{s - z}\right)$;

(c) $P(r_0, r, \phi - \theta)$ is a harmonic function of r and θ interior to the circle C_0 for each fixed s on C_0;

(d) $P(r_0, r, \phi - \theta)$ is an even periodic function of $\phi - \theta$, with period 2π;

(e) $P(r_0, 0, \phi - \theta) = 1$;

(f) $\dfrac{1}{2\pi}\displaystyle\int_0^{2\pi} P(r_0, r, \phi - \theta)d\phi = 1$ when $r < r_0$.

Property (a) is true because of expression (8) since $r < r_0$. Also, since $z/(s - z)$ and its complex conjugate $\overline{z}/(\overline{s} - \overline{z})$ have the same real parts, expression (8) and the second of equations (3) tells us that

$$P(r_0, r, \phi - \theta) = \text{Re}\left(\frac{s}{s - z} + \frac{z}{s - z}\right) = \text{Re}\left(\frac{s + z}{s - z}\right).$$

Thus P has property (b); and since the real part of an analytic function is harmonic, P has property (c). As for properties (d) and (e), we find from expression (7) that P has those properties. Finally, property (f) follows by writing $u(r, \theta) = 1$ in equation (6) and then referring to expression (7).

We conclude this introduction to the Poisson integral formula by writing expression (6) as

$$(9) \qquad u(r,\theta) = \frac{1}{2\pi}\int_0^{2\pi} P(r_0, r, \phi-\theta)u(r_0,\phi)\,d\phi \qquad (r < r_0).$$

We have assumed that f is analytic not only interior to C_0 but also on C_0 itself and that u is, therefore, harmonic in a domain which includes all points on that circle. In particular, u is continuous on C_0. The conditions will now be relaxed.

135. DIRICHLET PROBLEM FOR A DISK

Let F be a piecewise continuous function (Sec. 42) of θ on the interval $0 \leq \theta \leq 2\pi$. The ***Poisson integral transform*** of F is defined in terms of the Poisson kernel $P(r_0, r, \phi-\theta)$, introduced in Sec. 134, by means of the equation

$$(1) \qquad U(r,\theta) = \frac{1}{2\pi}\int_0^{2\pi} P(r_0, r, \phi-\theta)F(\phi)\,d\phi \qquad (r < r_0).$$

In this section, we shall prove that *the function $U(r,\theta)$ is harmonic inside the circle $r = r_0$ and*

$$(2) \qquad \lim_{\substack{r\to r_0 \\ r<r_0}} U(r,\theta) = F(\theta)$$

for each fixed θ at which F is continuous. Thus U is a solution of the Dirichlet problem for the disk $r < r_0$ in the sense that $U(r,\theta)$ is harmonic and approaches the boundary value $F(\theta)$ as the point (r,θ) approaches (r_0,θ) along a radius, except at the finite number of points (r_0,θ) where discontinuities of F may occur.

Applications of the solution will be made in Sec. 136. Turning now to the proof that the function $U(r,\theta)$ defined by equation (1) satisfies the stated Dirichlet problem, we note first that U is harmonic inside the circle $r = r_0$ because P is a harmonic function of r and θ there. More precisely, since F is piecewise continuous, integral (1) can be written as the sum of a finite number of definite integrals each of which has an integrand that is continuous in r, θ, and ϕ. The partial derivatives of those integrands with respect to r and θ are also continuous. Since the order of integration and differentiation with respect to r and θ can, then, be interchanged and since P satisfies Laplace's equation

$$r^2 P_{rr} + rP_r + P_{\theta\theta} = 0$$

in the polar coordinates r and θ (Exercise 1, Sec. 27), it follows that U satisfies that equation too.

In order to verify limit (2), we need to show that if F is continuous at θ, there corresponds to each positive number ε a positive number δ such that

$$(3) \qquad |U(r,\theta) - F(\theta)| < \varepsilon \qquad \text{whenever} \qquad 0 < r_0 - r < \delta.$$

We start by referring to property (f), Sec. 134, of the Poisson kernel and writing

$$U(r,\theta) - F(\theta) = \frac{1}{2\pi}\int_0^{2\pi} P(r_0, r, \phi - \theta)\,[F(\phi) - F(\theta)]\,d\phi.$$

For convenience, we let F be extended periodically, with period 2π, so that the integrand here is periodic in ϕ with that same period. Also, we agree that $0 < r < r_0$ because of the nature of the limit to be established.

Next, we observe that since F is continuous at θ, there is a small positive number α such that

$$(4) \qquad |F(\phi) - F(\theta)| < \frac{\varepsilon}{2} \qquad \text{whenever} \qquad |\phi - \theta| \le \alpha.$$

Assume now that $|\phi - \theta| \le \alpha$ and write

$$(5) \qquad U(r,\theta) - F(\theta) = I_1(r) + I_2(r)$$

where

$$I_1(r) = \frac{1}{2\pi}\int_{\theta-\alpha}^{\theta+\alpha} P(r_0, r, \phi - \theta)\,[F(\phi) - F(\theta)]\,d\phi,$$

$$I_2(r) = \frac{1}{2\pi}\int_{\theta+\alpha}^{\theta-\alpha+2\pi} P(r_0, r, \phi - \theta)\,[F(\phi) - F(\theta)]\,d\phi.$$

The fact that P is a positive function (Sec. 134), together with the first of inequalities (4) just above and property (f), Sec. 134, of that function, enables us to write

$$|I_1(r)| \le \frac{1}{2\pi}\int_{\theta-\alpha}^{\theta+\alpha} P(r_0, r, \phi - \theta)\,|F(\phi) - F(\theta)|\,d\phi$$

$$< \frac{\varepsilon}{4\pi}\int_0^{2\pi} P(r_0, r, \phi - \theta)\,d\phi = \frac{\varepsilon}{2}.$$

As for the integral $I_2(r)$, one can see from Fig. 192 in Sec. 134 that the denominator $|s - z|^2$ in expression (8) for $P(r_0, r, \phi - \theta)$ in that section has a (positive) minimum value m as the argument ϕ of s varies over the closed interval

$$\theta + \alpha \le \phi \le \theta - \alpha + 2\pi.$$

So, if M denotes an upper bound of the piecewise continuous function $|F(\phi) - F(\theta)|$ on the interval $0 \le \phi \le 2\pi$, it follows that

$$|I_2(r)| \le \frac{(r_0^2 - r^2)M}{2\pi m}\,2\pi < \frac{2Mr_0}{m}(r_0 - r) < \frac{2Mr_0}{m}\,\delta = \frac{\varepsilon}{2}$$

whenever $r_0 - r < \delta$ where

$$\delta = \frac{m\varepsilon}{4Mr_0}. \tag{6}$$

Finally, the results in the two preceding paragraphs tell us that

$$|U(r,\theta) - F(\theta)| \le |I_1(r)| + |I_2(r)| < \frac{\varepsilon}{2} + \frac{\varepsilon}{2} = \varepsilon$$

whenever $r_0 - r < \delta$, where δ is the positive number defined by equation (6). That is, statement (3) holds when that choice of δ is made.

According to expression (1), and since $P(r_0, 0, \phi - \theta) = 1$,

$$U(0,\theta) = \frac{1}{2\pi}\int_0^{2\pi} F(\phi)\, d\phi.$$

Thus *the value of a harmonic function at the center of the circle $r = r_0$ is the average of the boundary values on the circle.*

It is left to the exercises to prove that P and U can be represented by series involving the elementary harmonic functions $r^n \cos n\theta$ and $r^n \sin n\theta$ as follows:*

$$P(r_0, r, \phi - \theta) = 1 + 2\sum_{n=1}^{\infty}\left(\frac{r}{r_0}\right)^n \cos n(\phi - \theta) \qquad (r < r_0) \tag{7}$$

and

$$U(r,\theta) = \frac{1}{2}a_0 + \sum_{n=1}^{\infty}\left(\frac{r}{r_0}\right)^n (a_n \cos n\theta + b_n \sin n\theta) \qquad (r < r_0), \tag{8}$$

where

$$a_n = \frac{1}{\pi}\int_0^{2\pi} F(\phi)\cos n\phi\, d\phi \qquad (n = 0, 1, 2, \ldots), \tag{9}$$

$$b_n = \frac{1}{\pi}\int_0^{2\pi} F(\phi)\sin n\phi\, d\phi \qquad (n = 1, 2, \ldots). \tag{10}$$

136. EXAMPLES

The examples here illustrate much of the material in the last two sections.

EXAMPLE 1. Let us find the potential $V(r,\theta)$ inside a long hollow circular cylinder of unit radius, split lengthwise into two equal parts, when $V = 1$ on one of the parts and $V = 0$ on the other. This problem was solved by conformal mapping in Example 1, Sec. 123; and we recall how it was interpreted there as a Dirichlet problem

*These results are obtained, in somewhat different notation, when $r_0 = 1$ by the method of separation of variables in the authors' *Fourier Series and Boundary Value Problems,* 8th ed., Sec. 49, 2012.

for the disk $r < 1$, where $V = 0$ on the upper half of the boundary $r = 1$ and $V = 1$ on the lower half. (See Fig. 193.)

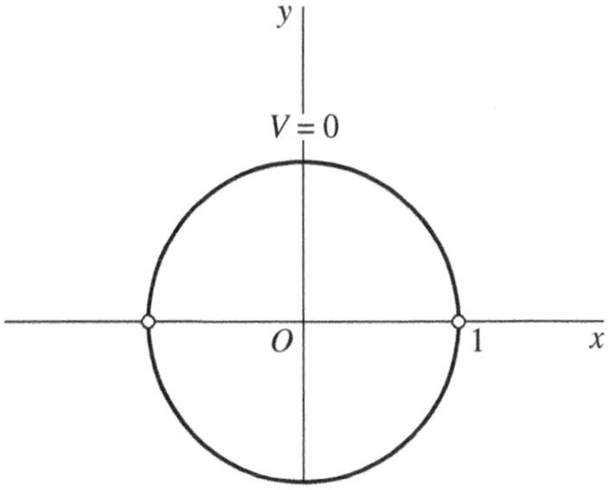

FIGURE 193

In equation (1), Sec. 135, write V for U, $r_0 = 1$, and

$$F(\phi) = \begin{cases} 0 & \text{when} \quad 0 < \phi < \pi, \\ 1 & \text{when} \quad \pi < \phi < 2\pi \end{cases}$$

to obtain

$$V(r,\theta) = \frac{1}{2\pi}\int_{\pi}^{2\pi} P(1, r, \phi - \theta)\, d\phi, \tag{1}$$

where (see Sec.134)

$$P(1, r, \phi - \theta) = \frac{1 - r^2}{1 + r^2 - 2r\cos(\phi - \theta)}.$$

An antiderivative of $P(1, r, \psi)$ is

$$\int P(1, r, \psi)\, d\psi = 2 \arctan\left(\frac{1+r}{1-r} \tan\frac{\psi}{2}\right), \tag{2}$$

the integrand here being the derivative with respect to ψ of the function on the right (see Exercise 3). So it follows from expression (1) that

$$\pi V(r,\theta) = \arctan\left(\frac{1+r}{1-r}\tan\frac{2\pi - \theta}{2}\right) - \arctan\left(\frac{1+r}{1-r}\tan\frac{\pi - \theta}{2}\right).$$

After simplifying the expression for $\tan[\pi V(r, \theta)]$ obtained from this last equation (see Exercise 4), we find that

$$V(r,\theta) = \frac{1}{\pi}\arctan\left(\frac{1 - r^2}{2r\sin\theta}\right) \qquad (0 \le \arctan t \le \pi), \tag{3}$$

where the stated restriction on the values of the arctangent function is physically evident. When expressed in rectangular coordinates, the solution here is the same as solution (5) in Sec. 123.

EXAMPLE 2. In Sec. 135 expression (8), with coefficients (9) and (10), can be used to find the steady temperatures $T(r, \theta)$ in a solid cylinder $r \le r_0$ of infinite length when there is a constant A such that

$$T(r_0, \theta) = A\cos\theta.$$

Using T instead of U, we find that

$$(4) \qquad T(r,\theta) = \frac{1}{2}a_0 + \sum_{n=1}^{\infty}\left(\frac{r}{r_0}\right)^n (a_n \cos n\theta + b_n \sin n\theta) \qquad (r < r_0)$$

where

$$a_0 = \frac{A}{\pi}\int_0^{2\pi} \cos\phi\, d\phi = 0$$

and, when $n = 1, 2, \ldots,$

$$a_n = \frac{A}{\pi}\int_0^{2\pi} \cos\phi\, \cos n\phi\, d\phi = \begin{cases} A \text{ if } n = 1 \\ 0 \text{ if } n > 1. \end{cases}$$

$$b_n = \frac{A}{\pi}\int_0^{2\pi} \cos\phi\, \sin n\phi\, d\phi = 0 \text{ for all } n.$$

(See Exercise 8, where these last two integrals are evaluated.)

If we substitute these values for the coefficients in series (4), we arrive at the desired temperature function:

$$(5) \qquad T(r,\theta) = \frac{A}{r_0}(r\cos\theta) = \frac{A}{r_0}x.$$

Note that (see Sec. 118) no heat flows across the plane $y = 0$, since $\partial T/\partial y = 0$ there.

EXERCISES

1. Use the Poisson integral transform (1), Sec. 135, to derive the expression

$$V(x,y) = \frac{1}{\pi}\arctan\left[\frac{1 - x^2 - y^2}{(x-1)^2 + (y-1)^2 - 1}\right] \qquad (0 \le \arctan t \le \pi)$$

for the electrostatic potential interior to a cylinder $x^2 + y^2 = 1$ when $V = 1$ on the first quadrant ($x > 0$, $y > 0$) of the cylindrical surface and $V = 0$ on the rest of that surface. Also, point out why $1 - V$ is the solution to Exercise 8, Sec. 123.

2. Let T denote the steady temperatures in a disk $r \le 1$, with insulated faces, when $T = 1$ on the arc $0 < \theta < 2\theta_0$ $(0 < \theta_0 < \pi/2)$ of the edge $r = 1$ and $T = 0$ on the rest of the edge. Use the Poisson integral transform (1), Sec. 135, to show that

$$T(x,y) = \frac{1}{\pi}\arctan\left[\frac{(1 - x^2 - y^2)y_0}{(x-1)^2 + (y-y_0)^2 - y_0^2}\right] \qquad (0 \le \arctan t \le \pi),$$

where $y_0 = \tan\theta_0$. Verify that this function T satisfies the boundary conditions.

3. Verify integration formula (2) in Example 1, Sec. 136, by differentiating the right-hand side there with respect to ψ.

Suggestion: The trigonometric identities

$$\cos^2\frac{\psi}{2} = \frac{1+\cos\psi}{2}, \qquad \sin^2\frac{\psi}{2} = \frac{1-\cos\psi}{2}$$

are useful in this verification.

4. With the aid of the trigonometric identities

$$\tan(\alpha-\beta) = \frac{\tan\alpha - \tan\beta}{1+\tan\alpha\tan\beta}, \qquad \tan\alpha + \cot\alpha = \frac{2}{\sin 2\alpha},$$

show how solution (3) in the example in Sec. 135 is obtained from the expression for $\pi V(r,\theta)$ just prior to that solution.

5. Let I denote this ***finite unit impulse function*** (Fig. 194):

$$I(h,\theta-\theta_0) = \begin{cases} 1/h & \text{when } \theta_0 \le \theta \le \theta_0 + h, \\ 0 & \text{when } 0 \le \theta < \theta_0 \text{ or } \theta_0 + h < \theta \le 2\pi, \end{cases}$$

where h is a positive number and $0 \le \theta_0 < \theta_0 + h < 2\pi$. Note that

$$\int_{\theta_0}^{\theta_0+h} I(h,\theta-\theta_0)\,d\theta = 1.$$

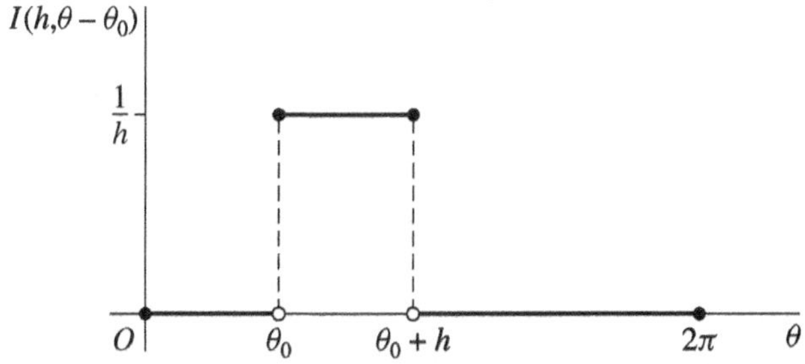

FIGURE 194

With the aid of a mean value theorem for definite integrals, show that

$$\int_0^{2\pi} P(r_0,r,\phi-\theta)\,I(h,\phi-\theta_0)\,d\phi = P(r_0,r,c-\theta)\int_{\theta_0}^{\theta_0+h} I(h,\phi-\theta_0)\,d\phi,$$

where $\theta_0 \le c \le \theta_0 + h$, and hence that

$$\lim_{\substack{h\to 0\\ h>0}} \int_0^{2\pi} P(r_0,r,\phi-\theta)\,I(h,\phi-\theta_0)\,d\phi = P(r_0,r,\theta-\theta_0) \qquad (r < r_0).$$

Thus the Poisson kernel $P(r_0,r,\theta-\theta_0)$ is the limit, as h approaches 0 through positive values, of the harmonic function inside the circle $r = r_0$ whose boundary values are represented by the impulse function $2\pi I(h,\theta-\theta_0)$.

6. Show that the expression in Exercise 7(*b*), Sec. 68, for the sum of a certain cosine series can be written

$$1 + 2\sum_{n=1}^{\infty} a^n \cos n\theta = \frac{1-a^2}{1-2a\cos\theta + a^2} \qquad (-1 < a < 1).$$

Thus show that the Poisson kernel (7), Sec. 134, has the series representation (7), Sec. 135.

7. Show that the series in representation (7), Sec. 135, for the Poisson kernel converges uniformly with respect to ϕ. Then obtain from formula (1) of that section the series representation (8) for $U(r, \theta)$ there.

8. Evaluate the integrals

$$\int_0^{2\pi} \cos\phi \cos n\phi d\phi \quad \text{and} \quad \int_0^{2\pi} \cos\phi \sin n\phi d\phi$$

in Example 2, Sec. 136.

Suggestion: Use the trigonometric identities

$$2\cos A \cos B = \cos(A - B) + \cos(A + B)$$

and

$$2\cos A \sin B = \sin(A + B) - \sin(A - B).$$

137. RELATED BOUNDARY VALUE PROBLEMS

Details of proofs of results given in this section are left to the exercises. The function F representing boundary values on the circle $r = r_0$ is assumed to be piecewise continuous.

Suppose that $F(2\pi - \theta) = -F(\theta)$. The Poisson integral transform (1) in Sec. 135 then becomes

$$U(r, \theta) = \frac{1}{2\pi} \int_0^{\pi} [P(r_0, r, \phi - \theta) - P(r_0, r, \phi + \theta)]F(\phi)\, d\phi. \tag{1}$$

This function U has zero values on the horizontal radii $\theta = 0$ and $\theta = \pi$ of the circle, as one would expect when U is interpreted as a steady temperature. Expression (1) thus solves *the Dirichlet problem for the semicircular region* $r < r_0$, $0 < \theta < \pi$, *where* $U = 0$ *on the diameter* AB *shown in* Fig. 195 *and*

$$\lim_{\substack{r \to r_0 \\ r < r_0}} U(r, \theta) = F(\theta) \qquad (0 < \theta < \pi) \tag{2}$$

for each fixed θ *at which* F *is continuous.*

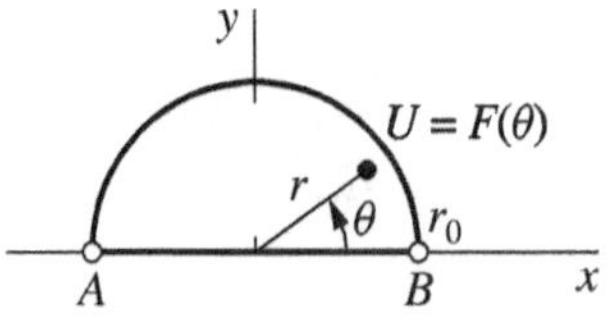

FIGURE 195

If $F(2\pi - \theta) = F(\theta)$, then

$$U(r, \theta) = \frac{1}{2\pi} \int_0^{\pi} [P(r_0, r, \phi - \theta) + P(r_0, r, \phi + \theta)]F(\phi)\, d\phi; \tag{3}$$

and $U_\theta(r, \theta) = 0$ when $\theta = 0$ or $\theta = \pi$. Hence expression (3) furnishes a function U that is *harmonic in the semicircular region* $r < r_0$, $0 < \theta < \pi$ *and satisfies condition* (2) *as well as the condition that its normal derivative be zero on the diameter* AB *shown in* Fig. 195.

The analytic function $z = r_0^2/Z$ maps the circle $|Z| = r_0$ in the Z plane onto the circle $|z| = r_0$ in the z plane, and it maps the exterior of the first circle onto the interior of the second (see Sec. 97). Writing

$$z = re^{i\theta} \quad \text{and} \quad Z = Re^{i\psi},$$

we see that

$$r = \frac{r_0^2}{R} \quad \text{and} \quad \theta = 2\pi - \psi.$$

The harmonic function $U(r, \theta)$ represented by expression (1), Sec. 135, is, then, transformed into the function

$$U\left(\frac{r_0^2}{R}, 2\pi - \psi\right) = -\frac{1}{2\pi}\int_0^{2\pi} \frac{r_0^2 - R^2}{r_0^2 - 2r_0R\cos(\phi + \psi) + R^2} F(\phi)\,d\phi,$$

which is harmonic in the domain $R > r_0$. Now, in general, if $u(r, \theta)$ is harmonic, so is $u(r, -\theta)$. [See Exercise 4.] Hence the function

$$H(R, \psi) = U\left(\frac{r_0^2}{R}, \psi - 2\pi\right),$$

or

(4) $$H(R, \psi) = -\frac{1}{2\pi}\int_0^{2\pi} P(r_0, R, \phi - \psi)F(\phi)\,d\phi \qquad (R > r_0),$$

is also harmonic. For each fixed ψ at which $F(\psi)$ is continuous, we find from condition (2), Sec. 135, that

(5) $$\lim_{\substack{R \to r_0 \\ R > r_0}} H(R, \psi) = F(\psi).$$

Thus expression (4) solves *the Dirichlet problem for the region exterior to the circle* $R = r_0$ in the Z plane (Fig. 196). We note from expression (8), Sec. 134, that the Poisson kernel $P(r_0, R, \phi - \psi)$ is negative when $R > r_0$. Also,

(6) $$\frac{1}{2\pi}\int_0^{2\pi} P(r_0, R, \phi - \psi)\,d\phi = -1 \qquad (R > r_0)$$

and

(7) $$\lim_{R \to \infty} H(R, \psi) = \frac{1}{2\pi}\int_0^{2\pi} F(\phi)\,d\phi.$$

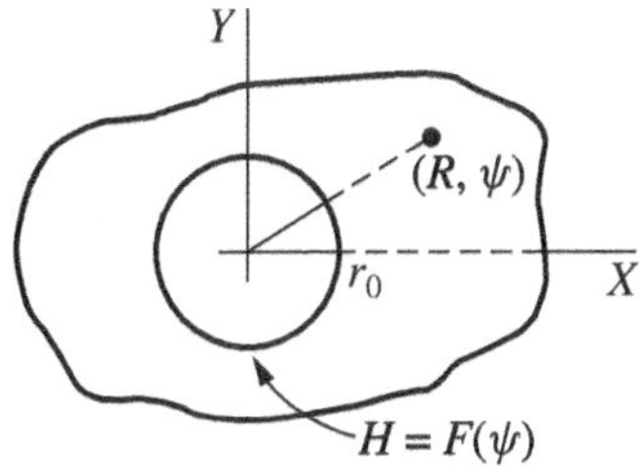

FIGURE 196

EXERCISES

1. Obtain the special case

(*a*) $H(R, \psi) = \dfrac{1}{2\pi} \displaystyle\int_0^\pi [P(r_0, R, \phi + \psi) - P(r_0, R, \phi - \psi)]F(\phi)\, d\phi;$

(*b*) $H(R, \psi) = -\dfrac{1}{2\pi} \displaystyle\int_0^\pi [P(r_0, R, \phi + \psi) + P(r_0, R, \phi - \psi)]F(\phi)\, d\phi$

of expression (4), Sec. 137, for the harmonic function $H(R, \psi)$ in the unbounded region $R > r_0, 0 < \psi < \pi$, shown in Fig. 197, if that function satisfies the boundary condition

$$\lim_{\substack{R \to r_0 \\ R > r_0}} H(R, \psi) = F(\psi) \qquad (0 < \psi < \pi)$$

on the semicircle and (*a*) it is zero on the rays BA and DE; (*b*) its normal derivative is zero on the rays BA and DE.

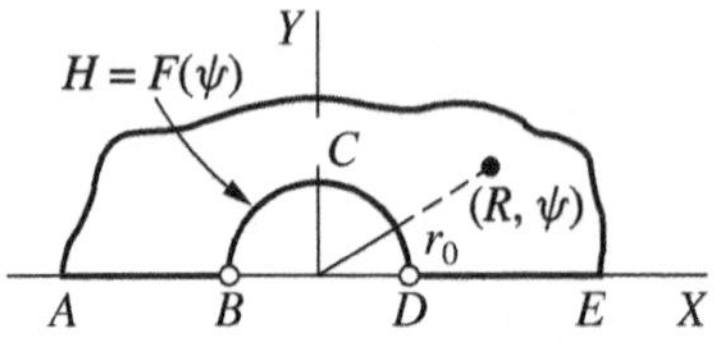

FIGURE 197

2. Give the details needed in establishing expression (1) in Sec. 137 as a solution of the Dirichlet problem stated there for the region shown in Fig. 195.

3. Give the details needed in establishing expression (3) in Sec. 137 as a solution of the boundary value problem stated there.

4. Obtain expression (4), Sec. 137, as a solution of the Dirichlet problem for the region exterior to a circle (Fig. 196). To show that $u(r, -\theta)$ is harmonic when $u(r, \theta)$ is harmonic, use the polar form

$$r^2 u_{rr}(r, \theta) + r u_r(r, \theta) + u_{\theta\theta}(r, \theta) = 0$$

of Laplace's equation.

5. State why equation (6), Sec. 137, is valid.

6. Establish limit (7), Sec. 137.

138. SCHWARZ INTEGRAL FORMULA

Let f be an analytic function of z throughout the half plane $\operatorname{Im} z \geq 0$ such that for some positive constants a and M, the order property

$$|z^a f(z)| < M \qquad (\operatorname{Im} z \geq 0) \tag{1}$$

is satisfied. For a fixed point z above the real axis, let C_R denote the upper half of a positively oriented circle of radius R centered at the origin, where $R > |z|$ (Fig. 198). Then, according to the Cauchy integral formula (Sec. 54),

$$f(z) = \frac{1}{2\pi i} \int_{C_R} \frac{f(s)\, ds}{s - z} + \frac{1}{2\pi i} \int_{-R}^{R} \frac{f(t)\, dt}{t - z}. \tag{2}$$

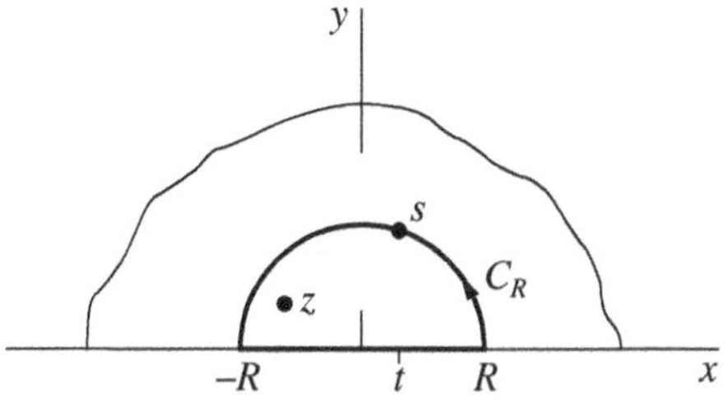

FIGURE 198

We find that the first of these integrals approaches 0 as R tends to ∞ since, in view of condition (1),

$$\left| \int_{C_R} \frac{f(s)\,ds}{s-z} \right| < \frac{M}{R^a(R-|z|)}\pi R = \frac{\pi M}{R^a(1-|z|/R)}.$$

Thus

$$f(z) = \frac{1}{2\pi i} \int_{-\infty}^{\infty} \frac{f(t)\,dt}{t-z} \qquad (\operatorname{Im} z > 0). \tag{3}$$

Condition (1) also ensures that the improper integral here converges.* The number to which it converges is the same as its Cauchy principal value (see Sec. 85), and representation (3) is a *Cauchy integral formula for the half plane* $\operatorname{Im} z > 0$.

When the point z lies below the real axis, the right-hand side of equation (2) is zero; hence integral (3) is zero for such a point. Thus, when z is above the real axis, we have the following expression, where c is an arbitrary complex constant:

$$f(z) = \frac{1}{2\pi i} \int_{-\infty}^{\infty} \left(\frac{1}{t-z} + \frac{c}{t-\overline{z}} \right) f(t)\,dt \qquad (\operatorname{Im} z > 0). \tag{4}$$

In the two cases $c = -1$ and $c = 1$, this reduces, respectively, to

$$f(z) = \frac{1}{\pi} \int_{-\infty}^{\infty} \frac{y f(t)}{|t-z|^2}\,dt \qquad (y > 0) \tag{5}$$

and

$$f(z) = \frac{1}{\pi i} \int_{-\infty}^{\infty} \frac{(t-x) f(t)}{|t-z|^2}\,dt \qquad (y > 0). \tag{6}$$

If $f(z) = u(x, y) + iv(x, y)$, it follows from equations (5) and (6) that the harmonic functions u and v are represented in the half plane $y > 0$ in terms of the boundary values of u by the expressions

$$u(x, y) = \frac{1}{\pi} \int_{-\infty}^{\infty} \frac{y u(t, 0)}{|t-z|^2}\,dt = \frac{1}{\pi} \int_{-\infty}^{\infty} \frac{y u(t, 0)}{(t-x)^2 + y^2}\,dt \qquad (y > 0) \tag{7}$$

*See, for instance, A. E. Taylor and W. R. Mann, *Advanced Calculus,* 3d ed., Chap. 22, 1983.

and

$$v(x, y) = \frac{1}{\pi} \int_{-\infty}^{\infty} \frac{(x - t)u(t, 0)}{(t - x)^2 + y^2}\, dt \qquad (y > 0). \tag{8}$$

Expression (7) is known as the ***Schwarz integral formula***, or the Poisson integral formula for the half plane. In the next section, we shall relax the conditions for the validity of expressions (7) and (8).

139. DIRICHLET PROBLEM FOR A HALF PLANE

Let F denote a real-valued function of x that is bounded for all x and continuous except for at most a finite number of finite jumps. When $y \geq \varepsilon$ and $|x| \leq 1/\varepsilon$, where ε is any positive constant, the integral

$$I(x, y) = \int_{-\infty}^{\infty} \frac{F(t)\, dt}{(t - x)^2 + y^2}$$

converges uniformly with respect to x and y, as do the integrals of the partial derivatives of the integrand with respect to x and y. Each of these integrals is the sum of a finite number of improper or definite integrals over intervals on which F is continuous; hence the integrand of each component integral is a continuous function of t, x, and y when $y \geq \varepsilon$. Consequently, each partial derivative of $I(x, y)$ is represented by the integral of the corresponding derivative of the integrand whenever $y > 0$.

If we write

$$U(x, y) = \frac{y}{\pi} I(x, y),$$

then U is the ***Schwarz integral transform*** of F, suggested by expression (7), Sec. 138:

$$U(x, y) = \frac{1}{\pi} \int_{-\infty}^{\infty} \frac{yF(t)}{(t - x)^2 + y^2}\, dt \qquad (y > 0). \tag{1}$$

Except for the factor $1/\pi$, the kernel here is $y/|t - z|^2$. It is the imaginary component of the function $1/(t - z)$, which is analytic in z when $y > 0$. It follows that the kernel is harmonic, and so it satisfies Laplace's equation in x and y. Because the order of differentiation and integration can be interchanged, the function (1) then satisfies that equation. Consequently, U *is harmonic when* $y > 0$.

To prove that

$$\lim_{\substack{y \to 0 \\ y > 0}} U(x, y) = F(x) \tag{2}$$

for each fixed x at which F is continuous, we substitute $t = x + y \tan \tau$ in integral (1) and write

$$U(x, y) = \frac{1}{\pi} \int_{-\pi/2}^{\pi/2} F(x + y \tan \tau)\, d\tau \qquad (y > 0). \tag{3}$$

As a consequence, if

$$G(x, y, \tau) = F(x + y \tan \tau) - F(x)$$

and α is some small positive constant,

$$\pi[U(x, y) - F(x)] = \int_{-\pi/2}^{\pi/2} G(x, y, \tau)\, d\tau = I_1(y) + I_2(y) + I_3(y) \tag{4}$$

where

$$I_1(y) = \int_{-\pi/2}^{(-\pi/2)+\alpha} G(x, y, \tau)\, d\tau, \qquad I_2(y) = \int_{(-\pi/2)+\alpha}^{(\pi/2)-\alpha} G(x, y, \tau)\, d\tau,$$

$$I_3(y) = \int_{(\pi/2)-\alpha}^{\pi/2} G(x, y, \tau)\, d\tau.$$

If M denotes an upper bound for $|F(x)|$, then $|G(x, y, \tau)| \le 2M$. For a given positive number ε, we select α so that $6M\alpha < \varepsilon$; and this means that

$$|I_1(y)| \le 2M\alpha < \frac{\varepsilon}{3} \quad \text{and} \quad |I_3(y)| \le 2M\alpha < \frac{\varepsilon}{3}.$$

We next show that corresponding to ε, there is a positive number δ such that

$$|I_2(y)| < \frac{\varepsilon}{3} \quad \text{whenever} \quad 0 < y < \delta.$$

To do this, we observe that since F is continuous at x, there is a positive number γ such that

$$|G(x, y, \tau)| < \frac{\varepsilon}{3\pi} \quad \text{whenever} \quad 0 < y|\tan\tau| < \gamma.$$

Now the maximum value of $|\tan\tau|$ as τ ranges from

$$-\frac{\pi}{2} + \alpha \quad \text{to} \quad \frac{\pi}{2} - \alpha$$

is

$$\tan\left(\frac{\pi}{2} - \alpha\right) = \cot\alpha.$$

Hence, if we write $\delta = \gamma\tan\alpha$, it follows that

$$|I_2(y)| < \frac{\varepsilon}{3\pi}(\pi - 2\alpha) < \frac{\varepsilon}{3} \quad \text{whenever} \quad 0 < y < \delta.$$

We have thus shown that

$$|I_1(y)| + |I_2(y)| + |I_3(y)| < \varepsilon \quad \text{whenever} \quad 0 < y < \delta.$$

Condition (2) now follows from this result and equation (4).

Expression (1) therefore solves *the Dirichlet problem for the half plane $y > 0$*, with the boundary condition (2). It is evident from the form (3) of expression (1) that $|U(x, y)| \le M$ in the half plane, where M is an upper bound of $|F(x)|$; that is, U is bounded. We note that $U(x, y) = F_0$ when $F(x) = F_0$, where F_0 is a constant.

According to expression (8) of Sec. 138, under certain conditions on F the function

$$V(x, y) = \frac{1}{\pi} \int_{-\infty}^{\infty} \frac{(x-t)F(t)}{(t-x)^2 + y^2}\, dt \qquad (y > 0) \tag{5}$$

is a harmonic conjugate of the function U given by equation (1). Actually, *equation* (5) *furnishes a harmonic conjugate of U if F is everywhere continuous, except for at most a finite number of finite jumps, and if F satisfies an order property*

$$|x^a F(x)| < M \qquad (a > 0).$$

For, under those conditions, we find that U and V satisfy the Cauchy–Riemann equations when $y > 0$.

Special cases of expression (1) when F is an odd or an even function are left to the exercises.

EXERCISES

1. Obtain as a special case of expression (1), Sec. 139, the expression

$$U(x, y) = \frac{y}{\pi} \int_0^{\infty} \left[\frac{1}{(t-x)^2 + y^2} - \frac{1}{(t+x)^2 + y^2} \right] F(t)\, dt \qquad (x > 0, y > 0)$$

for a bounded function U that is harmonic in the *first quadrant* and satisfies the boundary conditions

$$U(0, y) = 0 \qquad (y > 0),$$

$$\lim_{\substack{y \to 0 \\ y > 0}} U(x, y) = F(x) \qquad (x > 0, x \neq x_j),$$

where F is bounded for all positive x and continuous except for at most a finite number of finite jumps at the points x_j $(j = 1, 2, \ldots, n)$.

2. Let $T(x, y)$ denote the bounded steady temperatures in a plate $x > 0, y > 0$, with insulated faces, when

$$\lim_{\substack{y \to 0 \\ y > 0}} T(x, y) = F_1(x) \qquad (x > 0),$$

$$\lim_{\substack{x \to 0 \\ x > 0}} T(x, y) = F_2(y) \qquad (y > 0)$$

(Fig. 199). Here F_1 and F_2 are bounded and continuous except for at most a finite number of finite jumps. Write $x + iy = z$ and show with the aid of the expression obtained in Exercise 1 that

$$T(x, y) = T_1(x, y) + T_2(x, y) \qquad (x > 0, y > 0)$$

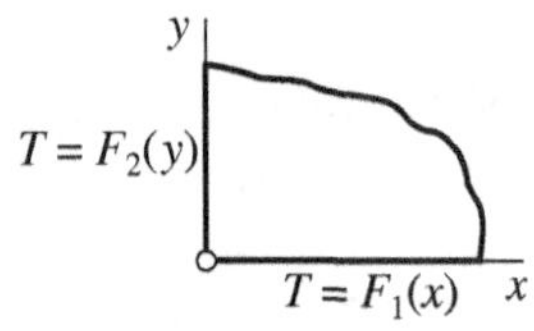

FIGURE 199

where

$$T_1(x, y) = \frac{y}{\pi} \int_0^\infty \left(\frac{1}{|t - z|^2} - \frac{1}{|t + z|^2} \right) F_1(t)\, dt,$$

$$T_2(x, y) = \frac{y}{\pi} \int_0^\infty \left(\frac{1}{|it - z|^2} - \frac{1}{|it + z|^2} \right) F_2(t)\, dt.$$

3. Obtain as a special case of expression (1), Sec. 139, the expression

$$U(x, y) = \frac{y}{\pi} \int_0^\infty \left[\frac{1}{(t - x)^2 + y^2} + \frac{1}{(t + x)^2 + y^2} \right] F(t)\, dt \qquad (x > 0, y > 0)$$

for a bounded function U that is harmonic in the *first quadrant* and satisfies the boundary conditions

$$U_x(0, y) = 0 \qquad (y > 0),$$

$$\lim_{\substack{y \to 0 \\ y > 0}} U(x, y) = F(x) \qquad (x > 0, x \neq x_j),$$

where F is bounded for all positive x and continuous except possibly for finite jumps at a finite number of points $x = x_j$ $(j = 1, 2, \ldots, n)$.

4. Interchange the x and y axes in Sec. 139 to write the solution

$$U(x, y) = \frac{1}{\pi} \int_{-\infty}^\infty \frac{x F(t)}{(t - y)^2 + x^2}\, dt \qquad (x > 0)$$

of the Dirichlet problem for the half plane $x > 0$. Then write

$$F(y) = \begin{cases} 1 & \text{when } |y| < 1, \\ 0 & \text{when } |y| > 1, \end{cases}$$

and obtain these expressions for U and its harmonic conjugate $-V$:

$$U(x, y) = \frac{1}{\pi} \left(\arctan \frac{y + 1}{x} - \arctan \frac{y - 1}{x} \right), \quad V(x, y) = \frac{1}{2\pi} \ln \frac{x^2 + (y + 1)^2}{x^2 + (y - 1)^2}$$

where $-\pi/2 \leq \arctan t \leq \pi/2$. Also, show that

$$V(x, y) + iU(x, y) = \frac{1}{\pi} [\text{Log}(z + i) - \text{Log}(z - i)],$$

where $z = x + iy$.

140. NEUMANN PROBLEMS

As in Sec. 134 and Fig. 192, we write

$$s = r_0 \exp(i\phi) \quad \text{and} \quad z = r \exp(i\theta) \quad (r < r_0).$$

When s is fixed, the function

$$(1) \qquad Q(r_0, r, \phi - \theta) = -2r_0 \ln|s - z| = -r_0 \ln \left[r_0^2 - 2r_0 r \cos(\phi - \theta) + r^2 \right]$$

is harmonic interior to the circle $|z| = r_0$ because it is the real component of

$$-2\,r_0 \log(z - s),$$

where the branch cut of $\log(z - s)$ is an outward ray from the point s. If, moreover, $r \neq 0$,

$$(2) \qquad Q_r(r_0, r, \phi - \theta) = -\frac{r_0}{r}\left[\frac{2r^2 - 2r_0 r\cos(\phi - \theta)}{r_0^2 - 2r_0 r\cos(\phi - \theta) + r^2}\right]$$

$$= \frac{r_0}{r}[P(r_0, r, \phi - \theta) - 1]$$

where P is the Poisson kernel (7) of Sec. 134.

These observations suggest that the function Q may be used to write an integral representation for a harmonic function U whose normal derivative U_r on the circle $r = r_0$ assumes prescribed values $G(\theta)$.

If G is piecewise continuous and U_0 is an arbitrary constant, the function

$$(3) \qquad U(r, \theta) = \frac{1}{2\pi}\int_0^{2\pi} Q(r_0, r, \phi - \theta)\, G(\phi)\, d\phi + U_0 \qquad (r < r_0)$$

is harmonic because the integrand is a harmonic function of r and θ. If the mean value of G over the circle $|z| = r_0$ is zero, so that

$$(4) \qquad \int_0^{2\pi} G(\phi)\, d\phi = 0,$$

then, in view of equation (2),

$$U_r(r, \theta) = \frac{1}{2\pi}\int_0^{2\pi} \frac{r_0}{r}[P(r_0, r, \phi - \theta) - 1]\, G(\phi)\, d\phi$$

$$= \frac{r_0}{r}\cdot\frac{1}{2\pi}\int_0^{2\pi} P(r_0, r, \phi - \theta)\, G(\phi)\, d\phi.$$

Now, according to equations (1) and (2) in Sec. 135,

$$\lim_{\substack{r \to r_0 \\ r < r_0}} \frac{1}{2\pi}\int_0^{2\pi} P(r_0, r, \phi - \theta)\, G(\phi)\, d\phi = G(\theta).$$

Hence

$$(5) \qquad \lim_{\substack{r \to r_0 \\ r < r_0}} U_r(r, \theta) = G(\theta)$$

for each value of θ at which G is continuous.

When G is piecewise continuous and satisfies condition (4), the expression

$$(6) \quad U(r, \theta) = -\frac{r_0}{2\pi}\int_0^{2\pi} \ln\left[r_0^2 - 2r_0 r\cos(\phi - \theta) + r^2\right] G(\phi)\, d\phi + U_0 \quad (r < r_0),$$

therefore, solves *the Neumann problem for the region interior to the circle* $r = r_0$, where $G(\theta)$ is the normal derivative of the harmonic function $U(r, \theta)$ at the boundary in the sense of condition (5). Note how it follows from equations (4) and (6) that since $\ln r_0^2$ is constant, U_0 is the value of U at the center $r = 0$ of the circle $r = r_0$.

The values $U(r, \theta)$ may represent steady temperatures in a disk $r < r_0$ with insulated faces. In that case, condition (5) states that the flux of heat into the disk through its edge is proportional to $G(\theta)$. Condition (4) is the natural physical requirement that the total rate of flow of heat into the disk be zero, since temperatures do not vary with time.

A corresponding expression for a harmonic function H in the region *exterior* to the circle $r = r_0$ can be written in terms of Q as

$$(7) \qquad H(R, \psi) = -\frac{1}{2\pi}\int_0^{2\pi} Q(r_0, R, \phi - \psi)\, G(\phi)\, d\phi + H_0 \qquad (R > r_0),$$

where H_0 is a constant. As before, we assume that G is piecewise continuous and that condition (4) holds. Then

$$H_0 = \lim_{R\to\infty} H(R, \psi)$$

and

$$(8) \qquad \lim_{\substack{R\to r_0\\ R>r_0}} H_R(R, \psi) = G(\psi)$$

for each point ψ at which G is continuous. Verification of expression (7), as well as special cases of expression (3) that apply to semicircular regions, is left to the exercises.

Turning now to a half plane, we let $G(x)$ be continuous for all real x, except possibly for a finite number of finite jumps, and let it satisfy an order property

$$(9) \qquad |x^a G(x)| < M \qquad (a > 1)$$

when $-\infty < x < \infty$. For each fixed real number t, the function $\text{Log}|z - t|$ is harmonic in the half plane $\text{Im}\, z > 0$. Consequently, the function

$$(10) \qquad U(x, y) = \frac{1}{\pi}\int_{-\infty}^{\infty} \ln|z - t|\, G(t)\, dt + U_0$$

$$= \frac{1}{2\pi}\int_{-\infty}^{\infty} \ln[(t - x)^2 + y^2]\, G(t)\, dt + U_0 \qquad (y > 0),$$

where U_0 is a real constant, is harmonic in that half plane.

The function (10) was written with the Schwarz integral transform (1), Sec. 139, in mind; for it follows from expression (10) that

$$(11) \qquad U_y(x, y) = \frac{1}{\pi}\int_{-\infty}^{\infty} \frac{y\, G(t)}{(t - x)^2 + y^2}\, dt \qquad (y > 0).$$

In view of equations (1) and (2) in Sec. 139, then,

$$(12) \qquad \lim_{\substack{y\to 0\\ y>0}} U_y(x, y) = G(x)$$

at each point x where G is continuous.

Expression (10) evidently solves *the Neumann problem for the half plane* $y > 0$, with boundary condition (12). But we have not presented conditions on G which are sufficient to ensure that the harmonic function U is bounded as $|z|$ increases.

When G is an odd function, expression (10) can be written

$$U(x, y) = \frac{1}{2\pi} \int_0^\infty \ln\left[\frac{(t-x)^2 + y^2}{(t+x)^2 + y^2}\right] G(t)\, dt \qquad (x > 0, y > 0). \tag{13}$$

This represents a function that is harmonic in the *first quadrant* $x > 0, y > 0$ and satisfies the boundary conditions

$$U(0, y) = 0 \qquad (y > 0), \tag{14}$$

$$\lim_{\substack{y \to 0 \\ y > 0}} U_y(x, y) = G(x) \qquad (x > 0). \tag{15}$$

EXERCISES

1. Establish expression (7), Sec. 140, as a solution of the Neumann problem for the region exterior to a circle $r = r_0$, using earlier results found in that section.

2. Obtain as a special case of expression (3), Sec. 140, the expression

$$U(r, \theta) = \frac{1}{2\pi} \int_0^\pi [Q(r_0, r, \phi - \theta) - Q(r_0, r, \phi + \theta)]\, G(\phi)\, d\phi$$

for a function U that is harmonic in the *semicircular region* $r < r_0, 0 < \theta < \pi$ and satisfies the boundary conditions

$$U(r, 0) = U(r, \pi) = 0 \qquad (r < r_0),$$
$$\lim_{\substack{r \to r_0 \\ r < r_0}} U_r(r, \theta) = G(\theta) \qquad (0 < \theta < \pi)$$

for each θ at which G is continuous.

3. Obtain as a special case of expression (3), Sec. 140, the expression

$$U(r, \theta) = \frac{1}{2\pi} \int_0^\pi [Q(r_0, r, \phi - \theta) + Q(r_0, r, \phi + \theta)]\, G(\phi)\, d\phi + U_0$$

for a function U that is harmonic in the *semicircular region* $r < r_0, 0 < \theta < \pi$ and satisfies the boundary conditions

$$U_\theta(r, 0) = U_\theta(r, \pi) = 0 \qquad (r < r_0),$$
$$\lim_{\substack{r \to r_0 \\ r < r_0}} U_r(r, \theta) = G(\theta) \qquad (0 < \theta < \pi)$$

for each θ at which G is continuous, provided that

$$\int_0^\pi G(\phi)\, d\phi = 0.$$

4. Let $T(x, y)$ denote the steady temperatures in a plate $x \geq 0, y \geq 0$. The faces of the plate are insulated, and $T = 0$ on the edge $x = 0$. The flux of heat (Sec. 118) into the plate along the segment $0 < x < 1$ of the edge $y = 0$ is a constant A, and the rest of that edge is insulated. Use expression (13), Sec. 140, to show that the flux out of the plate along the edge $x = 0$ is

$$\frac{A}{\pi} \ln\left(1 + \frac{1}{y^2}\right).$$

APPENDIX 2

TABLE OF TRANSFORMATIONS OF REGIONS (See Chap. 8)

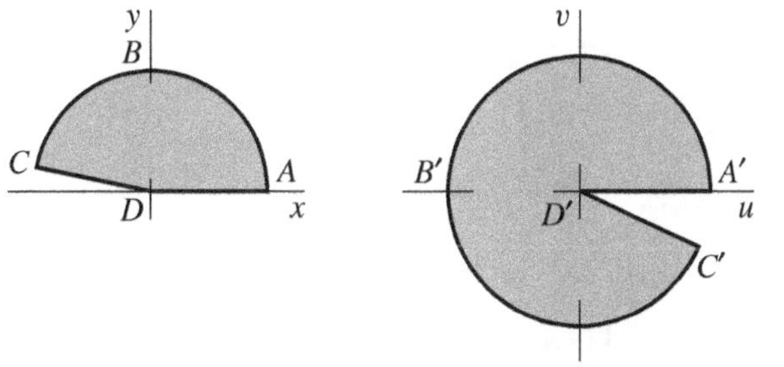

FIGURE 1
$w = z^2$.

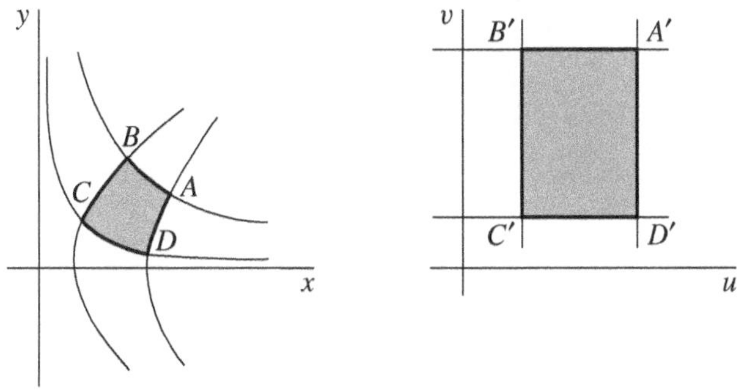

FIGURE 2
$w = z^2$.

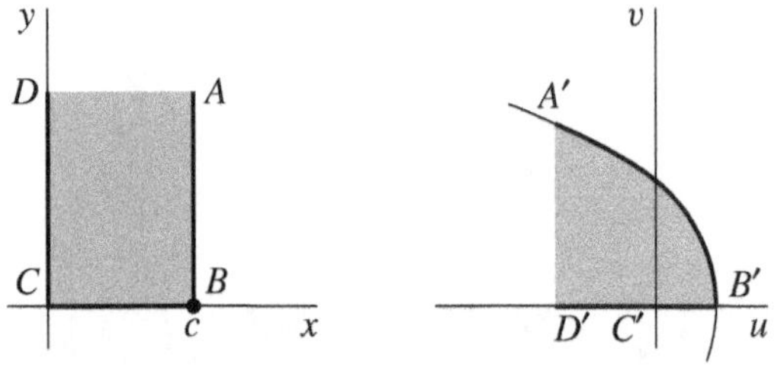

FIGURE 3
$w = z^2$;
$A'B'$ on parabola $v^2 = -4c^2(u - c^2)$.

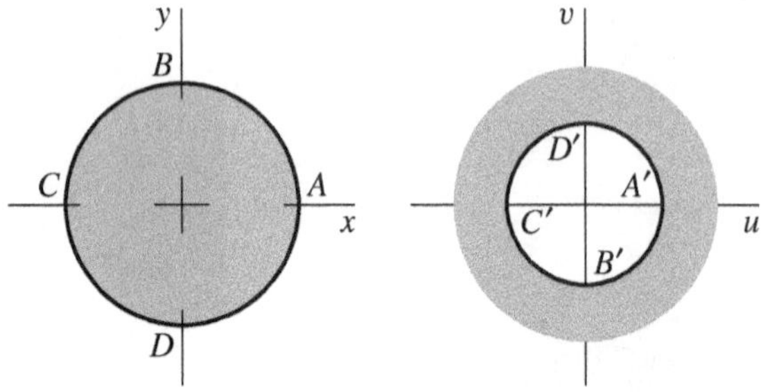

FIGURE 4
$w = 1/z$.

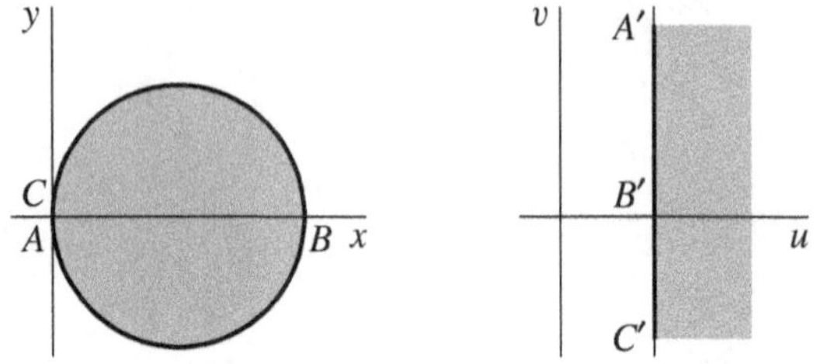

FIGURE 5
$w = 1/z$.

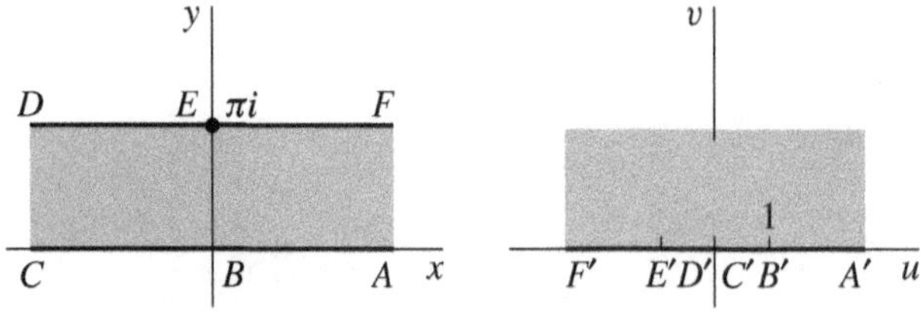

FIGURE 6
$w = \exp z$.

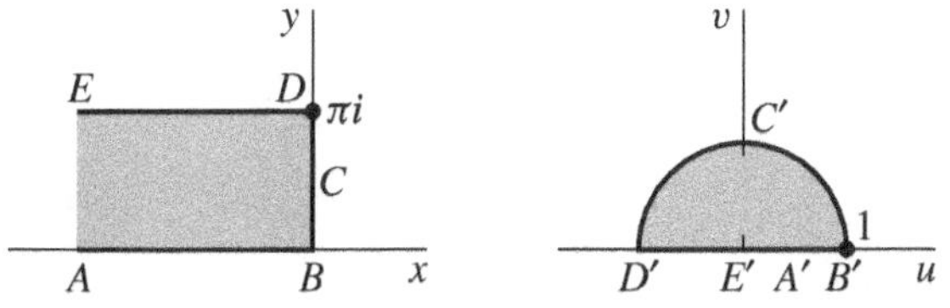

FIGURE 7
$w = \exp z$.

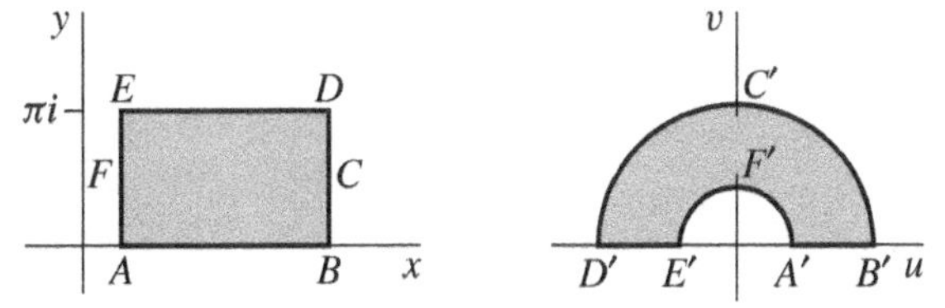

FIGURE 8
$w = \exp z$.

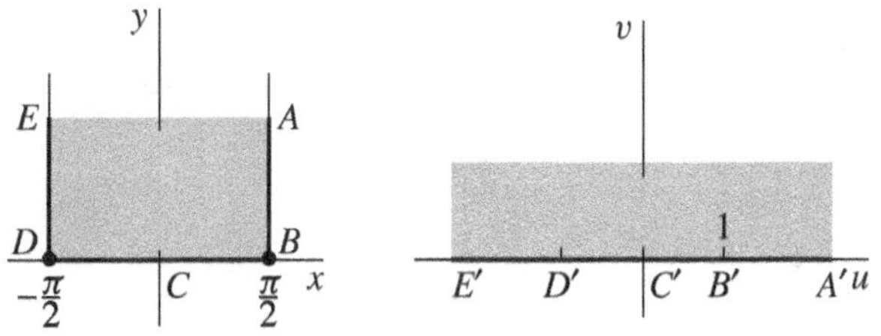

FIGURE 9
$w = \sin z$.

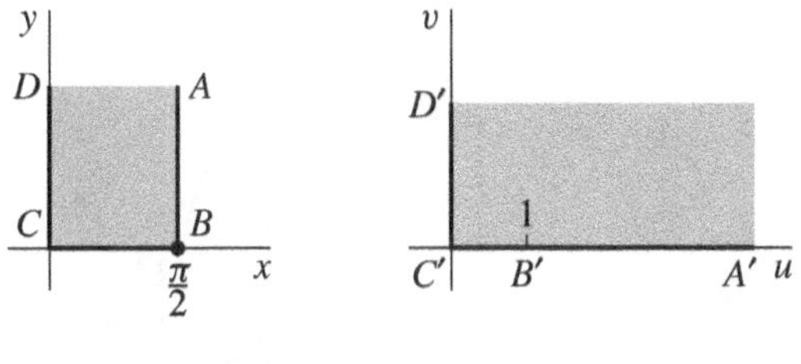

FIGURE 10
$w = \sin z$.

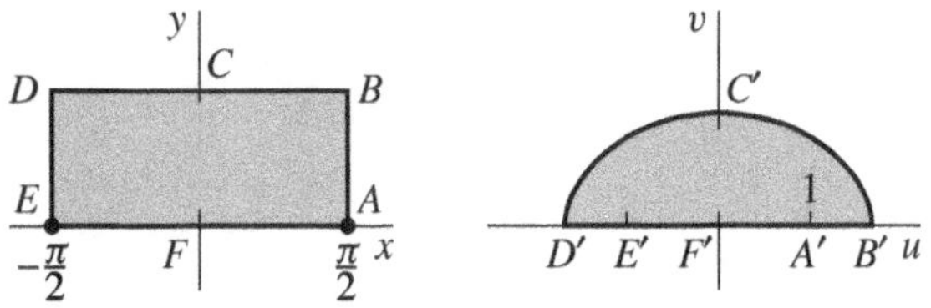

FIGURE 11
$w = \sin z$; BCD on line $y = b$ $(b > 0)$,

$B'C'D'$ on ellipse $\dfrac{u^2}{\cosh^2 b} + \dfrac{v^2}{\sinh^2 b} = 1$.

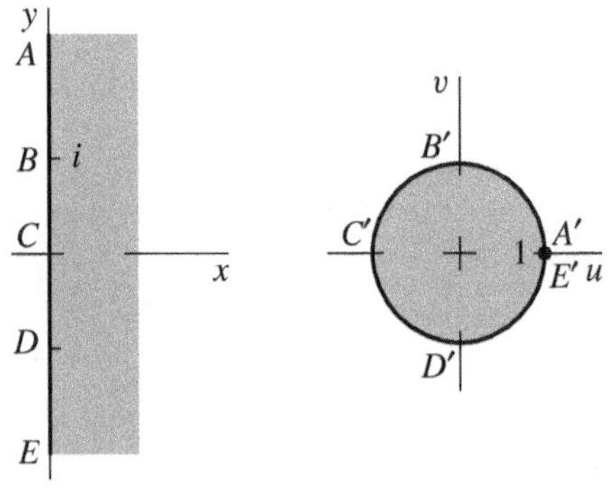

FIGURE 12

$$w = \frac{z-1}{z+1}.$$

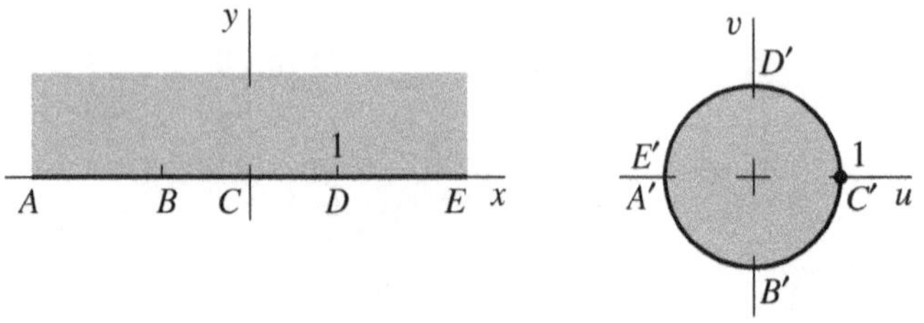

FIGURE 13

$$w = \frac{i-z}{i+z}.$$

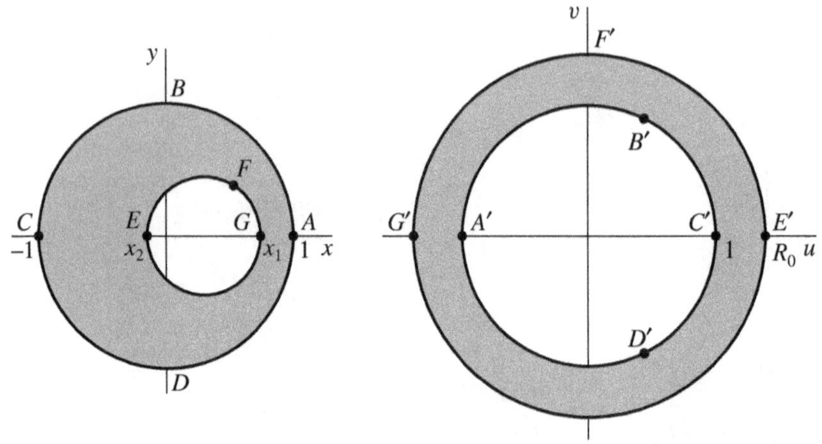

FIGURE 14

$$w = \frac{z-a}{az-1};\ a = \frac{1 + x_1x_2 + \sqrt{(1-x_1^2)(1-x_2^2)}}{x_1 + x_2},$$

$$R_0 = \frac{1 - x_1x_2 + \sqrt{(1-x_1^2)(1-x_2^2)}}{x_1 - x_2} \quad (a > 1 \text{ and } R_0 > 1 \text{ when } -1 < x_2 < x_1 < 1).$$

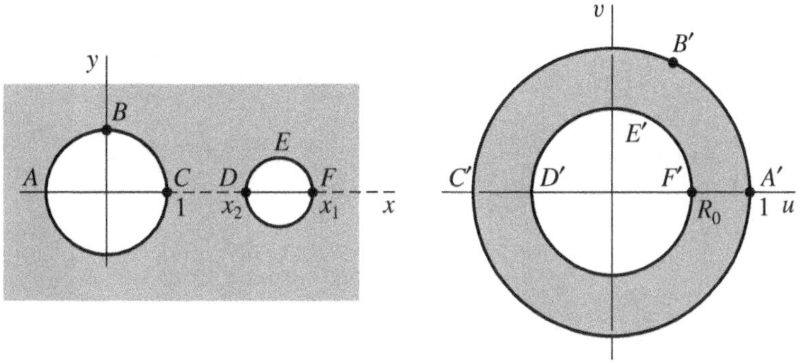

FIGURE 15

$$w = \frac{z-a}{az-1};\ a = \frac{1 + x_1x_2 + \sqrt{(x_1^2-1)(x_2^2-1)}}{x_1+x_2},$$

$$R_0 = \frac{x_1x_2 - 1 - \sqrt{(x_1^2-1)(x_2^2-1)}}{x_1-x_2}\quad (x_2 < a < x_1 \text{ and } 0 < R_0 < 1 \text{ when } 1 < x_2 < x_1).$$

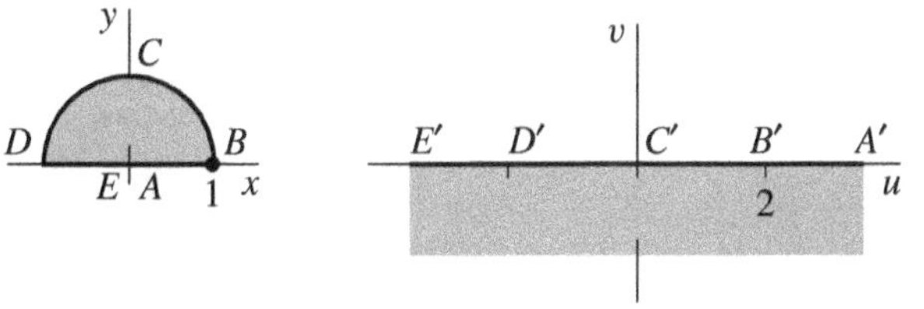

FIGURE 16

$$w = z + \frac{1}{z}.$$

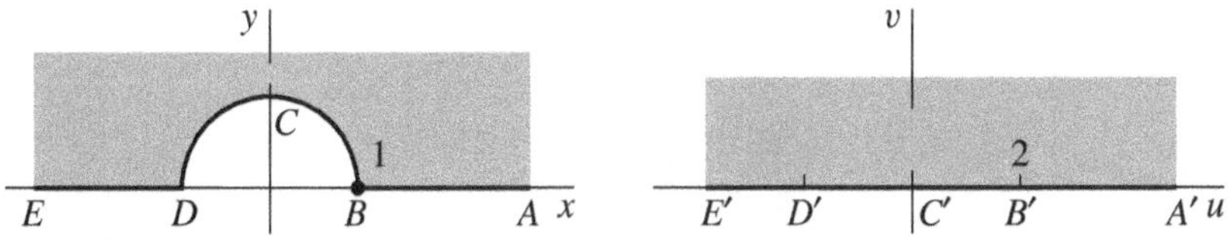

FIGURE 17

$$w = z + \frac{1}{z}.$$

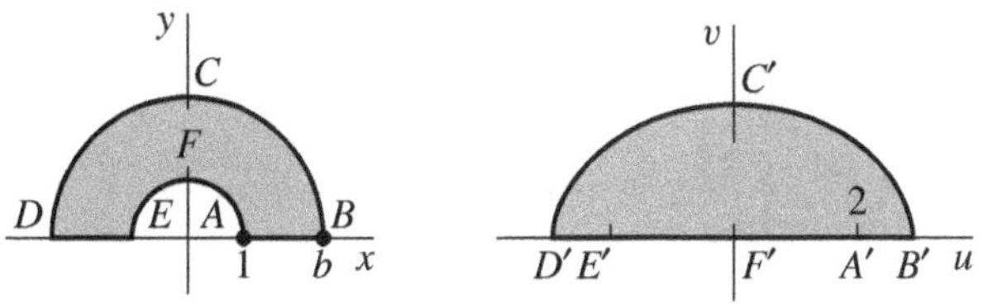

FIGURE 18

$$w = z + \frac{1}{z};\ B'C'D' \text{ on ellipse } \frac{u^2}{(b+1/b)^2} + \frac{v^2}{(b-1/b)^2} = 1.$$

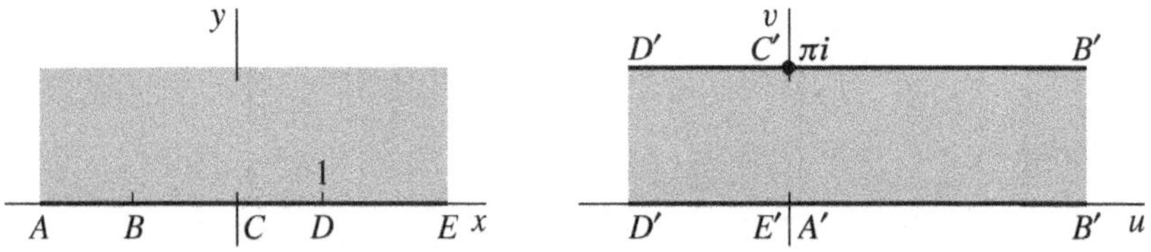

FIGURE 19

$w = \text{Log}\,\dfrac{z-1}{z+1}$; $z = -\coth\dfrac{w}{2}$.

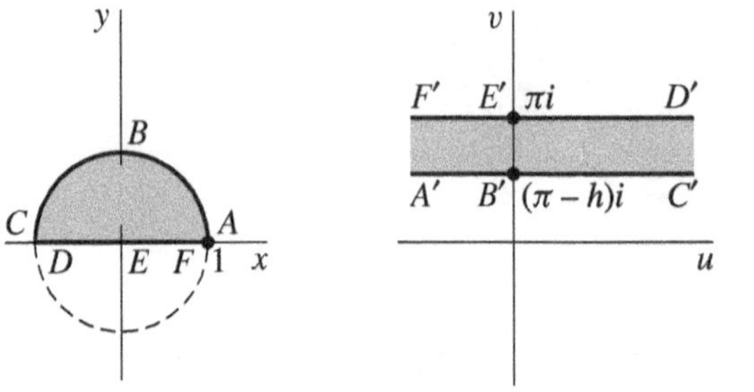

FIGURE 20

$w = \text{Log}\,\dfrac{z-1}{z+1}$;

ABC on circle $x^2 + (y + \cot h)^2 = \csc^2 h \quad (0 < h < \pi)$.

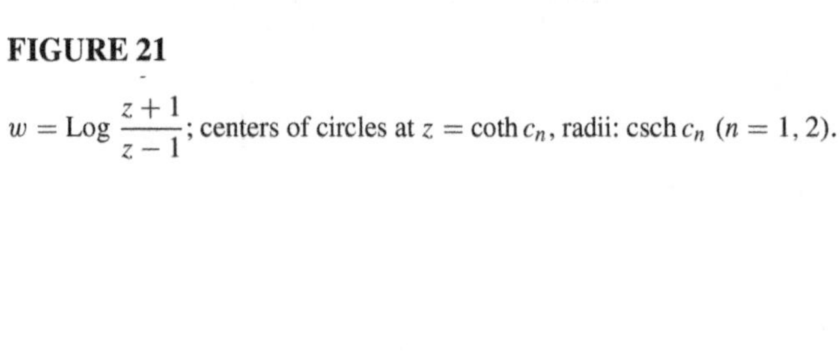

FIGURE 21

$w = \text{Log}\,\dfrac{z+1}{z-1}$; centers of circles at $z = \coth c_n$, radii: $\text{csch}\,c_n$ $(n = 1, 2)$.

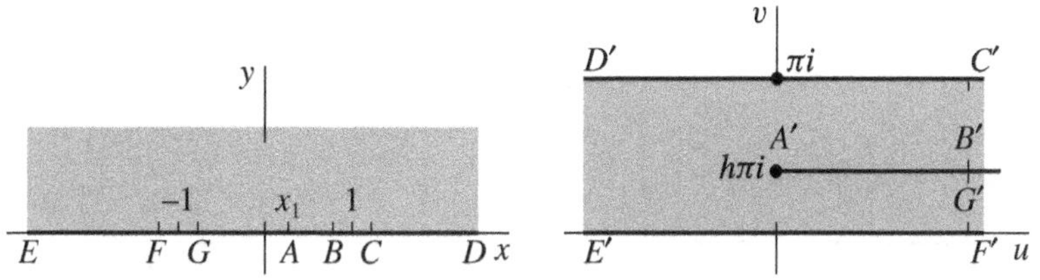

FIGURE 22

$$w = h \ln \frac{h}{1-h} + \ln 2(1-h) + i\pi - h\,\mathrm{Log}(z+1) - (1-h)\,\mathrm{Log}(z-1);\; x_1 = 2h - 1.$$

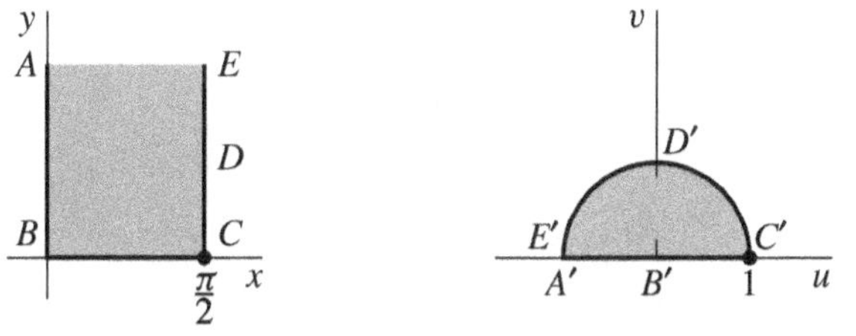

FIGURE 23

$$w = \left(\tan \frac{z}{2}\right)^2 = \frac{1-\cos z}{1+\cos z}.$$

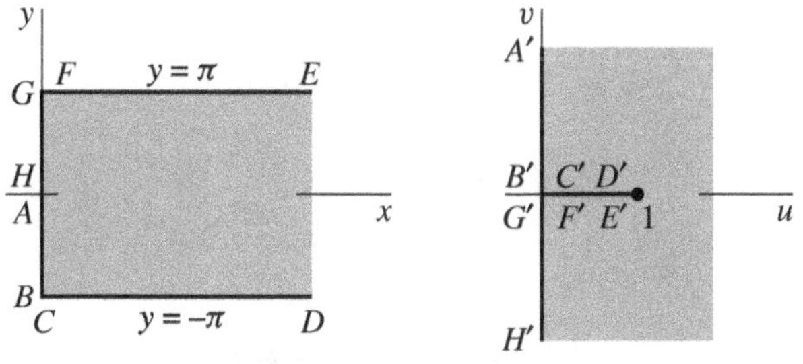

FIGURE 24

$$w = \coth \frac{z}{2} = \frac{e^z + 1}{e^z - 1}.$$

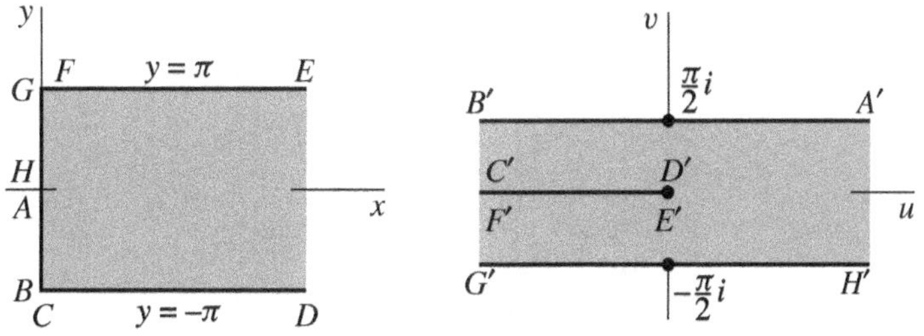

FIGURE 25

$$w = \mathrm{Log}\left(\coth \frac{z}{2}\right).$$

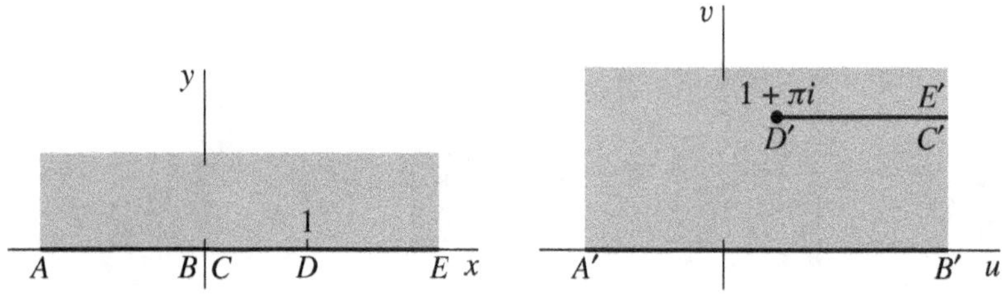

FIGURE 26
$w = \pi i + z - \operatorname{Log} z.$

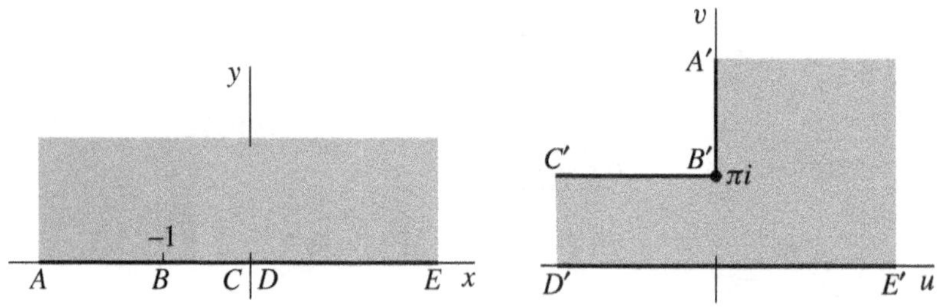

FIGURE 27
$$w = 2(z+1)^{1/2} + \operatorname{Log}\frac{(z+1)^{1/2}-1}{(z+1)^{1/2}+1}.$$

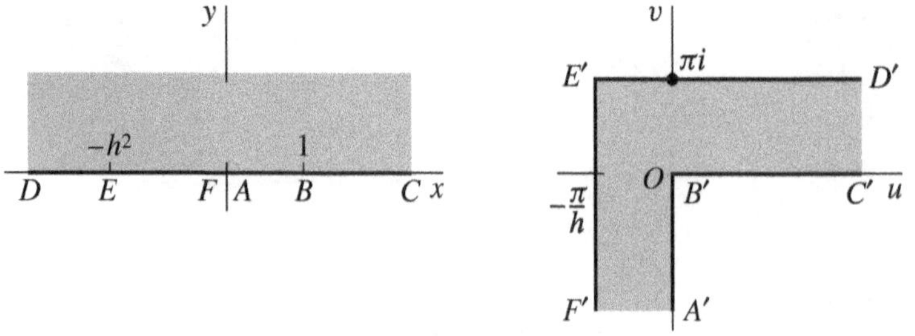

FIGURE 28
$$w = \frac{i}{h}\operatorname{Log}\frac{1+iht}{1-iht} + \operatorname{Log}\frac{1+t}{1-t};\ t = \left(\frac{z-1}{z+h^2}\right)^{1/2}.$$

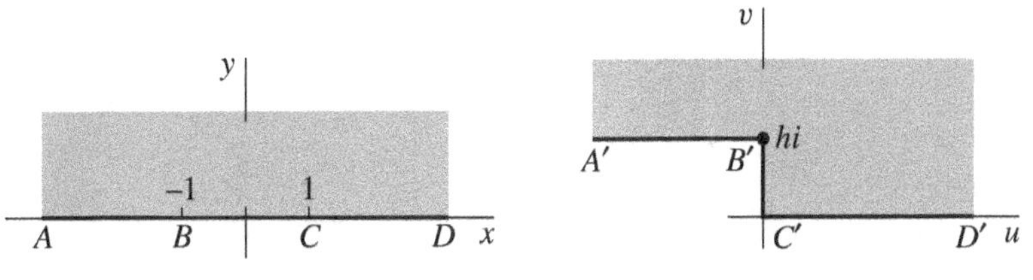

FIGURE 29

$$w = \frac{h}{\pi}[(z^2-1)^{1/2} + \cosh^{-1} z].^*$$

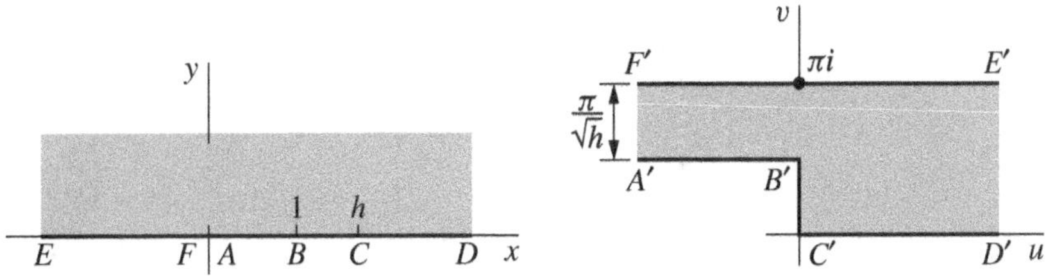

FIGURE 30

$$w = \cosh^{-1}\left(\frac{2z-h-1}{h-1}\right) - \frac{1}{\sqrt{h}}\cosh^{-1}\left[\frac{(h+1)z-2h}{(h-1)z}\right].$$

*See Exercise 3, Sec. 133.

APPENDIX 1

BIBLIOGRAPHY

The following list of supplementary books is far from exhaustive. Further references can be found in many of the books listed here.

Ahlfors, L. V.: *Complex Analysis* (3d ed.), McGraw-Hill Higher Education, Burr Ridge, IL, 1979.

Antimirov, M. Ya., A. A. Kolyshkin, and R.Vaillancourt: *Complex Variables*, Academic Press, San Diego, 1998.

Asmar, N. H.: *Applied Complex Analysis with Partial Differential Equations*, Prentice-Hall, Inc., Upper Saddle River, NJ, 2002.

Bak, J., and D. J. Newman: *Complex Analysis* (2d ed.), Springer-Verlag, New York, 1997.

Bieberbach, L.: *Conformal Mapping*, American Mathematical Society, Providence, RI, 2000.

Boas, R. P.: *Invitation to Complex Analysis* (2d ed.), The Mathematical Association of America, Washington, DC, 2010.

______: Yet Another Proof of the Fundamental Theorem of Algebra, *Amer. Math. Monthly*, Vol. 71, No. 2, p. 180, 1964.

Bowman F.: *Introduction to Elliptic Functions, with Applications*, English Universities Press, London, 1953.

Brown, G. H., C. N. Hoyler, and R. A. Bierwirth: *Theory and Application of Radio-Frequency Heating*, D. Van Nostrand Company, Inc., New York, 1947.

Brown, J. W., and R. V. Churchill: *Fourier Series and Boundary Value Problems* (8th ed.), The McGraw-Hill Companies, Inc., New York, 2012.

Carathéodory, C.: *Conformal Representation*, Dover Publications, Inc., Mineola, NY, 1952.

______: *Theory of Functions of a Complex Variable*, American Mathematical Society, Providence, RI, 1954.

Churchill, R. V.: *Operational Mathematics*, 3d ed., McGraw-Hill Book Company, New York, 1972.

Conway, J. B.: *Functions of One Complex Variable* (2d ed.), 6th Printing, Springer-Verlag, New York, 1997.

Copson, E. T.: *Theory of Functions of a Complex Variable*, Oxford University Press, London, 1962.

D'Angelo, J. P.: *An Introduction to Complex Analysis and Geometry*, American Mathematical Society, Providence, RI, 2010.

Dettman, J. W.: *Applied Complex Variables*, Dover Publications, Inc., Mineola, NY, 1984.

Evans, G. C.: *The Logarithmic Potential, Discontinuous Dirichlet and Neumann Problems*, American Mathematical Society, Providence, RI, 1927.

Fisher, S. D.: *Complex Variables* (2d ed.), Dover Publications, Inc., Mineola, NY, 1999.

Flanigan, F. J.: *Complex Variables: Harmonic and Analytic Functions*, Dover Publications, Inc., Mineola, NY, 1983.

Fourier, J.: *The Analytical Theory of Heat*, translated by A. Freeman, Dover Publications, Inc., Mineola, NY, 2003.

Hayt, W. H., Jr. and J. A. Buck: *Engineering Electromagnetics* (7th ed.), McGraw-Hill Higher Education, Burr Ridge, IL, 2006.

Henrici, P.: *Applied and Computational Complex Analysis*, Vols. 1, 2, and 3, John Wiley & Sons, Inc., New York, 1988, 1991, and 1993.

Hille, E.: *Analytic Function Theory*, Vols. 1 and 2, (2d ed.), Chelsea Publishing Co., New York, 1973.

Jeffrey, A.: *Complex Analysis and Applications* (2d ed.), CRC Press, Boca Raton, FL, 2005.

Kaplan, W.: *Advanced Calculus* (5th ed.), Addison-Wesley Higher Mathematics, Boston, MA, 2003.

______: *Advanced Mathematics for Engineers*, TechBooks, Marietta, OH, 1992.

Kellogg, O. D.: *Foundations of Potential Theory*, Dover Publications, Inc., Mineola, NY, 1953.

Knopp, K.: *Elements of the Theory of Functions*, translated by F. Bagemihl, Dover Publications, Inc., Mineola, NY, 1952.

______: *Problem Book in the Theory of Functions*, Dover Publications, Inc., Mineola, NY, 2000.

Kober, H.: *Dictionary of Conformal Representations*, Dover Publications, Inc., Mineola, NY, 1952.

Krantz, S. G.: *A Guide to Complex Variables* (Guide #1), The Mathematical Association of America, Washington, DC, 2008.

______: *Complex Analysis: The Geometric Viewpoint* (2d ed.,) Carus Mathematical Monograph Series, The Mathematical Association of America, Washington, DC, 2004.

______: *Handbook of Complex Variables*, Birkhauser Boston, Cambridge, MA, 2000.

Krzyż, J. G.: *Problems in Complex Variable Theory*, Elsevier Science, New York, 1972.

Lang, S.: *Complex Analysis* (3d ed.), Springer-Verlag, New York, 1993.

Lebedev, N. N.: *Special Functions and Their Applications* (rev. ed.), translated by R. Silverman, Dover Publications, Inc., Mineola, NY, 1972.

Levinson, N., and R. M. Redheffer: *Complex Variables*, The McGraw-Hill Companies, Inc., New York, 1988.

Love, A. E.: *Treatise on the Mathematical Theory of Elasticity* (4th ed.), Dover Publications, Inc., Mineola, NY, 1944.

Markushevich, A. I.: *Theory of Functions of a Complex Variable* (2d ed.), 3 vols. in one, American Mathematical Society, Providence, RI, 1977.

Marsden, J. E., and M. J. Hoffman: *Basic Complex Analysis* (3d ed.), W. H. Freeman and Company, New York, 1999.

Mathews, J. H., and R. W. Howell: *Complex Analysis for Mathematics and Engineering*, (5th ed.), Jones and Bartlett Publishers, Sudbury, MA, 2006.

Milne-Thomson, L. M., *Theoretical Hydrodynamics* (5th ed.), Dover Publications, Inc., Mineola, NY, 1996.

Mitrinović, D. S.: *Calculus of Residues*, P. Noordhoff, Ltd., Groningen, 1966.

Nahin, P. J.: *An Imaginary Tale: The Story of* $\sqrt{-1}$, Princeton University Press, Princeton, NJ, 1998.

Nehari, Z.: *Conformal Mapping*, Dover Publications, Inc., Mineola, NY, 1975.

Newman, M. H. A.: *Elements of the Topology of Plane Sets of Points* (2d ed.), Dover Publications, Inc., Mineola, NY, 1999.

Oppenheim, A. V., R. W. Schafer, and J. R. Buck: *Discrete-Time Signal Processing* (2d ed.), Prentice-Hall PTR, Paramus, NJ, 1999.

Pennisi, L. L.: *Elements of Complex Variables* (2d ed.), Holt, Rinehart & Winston, Inc., Austin, TX, 1976.

Rubenfeld, L. A.: *A First Course in Applied Complex Variables*, John Wiley & Sons, Inc., New York, 1985.

Saff, E. B., and A. D. Snider: *Fundamentals of Complex Analysis* (3d ed.), Prentice-Hall PTR, Paramus, NJ, 2003.

Shaw, W. T.: *Complex Analysis with Mathematica*, Cambridge University Press, Cambridge, 2006.

Silverman, R. A.: *Complex Analysis with Applications*, Dover Publications, Inc., Mineola, NY, 1984.

Sokolnikoff, I. S.: *Mathematical Theory of Elasticity* (2d ed.), Krieger Publishing Company, Melbourne, FL, 1983.

Springer, G.: *Introduction to Riemann Surfaces* (2d ed.), American Mathematical Society, Providence, RI, 1981.

Streeter, V. L., E. B. Wylie, and K. W. Bedford: *Fluid Mechanics* (9th ed.), McGraw-Hill Higher Education, Burr Ridge, IL, 1997.

Taylor, A. E., and W. R. Mann: *Advanced Calculus* (3d ed.), John Wiley & Sons, Inc., New York, 1983.

Thron, W. J.: *Introduction to the Theory of Functions of a Complex Variable*, John Wiley & Sons, Inc., New York, 1953.

Timoshenko, S. P., and J. N. Goodier: *Theory of Elasticity* (3d ed.), The McGraw-Hill Companies, New York, 1970.

Titchmarsh, E. C.: *Theory of Functions* (2d ed.), Oxford University Press, Inc., New York, 1976.

Volkovyskii, L. I., G. L. Lunts, and I. G. Aramanovich: *A Collection of Problems on Complex Analysis*, Dover Publications, Inc., Mineola, NY, 1992.

Wen, G.-C.: *Conformal Mappings and Boundary Value Problems*, Translations of Mathematical Monographs, Vol. 106, American Mathematical Society, Providence, RI, 1992.

Whittaker, E. T., and G. N. Watson: *A Course of Modern Analysis* (4th ed.), Cambridge University Press, New York, 1996.

Wunsch, A. D.: *Complex Variables with Applications* (3d ed.), Pearson Education, Inc., Boston, 2005.

INDEX

Note: Page numbers followed by *n* refer to footnotes.